3.2 THE DIFFERENCE OF TWO SQUARES; THE SUM AND DIFFERENCE OF TWO CUBES

$$x^2 - y^2 = (x + y)(x - y)$$
$$x^3 + y^3 = (x + y)(x^2 - xy + y^2)$$
$$x^3 - y^3 = (x - y)(x^2 + xy + y^2)$$

3.3 FACTORING TRINOMIALS

$$x^2 + 2xy + y^2 = (x + y)^2$$
$$x^2 - 2xy + y^2 = (x - y)^2$$

4.1 LINEAR EQUATIONS AND THEIR SOLUTIONS

If a, b, and c are real numbers, if there are no divisions by 0, and if $a = b$, then

$$a + c = b + c \qquad a - c = b - c$$
$$ac = bc \qquad \frac{a}{c} = \frac{b}{c}$$

4.4 SOLVING EQUATIONS BY FACTORING

If $ab = 0$, then $a = 0$ or $b = 0$.

4.5 ABSOLUTE VALUE EQUATIONS

$|x| = k$ is equivalent to $x = k$ or $x = -k$.

4.6 LINEAR INEQUALITIES

If a, b, and c are real numbers, if there are no divisions by 0, and if $a < b$, then

$$a + c < b + c \qquad a - c < b - c$$
$$ac < bc \quad (c > 0) \qquad ac > bc \ (c < 0)$$
$$\frac{a}{c} < \frac{b}{c} \quad (c > 0) \qquad \frac{a}{c} > \frac{b}{c} \ (c < 0)$$

$c < x < d$ is equivalent to $c < x$ and $x < d$.

4.7 INEQUALITIES CONTAINING ABSOLUTE VALUES

$|x| < k$ is equivalent to $-k < x < k$.
$|x| > k$ is equivalent to $x < -k$ or $x > k$.

6.1 RATIONAL EXPONENTS

If all expressions represent real numbers, then
$$(a^{1/n})^n = a$$
$$a^{m/n} = (a^{1/n})^m = (a^m)^{1/n}$$
$$a^{-m/n} = \frac{1}{a^{m/n}}$$

6.2 RADICALS

If all expressions represent real numbers, then
$$a^{1/n} = \sqrt[n]{a} \qquad (\sqrt[n]{a})^n = a$$
$$x^{m/n} = \sqrt[n]{x^m} = (\sqrt[n]{x})^m$$
$$\sqrt[n]{a^n} = |a| \quad \text{if } n \text{ is even}$$
$$\sqrt[n]{a^n} = a \quad \text{if } n \text{ is odd}$$
$$\sqrt[n]{ab} = \sqrt[n]{a}\,\sqrt[n]{b} \qquad \sqrt[n]{\frac{a}{b}} = \frac{\sqrt[n]{a}}{\sqrt[n]{b}}$$

6.6 RADICAL EQUATIONS

If a, b, and c are real numbers and if $a = b$, then
$$a^n = b^n$$

7.1 THE RECTANGULAR COORDINATE SYSTEM

If $P(x_1, y_1)$ and $Q(x_2, y_2)$ are two points on a line, then the distance between P and Q is
$$d = \sqrt{(x_2 - x_1)^2 + (y_2 - y_1)^2} \quad \text{distance formula}$$

The coordinates of the midpoint of line segment PQ are
$$\left(\frac{x_1 + x_2}{2}, \frac{y_1 + y_2}{2} \right) \quad \text{midpoint formula}$$

7.2 SLOPE OF A NONVERTICAL LINE

The slope of a nonvertical line passing through $P(x_1, y_1)$ and $Q(x_2, y_2)$ is given by
$$m = \frac{y_2 - y_1}{x_2 - x_1} \quad (x_2 \neq x_1)$$

7.3 EQUATIONS OF LINES

$y - y_1 = m(x - x_1)$	point–slope form of a line
$y = mx + b$	slope–intercept form of a line
$Ax + By = C$	general form of a line
$y = k$	a horizontal line
$x = k$	a vertical line

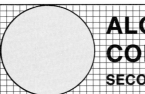

ALGEBRA FOR COLLEGE STUDENTS

SECOND EDITION

Books in the Gustafson and Frisk Series

BEGINNING ALGEBRA,   Second Edition
INTERMEDIATE ALGEBRA,   Second Edition
ALGEBRA FOR COLLEGE STUDENTS,   Second Edition
COLLEGE ALGEBRA,   Third Edition
PLANE TRIGONOMETRY,   Second Edition
COLLEGE ALGEBRA AND TRIGONOMETRY,   Second Edition
FUNCTIONS AND GRAPHS

ALGEBRA FOR COLLEGE STUDENTS

SECOND EDITION

R. David Gustafson
Rock Valley College

Peter D. Frisk
Rock Valley College

Brooks/Cole Publishing Company
Pacific Grove, California

Brooks/Cole Publishing Company
A Division of Wadsworth, Inc.

Printed in the United States of America

10   9   8   7   6   5   4   3   2

Library of Congress Cataloging-in-Publication Data
Gustafson, R. David (Roy David), [date]
    Algebra for college students.

    Includes index.
    1. Algebra.   I. Frisk, Peter D., [date]
II. Title.
QA154.2.G864   1988   512.9   87-29997
ISBN 0-534-08994-1

Sponsoring Editor: *Jeremy Hayhurst*
Editorial Assistant: *Maxine Westby*
Production Editor: *Ellen Brownstein*
Manuscript Editor: *Linda Thompson*
Permissions Editor: *Carline Haga*
Interior and Cover Design: *Roy R. Neuhaus*
Cover Photo: *Lee Hocker*
Art Coordinator: *Lisa Torri*
Interior Illustration: *Lori Heckelman*
Typesetting: *Syntax International, Singapore*
Cover Printing: *Phoenix Color Corp., Long Island City, New York*
Printing and Binding: *R. R. Donnelley & Sons, Crawfordsville, Indiana*

To Our Students

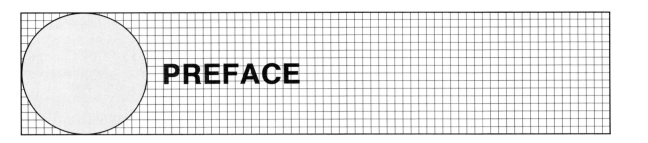

PREFACE

TO THE INSTRUCTOR

In most colleges the mathematical backgrounds of algebra students are quite varied. Some students have recently completed a beginning course in algebra, while others have not studied algebra for years. In this mixture, many students grasp algebra quickly, while others find the concepts to be difficult. To minimize the problems caused by this heterogeneous group, we have prepared a text that meets the needs of a variety of students in many different teaching situations. For example, in *Algebra for College Students, Second Edition*, less-able students will appreciate the nontechnical writing style, the author's notes in the examples, and the review of basic algebra. Good students will appreciate the comprehensive coverage of topics and the challenging problems that appear at the end of most exercise sets.

This text will be effective for students who need a thorough review of basic algebra before proceeding to advanced topics. It will be especially useful for students who need more than one semester of algebra in college or for students who plan to enroll in an expanded one-semester course. Selected chapters can easily support either a traditional intermediate algebra course or a traditional college algebra course.

Because this text contains an abundant supply of worked examples and exercises with the odd-numbered answers provided, students can learn a great deal on their own.

The second edition of *Algebra for College Students* retains the basic philosophy of the highly successful first edition. However, we have made some significant improvements, such as:

1. The chapter on factoring has been reorganized and expanded to cover the **key number method** of factoring trinomials. A new section summarizing factoring techniques has been added.
2. The chapter on solving equations now precedes the chapter on fractions. This permits students to get to applications more quickly. Because equations containing fractions remain in Chapter 5, the work with equations is now spread over two chapters and word problems are distributed more evenly throughout the text.
3. The chapter on radicals has been rewritten using simpler and more concise language.

4. The chapters on functions and graphing have been reorganized. The material on slope of a nonvertical line and writing equations of lines now precedes the discussion of functions. This provides students with preparatory material before they encounter more formal aspects of functions.

5. The chapter on logarithms has been expanded to include more work with base-10 and base-*e* exponential functions, more work with natural logarithms, and many more applications of the exponential and logarithmic functions.

6. Many more word problems have been included throughout the text.

We think you will like this text because of the following features:

Review It includes a thorough and continuing review of basic topics. Skills taught early in the course are used throughout the text. This provides a built-in redundancy that allows students several opportunities to review or even relearn material. This constant review helps improve student confidence and helps reduce student attrition.

Many Exercises It contains over 4600 exercises. Each exercise set is carefully graded and contains an ample supply of both drill and challenging problems. Answers to the odd-numbered exercises are provided in an appendix.

Comprehensive It covers all of the topics that are essential to provide a strong background for work in a precalculus, finite mathematics, or statistics course.

Mathematically Honest The mathematical developments preserve the integrity of the mathematics, but they are not so rigorous as to confuse students.

Teacher Support A Test Manual containing three tests for each chapter is available in hard copy format. For compiling individualized examinations, a computer-based test bank of test items with EXPTEST®, a full-featured test-generating system, is available to those who adopt the text. An Instructor's Manual is available, which gives the answers to all of the even-numbered exercises.

We think your students will like the text because it has the following features:

Informal Writing The text is written for students to read. The writing is informal rather than technical and is at the tenth grade reading level on the Fry Readability Test.

Worked Examples   There are more than 450 worked examples, many including author's notes to explain each step in the solution process.

Functional Use of Second Color   It makes use of color, not just to highlight important definitions and theorems, but to "point" to terms and expressions that you would point to in a classroom discussion.

Review Exercises   Each chapter concludes with a chapter summary, review exercises, and a sample chapter test. Cumulative review exercises appear throughout the text.

Applications   Applications in the form of word problems appear throughout the text.

Summary of Information   Key formulas and ideas are listed inside the front and back covers for quick reference.

Student Support   A Student's Solutions Manual is available that provides completely worked solutions to the even-numbered exercises that are not multiples of four. A student Study Guide is also available.

ORGANIZATION AND COVERAGE

Several of the chapters are independent from the others to allow for flexibility in the sequencing of topics. The following diagram shows how the chapters are interrelated:

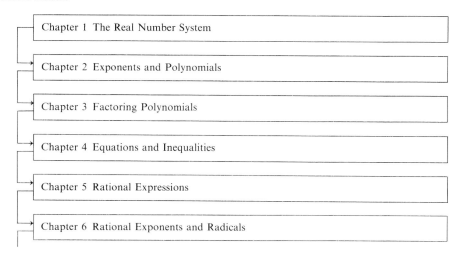

Chapter 1 The Real Number System

Chapter 2 Exponents and Polynomials

Chapter 3 Factoring Polynomials

Chapter 4 Equations and Inequalities

Chapter 5 Rational Expressions

Chapter 6 Rational Exponents and Radicals

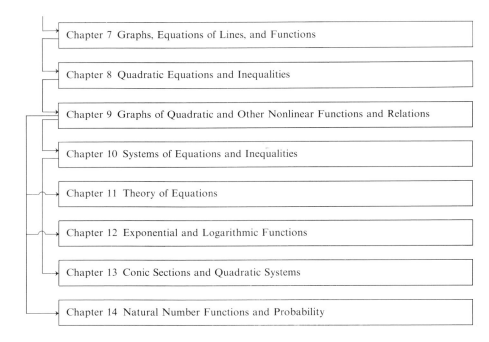

CALCULATORS

We encourage the use of calculators and believe that students should learn calculator skills in the mathematics classroom. Then they will be able to use a calculator in science and business classes and for nonacademic purposes.

ACCURACY

Dozens of mathematics teachers have reviewed either all or a portion of this text. We are grateful for their many constructive criticisms and helpful suggestions. Both authors have independently worked all of the exercises as have two other problem checkers.

TO THE STUDENT

Because we believe that many students who read this book do not intend to major in mathematics, we have written it in an informal, rather than a technical, way. We have provided an extensive number of worked examples and have tried to present them in a way that will make sense to you. This text has been written for you to read and we think that you will find the explanations helpful. If you do not bother to follow the explanations carefully, much of the value of this text will be lost. What you learn here will be of great value to you both in other course work and in your chosen occupation.

We suggest that you consider keeping your text after completing this course. It will be a good source of reference and will keep the material that you learned here at your fingertips.

We wish you well.

ACKNOWLEDGMENTS

We are grateful to the following people who reviewed the entire text at various levels of its development.

Dale Boye
Schoolcraft College

Lee R. Clancy
Golden West College

Joseph W. Colen
Jackson State University

Robert B. Eicken
Illinois Central College

George Grisham
Bradley University

David W. Hansen
Monterey Peninsula College

Steven Hatfield
Marshall University

Libby W. Holt
Florida Community College

John Hooker
Souther Illinois University

Herbert Kasube
Bradley University

Maureen McCarthy
Santa Rosa Junior College

L. Dwayne Snider
Tarleton State University

Lora L. Stewart
Cosumnes River College

Ray Tebbetts
San Antonio College

We wish to thank Diane Koenig, who read the entire text and worked every problem. Our thanks also go to William Hinrichs, Darrell Ropp, David Hinde, Jerry Frang, Gary Schultz, and James Yarwood for their helpful comments and suggestions. We thank Archie Strole for his suggested inclusion of the key number method for factoring trinomials.

We also thank Jeremy Hayhurst, Steven Bailey, Ellen Brownstein, Roy Neuhaus, Lisa Torri, Linda Thompson, and Jeanne Wyatt for their valuable assistance in the creation of this textbook.

R. David Gustafson
Peter D. Frisk

CONTENTS

ALGEBRA FOR
COLLEGE STUDENTS
SECOND EDITION

1 The Real Number System

Algebra is the result of contributions from many cultures over thousands of years. Possibly some algebra was known to the ancient Babylonians, although its first recorded traces are found in the writings of an Egyptian priest named Ahmes, who lived before 1700 B.C. Diophantus, a Greek who lived around A.D. 300, was the first to use special symbols to represent unknown quantities. He is famous for his work with equations. The first known woman mathematician, a Greek scholar named Hypatia, studied and explained the work of Diophantus. Within one hundred years of her death in A.D. 415, the Arabians were using + and − signs and were working with fractions. The symbols we now use to write numbers were developed by the Hindu and Arabic cultures. They were introduced to the West by the thirteenth century Italian merchant Leonardo of Pisa, also known as Fibonacci. The name *algebra* comes from the title of a book written by the Arabian mathematician Al-Khowarazmi around A.D. 800. Its title, *Ihm al-jabr wa'l muqabalah*, means restoration and reduction, a process then used to solve equations.

During the middle ages there was little further development of algebra. Not until the sixteenth century did scholars again become interested in mathematics. At that time, France and Spain were at war. François Viète, a French lawyer with an interest in mathematics, devised a system to break the codes the Spaniards used to send secret messages. His system developed the algebraic notation that we still use today.

Because the concept of *number* is basic in algebra, we begin by discussing the various sets of real numbers.

1.1 SETS OF NUMBERS

A **set** is a collection of objects. To denote a set, we often use braces to enclose a list of its **members** or **elements**. For example, the notation

$$\{a, b, c\}$$

denotes the set with elements a, b, and c. To indicate that b is an element of this set, we write

$$b \in \{a, b, c\} \qquad \text{Read } \in \text{ as "is an element of."}$$

1

The expression

$$d \notin \{a, b, c\}$$

indicates that d is not an element of $\{a, b, c\}$.

Capital letters are used to name sets. For example, the expression

$$A = \{a, e, i, o, u\}$$

means that A is the set containing the vowels a, e, i, o, and u.

In **set-builder notation** a rule is given that establishes membership in a set. The set of vowels in the English alphabet, for example, can be denoted as

$$V = \{x : x \text{ is a vowel of the English alphabet.}\}$$

The statement above is read as "V is the set of all letters x such that x represents a vowel of the English alphabet." Because x can represent many different elements of the set, x is called a **variable**.

When two sets such as A and V have exactly the same elements, we say that they are equal, and we write $A = V$.

If $B = \{a, c, e\}$ and $A = \{a, b, c, d, e\}$, each element of B is also an element of A. When this is so, we say that B is a **subset** of A. In symbols, we write

$$B \subseteq A \qquad \text{Read as "}B\text{ is a subset of }A\text{."}$$

Because every element in set A is an element in set A, set A is a subset of itself. In symbols,

$$A \subseteq A$$

In general, any set is a subset of itself. The expression

$$A \nsubseteq B$$

indicates that A is not a subset of B.

A set with no elements is called the **empty set**, or **null set**, and is denoted as $\varnothing$. Thus,

$$\varnothing = \{\quad\}$$

The empty set is considered to be a subset of every set.

If the elements of some set A are joined with the elements of some set B, the **union** of set A and set B is formed. The union of set A and set B is denoted as

$$A \cup B \qquad \text{Read as "the union of set }A\text{ and set }B\text{."}$$

The elements of $A \cup B$ are *either* elements of set A, *or* elements of set B, *or both*.

The set of elements that are common to set A and set B is called the **intersection** of set A and set B. The intersection of set A and set B is denoted as

$$A \cap B \qquad \text{Read as "the intersection of set }A\text{ and set }B\text{."}$$

The elements of $A \cap B$ are elements of *both* set A *and* set B. If A and B have no elements in common, then $A \cap B = \varnothing$, and the sets A and B are said to be **disjoint**.

Example 1   If $A = \{a, e, i, o, u\}$ and $B = \{a, b, c, d, e\}$, find   **a.** $A \cup B$,   **b.** $A \cap B$,   and   **c.** $(A \cap \varnothing) \cup B$.

Solution   **a.** $A \cup B = \{a, b, c, d, e, i, o, u\}$

b. $A \cap B = \{a, e\}$

c. $(A \cap \varnothing) \cup B = \varnothing \cup B$ Do the work in parentheses first.

$= B$

$= \{a, b, c, d, e\}$ ■

Sets of Numbers

The set of numbers that we use for counting is called the set of **natural numbers** or the set of **counting numbers**.

Definition.   The **natural numbers** are the numbers

1, 2, 3, 4, 5, 6, 7, 8, 9, . . .

The three dots used in the previous definition, called the **ellipsis**, indicate that the list of natural numbers continues endlessly. If a set, such as the set of natural numbers, has an unlimited number of elements, it is called an **infinite set**. If a set has a limited number of elements, it is called a **finite set**.

Two important subsets of the natural numbers are the **prime numbers** and the **composite numbers**.

Definition.   A **prime number** is any natural number greater than 1 that is divisible without a remainder only by itself and by 1.

A **composite number** is any natural number greater than 1 that is not a prime number.

The prime numbers less than 20 are

2, 3, 5, 7, 11, 13, 17, and 19

and the composite numbers less than 20 are

4, 6, 8, 9, 10, 12, 14, 15, 16, and 18

If we join 0 to the set of natural numbers, we have the set of **whole numbers**.

Definition.   The **whole numbers** are the numbers

0, 1, 2, 3, 4, 5, 6, 7, 8, 9, . . .

It is often necessary to use numbers that indicate direction as well as quantity—for example, profit or loss, temperatures above or below 0, and gains or losses in the stock market. To do so, we must extend the set of whole numbers to include the negatives of the natural numbers. These negatives are denoted with − signs. For example, the negative of 7 is written as −7 and is read as "negative 7." The union of the set of whole numbers and the set of negatives of the natural numbers forms the set of **integers**.

Definition.   The **integers** are the numbers

$$\dots, -7, -6, -5, -4, -3, -2, -1, 0, 1, 2, 3, 4, 5, 6, 7, \dots$$

Integers that are divisible by 2 are called **even integers**, and integers that are not divisible by 2 are called **odd integers**. Because $\frac{0}{2} = 0$, 0 is an even integer. The even integers from −10 to 10 are

$$-10, -8, -6, -4, -2, 0, 2, 4, 6, 8, 10$$

and the odd integers between −10 and 10 are

$$-9, -7, -5, -3, -1, 1, 3, 5, 7, 9$$

If two integers are added, subtracted, or multiplied, the result is always another integer. However, the result obtained when two integers are divided is not always another integer. For example, when 8 is divided by 5, we obtain the fraction $\frac{8}{5}$. When an integer is divided by a nonzero integer, the result is called a **rational number**. The numbers

$$\frac{2}{3}, \qquad -\frac{44}{23}, \qquad 16, \qquad \text{and} \qquad -0.25$$

are examples of rational numbers. The number 16 is rational because it can be written as the fractions $\frac{16}{1}, \frac{32}{2}, \frac{48}{3}$, and so on. The number -0.25 is rational because it can be written as the fraction $-\frac{1}{4}$.

We note that $\frac{8}{4} = 2$ because $4(2) = 8$, that $\frac{24}{8} = 3$ because $8(3) = 24$, and that $\frac{0}{9} = 0$ because $9(0) = 0$. However, the fraction $\frac{5}{0}$ is undefined because there is no number that when multiplied by 0 gives 5. The fraction $\frac{0}{0}$ is undefined also because *all* numbers when multiplied by 0 give 0. Thus, it is understood that *the denominator of a fraction can never be* 0. We emphasize this important fact in the following definition.

Definition.   A **rational number** is any number that can be written in the form a/b, where a and b are integers and b is not 0.

Example 2   **a.**   The fraction $\frac{5}{3}$ is a rational number because it is the quotient of two integers and the denominator is not 0.

b.   The number -7 is rational because it can be written in the form $-\frac{7}{1}$, $-\frac{14}{2}$, $-\frac{21}{3}$, and so on.

c.   The number 0.125 is rational because it can be written in the form $\frac{1}{8}$.

d.   The number $-0.666\ldots$ is rational because it can be written as $-\frac{2}{3}$.   ■

Every rational number written in fractional form can be written in decimal form. For example, to change $\frac{3}{4}$ to a decimal fraction, we divide 3 by 4 to obtain 0.75.

$$
\begin{array}{r}
0.75 \\
4\,)\overline{3.00} \\
2\,8 \\ \hline
20 \\
20 \\ \hline
0
\end{array}
$$

Because the division leaves a remainder of 0, the division stops and the quotient 0.75 is called a **terminating decimal**. If we change a fraction such as $\frac{421}{990}$ to a decimal fraction, we obtain $0.4252525\ldots$, called a **repeating decimal**, in which the block of digits "25" repeats forever.

$$
\begin{array}{r}
0.4252\,5\ldots \\
990\,)\overline{421.0000} \\
3960 \\ \hline
2500 \\
1980 \\ \hline
5200 \\
4950 \\ \hline
250
\end{array}
$$

The repeating decimal $0.4252525\ldots$ is often written as $0.4\overline{25}$, where the overbar indicates the repeating block of digits.

It can be shown that all decimal forms of rational numbers are either terminating or repeating decimals.

It is easy to write a terminating decimal as a rational number in fractional form. For example, to write 0.25 as a fraction we note that 0.25 means $\frac{25}{100}$ and that $\frac{25}{100}$ can be simplified to obtain $\frac{1}{4}$.

$$
0.25 = \frac{25}{100} = \frac{25 \cdot 1}{25 \cdot 4} = \frac{\cancel{25} \cdot 1}{\cancel{25} \cdot 4} = \frac{1}{4} \qquad \text{Read } 25 \cdot 1 \text{ as "25 times 1."}
$$

In Chapter 4 we will show that any repeating decimal can be written as a rational number in fractional form.

Because it is possible both to write rational numbers in fractional form as terminating or repeating decimals and to write terminating and repeating decimals as rational numbers in fractional form, these two sets of numbers are one and the same. Thus, the set of rational numbers is equal to the set of all decimals that either terminate or repeat.

Numbers whose decimal representations neither terminate nor repeat are called **irrational numbers**. For example, the decimal

$$0.31\ 331\ 3331\ldots$$

follows a pattern, but it will never have a repeating block of digits. Thus, it represents an irrational number. Other examples of irrational numbers are $\sqrt{3}$ (the square root of 3) and $-\pi$ (negative pi).

$$\sqrt{3} = 1.7320508075 \qquad \text{and} \qquad -\pi = -3.141592653\ldots$$

If **R** is used to represent the set of rational numbers and **H** is used to represent the set of irrational numbers, the union of set **R** and set **H** is the set of all decimals. This set, denoted as $\mathscr{R}$, is called the set of **real numbers**. In symbols, we write

$$\mathbf{R} \cup \mathbf{H} = \mathscr{R}$$

Since there are no real numbers that are both rational and irrational, sets **R** and **H** are disjoint. Thus,

$$\mathbf{R} \cap \mathbf{H} = \varnothing$$

The relationship of the sets of numbers developed thus far is shown in Figure 1-1. Each set of numbers in the figure is a subset of those sets that precede it.

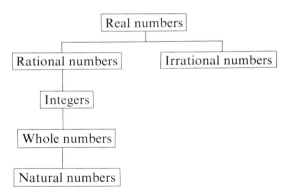

Figure 1-1

■ EXERCISE 1.1

In Exercises 1–6, $A = \{1, 3, 5, 9\}$, $B = \{3, 5, 9, 11\}$, and $C = \{x : x$ is an odd integer.$\}$. Insert either an $\in$ or a $\subseteq$ symbol to make a true statement.

1. $A \underline{\quad} C$

2. $3 \underline{\quad} A$

3. $9 \underline{\quad} B$

4. $\{3, 5\} \underline{\quad} C$

5. $\varnothing \underline{\quad} B$

6. $A \underline{\quad} A$

In Exercises 7–10, list the elements in each set, if possible.

7. $\{x : x$ is a prime number less than 10.$\}$

8. $\{x:x$ is a composite number between 3 and 7.$\}$

9. $\{x : x$ is a number that is both rational and irrational.$\}$

10. $\{x : x$ is the name of a state in the United States beginning with the letter I$\}$

In Exercises 11–18, $A = \{2, 3, 5, 7\}$, $B = \{2, 4, 6, 8, 10\}$, and $C = \{1, 3, 5, 7, 9\}$. Find each set.

11. $A \cup B$ **12.** $A \cap C$ **13.** $B \cap C$ **14.** $A \cup C$

15. $(C \cap \varnothing) \cap B$ **16.** $B \cup (\varnothing \cap C)$ **17.** $(A \cup B) \cap C$ **18.** $(A \cap B) \cup C$

In Exercises 19–24, tell whether each set is a finite or an infinite set.

19. $\{x : x$ is a prime number.$\}$

20. $\{1, 2, 3, 4, 5, 6, 7, 8\}$

21. $\{x : x$ is a natural number that is neither prime nor composite.$\}$

22. $\{x : x$ is an even integer.$\}$

23. $\{x : x$ is a rational number.$\}$

24. $\{x : x$ is a state in the United States.$\}$

In Exercises 25–36, simplify each expression, if necessary. Then classify each number as a natural number, a whole number, an integer, a rational number, an irrational number, and/or a real number. Most numbers will be in many classifications.

25. 2 **26.** -2 **27.** 0 **28.** $\dfrac{2}{3}$

29. 0.75 **30.** $0.333\ldots$ **31.** $-\dfrac{8}{9}$ **32.** $-3.\overline{15}$

33. $\dfrac{20}{4}$ **34.** $\dfrac{4}{8}$ **35.** $0.232232223\ldots$ **36.** $-2.373373337\ldots$

In Exercises 37–48, simplify each expression, if necessary, and classify each result as an even integer, an odd integer, a prime number, and/or a composite number. Some numbers will be in more than one classification.

37. 8 **38.** -5 **39.** -9 **40.** 4 **41.** $\dfrac{12}{6}$ **42.** $8 - 5$

43. 0 **44.** 1 **45.** $3(5)$ **46.** -16 **47.** $\dfrac{0}{4}$ **48.** 2

In Exercises 49–68, identify each statement as true or false. If a statement is true, give an example to confirm that it is true. If a statement is false, give an example to show that it is false. If a statement is sometimes true and sometimes false, consider it to be a false statement.

49. The product of two natural numbers is a natural number.

50. The sum of two natural numbers is a natural number.

51. All of the whole numbers are natural numbers.

52. All of the natural numbers are integers.

53. The sum of two prime numbers is a prime number.

54. The product of two prime numbers is a prime number.

55. The sum of two even integers is even.

56. The product of two even integers is even.

57. The sum of two odd integers is odd.

58. The product of two odd integers is odd.

59. The sum of two composite numbers is a composite number.

60. The product of two composite numbers is composite.

61. The product of two prime numbers is composite.

62. The sum of two prime numbers is composite.

63. The sum of 0 and any natural number is a natural number.

64. The product of 0 and any natural number is a natural number.

65. The only even prime number is 2.

66. The negative of a prime number is also prime.

67. Every integer is a rational number.

68. No rational number is an integer.

In Exercises 69–72, write each rational number as a decimal. Then classify the decimal as a terminating or a repeating decimal.

69. $\dfrac{7}{8}$ **70.** $\dfrac{7}{3}$ **71.** $-\dfrac{11}{15}$ **72.** $-\dfrac{19}{16}$

In Exercises 73–76, write each terminating decimal as a rational number in fractional form.

73. 0.5   **74.** 0.2   **75.** 0.75   **76.** 0.125

1.2 EQUALITY AND PROPERTIES OF REAL NUMBERS

If two variables such as a and b represent the same number, we say that a and b are equal, and we write $a = b$. To show that a and b are not equal, we write $a \neq b$, where the symbol $\neq$ means "is not equal to." There are several properties of equality that we shall use throughout this book.

Properties of Equality.   If a, b, and c are real numbers, then

$a = a$	The reflexive property
If $a = b$, then $b = a$.	The symmetric property
If $a = b$ and $b = c$, then $a = c$.	The transitive property

---

The reflexive property of equality states that any number is equal to itself. The symmetric property states that if one number is equal to a second, then the second number is equal to the first. The transitive property states that if one number is equal to a second and the second number is equal to a third, then the first number is equal to the third.

Another property of equality enables us to substitute a quantity for its equal in any mathematical expression without changing the meaning of the expression.

> **The Substitution Property.**   If a and b are real numbers and $a = b$, then b can be substituted for a in any mathematical expression to obtain an equivalent expression.

Example 1   Each statement is true because of the given reason.

  a. $x - 4 = x - 4$ The reflexive property

  b. If $5x = 3y$, then $3y = 5x$.   The symmetric property

  c. If $3x = 8$ and $8 = 2y$, then $3x = 2y$.   The transitive property

  d. If $x + 3 = xy$ and $x = 9$, then $9 + 3 = 9y$.   The substitution property ■

There are many properties involving operations on the real numbers.

> **The Closure Properties.**   If a, b, and c are real numbers, then
>
> $a + b$ (the sum of a and b) is a real number.
>
> $a - b$ (the difference of a and b) is a real number.
>
> $a \cdot b$ (the product of a and b) is a real number.
>
> $\dfrac{a}{b}$ (the quotient of a and b) is a real number, provided that $b \neq 0$.

The product of a and b is often written as $a(b)$, $(a)(b)$, or just ab.

Because of the closure properties, the sum, difference, product, and quotient of any two real numbers is, again, a real number (provided there are no divisions by 0).

> **The Associative Properties.**   If a, b, and c are real numbers, then
>
> $(a + b) + c = a + (b + c)$ The associative property of addition
>
> $(ab)c = a(bc)$ The associative property of multiplication

The associative properties enable us to group, or associate, the numbers in a sum, or the numbers in a product, in any way that we wish and still be assured of the same answer. For example,

$$(2 + 3) + 4 = 5 + 4 \qquad \text{and} \qquad 2 + (3 + 4) = 2 + 7$$
$$= 9 \qquad\qquad\qquad\qquad = 9$$

The answer is 9 regardless of how we group the numbers in this sum. Likewise,

$$(2 \cdot 3) \cdot 4 = 6 \cdot 4 \qquad \text{and} \qquad 2 \cdot (3 \cdot 4) = 2 \cdot 12$$
$$= 24 \qquad\qquad\qquad\qquad = 24$$

The product is 24 regardless of how we group the numbers in this product.

Example 2   Use an associative property to simplify the expression $3 + (2 + a)$.

Solution $3 + (2 + a) = (3 + 2) + a$ Use the associative property of addition.
                               $= 5 + a$ ■

The Commutative Properties.   If a and b are real numbers, then

$a + b = b + a$ The commutative property of addition

$ab = ba$ The commutative property of multiplication

The commutative properties enable us to add or multiply two numbers in either order. We can add the first number to the second, or the second number to the first. The results are the same. Likewise, we can multiply the first number by the second, or the second number by the first, and the results are the same. For example,

$2 + 3$ and $3 + 2$ are both 5.

$7 \cdot 9$ and $9 \cdot 7$ are both 63.

Example 3   Use a commutative and an associative property to simplify the expression $(3a)4$.

Solution $(3a)4 = 4(3a)$ Use the commutative property of multiplication.
                         $= (4 \cdot 3)a$ Use the associative property of multiplication.
                         $= 12a$ ■

The Distributive Property.   If a, b, and c are real numbers, then

$a(b + c) = ab + ac$

Because of the distributive property, there are two ways of evaluating certain expressions that involve both a multiplication and an addition: We can either add first and then multiply, or multiply first and then add. Either way, the answer is the same. For example, $2(3 + 7)$ can be computed in two ways. One way is to perform the indicated addition and then the multiplication.

$$2(3 + 7) = 2 \cdot 10$$
$$= 20$$

The other way is to distribute the multiplication by 2 by first multiplying each number within the parentheses by 2 and then adding.

$$2(3 + 7) = 2 \cdot 3 + 2 \cdot 7$$
$$= 6 + 14$$
$$= 20$$

Either way, the answer is 20.

A more general form of the distributive property is called the **extended distributive property**:

$$a(b + c + d + e + \cdots) = ab + ac + ad + ae + \cdots$$

Example 4   Use the extended distributive property to simplify the expression $2(x + y + 7)$.

Solution
$$2(x + y + 7) = 2x + 2y + 2(7)$$
$$= 2x + 2y + 14$$ ■

Because adding 0 to a number leaves that number identically the same, 0 is called the **identity for addition**.

> **The Identity Element for Addition.**   There is a unique number 0, called the **additive identity**, such that
>
> $$0 + a = a + 0 = a$$

Another property of 0, called the **multiplication property of zero**, states that the product of any number and 0 is 0.

$$a \cdot 0 = 0 \cdot a = 0$$

Because multiplying a number by 1 leaves that number identically the same, 1 is called the **identity for multiplication**.

> **The Identity Element for Multiplication.**   There is a unique number 1, called the **multiplicative identity**, such that
>
> $$1 \cdot a = a \cdot 1 = a$$

If the sum of two numbers is 0, the numbers are called **additive inverses** or **negatives** of each other.

The Additive Inverse Elements.   For each real number a, there is a single number $-a$ such that

$$a + (-a) = -a + a = 0$$

The number $-a$ is called the **additive inverse** or the **negative** of a. Also, a is called the additive inverse or the negative of $-a$.

Because of the previous definition, the sum of a number and its negative is 0. For example,

$$5 + (-5) = 0 \qquad \text{and} \qquad -7 + 7 = 0$$

The symbol $-(-6)$ is read as "the negative of negative 6." Because the sum of two numbers that are negatives is 0, we have

$$-6 + [-(-6)] = 0$$

but

$$-6 + \quad 6 \quad = 0$$

Because -6 has only one additive inverse, it follows that

$$-(-6) = 6$$

In general, we have the following rule:

The Double Negative Rule.   If a represents any number, then

$$-(-a) = a$$

If the product of two numbers is 1, the numbers are called **multiplicative inverses** or **reciprocals** of each other.

The Multiplicative Inverse Elements.   For every nonzero real number a, there exists a single real number $\dfrac{1}{a}$ such that

$$a \cdot \frac{1}{a} = \frac{1}{a} \cdot a = 1$$

The number $\dfrac{1}{a}$ is called the **multiplicative inverse**, or the **reciprocal**, of a.

Also, a is called the multiplicative inverse, or the reciprocal, of $\dfrac{1}{a}$.

The existence of multiplicative inverse elements guarantees that whatever nonzero real number we start with, another real number can be found so that their product is 1. For example, the reciprocal, or multiplicative inverse, of 5 is $\frac{1}{5}$ because $5 \cdot \frac{1}{5} = 1$. The reciprocal of $-\frac{3}{2}$ is $-\frac{2}{3}$ because $(-\frac{3}{2})(-\frac{2}{3}) = 1$. A reciprocal for 0 does not exist because $\frac{1}{0}$ is an undefined mathematical expression.

Example 5   The statements in the left column are true because of the properties listed in the right column.

$2 + 7$ is a real number	The closure property for addition
$2(7)$ is a real number	The closure property for multiplication
$9 + 3 = 3 + 9$	The commutative property for addition
$8 \cdot 3 = 3 \cdot 8$	The commutative property for multiplication
$9 + (2 + 3) = (9 + 2) + 3$	The associative property for addition
$2(xy) = (2x)y$	The associative property for multiplication
$2(x + 3) = 2x + 2 \cdot 3$	The distributive property
$(a + b) + c = c + (a + b)$	The commutative property for addition
$37 + 0 = 37$	The identity property for addition
$17 \cdot 1 = 17$	The identity property for multiplication
$\frac{3}{7} + \left(-\frac{3}{7}\right) = 0$	The additive inverse property
$\frac{4}{5} \cdot \frac{5}{4} = 1$	The multiplicative inverse property ■

■ EXERCISE 1.2

In Exercises 1–4, insert either an = or an ≠ symbol to make a true statement.

1. $3 \_\_ 2 + 1$ **2.** $\frac{2}{3} \_\_ \frac{3}{4}$ **3.** $\pi \_\_ 3$ **4.** $0.375 \_\_ \frac{3}{8}$

In Exercises 5–12, tell which property of equality justifies each statement.

5.   If $a = b + c$, then $b + c = a$.   **6.**   If $x = y + z$ and $z = 3$, then $x = y + 3$.

7. $a + b + c = a + b + c$ **8.**   If $a = 37$ and $37 = b$, then $a = b$.

9.   If $x = y + z$ and $y + z = 10$, then $x = 10$.   **10.**   If $x + y = c + d$, then $c + d = x + y$.

11.   If $3x = 3y$ and $y = 4$, then $3x = 3(4)$.   **12.** $(a + b) + c = (a + b) + c$

In Exercises 13–16, use an associative property to help simplify each expression.

13. $5 + (2 + x)$ **14.** $(a + 3) + 4$ **15.** $5(3b)$ **16.** $3(2x)$

In Exercises 17–20, use a commutative property and then an associative property to help simplify each expression.

17. $(3 + b) + 7$ **18.** $7 + (a + 3)$ **19.** $(3y)2$ **20.** $(5z)3$

In Exercises 21–24, use the distributive property to remove parentheses and then simplify, if possible.

21. $3(x + 2)$ **22.** $2(3y + 4)$ **23.** $5(x + y + 4)$ **24.** $9(3 + a + b)$

In Exercises 25–40, tell which property of the real numbers justifies each statement.

25. $3(4)$ is a real number.   **26.** $5 + 5$ is a real number.

27. $3 + 7 = 7 + 3$ **28.** $2(9 \cdot 13) = (2 \cdot 9)13$

29. $3(2 + 5) = 3 \cdot 2 + 3 \cdot 5$ **30.** $1 \cdot 3 = 3 \cdot 1$

31. $81 + 0 = 0 + 81$ **32.** $3(9 + 2) = 3 \cdot 9 + 3 \cdot 2$

33. $81 + 0 = 81$ **34.** $3 + (9 + 0) = (9 + 0) + 3$

35. $5 \cdot \dfrac{1}{5} = 1$ **36.** $a + (3 + y) = (a + 3) + y$

37. $2 + (7 + 8) = (2 + 7) + 8$ **38.** $1 \cdot 3 = 3$

39. $(2 \cdot 3)4 = 4(2 \cdot 3)$ **40.** $8 + (-8) = 0$

*In Exercises 41–52, find the **additive inverse** of each number. If necessary, simplify the expression first, and then find the additive inverse of the result.*

41. 1 **42.** 3 **43.** -8 **44.** -7 **45.** 0 **46.** $\dfrac{1}{2}$

47. π **48.** a **49.** $2 + 8$ **50.** $5 - 3$ **51.** $-(7 - 4)$ **52.** $-\dfrac{8}{2}$

*In Exercises 53–60, find the **multiplicative inverse** (the reciprocal) of each number, provided one exists.*

53. 1 **54.** 3 **55.** $\dfrac{1}{2}$ **56.** $-\dfrac{7}{5}$

57. -0.25 **58.** $0.333 \ldots$ **59.** 0 **60.** 1.25

In Exercises 61–64, give a reason for each step in each proof.

61. Prove that $(a + b) + c = a + (c + b)$.

$$(a + b) + c = a + (b + c) \quad \underline{\hspace{4cm}}$$
$$= a + (c + b) \quad \underline{\hspace{4cm}}$$

62. Prove that $a(b + c) = ca + ba$.

$$a(b + c) = ab + ac \quad \underline{\hspace{4cm}}$$
$$= ac + ab \quad \underline{\hspace{4cm}}$$
$$= ca + ab \quad \underline{\hspace{4cm}}$$
$$= ca + ba \quad \underline{\hspace{4cm}}$$

63. Prove that $(b + c)a = ba + ca$.

$$(b + c)a = a(b + c) \quad \underline{\hspace{4cm}}$$
$$= ab + ac \quad \underline{\hspace{4cm}}$$
$$= ba + ac \quad \underline{\hspace{4cm}}$$
$$= ba + ca \quad \underline{\hspace{4cm}}$$

64. Prove that $(ab)(cd) = (ad)(bc)$.

$$(ab)(cd) = (cd)(ab) \quad \underline{\hspace{4cm}}$$
$$= c[d(ab)] \quad \underline{\hspace{4cm}}$$
$$= c[(da)b] \quad \underline{\hspace{4cm}}$$
$$= c[(ad)b] \quad \underline{\hspace{4cm}}$$
$$= [(ad)b]c \quad \underline{\hspace{4cm}}$$
$$= (ad)(bc) \quad \underline{\hspace{4cm}}$$

1.3   INEQUALITIES AND GRAPHS OF SETS OF REAL NUMBERS

Sets of numbers can be pictured, or graphed, on a number line. To do so, we construct a number line by choosing some point on a line (called the **origin**) and giving it a number value (a **coordinate**) of 0. We then locate points that are equal distances to the right and to the left of 0, and label them with coordinates, as shown in Figure 1-2. The point on the number line corresponding to the real number -4 is the point with coordinate -4. The point corresponding to the real number $\frac{13}{2}$ is the point midway between the points with coordinates 6 and 7. The point corresponding to the real number π is the point with coordinate $3.14159\ldots$. To every real number there corresponds exactly one point on the number line, called its **graph**, and to each point there corresponds exactly one real number, which is its coordinate.

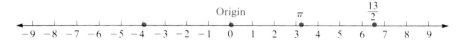

Figure 1-2

Real numbers such as 5 and 25.347 that are to the right of 0 are called **positive numbers**. Sometimes these numbers are preceded by a $+$ sign:

$$+5 = 5 \qquad +25.347 = 25.347 \qquad +\pi = \pi$$

Real numbers such as -4 and $-\frac{17}{2}$ that are to the left of 0 are called **negative numbers**. The number 0 is neither positive nor negative.

Example 1   Graph the set of even integers between -5 and 5.

Solution   The graph of the set of even integers between -5 and 5 includes the points with coordinates -4, -2, 0, 2, and 4. The graph is shown in Figure 1-3.

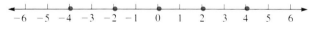

Figure 1-3   ■

If a point lies to the right of a second point on the number line, its coordinate is the greater. For example, on the number line the point with coordinate 4 lies to the right of the point with coordinate -2. Thus,

$$4 > -2 \qquad \text{Read as "4 is greater than negative 2."}$$

If a point on the number line is to the left of another, its coordinate is the smaller. The point with coordinate -5, for example, lies to the left of the point with coordinate -1. Thus,

$$-5 < -1 \qquad \text{Read as "negative 5 is less than negative 1."}$$

Two other common inequality symbols are

$\leq$ Read as "is less than or equal to."

and

$\geq$ Read as "is greater than or equal to."

Example 2 **a.** $-7 > -10$ because -7 is to the right of -10 on the number line.

b. $5 < 8$ because   5 is to the left of 8 on the number line.

c. $15 \leq 15$ because $15 = 15$.

d. $20 \geq -19$ because $20 > -19$.   ∎

Inequality statements can be written so that the inequality symbol points in the opposite direction. For example, the inequality

$-3 \leq 9$ can be written as $9 \geq -3$.

To say that a number is not less than 0, we write $x \not< 0$. This is equivalent to saying that $x \geq 0$. Likewise,

$x \not> 0$ is equivalent to $x \leq 0$.
$x \not\geq 0$ is equivalent to $x < 0$.
$x \not\leq 0$ is equivalent to $x > 0$.
$x \neq 0$ is equivalent to $x < 0$ or $x > 0$.

If a and b are two numbers, either a and b are equal or they are not. If they are not equal, then one or the other must be the larger. The possibilities are summed up in the following property.

The Trichotomy Property.   If a and b are real numbers, then exactly one of the following statements is true:

$a < b$ or $a = b$ or $a > b$

Many of the inequality relationships have a transitive property.

The Transitive Property of Inequality.   If a, b, and c are real numbers, then

If $a < b$ and $b < c$, then $a < c$.

A similar statement is true for the $>$, $\leq$, and $\geq$ symbols.

Example 3 **a.** By the trichotomy property, if x is a real number, then

$$x < 5 \quad \text{or} \quad x = 5 \quad \text{or} \quad x > 5$$

b. By the transitive property,

if $x > 12$ and $12 > 5$, then $x > 5$. ∎

Graphs of sets of real numbers are often portions of the number line, called **intervals**. For example, Figure 1-4 shows the graph of all real numbers greater than 3. The open circle at 3 indicates that 3 is *not* included. This interval, which includes no endpoints, is called an **open interval** and is denoted by the inequality

$$x > 3$$

In **interval notation** this interval is denoted as $(3, \infty)$, where the symbol ∞ is read as "infinity." In this notation the parentheses indicate that neither endpoint is included.

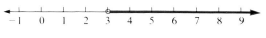

Figure 1-4

The interval shown in Figure 1-5 includes all real numbers x such that $x \le -3$. The solid circle at -3 indicates that -3 is included. Because exactly one endpoint is included in the graph, this interval is called a **half-open interval**. In interval notation, it is denoted as $(-\infty, -3]$. The bracket indicates that the endpoint with coordinate -3 is included.

Figure 1-5

To graph the set of real numbers between -4 and 2 (see Figure 1-6), we graph the open interval denoted by the inequalities

$$x > -4 \quad \text{and} \quad x < 2$$

or, more briefly, by the double inequality

$$-4 < x < 2 \qquad \text{Read as "-4 is less than x, which, in turn, is less than 2."}$$

In interval notation this open interval is expressed as $(-4, 2)$.

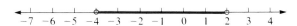

Figure 1-6

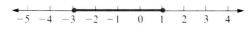

Figure 1-7

The interval shown in Figure 1-7, called a **closed interval**, includes two endpoints. It is denoted by the double inequality $-3 \leq x \leq 1$, or in interval notation by $[-3, 1]$. The brackets indicate that both endpoints are included.

The half-open interval shown in Figure 1-8 is denoted by the double inequality $0 \leq x < 5$, or in interval notation by $[0, 5)$.

Figure 1-8

Example 4   If $A = (-2, 4)$ and $B = [1, 5)$, find the graph of

a. $A \cup B$ and   **b.** $A \cap B$.

Solution   **a.**   The union of intervals A and B is the set of all real numbers that are elements of either set A or set B or both. Numbers between -2 and 4 are in set A, and numbers between 1 and 5 (including 1) are in set B. Numbers between -2 and 5 are in at least one of these sets. To see this, refer to Figure 1.9(a). Thus,

$$A \cup B = (-2, 4) \cup [1, 5) = (-2, 5)$$

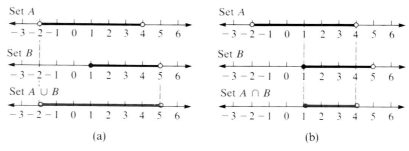

Figure 1-9

b.   The intersection of intervals A and B is the set of all real numbers that are elements of both set A and set B. The numbers that are in both of these sets are those numbers between 1 and 4 (including 1). To see this, refer to Figure 1-9(b). Thus,

$$A \cap B = (-2, 4) \cap [1, 5) = [1, 4)$$ ∎

The **absolute value** of any real number a, denoted as $|a|$, is the distance on the number line between the origin and the point with coordinate a. Because the points shown in Figure 1-10 with coordinates of 3 and -3 both lie 3 units

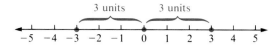

Figure 1-10

from 0,

$$|3| = |-3| = 3$$

Similarly, because the points with coordinates -15 and 15 both lie 15 units from 0,

$$|-15| = |15| = 15$$

In general, for any real number a,

$$|a| = |-a|$$

The absolute value of a number can be defined more formally as follows:

> **Definition.**   If $x \geq 0$, then $|x| = x$.
> If $x < 0$, then $|x| = -x$.

The previous definition indicates that if x is a positive number or 0, then x is its own absolute value. However, if x is a negative number, then $-x$ (which is a positive number) is the absolute value of x. Thus, $|x|$ always represents a nonnegative number. In general, for all x

$$|x| \geq 0$$

Example 5   **a.** $|8| = 8$ **b.** $|-4| = -(-4) = 4$

c. $|0| = 0$ **d.** $-|7| = -7$

e. $-|-7| = -(7)$ **f.** $|7 - 2| - (-3) = |5| + 3$
$$= -7 \qquad\qquad\qquad = 5 + 3$$
$$= 8 \qquad \blacksquare$$

▬ EXERCISE 1.3

In Exercises 1–4, graph each set on the number line.

1.   The set of prime numbers less than 10.

2.   The set of negative integers between -10 and 0.

3.   The set of odd integers between 10 and 20.

4.   The set of composite numbers less than 10.

In Exercises 5–10, insert one of the symbols $<$ or $>$ to make a true statement.

5.   5 __ 9

6.   9 __ 0

7. -5 __ -10

8. -3 __ 10

9. -7 __ 7

10.   6 __ -6

In Exercises 11–16, rewrite each statement with the inequality symbol pointing in the opposite direction.

11. $19 > 12$ **12.** $-3 \geq -5$ **13.** $-6 \leq -5$ **14.** $-10 < 13$

15. $5 \geq -3$ **16.** $-10 \leq 0$

In Exercises 17–20, rewrite each statement using one of the symbols $<$ or $>$.

17. $x \nleq 3$ **18.** $y \ngeq 4$ **19.** $z \ngeq 4$ **20.** $t \nleq -2$

In Exercises 21–24, rewrite each expression using one of the symbols $\leq$ or $\geq$.

21. $x \nless 7$ **22.** $x \ngtr 3$ **23.** $x \ngtr -3$ **24.** $x \nless -7$

In Exercises 25–36, graph each interval on the number line.

25. $x > 3$ **26.** $x < 0$ **27.** $-3 < x < 2$ **28.** $-5 \leq x < 2$

29. $0 < x \leq 5$ **30.** $-4 \leq x \leq -2$ **31.** $(-2, \infty)$ **32.** $(-\infty, 4]$

33. $[-6, 9]$ **34.** $(-1, 3)$ **35.** $(2, 4]$ **36.** $[-5, 2]$

In Exercises 37–42, A, B, and C are intervals with $A = [-4, 4]$, $B = (0, 6)$, and $C = [2, 8)$. Graph each set.

37. $A \cap C$ **38.** $B \cup C$ **39.** $A \cup C$ **40.** $A \cap B$

41. $A \cap B \cap C$ **42.** $A \cup B \cup C$

In Exercises 43–52, write each expression without using absolute value symbols.

43. $|20|$ **44.** $|-20|$ **45.** $-|-6|$ **46.** $-|8|$

47. $|-5| + |0|$ **48.** $-|0| + |-4|$

49. $|-15| - |10| - (-2)$ **50.** $|-4| - |-4| - (-4)$

51. $|5 - 3| - (-|-1|)$ **52.** $|18 - 5| - (-|-18|)$

53. How many integers have an absolute value that is less than 50?

54. How many odd integers have an absolute value between 20 and 40?

55. What numbers are equal to their own absolute values?

56. What numbers when added to their own absolute values give a sum of 0?

57. What numbers must x and y be if $|x| + |y| = 0$?

58. What numbers must x and y be if $|x + y| = 0$?

59. Does the absolute value of the product of two numbers equal the product of their absolute values? Explain.

60. Does the absolute value of the sum of two numbers equal the sum of their absolute values? Explain.

61. If $|x| = 3$, what numbers could x be?

62. If $|x| = 7$, what numbers could x be?

1.4 ARITHMETIC OF REAL NUMBERS

If x and y are added, the result (denoted by $x + y$) is called their **sum**. Each of the numbers x and y is called a **term** of that sum.

Suppose we wish to add the numbers $+2$ and $+3$. Because the positive direction on the number line is to the right, we can represent $+2$ with an arrow

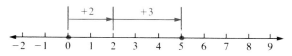

Figure 1-11

of length 2 pointing to the right. Likewise, we can represent $+3$ with an arrow of length 3 also pointing to the right. To find the sum $(+2) + (+3)$, we start at the origin and place the arrows end to end as in Figure 1-11. The endpoint of the second arrow is the point with coordinate $+5$. Thus,

$$+2 + (+3) = +5$$

We can represent the numbers in the addition problem

$$(-2) + (-3)$$

with arrows as in Figure 1-12. We represent -2 with an arrow of length 2 that begins at the origin and points to the left. Then using -2 as a starting point, we represent -3 with an arrow of length 3 that also points to the left. Because the endpoint of the final arrow has coordinate -5,

$$(-2) + (-3) = -5$$

Figure 1-12

Because two numbers with like signs are represented by arrows pointing in the same direction, we have the following rule:

Adding Real Numbers with Like Signs.   If two real numbers a and b have the same sign, their sum is found by adding their absolute values and using their common sign.

Example 1   **a.** $+4 + (+6) = +(|+4| + |+6|)$ **b.** $-4 + (-6) = -(|-4| + |-6|)$
$= +(4 + 6)$ $= -(4 + 6)$
$= +10$ $= -10$ ■

Two real numbers with unlike signs can be represented by arrows that point in opposite directions. For example, to add -6 and $+2$, we refer to the number line in Figure 1-13 where the number -6 is represented by an arrow of length 6 that begins at the origin and points to the left. The arrow representing $+2$

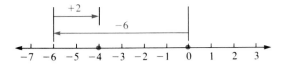

Figure 1-13

begins at -6, has length 2, and points to the right. The endpoint of this final arrow is the point with coordinate -4. Thus,

$$(-6) + (+2) = -4$$

The arrows in Figure 1-14 represent the numbers in the addition problem

$$(+7) + (-4)$$

The first arrow begins at the origin, has length 7, and points to the right. The second arrow begins at point 7, has length 4, and points to the left. The endpoint of the final arrow is the point with coordinate $+3$. Thus,

$$(+7) + (-4) = +3$$

Figure 1-14

Because two real numbers with unlike signs are represented by arrows pointing in opposite directions, we have the following rule:

> **Adding Real Numbers with Unlike Signs.**   If two real numbers a and b have unlike signs, their sum is found by subtracting their absolute values (the smaller from the larger) and using the sign of the number with the greater absolute value.

Example 2   **a.** $\begin{aligned} +6 + (-5) &= +(|+6| - |-5|) \\ &= +(6 - 5) \\ &= +1 \end{aligned}$ **b.** $\begin{aligned} -2 + (+5) &= +(|+5| - |-2|) \\ &= +(5 - 2) \\ &= +3 \end{aligned}$

c. $\begin{aligned} 6 + (-9) &= -(|-9| - |6|) \\ &= -(9 - 6) \\ &= -3 \end{aligned}$ **d.** $\begin{aligned} -10 + (4) &= -(|-10| - |4|) \\ &= -(10 - 4) \\ &= -6 \end{aligned}$ ■

It is always possible to express a subtraction problem as an equivalent addition problem. For example, we can think of the subtraction problem

$$7 - 4$$

as the addition problem

$$7 + (-4)$$

because they have the same answer:

$$7 - 4 = 3 \quad \text{and} \quad 7 + (-4) = 3$$

We use this idea to define the **difference** (the answer to a subtraction problem) when b is to be subtracted from a.

Subtracting Real Numbers.   If a and b are real numbers, then

$$a - b = a + (-b)$$

Example 3   Evaluate   **a.** $12 - 4$,   **b.** $-13 - 5$, and   **c.** $-14 - (-6)$.

Solution   Use the rule for finding the difference of two real numbers:

a. $12 - 4 = 12 + (-4)$ **b.** $-13 - 5 = -13 + (-5)$
$\qquad\qquad = 8$ $\qquad\qquad\qquad\qquad = -18$

c. $-14 - (-6) = -14 + [-(-6)]$
$\qquad\qquad\quad = -14 + 6$ Use the double negative rule.
$\qquad\qquad\quad = -8$ ■

The result of multiplying two numbers x and y is called the **product** of x and y. Each of the numbers x and y is called a **factor** of that product. Multiplication by a positive number can be thought of as repeated addition. The expression $5(4)$, for example, means that 4 is to be used as a term in an indicated sum five times. Thus,

$$5(4) = 4 + 4 + 4 + 4 + 4$$
$$\quad = 20$$

Likewise, the expression $5(-4)$ means that -4 is to be used as a term in a sum five times. Thus,

$$5(-4) = (-4) + (-4) + (-4) + (-4) + (-4)$$
$$\quad = -20$$

If multiplication by a positive number means repeated addition, then it is reasonable to assume that multiplication by a negative number means repeated subtraction. The expression $-5(4)$ means that 4 is to be used as a term in a repeated subtraction five times. Thus,

$$-5(4) = -4 - 4 - 4 - 4 - 4$$
$$= -4 + (-4) + (-4) + (-4) + (-4)$$
$$= -20$$

Likewise, the expression $-5(-4)$ means that -4 is to be used as a term in a repeated subtraction five times. Thus,

$$-5(-4) = -(-4) - (-4) - (-4) - (-4) - (-4)$$
$$= 4 + [-(-4)] + [-(-4)] + [-(-4)] + [-(-4)]$$
$$= 4 + 4 + 4 + 4 + 4$$
$$= 20$$

Note that the products $5(4)$ and $-5(-4)$ both equal $+20$, and that the products $5(-4)$ and $-5(4)$ both equal -20. These results suggest the following rule:

Multiplying Real Numbers.
1. The product of two real numbers with like signs is the positive product of their absolute values.
2. The product of two real numbers with unlike signs is the negative of the product of their absolute values.

Note that, if x is any real number, then $x \cdot 0 = 0 \cdot x = 0$.

Example 4   Use the rules for multiplying real numbers to find each product:

   a. $4(-7)$,   **b.** $-5(-6)$,   **c.** $-7(6)$, and   **d.** $8(6)$.

Solution   **a.** $4(-7) = -(|4| \cdot |-7|)$ **b.** $-5(-6) = +(|-5| \cdot |-6|)$
             $= -(4 \cdot 7)$ $= +(5 \cdot 6)$
             $= -28$ $= +30$

   c. $-7(6) = -(|-7| \cdot |6|)$ **d.** $8(6) = +(|8| \cdot |6|)$
             $= -(7 \cdot 6)$ $= +(8 \cdot 6)$
             $= -42$ $= +48$ ∎

Just as subtraction is defined in terms of addition, division is defined in terms of multiplication. When x is divided by a nonzero number y, the result is called the **quotient** of x and y, and we can write

$$\frac{x}{y} = q$$

The quotient q is that number which, when multiplied by y, gives x.

$$yq = x$$

This special relationship can be used to develop the rules for dividing one real number by a nonzero real number. We consider four divisions:

$$\frac{+10}{+2} = +5 \quad \text{because} \quad +2(+5) = +10.$$

$$\frac{-10}{-2} = +5 \quad \text{because} \quad -2(+5) = -10.$$

$$\frac{+10}{-2} = -5 \quad \text{because} \quad -2(-5) = +10.$$

$$\frac{-10}{+2} = -5 \quad \text{because} \quad +2(-5) = -10.$$

The results of the previous examples suggest that the rules for dividing real numbers are very similar to the rules for multiplying real numbers.

Dividing Real Numbers.

1. The quotient of two real numbers with like signs is the positive quotient of their absolute values.
2. The quotient of two real numbers with unlike signs is the negative of the quotient of their absolute values.
3. Division by 0 is undefined.

Note that, if x is any nonzero number, then $\dfrac{0}{x} = 0$.

Example 5   Use the rules for dividing real numbers to find each quotient:

$$\textbf{a.} \quad \frac{36}{18}, \quad \textbf{b.} \quad \frac{-44}{11}, \quad \textbf{c.} \quad \frac{27}{-9}, \text{ and} \quad \textbf{d.} \quad \frac{-64}{-8}$$

Solution   **a.**
$$\frac{36}{18} = +\frac{|36|}{|18|}$$
$$= \frac{36}{18}$$
$$= 2$$

b.
$$\frac{-44}{11} = -\frac{|-44|}{|11|}$$
$$= -\frac{44}{11}$$
$$= -4$$

c.
$$\frac{27}{-9} = -\frac{|27|}{|-9|}$$
$$= -\frac{27}{9}$$
$$= -3$$

d.
$$\frac{-64}{-8} = +\frac{|-64|}{|-8|}$$
$$= \frac{64}{8}$$
$$= 8$$

■

Order of Operations

The expression $2 \cdot 3 + 4$ seems to have two answers depending upon whether the addition or the multiplication is done first. If we were to add first, the answer would be $2(3 + 4) = 2 \cdot 7 = 14$. If we were to multiply first, the answer would be $(2 \cdot 3) + 4 = 6 + 4 = 10$. Unless there is agreement on which operation is to be done first, there is no way of knowing which of these answers is correct. To remove this ambiguity, mathematicians agree on the following order of operations.

> **Order of Operations.**   Unless grouping symbols indicate otherwise, perform the multiplications and/or divisions, in order from left to right. After that, perform the additions and/or subtractions, in order from left to right.

Example 6   Calculate: **a.** $2 \cdot 3 + 4$,   **b.** $2(3 + 4)$,   **c.** $10 \div 5 \cdot 2$, and   **d.** $10 \div (5 \cdot 2)$.

Solution   **a.**   Because parentheses do not indicate otherwise, the multiplication is done first, followed by the addition.

$$2 \cdot 3 + 4 = 6 + 4$$
$$= 10$$

b.   Here the parentheses indicate that the addition must be done first.

$$2(3 + 4) = 2 \cdot 7$$
$$= 14$$

c.   With the absence of grouping symbols to indicate otherwise, the multiplications and/or divisions are done in the order in which they are encountered (from left to right).

$$10 \div 5 \cdot 2 = (10 \div 5)2$$
$$= 2 \cdot 2$$
$$= 4$$

d.   The parentheses indicate that the multiplication is to be done first. Hence,

$$10 \div (5 \cdot 2) = 10 \div 10$$
$$= 1$$ ∎

Example 7   Perform the following calculations: **a.** $5 \cdot 3 - 6 \div 3 + 1$,   **b.** $5(3 - 6) \div 3 + 1$, and   **c.** $5(3 - 6 \div 3) + 1$.

Solution   **a.**   Do the multiplications and divisions first, and then the additions and subtractions, from left to right.

$$5 \cdot 3 - 6 \div 3 + 1 = 15 - 2 + 1$$
$$= 13 + 1$$
$$= 14$$

b.   The parentheses indicate that a subtraction must be done first, then the multiplications and divisions in order from left to right. The addition is done last.

$$5(3 - 6) \div 3 + 1 = 5(-3) \div 3 + 1$$
$$= -15 \div 3 + 1$$
$$= -5 + 1$$
$$= -4$$

c.   The operations within the parentheses must be done first; and within the parentheses, the division has priority over the subtraction.

$$5(3 - 6 \div 3) + 1 = 5(3 - 2) + 1$$
$$= 5 \cdot 1 + 1$$
$$= 5 + 1$$
$$= 6 \qquad \blacksquare$$

Often, we will encounter arithmetic that needs to be done in both the numerator and denominator of a fraction. To simplify such a fraction, we carry out all indicated operations in the numerator and the denominator separately. Then we simplify the fraction, if possible.

Example 8   If $a = 2$, $b = -3$, and $c = -5$, evaluate $\dfrac{ab + 3c}{b(c - a)}$.

Solution   Substitute 2 for a, -3 for b, -5 for c, do the work in the numerator and denominator separately, and then simplify.

$$\frac{ab + 3c}{b(c - a)} = \frac{2(-3) + 3(-5)}{-3(-5 - 2)}$$
$$= \frac{-6 + (-15)}{-3(-7)}$$
$$= \frac{-21}{21}$$
$$= -1 \qquad \blacksquare$$

Properties of Fractions

In algebra we will often encounter fractions. We summarize the properties of arithmetic fractions here and will discuss algebraic fractions in detail in Chapter 5.

Properties of Fractions.   If no denominators are 0, then

1. $\dfrac{a}{b} = \dfrac{c}{d}$ if and only if $ad = bc$

2. $\dfrac{a}{1} = a$ and   if $a \neq 0$, $\dfrac{a}{a} = 1$

3. If $k \neq 0$, $\dfrac{a}{b} = \dfrac{ak}{bk}$

4. $\dfrac{a}{b} \cdot \dfrac{c}{d} = \dfrac{ac}{bd}$ and $\dfrac{a}{b} \div \dfrac{c}{d} = \dfrac{a}{b} \cdot \dfrac{d}{c} = \dfrac{ad}{bc}$

5. $\dfrac{a}{b} + \dfrac{c}{b} = \dfrac{a+c}{b}$ and $\dfrac{a}{b} - \dfrac{c}{b} = \dfrac{a-c}{b}$

6. $-\dfrac{a}{b} = \dfrac{-a}{b} = \dfrac{a}{-b}$

Property 1 points out that fractions are equal if the same product occurs when "cross multiplying." For example,

$$\frac{2}{3} = \frac{8}{12} \quad \text{because} \quad \begin{aligned} 2(12) &= 3(8) \\ 24 &= 24 \end{aligned}$$

Property 2 points out that any number divided by 1 is left unchanged and that any nonzero number divided by itself is 1.

Property 3 is used to simplify fractions because it enables us to simplify fractions containing common factors in both the numerator and the denominator. For example, to simplify the fraction $\frac{27}{90}$ we proceed as follows:

$$\frac{27}{90} = \frac{9 \cdot 3}{9 \cdot 10} = \frac{\cancel{9} \cdot 3}{\cancel{9} \cdot 10} = \frac{3}{10}$$

Property 3 is also used to build fractions. For example, to write the fraction $\frac{3}{4}$ as a fraction with a denominator of 20 we use Property 3 and multiply both the numerator and the denominator of $\frac{3}{4}$ by 5:

$$\frac{3}{4} = \frac{3 \cdot 5}{4 \cdot 5} = \frac{15}{20}$$

Property 4 asserts that the product of two fractions is found by multiplying their numerators and multiplying their denominators, and that the quotient of two fractions is found by inverting the **divisor** (the fraction following the $\div$ symbol) and multiplying. For example,

$$\frac{1}{3} \cdot \frac{2}{5} = \frac{1 \cdot 2}{3 \cdot 5} = \frac{2}{15}$$

$$\frac{3}{7} \cdot \frac{21}{5} = \frac{3 \cdot 21}{7 \cdot 5} = \frac{3 \cdot 3 \cdot \cancel{7}}{\cancel{7} \cdot 5} = \frac{3 \cdot 3}{5} = \frac{9}{5}$$

and

$$\frac{3}{7} \div \left(-\frac{5}{4}\right) = \frac{3}{7} \cdot \left(-\frac{4}{5}\right) = -\frac{3 \cdot 4}{7 \cdot 5} = -\frac{12}{35}$$

Property 5 enables us to add or subtract fractions with common denominators. To add or subtract fractions with unlike denominators, we must use Property 3 to build the fractions into fractions with common denominators. For example,

$$\frac{6}{7} - \frac{2}{7} = \frac{6}{7} + \left(-\frac{2}{7}\right) = \frac{6 + (-2)}{7} = \frac{4}{7}$$

$$\frac{3}{5} + \frac{4}{7} = \frac{3 \cdot 7}{5 \cdot 7} + \frac{4 \cdot 5}{7 \cdot 5} = \frac{21}{35} + \frac{20}{35} = \frac{41}{35}$$

$$\frac{5}{6} - \frac{3}{4} = \frac{5 \cdot 2}{6 \cdot 2} - \frac{3 \cdot 3}{4 \cdot 3} = \frac{10}{12} - \frac{9}{12} = \frac{1}{12}$$

We need not write a fraction such as $\frac{41}{35}$ as the mixed number $1\frac{6}{35}$. In algebra, **improper fractions** (fractions with numerators greater than their denominators) are preferred.

Property 6 points out that a $-$ sign placed in front of a fraction can be written in either the numerator or the denominator of the fraction. For example,

$$-\frac{2}{3} = \frac{-2}{3} = \frac{2}{-3}$$

■ EXERCISE 1.4

In Exercises 1–50, perform the indicated operations.

1.	$-3 + (-5)$	**2.**	$2 + (+8)$	**3.**	$-7 + (-2)$	**4.**	$3 + (-5)$
5.	$2 + (-8)$	**6.**	$-5 + 3$	**7.**	$-7 + 2$	**8.**	$3 + (-7)$
9.	$8 + (-2)$	**10.**	$-17 + (-8)$	**11.**	$0 - (-17)$	**12.**	$0 - 21$
13.	$0 - 93$	**14.**	$0 - (-57)$	**15.**	$3 - 5$	**16.**	$3 - (-4)$
17.	$-3 - 4$	**18.**	$-11 - (-17)$	**19.**	$-33 - (-33)$	**20.**	$14 - (-13)$
21.	$-2(6)$	**22.**	$3(-5)$	**23.**	$-3(-7)$	**24.**	$-2(-5)$
25.	$\dfrac{-8}{4}$	**26.**	$\dfrac{25}{-5}$	**27.**	$\dfrac{-16}{-4}$	**28.**	$\dfrac{2-6}{-8-(-12)}$
29.	$\dfrac{9-5}{5-9}$	**30.**	$\dfrac{8+2}{3-8}$	**31.**	$3 - 2 - 1$	**32.**	$5 - 3 - 1$

33. $3 - (2 - 1)$ **34.** $5 - (3 - 1)$ **35.** $2 - 3 \cdot 5$ **36.** $6 + 4 \cdot 7$

37. $8 \div 4 \div 2$ **38.** $50 \div 10 \div 5$ **39.** $8 \div (4 \div 2)$ **40.** $50 \div (10 \div 5)$

41. $2 + 6 \div 3 - 5$ **42.** $6 - 8 \div 4 - 2$ **43.** $(2 + 6) \div (3 - 5)$ **44.** $(6 - 8) \div (4 - 2)$

45. $\dfrac{3(8 + 4)}{2 \cdot 3 - 9}$ **46.** $\dfrac{5(4 - 1)}{3 \cdot 2 + 5 \cdot 3}$ **47.** $\dfrac{100(2 - 4)}{1000 \div 10 \div 10}$ **48.** $\dfrac{8(3) - 4(6)}{5(3) + 3(-7)}$

49. $\dfrac{5 \div (2 - 3)}{5(2 - 3)}$ **50.** $\dfrac{4(3 - 7)}{4(3) - 7}$

In Exercises 51–58, a = 3, b = −2, c = −1, and d = 2. Evaluate each expression.

51. $ab + cd$ **52.** $ad + bc$ **53.** $a(b + c)$ **54.** $d(b + a)$

55. $\dfrac{ad + c}{cd + b}$ **56.** $\dfrac{ab + d}{bd + a}$ **57.** $\dfrac{ac - bd}{cd - ad}$ **58.** $\dfrac{bc - ad}{bd + ac}$

In Exercises 59–64, a = −1, b = 3, c = −3, and d = −2. Evaluate each expression.

59. $ad - d$ **60.** $db - d$ **61.** $\dfrac{ad + dc - bd}{(a - d)(b + d)}$ **62.** $\dfrac{ab - bc + cd}{(a - c)(b - d)}$

63. $\dfrac{(a + c)(b - d)}{(a + b \cdot d)(-c)}$ **64.** $\dfrac{(c \cdot d - b + a)(a - b \cdot c + d)}{(c - d \cdot c)(-b + c)(c - d)}$

In Exercises 65–74, use signed numbers to solve each problem.

65. One day Scott earned $22.17 mowing lawns and $39.56 painting a picnic bench. How much did he earn?

66. Wendy lost 3 pounds after an illness. She then dieted and lost 11 pounds. How much weight did Wendy lose?

67. The temperature rose 7 degrees in 1 hour. It then dropped 3 degrees in the next hour. What was the net change in the temperature?

68. An army retreated 2300 meters. After regrouping, they moved forward 1750 meters. The next day they gained another 1875 meters. What was the army's net gain (or loss)?

69. Sally had $437 in a bank account. One month, she had deposits of $25, $37, and $45. That same month, she had withdrawals of $17, $83, and $22. How much was in her account at the end of the month?

70. If the temperature is dropping 4 degrees each hour, how much warmer was it 3 hours ago?

71. In Las Vegas, Harry lost $30 per hour playing the slot machines. How much did he lose after gambling for 15 hours?

72. The flow of water from a pipe is filling a pool at the rate of 23 gallons per minute. How much less water was in the pool 5 hours ago?

73. If a drain is emptying a pool at the rate of 12 gallons per minute, how much more water was in the pool 2 hours ago?

74. John worked all day mowing lawns. He was paid $8 per hour. If he had $94 in his pocket at the end of an 8-hour day, how much money did he have before he started working?

In Exercises 75–76, tell whether the given fractions are equal.

75. $\dfrac{14}{15}, \dfrac{42}{45}$ **76.** $\dfrac{11}{13}, \dfrac{133}{169}$

In Exercises 77–80, simplify each fraction.

77. $\dfrac{12}{15}$

78. $-\dfrac{18}{36}$

79. $-\dfrac{48}{72}$

80. $\dfrac{539}{637}$

In Exercises 81–92, perform the indicated operations and simplify the answer, if possible.

81. $\dfrac{1}{4} \cdot \dfrac{3}{5}$

82. $-\dfrac{3}{5}\left(\dfrac{20}{27}\right)$

83. $-\dfrac{2}{3} \div \left(-\dfrac{3}{7}\right)$

84. $\dfrac{1}{4} \div \dfrac{3}{5}$

85. $-\dfrac{3}{5} \div \dfrac{9}{15}\left(-\dfrac{5}{27}\right)$

86. $\dfrac{1}{3} \div \dfrac{3}{4} \cdot \dfrac{5}{3} \div \dfrac{1}{2}$

87. $\dfrac{2}{3} + \dfrac{4}{3}$

88. $\dfrac{9}{14} - \dfrac{3}{14}$

89. $\dfrac{2}{5} - \dfrac{7}{9}$

90. $\dfrac{2}{3} + \dfrac{4}{5}$

91. $-\dfrac{3}{5}\left(\dfrac{1}{7} + \dfrac{2}{3}\right)$

92. $\dfrac{2}{3}\left(-\dfrac{3}{4} + \dfrac{1}{3}\right)$

93. Jim baked 4 dozen cookies, and took two-thirds of them to a bake sale. How many were left for his family to eat?

94. One dessert recipe calls for 8 eggs, while another recipe requires only three-fourths of that number. How many eggs will Jim need to make both desserts?

95. Sandy lost 15 pounds on a recent diet. Following the same diet, Jane lost one-third as much as Sandy, and Sue lost two-fifths as much as Sandy. How many pounds did Sandy, Jane, and Sue lose combined?

96. In January, Stu earned $3000 in commissions. In February, his commissions dropped to five-sixths of January's earnings, and during March, commissions were only two-fifths of January's. How much did Stu earn in commissions during the first quarter of that year?

CHAPTER SUMMARY

Key words

absolute value (1.3)	*null set* (1.1)
closed interval (1.3)	*open interval* (1.3)
coordinate (1.3)	*origin* (1.3)
difference (1.4)	*positive numbers* (1.3)
disjoint sets (1.1)	*product* (1.4)
element of a set (1.1)	*quotient* (1.4)
ellipsis (1.1)	*reciprocal* (1.2)
empty set (1.1)	*repeating decimal* (1.1)
factor (1.4)	*set* (1.1)
finite set (1.1)	*set-builder notation* (1.1)
graph (1.3)	*subset* (1.1)
half-open interval (1.3)	*sum* (1.4)
improper fraction (1.4)	*term* (1.4)
infinite set (1.1)	*terminating decimal* (1.1)
intersection of two sets (1.1)	*union of two sets* (1.1)
interval (1.3)	*variable* (1.1)
negative numbers (1.3)	

Key Ideas

(1.1)   Two sets are equal if they have the same elements.

The **natural numbers** are the numbers 1, 2, 3, 4, 5, . . .

A **prime number** is a natural number greater than 1 that is divisible without remainder only by itself and 1.

A **composite number** is a natural number greater than 1 that is not a prime number.

The **whole numbers** are the numbers 0, 1, 2, 3, 4, 5, . . .

The **integers** are the numbers . . . , -4, -3, -2, -1, 0, 1, 2, 3, 4, . . .

If an integer n is divisible by 2, then n is an **even integer**.

If an integer n is not divisible by 2, then n is an **odd integer**.

A **rational number** is any number that can be written as a fraction with an integer numerator and a nonzero integer denominator. Any rational number can be written in decimal form as either a terminating or a repeating decimal.

An **irrational number** is any number that can be written in decimal form as a nonterminating, nonrepeating decimal.

A **real number** is any number that can be written in decimal form.

(1.2)   The **reflexive property**: $a = a$.

The **symmetric property**:   If $a = b$, then $b = a$.

The **transitive property**:   If $a = b$ and $b = c$, then $a = c$.

The **substitution property**:   In any expression a quantity can be substituted for its equal without changing the meaning of the expression.

The **closure properties**: $a + b$ is a real number.

$\qquad\qquad\qquad\qquad\qquad$ $a - b$ is a real number.

$\qquad\qquad\qquad\qquad\qquad$ ab is a real number.

$\qquad\qquad\qquad\qquad\qquad$ $\dfrac{a}{b}$ is a real number, provided that $b \neq 0$.

The **associative properties**: $(a + b) + c = a + (b + c)$, and $(ab)c = a(bc)$.

The **commutative properties**: $a + b = b + a$, and $ab = ba$.

The **distributive property**: $a(b + c) = ab + ac$.

0 is the **additive identity**: $a + 0 = 0 + a = a$.

1 is the **multiplicative identity**: $a \cdot 1 = 1 \cdot a = a$.

$-a$ is the **negative** (or **additive inverse**) of a: $a + (-a) = 0$.

The **double negative rule**: $-(-a) = a$.

$\dfrac{1}{a}$ is the **multiplicative inverse** (or **reciprocal**) of a: $a\left(\dfrac{1}{a}\right) = 1$, provided $a \neq 0$.

(1.3)   The **trichotomy property**: $a < b$ or $a = b$ or $a > b$.

The **transitive property** for $<$:   If $a < b$ and $b < c$, then $a < c$. A similar statement is true for $>$, $\leq$, and $\geq$.

$|x| = x$ if $x \geq 0$ and $|x| = -x$ if $x < 0$.

$|x| \geq 0$.

(1.4)   To add two numbers with like signs, add their absolute values and use their common sign.

To add two numbers with unlike signs, find the difference of their absolute values and use the sign of the number with the greater absolute value.

The difference $a - b$ is equivalent to $a + (-b)$.

The product of two numbers with like signs is the positive product of their absolute values.

The product of two numbers with unlike signs is the negative of the product of their absolute values.

The quotient of two numbers with like signs is the positive quotient of their absolute values.

The quotient of two numbers with unlike signs is the negative of the quotient of their absolute values.

Division by 0 is undefined.

Unless parentheses indicate otherwise, do multiplications and/or divisions first, in order from left to right. Then do the additions and/or subtractions, from left to right. In a fraction, perform the operations within the numerator and denominator separately. Then simplify the fraction, if possible.

Properties of fractions: If no denominators are 0, then

$\dfrac{a}{b} = \dfrac{c}{d}$ if and only if $ad = bc$.

$\dfrac{a}{1} = a$ and   if $a \neq 0$, $\dfrac{a}{a} = 1$.

If $k \neq 0$, $\dfrac{a}{b} = \dfrac{ak}{bk}$.

$$\dfrac{a}{b} \cdot \dfrac{c}{d} = \dfrac{ac}{bd} \quad \text{and} \quad \dfrac{a}{b} \div \dfrac{c}{d} = \dfrac{a}{b} \cdot \dfrac{d}{c} = \dfrac{ad}{bc}.$$

$$\dfrac{a}{b} + \dfrac{c}{b} = \dfrac{a + c}{b} \quad \text{and} \quad \dfrac{a}{b} - \dfrac{c}{b} = \dfrac{a - c}{b}$$

$$-\dfrac{a}{b} = \dfrac{-a}{b} = \dfrac{a}{-b}.$$

━━━━━━ REVIEW EXERCISES ━━━━━━

In Review Exercises 1–6, $A = \{1, 2, 4, 6, 8, 9\}$, $B = \{1, 2, 4, 9\}$, and $C = \{3, 5, 7, 9\}$. Tell whether each statement is true. If a statement is false, change the symbol between the letters to make it true.

1. $4 \in A$ **2.** $B \subseteq C$ **3.** $B \in A$ **4.** $\{3, 7\} \subseteq C$

5. $\varnothing \subseteq B$ **6.** $\varnothing \in C$

In Review Exercises 7–14, simplify each expression, if necessary, and classify the result as a natural number, whole number, integer, rational number, irrational number, and/or real number. Most numbers will be in several classifications.

7. -10 **8.** $\dfrac{4}{2}$ **9.** π **10.** $\sqrt{7}$

11. $-\dfrac{8}{9}$ **12.** 17 **13.** $5 - 5$ **14.** $6 - 8$

In Review Exercises 15–22, classify each integer as an even, odd, prime, or composite number.

15. 10 **16.** -8 **17.** -11 **18.** 7

19. 1 **20.** 0 **21.** -1 **22.** 2

In Review Exercises 23–34, state the property of equality or the property of real numbers that justifies each statement.

23. $3(4 + 2) = 3 \cdot 4 + 3 \cdot 2$ **24.** If $3 = 2 + 1$, then $2 + 1 = 3$.

25. $3 + (x + 7) = (x + 7) + 3$ **26.** $3 + (x + 7) = (3 + x) + 7$

27. $3 + 0 = 3$ **28.** $3 + (-3) = 0$

29. $xy = xy$ **30.** $5(3) = 3(5)$

31. $3(xy) = (3x)y$ **32.** $3x \cdot 1 = 3x$

33. $a\left(\dfrac{1}{a}\right) = 1 \quad (a \neq 0)$ **34.** If $x = 7$ and $7 = y$, then $x = y$.

In Review Exercises 35–38, find the additive inverse and the multiplicative inverse (the reciprocal), if any, of each number.

35. 1 **36.** -3 **37.** 0 **38.** $\dfrac{1}{3}$

In Review Exercises 39–40, write each expression using $<$ and $>$ symbols.

39. $a \ngeq 4$ **40.** $a \neq b$

In Review Exercises 41–42, write each expression so that the inequality symbol points in the opposite direction.

41. $3 \leq 10$ **42.** $-4 > -8$

43. Graph the set of prime numbers between 20 and 30.

44. Graph the set of composite numbers between 5 and 13.

In Review Exercises 45–50, graph each interval.

45. $x \geq -4$ **46.** $-2 < x \leq 6$

47. $(-2, 3)$ **48.** $[2, 6]$ **49.** $(2, \infty)$ **50.** $(-\infty, -1)$

In Review Exercises 51–54, write each expression without using absolute value symbols.

51. $|0|$ **52.** $|-1|$ **53.** $-|-8|$ **54.** $|3 - 8|$

In Review Exercises 55–70, perform the indicated operations and simplify, if possible.

55. $3 + (-5)$ **56.** $5 - 3$ **57.** $-2 + 5$ **58.** $-3 - 5$

59. $-8 - (-3)$ **60.** $7 - (-9)$ **61.** $4(-3)$ **62.** $-3(8)$

63. $-4(3 - 6)$ **64.** $3[8 - (-1)]$ **65.** $\dfrac{-8}{2}$ **66.** $\dfrac{8}{-4}$

67. $\dfrac{-16}{-4}$ **68.** $\dfrac{-25}{-5}$ **69.** $\dfrac{3 - 8}{10 - 5}$ **70.** $\dfrac{|-32 - 8|}{6 - 16}$

In Review Exercises 71–78, $a = 5$, $b = -2$, $c = -3$, and $d = 2$. Simplify each expression.

71. $\dfrac{3a - 2b}{cd}$ **72.** $\dfrac{3b + 2d}{ac}$ **73.** $\dfrac{ab + cd}{c(b - d)}$ **74.** $\dfrac{ac - bd}{a(d + c)}$

75. $\dfrac{a(b + d) + c}{ad - bc}$ **76.** $\dfrac{b(c - d) - a}{a + c(b - d)}$ **77.** $\dfrac{ac}{-4b} + \dfrac{bc}{-2d}$ **78.** $\dfrac{ab}{c} - \dfrac{-5b}{a - d}$

CHAPTER ONE TEST

In Problems 1–4, $A = \{1, 2, 3, 4\}$, $B = \{3, 4, 5, 6\}$, and $C = \{5, 6, 7, 8\}$. Insert either an $\in$ or a $\subseteq$ symbol to make a true statement.

1. $3 \_\_ A$ **2.** $\varnothing \_\_ B$ **3.** $A \cap B \_\_ B$ **4.** $\{7, 8\} \_\_ C$

In Problems 5–8, $A = \{1, 2, 3, 4\}$, $B = \{3, 4, 5, 6\}$, and $C = \{5, 6, 7, 8\}$. Find each set.

5. $A \cup B$ **6.** $A \cap B \cap C$ **7.** $(A \cup \varnothing) \cap C$ **8.** $A \cup B \cup C$

In Problems 9–12, let $A = \{-2, 0, 1, 2, \frac{6}{5}, 5, \sqrt{7}\}$.

9. List the elements in A that are natural numbers.   **10.** List the elements in A that are integers.

11. List the elements in A that are rational numbers.

12. List the elements in A that are irrational numbers.

13. Express the fraction $\dfrac{7}{9}$ as a decimal.

In Problems 14–18, tell which property of equality or property of real numbers justifies each statement.

14. $3 = 3$

15. $3 + 5 = 5 + 3$

16. $a(b + c) = ab + ac$

17. $7 + (4 + 3) = (7 + 4) + 3$

18. $(4 \cdot 3) \cdot 5 = 5 \cdot (4 \cdot 3)$

In Problems 19–20, graph each set on the number line.

19. The set of odd integers between -4 and 6.

20. The set of prime numbers less than 12.

In Problems 21–22, graph each interval on the number line.

21. $-2 \leq x < 4$

22. $[-1, 3)$

In Problems 23–24, write each expression in simplest form without using absolute value symbols.

23. $-|8 - 5|$

24. $|-5| - |2| + |0|$

In Problems 25–30, $a = 2$, $b = -3$, and $c = 4$. Evaluate each expression.

25. ab

26. $a + bc$

27. $ab - bc$

28. $b(a + c)$

29. $\dfrac{-3b + a}{ac - b}$

30. $\dfrac{(4a + b)(b + 2c)}{-4c - ab}$

2 Exponents and Polynomials

One of the most common expressions in algebra is the polynomial. Because polynomials often involve exponents, we begin this chapter by discussing the properties of exponents.

2.1 EXPONENTS

Multiplication indicates repeated addition. For example, $4x$ means $x + x + x + x$ and $3y$ means $y + y + y$. The number 4, called the **numerical coefficient**, or simply **coefficient**, of the expression $4x$, indicates that x is to be used as a term in an addition four times. The coefficient 3 of the expression $3y$ indicates that y is to be used as a term three times.

Exponents are used to indicate repeated multiplication. For example,

$y^2 = y \cdot y$	Read y^2 as "y to the second power" or "y squared."
$z^3 = z \cdot z \cdot z$	Read z^3 as "z to the third power" or "z cubed."
$x^4 = x \cdot x \cdot x \cdot x$	Read x^4 as "x to the fourth power."

These examples suggest the following definition:

Definition. If n is a natural number, then

$$x^n = \overbrace{x \cdot x \cdot x \cdots \cdot x}^{n \text{ factors of } x}$$

The exponential expression x^n is called a **power of x**. In this expression, x is called the **base** and n is the exponent. A natural number exponent tells how many times the base of an exponential expression is to be used as a factor in a product.

Example 1 **a.** $2^5 = 2 \cdot 2 \cdot 2 \cdot 2 \cdot 2$
$\qquad = 32$

b. $(-2)^5 = (-2)(-2)(-2)(-2)(-2)$
$\qquad = -32$

37

c. $\quad -4^4 = -(4^4)$

$\qquad = -(4 \cdot 4 \cdot 4 \cdot 4)$

$\qquad = -256$

d. $\quad (-4)^4 = (-4)(-4)(-4)(-4)$

$\qquad\qquad = 256$

e. $\quad 8a^2 = 8(a^2)$

$\qquad = 8aa$

f. $\quad (8a)^2 = (8a)(8a)$

$\qquad\qquad = 64a^2$ ■

It is important to note the difference between $-x^n$ and $(-x)^n$, and between ax^n and $(ax)^n$:

$$-x^n = -\overbrace{(x \cdot x \cdot x \cdot \cdots \cdot x)}^{n \text{ factors of } x}$$

$$(-x)^n = \overbrace{(-x)(-x)(-x) \cdot \cdots \cdot (-x)}^{n \text{ factors of } -x}$$

$$ax^n = a \cdot \overbrace{x \cdot x \cdot x \cdot \cdots \cdot x}^{n \text{ factors of } x}$$

$$(ax)^n = \overbrace{(ax)(ax)(ax) \cdot \cdots \cdot (ax)}^{n \text{ factors of } ax}$$

Several properties of exponents follow directly from the definition of *expo-nent*. Because x^5 means that x is to be used as a factor five times, and x^3 means that x is to be used as a factor three times, the product $x^5 \cdot x^3$ indicates that x is to be used as a factor eight times:

$$x^5 x^3 = \overbrace{x \cdot x \cdot x \cdot x \cdot x}^{5 \text{ factors of } x} \cdot \overbrace{x \cdot x \cdot x}^{3 \text{ factors of } x} = \overbrace{x \cdot x \cdot x \cdot x \cdot x \cdot x \cdot x \cdot x}^{8 \text{ factors of } x}$$

In general,

$$x^m x^n = \overbrace{x \cdot x \cdot x \cdot \cdots \cdot x}^{m \text{ factors of } x} \cdot \overbrace{x \cdot x \cdot \cdots \cdot x}^{n \text{ factors of } x} = \overbrace{x \cdot x \cdot x \cdot x \cdot \cdots \cdot x}^{m + n \text{ factors of } x}$$

Thus, to multiply exponential expressions with the same base, we keep the same base and add the exponents.

The Product Rule of Exponents.   If m and n are natural numbers, then

$$x^m x^n = x^{m+n}$$

Note that the product rule of exponents applies only to exponential expressions with the same base. The expression $x^5 y^3$, for example, cannot be simplified because the bases of the exponential expressions are different.

Example 2   **a.** $x^{11}x^5 = x^{11+5}$ **b.** $a^5a^4a^3 = (a^5a^4)a^3$
$= x^{16}$ $= a^9a^3$
$= a^{12}$

c. $a^2b^3a^3b^2 = a^2a^3b^3b^2$ **d.** $8x^4x^4 = 8x^{4+4}$
$= a^5b^5$ $= 8x^8$ ■

To find another property of exponents, we simplify the expression $(x^4)^3$. This expression means "x^4 cubed" or $x^4 \cdot x^4 \cdot x^4$, which can be written as x^{12} because it is the product of 12 factors of x. Thus,

$$(x^4)^3 = x^{4 \cdot 3} = x^{12}$$

In general,

$$(x^m)^n = \overbrace{x^m \cdot x^m \cdot x^m \cdot \cdots \cdot x^m}^{n \text{ factors of } x^m} = \overbrace{x \cdot x \cdot x \cdot x \cdot x \cdots \cdot x}^{mn \text{ factors of } x} = x^{mn}$$

Thus, to raise an exponential expression to a power, we keep the same base and multiply the exponents.

To raise a product to a power, we raise each factor to that power.

$$(xy)^n = \overbrace{(xy)(xy)(xy) \cdot \cdots \cdot (xy)}^{n \text{ factors of } xy} = \overbrace{xxx \cdots \cdot x}^{n \text{ factors of } x} \cdot \overbrace{yyy \cdots \cdot y}^{n \text{ factors of } y} = x^n y^n$$

To raise a fraction to a power, we raise both the numerator and the denominator to that power:

$$\left(\frac{x}{y}\right)^n = \overbrace{\left(\frac{x}{y}\right)\left(\frac{x}{y}\right)\left(\frac{x}{y}\right) \cdot \cdots \cdot \left(\frac{x}{y}\right)}^{n \text{ factors of } \frac{x}{y}}$$

$$= \frac{\overbrace{xxx \cdots \cdot x}^{n \text{ factors of } x}}{\underbrace{yyy \cdots \cdot y}_{n \text{ factors of } y}}$$

Recall that we multiply fractions by multiplying the numerators and multiplying the denominators.

$$= \frac{x^n}{y^n}$$

The previous three results are often called the **power rules of exponents**.

The Power Rules of Exponents.   If m and n are natural numbers, then

$$(x^m)^n = x^{mn} \qquad (xy)^n = x^n y^n \qquad \left(\frac{x}{y}\right)^n = \frac{x^n}{y^n} \quad (y \neq 0)$$

Example 3   **a.** $(3^2)^3 = 3^{2 \cdot 3}$ **b.** $(x^{11})^5 = x^{11 \cdot 5}$

$\qquad\qquad\qquad\qquad\quad = 3^6 \qquad\qquad\qquad\qquad\qquad = x^{55}$

$\qquad\qquad\qquad\qquad\quad = 729$

        c. $(x^2 x^3)^6 = (x^5)^6$ **d.** $(x^2)^4 (x^3)^2 = x^8 x^6$

$\qquad\qquad\qquad\qquad\quad = x^{30} \qquad\qquad\qquad\qquad\qquad = x^{14}$ ∎

Example 4   **a.** $(x^2 y)^3 = (x^2)^3 y^3$ **b.** $(x^3 y^4)^4 = (x^3)^4 (y^4)^4$

$\qquad\qquad\qquad\qquad\qquad = x^6 y^3 \qquad\qquad\qquad\qquad\qquad = x^{12} y^{16}$

       c. $\left(\dfrac{x}{y^2}\right)^4 = \dfrac{x^4}{(y^2)^4}$ **d.** $\left(\dfrac{x^3}{y^4}\right)^2 = \dfrac{(x^3)^2}{(y^4)^2}$

$\qquad\qquad\qquad\qquad\quad = \dfrac{x^4}{y^8} \qquad\qquad\qquad\qquad\qquad = \dfrac{x^6}{y^8}$ ∎

Until now we have defined only natural-number exponents. We can, however, extend the definition to include other exponents. For example, if we assume that the rules for natural-number exponents hold for exponents of 0, we can write

$$x^0 x^n = x^{0+n} = x^n = 1x^n$$

Because $x^0 x^n = 1x^n$, it follows that if $x \neq 0$, then $x^0 = 1$. Thus, we make the following definition:

Definition.   If $x \neq 0$, then

$$x^0 = 1$$

Furthermore, if we assume that the rules for natural-number exponents hold for exponents that are negative integers, then if $x \neq 0$, we can write

$$x^{-n} x^n = x^{-n+n} = x^0 = 1$$

However, because

$$\frac{1}{x^n} \cdot x^n = 1$$

we make the following definition:

Definition.   If n is an integer and $x \neq 0$, then

$$x^{-n} = \frac{1}{x^n} \qquad \text{and} \qquad \frac{1}{x^{-n}} = x^n$$

Because of the two previous definitions, all of the rules for natural-number exponents hold for integer exponents.

Example 5   **a.** $(3x)^0 = 1$ **b.** $3x^0 = 3(x^0)$
$$= 3(1)$$
$$= 3$$

c. $x^{-5} = \dfrac{1}{x^5}$ **d.** $\dfrac{1}{x^{-6}} = x^6$

e. $x^{-5}x^3 = x^{-5+3}$ **f.** $(x^{-3})^{-2} = x^{(-3)(-2)}$
$$= x^{-2}$$ $$= x^6$$
$$= \dfrac{1}{x^2}$$

■

To develop the quotient rule for exponents, we proceed as follows:

$$\frac{x^m}{x^n} = x^m\left(\frac{1}{x^n}\right) = x^m x^{-n} = x^{m+(-n)} = x^{m-n}$$

Thus, to divide two exponential expressions with the same nonzero base, we keep the same base and subtract the exponents.

The Quotient Rule for Exponents.   If m and n are integers and $x \neq 0$, then

$$\frac{x^m}{x^n} = x^{m-n}$$

Example 6   **a.** $\dfrac{a^5}{a^3} = a^{5-3}$ **b.** $\dfrac{x^{-5}}{x^{11}} = x^{-5-11}$
$$= a^2$$ $$= x^{-16}$$
$$= \dfrac{1}{x^{16}}$$

c. $\dfrac{x^4x^3}{x^{-5}} = \dfrac{x^7}{x^{-5}}$ **d.** $\dfrac{(x^2)^3}{(x^3)^2} = \dfrac{x^6}{x^6}$
$$= x^{7-(-5)}$$ $$= x^{6-6}$$
$$= x^{12}$$ $$= x^0$$
$$= 1$$

e. $\dfrac{x^2 y^3}{xy^4} = x^{2-1} y^{3-4}$

$= xy^{-1}$

$= x\left(\dfrac{1}{y}\right)$

$= \dfrac{x}{y}$

f. $\left(\dfrac{a^{-2}b^3}{a^2 a^3 b^4}\right)^3 = \left(\dfrac{a^{-2}b^3}{a^5 b^4}\right)^3$

$= (a^{-2-5}b^{3-4})^3$

$= (a^{-7}b^{-1})^3$

$= a^{-21}b^{-3}$

$= \dfrac{1}{a^{21}b^3}$ ■

Note that part a of Example 6 could be simplified by using Property 3 of fractions:

$$\frac{a^5}{a^3} = \frac{a \cdot a \cdot a \cdot a \cdot a}{a \cdot a \cdot a} = \frac{\not{a} \cdot \not{a} \cdot \not{a} \cdot a \cdot a}{\not{a} \cdot \not{a} \cdot \not{a}} = a^2$$

One final property often is used to simplify exponential expressions.

Theorem.   If n is an integer, $x \neq 0$, and $y \neq 0$, then

$$\left(\frac{x}{y}\right)^{-n} = \left(\frac{y}{x}\right)^{n}$$

This theorem states that a fraction, when raised to the power $-n$ is equal to the reciprocal of that fraction raised to the power n.

To prove this theorem, we proceed as follows:

$$\left(\frac{x}{y}\right)^{-n} = \frac{x^{-n}}{y^{-n}}$$

$$= \frac{x^{-n} x^n y^n}{y^{-n} x^n y^n}$$ Multiply both numerator and denominator by $x^n y^n$.

$$= \frac{x^0 y^n}{y^0 x^n}$$

$$= \frac{y^n}{x^n}$$

$$= \left(\frac{y}{x}\right)^n$$ □

Example 7   **a.** $\left(\dfrac{2}{3}\right)^{-4} = \left(\dfrac{3}{2}\right)^{4}$

$= \dfrac{81}{16}$

b. $\left(\dfrac{y^2}{x^3}\right)^{-3} = \left(\dfrac{x^3}{y^2}\right)^{3}$

$= \dfrac{x^9}{y^6}$

c. $\left(\dfrac{4x^{-2}}{3y^3}\right)^{-4} = \left(\dfrac{3y^3}{4x^{-2}}\right)^4$ **d.** $\left(\dfrac{a^{-2}b^3}{a^2a^3b^4}\right)^{-3} = \left(\dfrac{a^2a^3b^4}{a^{-2}b^3}\right)^3$

$$= \dfrac{81y^{12}}{256x^{-8}}$$

$$= \dfrac{81y^{12}x^8}{256x^{-8}x^8}$$

$$= \dfrac{81y^{12}x^8}{256x^0}$$

$$= \dfrac{81y^{12}x^8}{256}$$

$$= \left(\dfrac{a^5b^4}{a^{-2}b^3}\right)^3$$

$$= (a^{5-(-2)}b^{4-3})^3$$

$$= (a^7b)^3$$

$$= a^{21}b^3$$

■

We summarize the rules of exponents as follows:

Rules for Exponents.

If n is a natural number, then $x^n = \overbrace{x \cdot x \cdot x \cdot \cdots \cdot x}^{n \text{ factors of } x}$.

If $x \neq 0$, then $x^0 = 1$.

For all integers n, $x^{-n} = \dfrac{1}{x^n}$ and $\dfrac{1}{x^{-n}} = x^n$, provided $x \neq 0$.

If there are no divisions by zero, then for all integers m and n,

$$x^m x^n = x^{m+n} \qquad (x^m)^n = x^{mn}$$

$$(xy)^n = x^n y^n \qquad \left(\dfrac{x}{y}\right)^n = \dfrac{x^n}{y^n}$$

$$\dfrac{x^m}{x^n} = x^{m-n} \qquad \left(\dfrac{x}{y}\right)^{-n} = \left(\dfrac{y}{x}\right)^n$$

In Chapter 1 we agreed that multiplications and divisions take priority over additions and subtractions. For example, $3 \cdot 4 + 5$ means $(3 \cdot 4) + 5$, rather than $3(4 + 5)$. To avoid any confusion when simplifying expressions containing exponents, we will follow this convention: *Unless parentheses indicate otherwise, we find the power of each base first, and then follow the priority rules given in Section 1.4.* Thus, $5 \cdot 2^3$ means $5(2^3)$ or $5(8) = 40$. However, $(5 \cdot 2)^3$ means 10^3, or 1000, because parentheses indicate that the multiplication is to be done first.

Example 8   Evaluate   **a.** $3x^2y^3$,   **b.** $(3x)^2y^3$,   **c.** $-z^4$, and   **d.** $(-z)^4$ for $x = 2$, $y = -1$, and $z = 3$.

Solution   **a.** $3x^2y^3 = 3(2)^2(-1)^3 = 3(4)(-1) = -12$

      b. $(3x)^2y^3 = (3 \cdot 2)^2(-1)^3 = 6^2(-1) = -36$

c. $-z^4 = -(3)^4 = -81$

d. $(-z)^4 = (-3)^4 = 81$ ∎

Example 9 Simplify each expression. Assume that neither a nor x is zero.

a. $\dfrac{a^n a}{a^2} = \dfrac{a^{n+1}}{a^2} = a^{n+1-2} = a^{n-1}$

b. $\dfrac{x^3 x^2}{x^n} = \dfrac{x^5}{x^n} = x^{5-n}$

c. $\left(\dfrac{x^n}{x^2}\right)^2 = \dfrac{x^{2n}}{x^4} = x^{2n-4}$ ∎

■ EXERCISE 2.1

In Exercises 1–78, simplify each expression and write all answers without using negative exponents. Assume that no denominators are 0.

1. 3^2

2. 3^4

3. -3^2

4. -3^4

5. $(-3)^2$

6. $(-3)^3$

7. $(-2x)^5$

8. $(-3a)^3$

9. $-(2x)^7$

10. $(-2a)^4$

11. $(-2x)^6$

12. $(-3y)^5$

13. 5^{-2}

14. 5^{-4}

15. -5^{-2}

16. -5^{-4}

17. $(-5)^{-2}$

18. $(-5)^{-4}$

19. 8^0

20. 9^0

21. -8^0

22. -9^0

23. $(-8)^0$

24. $(-9)^0$

25. $x^2 x^3$

26. $y^3 y^4$

27. $k^0 k^7$

28. $x^8 x^{11}$

29. $x^2 x^3 x^5$

30. $y^3 y^7 y^2$

31. $p^9 p p^0$

32. $z^7 z^0 z$

33. $aba^3 b^4$

34. $x^2 y^3 x^3 y^2$

35. $(-x)^2 y^4 x^3$

36. $-x^2 y^7 z^3 y^3 x^{-2}$

37. $(x^4)^7$

38. $(y^7)^5$

39. $(b^{-8})^9$

40. $(z^{12})^2$

41. $(x^3 y^2)^4$

42. $(x^2 y^5)^2$

43. $(r^{-3} s)^3$

44. $(m^5 n^2)^{-3}$

45. $(a^2 a^3)^4$

46. $(bb^2 b^3)^4$

47. $(-d^2)^3 (d^{-3})^3$

48. $(c^3)^2 (c^4)^{-2}$

49. $(x^{-2} y x^3 y^4)^2$

50. $(-a^2 b^{-4} a^3 b^2)^3$

51. $\left(\dfrac{a^3}{b^2}\right)^5$

52. $\left(\dfrac{a^2}{b^3}\right)^4$

53. $\left(\dfrac{a^{-3}}{b^{-2}}\right)^{-2}$

54. $\left(\dfrac{k^{-3}}{k^{-4}}\right)^{-1}$

55. $\dfrac{a^4 a^4}{a^3}$

56. $\dfrac{c^3 c^4}{c^2}$

57. $\dfrac{c^{12} c^5}{(c^5)^2}$

58. $\dfrac{(a^3)^{11}}{a^2 a^3}$

59. $\dfrac{m^9 m^{-2}}{(m^2)^3}$

60. $\dfrac{a^{10} a^{-3}}{a^5 a^{-2}}$

61. $\dfrac{1}{a^{-4}}$

62. $\dfrac{3}{b^{-5}}$

63. $\dfrac{m^5 m^{-7}}{m^2 m^{-5}}$

64. $\dfrac{(a^{-2})^3}{a^3 a^{-4}}$

65. $\left(\dfrac{4a^{-2} b}{3ab^{-3}}\right)^3$

66. $\left(\dfrac{2ab^{-3}}{3a^{-2} b^2}\right)^2$

67. $\left(\dfrac{3a^{-2} b^2}{17a^2 b^3}\right)^0$

68. $\left(\dfrac{-3x^{-2} y^5}{7xy^4}\right)^0$

69. $\left(\dfrac{-2a^4b}{a^{-3}b^2}\right)^{-3}$

70. $\left(\dfrac{-3x^{-5}y^2}{-9x^5y^{-2}}\right)^{-2}$

71. $\left(\dfrac{2a^3b^2}{3a^{-3}b^2}\right)^{-3}$

72. $\left(\dfrac{3x^5y^{-2}}{2x^5y^{-2}}\right)^{-4}$

73. $\dfrac{(3x^2)^{-2}}{x^3x^{-4}x^0}$

74. $\dfrac{y^{-3}y^{-4}y^0}{(2y^{-2})^3}$

75. $\dfrac{-3x^{-2}y^2}{(-2x^{-3})^0}$

76. $\dfrac{-4x^{-2}x^2(y^0)^2}{(-4x^2y^{-4})^0}$

77. $\dfrac{(4m^{-2}n^{-3})^{-2}(m^{-4}n^{-3})^2}{-3m^{-4}n^{-3}}$

78. $\dfrac{(3t^2s^{-2})^{-1}(2^{-3}ts^{-4})^{-2}}{(6t^2s^{-3})^{-2}}$

In Exercises 79–90, evaluate each expression if $x = -2$ and $y = 3$.

79. x^2y^3

80. x^3y^2

81. x^y

82. y^x

83. $\dfrac{x^{-3}}{y^3}$

84. $\dfrac{x^2}{y^{-3}}$

85. $(xy^2)^{-2}$

86. $(x^3y)^{-3}$

87. $-y^3x^{-1}$

88. $-y^3x^{-2}$

89. $(-yx^{-1})^3$

90. $(-y)^3x^{-2}$

In Exercises 91–98, simplify each expression.

91. $\dfrac{a^na^3}{a^4}$

92. $\dfrac{b^9b^7}{b^n}$

93. $\left(\dfrac{b^n}{b^3}\right)^3$

94. $\left(\dfrac{a^2}{a^n}\right)^4$

95. $\dfrac{a^{-n}a^2}{a^3}$

96. $\dfrac{a^na^{-2}}{a^4}$

97. $\dfrac{a^{-n}a^{-2}}{a^{-4}}$

98. $\dfrac{a^n}{a^{-3}a^5}$

99. Show that, if m is a natural number, $(xy)^m = x^my^m$.

100. Show that, if m is a natural number and if $y \neq 0$, then $\left(\dfrac{x}{y}\right)^m = \dfrac{x^m}{y^m}$.

101. Construct an example to show that $x^mx^n = x^{m+n}$ when m is a negative integer and n is a positive integer.

102. Construct an example to show that $x^mx^n = x^{m+n}$ when both m and n are negative integers.

103. Construct an example to show that $(x^m)^n = x^{mn}$ when m is a negative integer and n is a positive integer.

104. Construct an example to show that $(x^m)^n = x^{mn}$ when both m and n are negative integers.

105. Construct an example to show that $\dfrac{x^m}{x^n} = x^{m-n}$ when both m and n are negative integers and x is not zero.

106. Construct an example to show that $\left(\dfrac{y}{x}\right)^m = \dfrac{y^m}{x^m}$ when m is a negative integer and x is not zero.

107. Construct an example using numbers to show that $x^m + x^n$ is *not* equal to x^{m+n}.

108. Construct an example using numbers to show that $x^m + y^m$ is *not* equal to $(x + y)^m$.

In Exercises 109–116, use a calculator to verify that each statement is true.

109. $(3.68)^0 = 1$

110. $(2.1)^4(2.1)^3 = (2.1)^7$

111. $(7.2)^2(2.7)^2 = [(7.2)(2.7)]^2$

112. $(3.7)^2 + (4.8)^2 \neq (3.7 + 4.8)^2$

113. $(3.2)^2(3.2)^{-2} = 1$

114. $[(5.9)^3]^2 = (5.9)^6$

115. $(7.23)^{-3} = \dfrac{1}{(7.23)^3}$

116. $\left(\dfrac{5.4}{2.7}\right)^{-4} = \left(\dfrac{2.7}{5.4}\right)^4$

2.2 SCIENTIFIC NOTATION

Scientists often deal with very large and with very small numbers. For example, the speed of light is approximately 29,980,000,000 centimeters per second, and the mass of a hydrogen atom is 0.000000000000000000000001673 gram. The large number of zeros in these numbers makes them difficult to read and hard to remember. However, the use of exponents makes it possible for scientists to write such numbers more compactly in a form called **scientific notation**.

> **Definition.**   A number is written in **scientific notation** if it is written as the product of a number between 1 (including 1) and 10, and an appropriate power of 10.

Example 1   Change   **a.**   29,980,000,000 and   **b.**   0.000000000000000000000001673 to scientific notation.

Solution   **a.**   To write the number 29,980,000,000 in scientific notation, you must express that number as a product of a number between 1 and 10, and some power of 10. The number 2.998 lies between 1 and 10. To get the number 29,980,000,000 the decimal point in 2.998 must be moved 10 places to the right. This is accomplished by multiplying 2.998 by 10^{10}. Hence, the number 29,980,000,000 written in scientific notation is 2.998×10^{10}.

b.   To write the number 0.000000000000000000000001673 in scientific notation, you must express that number as a product of a number between 1 and 10, and some power of 10. To get the number 0.000000000000000000000001673, the decimal point in 1.673 must be moved 24 places to the left. This is accomplished by dividing 1.673 by 10^{24}. This is equivalent to multiplying 1.673 by $1/10^{24}$, or by 10^{-24}. Hence, the number 0.000000000000000000000001673 written in scientific notation is 1.673×10^{-24}.   ∎

Example 2   Change   **a.** 93,000,000 and   **b.** 0.0000000667   to scientific notation.

Solution   **a.** $93,000,000 = 9.3 \times 10^7$ because 9.3 is a number between 1 and 10, and $9.3 \times 10^7 = 93,000,000$.

b. $0.0000000667 = 6.67 \times 10^{-8}$ because 6.67 is between 1 and 10, and

$$6.67 \times 10^{-8} = 6.67 \times \frac{1}{100,000,000} = 0.0000000667$$ ∎

Example 3   Change   **a.** 3.7×10^5 and   **b.** 1.1×10^{-3} to standard notation.

Solution   **a.**   Because $10^5 = 100,000$, it follows that $3.7 \times 10^5 = 370,000$.

b.   Because $10^{-3} = \frac{1}{1000}$, it follows that $1.1 \times 10^{-3} = 0.0011$.   ∎

Study each of the following numbers written in both scientific and standard notation. In each case, note that the exponent gives the number of places that the decimal point moves, and the sign of the exponent indicates the direction that it moves:

$$5.32 \times 10^4 = 5\,3\,2\,0\,0$$
4 places to the right

$$6.45 \times 10^7 = 6\,4\,5\,0\,0\,0\,0\,0$$
7 places to the right

$$5.37 \times 10^{-4} = 0.\,0\,0\,0\,5\,3\,7$$
4 places to the left

$$5.234 \times 10^{-2} = 0.\,0\,5\,2\,3\,4$$
2 places to the left

$$5.89 \times 10^0 = 5.\,8\,9$$
no movement of the decimal point

Example 4   Change   **a.** 47.2×10^{-3} and   **b.** 0.043×10^{-2} to scientific notation.

Solution   Neither number is in scientific notation because the first factors are not between 1 and 10. You can, however, change these numbers to scientific notation as follows:

a. $47.2 \times 10^{-3} = (4.72 \times 10^1) \times 10^{-3} = 4.72 \times (10^1 \times 10^{-3}) = 4.72 \times 10^{-2}$

b. $0.043 \times 10^{-2} = (4.3 \times 10^{-2}) \times 10^{-2} = 4.3 \times (10^{-2} \times 10^{-2}) = 4.3 \times 10^{-4}$ ■

Another advantage of scientific notation becomes evident when we must multiply and divide combinations of very large and very small numbers. For example, the fraction

$$\frac{(0.0000064)(24,000,000,000)}{0.000000048}$$

can be evaluated by ordinary arithmetic. However, there is an easier way: change each number to scientific notation. Next do the arithmetic on the numbers and on the exponential expressions separately. Finally, write the answer in standard notation, if desired.

$$\frac{(0.0000064)(24,000,000,000)}{0.000000048} = \frac{(6.4 \times 10^{-6})(2.4 \times 10^{10})}{4.8 \times 10^{-8}}$$

$$= \frac{(6.4)(2.4)}{4.8} \cdot \frac{10^{-6}\,10^{10}}{10^{-8}}$$

$$= 3.2 \times 10^{12}$$

$$= 3,200,000,000,000$$

Example 5   Evaluate $\dfrac{(1,920,000)(0.0015)}{(0.000032)(45,000)}$.

Solution   First, express all numbers in scientific notation to get

$$\frac{(1.92 \times 10^6)(1.5 \times 10^{-3})}{(3.2 \times 10^{-5})(4.5 \times 10^4)}$$

Then do the arithmetic on the numbers and exponents separately.

$$\frac{(1.92)(1.5)}{(3.2)(4.5)} \cdot \frac{10^6}{10^{-5}} \frac{10^{-3}}{10^4} = 0.2 \cdot \frac{10^3}{10^{-1}}$$

$$= \mathbf{0.2 \cdot 10^4}$$

$$= \mathbf{2.0 \cdot 10^{-1} \cdot 10^4} \qquad 0.2 = 2.0 \times 10^{-1}$$

$$= 2.0 \cdot 10^3$$

$$= 2000$$ ∎

■ EXERCISE 2.2

In Exercises 1–20, change each expression to scientific notation.

1.	3,900	**2.**	1,700	**3.**	0.0078	**4.**	0.068
5.	17,600,000	**6.**	89,800,000	**7.**	0.0000096	**8.**	0.000000467
9.	323×10^5	**10.**	689×10^9	**11.**	$6,000 \times 10^{-7}$	**12.**	$76,543 \times 10^{-5}$
13.	0.0527×10^5	**14.**	0.0298×10^3	**15.**	0.0317×10^{-2}	**16.**	0.0012×10^{-3}
17.	731.0×10^4	**18.**	817.6×10^3	**19.**	$9,137 \times 10^{-2}$	**20.**	1000×10^{-3}

In Exercises 21–32, change each expression to standard notation.

21.	2.7×10^2	**22.**	7.2×10^3	**23.**	3.23×10^{-3}	**24.**	6.48×10^{-2}
25.	7.96×10^5	**26.**	9.67×10^6	**27.**	3.7×10^{-4}	**28.**	4.12×10^{-5}
29.	5.23×10^0	**30.**	8.67×10^0	**31.**	23.65×10^9	**32.**	75.62×10^{-9}

In Exercises 33–40, use the method of Example 5 to simplify each expression. Give all answers in standard notation.

33. $\dfrac{(0.006)(0.008)}{0.0012}$ **34.** $\dfrac{(600)(80,000)}{120,000}$

35. $\dfrac{(640,000)(2,700,000)}{120,000}$ **36.** $\dfrac{(0.0000013)(0.000090)}{0.00039}$

37. $\dfrac{(220,000)(0.000009)}{0.00033}$ **38.** $\dfrac{(0.00024)(96,000,000)}{640,000,000}$

39. $\dfrac{(320,000)^2(0.0009)}{(12,000)^2}$ **40.** $\dfrac{(0.000012)^2(49,000)^2}{0.021}$

41. The speed of sound (in air) is 3.31×10^4 centimeters per second. Use scientific notation to compute the speed of sound in centimeters per hour.

42. Calculate the volume of a tank that has dimensions of 3000 by 7000 by 4000 millimeters. Use scientific notation to perform the calculation, and express the answer in scientific notation.

43. The mass of a proton is 0.000000000000000000000000167248 gram. Express the mass of 1 million protons using scientific notation.

44. The speed of light (in a vacuum) is approximately 30,000,000,000 centimeters per second. Find the speed of light in miles per hour, and express your answer in scientific notation. There are approximately 160,000 centimeters in 1 mile.

45. The moon is approximately 235,000 miles from the earth. Express this distance in inches using scientific notation.

46. One *angstrom* is 0.0000001 millimeter. One inch is 25.4 millimeters. Use scientific notation to express the number of angstroms in an inch.

47. One *astronomical unit* (AU) is the distance from the earth to the sun—93,000,000 miles. Halley's comet ranges from 0.6 to 18 AU from the sun. Use scientific notation to express the comet's range in miles.

48. Light travels 300,000,000 meters per second. A *light-year* is the distance that light would travel in one year. Use scientific notation to express the number of meters in 1 light-year.

49. Light travels 186,000 miles per second. A *parsec* is 3.26 light-years. The star Alpha Centauri is 1.3 parsecs from the earth. Use scientific notation to express this distance in miles.

50. The moon is approximately 378,196 kilometers from the earth. Use scientific notation to express this distance in feet. (*Hint:* 1 mile $\approx$ 1.61 kilometers. Read "$\approx$" as "is approximately equal to.")

Most calculators have either 8- or 10-digit displays. When doing arithmetic involving very large or very small numbers, it is common to get answers requiring more than 8 or 10 digits. To solve this problem, many scientific calculators give answers to such problems in scientific notation. In Exercises 51–56, evaluate each expression using a calculator. Note that each answer is given in scientific notation.

51. $(23,437)^3$

52. $(0.00034)^4$

53. $(63,480)(893,322)$

54. $(0.0000413)(0.0000049)^2$

55. $\dfrac{(69.4)^8(73.1)^2}{(0.0043)^3}$

56. $\dfrac{(0.0031)^4(0.0012)^5}{(0.0456)^{-7}}$

2.3 ADDING AND SUBTRACTING POLYNOMIALS

A fundamental expression in algebra is the **polynomial**.

> **Definition.** A **polynomial in one variable**, say x, is the sum of one or more terms of the form ax^n, where a is a real number and n is a whole number.

The expressions

$$3x^2 + 2x + 3$$

$$\frac{3}{2}x^5 - \frac{7}{3}x^4 - \frac{8}{3}x^3$$

$$19x^{20} - 22.2x^{15} + \sqrt{3}x^{14} + 4.5x^{11} - 17x^2$$

are polynomials in x.

> **Definition.**   A **polynomial in several variables**, say x, y, and z, is the sum of one or more terms of the form $ax^m y^n z^p$, where a is a real number and m, n, and p are whole numbers.

The expressions

$$3xy$$
$$5x^2 y + 2yz^3 - 3xz$$
$$u^2 v^2 w^2 + x^3 y^3 + 1$$

are polynomials in several variables.

If a polynomial has a single term, it is called a **monomial**. If it has two terms, it is called a **binomial**. If it has three terms, it is called a **trinomial**. Here are some examples of each:

Monomials	Binomials	Trinomials
$2x^3$	$2x^4 + 5$	$2x^3 + 4x^2 + 3$
$x^2 y$	$-17t^{45} - 3xy$	$3xy^3 - x^2 y^3 + 7y$
$3x^3 y^5 z^2$	$32x^{13} y^5 + 47x^3 yz$	$-12x^5 y^2 + 13x^4 y^3 - 7x^3 y^3$

> **Definition.**   If $a \neq 0$, the **degree of the monomial ax^n** is n. The degree of a monomial containing several variables is the sum of the exponents of those variables.

By the previous definition,

$3x^4$ is a monomial of degree 4.

$4^7 x^2 y^3$ is a monomial of degree 5.   The sum of the exponents of x and y is 5.

$-18x^3 y^2 z^{12}$ is a monomial of degree 17.

3 is a monomial of degree 0. $3 = 3x^0$

The monomial 0 is of undefined degree because, by definition of the degree of a monomial, a cannot be zero.

> **Definition.**   The **degree of a polynomial** is the degree of the term with largest degree that is contained within the polynomial.

By the previous definition,

$3x^5 + 4x^2 + 7$ is a trinomial of degree 5.

$7x^2 y^8 - 3xy$ is a binomial of degree 10.

$3x + 2y - xy$ is a trinomial of degree 2.

$18x^2y^3 - 12x^7y^2 + 3x^9y^3 - 3$ is a polynomial of degree 12.

Polynomials in one variable can be denoted by symbols such as

$P(x)$ Read $P(x)$ as "P of x."

where the letter within the parentheses represents the variable of the polynomial. As we read each of the polynomials

$$P(x) = 3x^2 + 4x + 5$$
$$Q(y) = 5y^4 + 3y^3 + 4y^2 - 3y - 4$$
$$R(z) = 2z^3 - 3z^2 + 7z + 1$$

from left to right, the degrees of successive terms get smaller. When this is so, we say the polynomials are written in descending powers of their variables. In the polynomial

$$3 - 2x + 3x^2 + 4x^3 - 7x^4$$

the exponents of x increase. When this is so, we say the polynomial is written in ascending powers of x. In the polynomial

$$x^5 - 5x^4y + 10x^3y^2 - 10x^2y^3 + 5xy^4 - y^5$$

the exponents of x decrease and the exponents of y increase. We say the polynomial is written in descending powers of x and in ascending powers of y.

The symbol $P(x)$ gives a convenient way to indicate the value of a polynomial at different values of x. For example, $P(0)$ represents the value of the polynomial $P(x)$ when $x = 0$. Likewise $P(-5)$ represents the value of $P(x)$ when $x = -5$.

Example 1   Consider the trinomial $P(x) = 3x^2 - 2x + 7$. Find   **a.** $P(0)$,   **b.** $P(4)$,   **c.** $P(-5)$, and   **d.** $P(-x)$.

Solution   **a.** $P(0) = 3(0)^2 - 2(0) + 7 = 7$

         b. $P(4) = 3(4)^2 - 2(4) + 7 = 47$

         c. $P(-5) = 3(-5)^2 - 2(-5) + 7 = 92$

         d. $P(-x) = 3(-x)^2 - 2(-x) + 7 = 3x^2 + 2x + 7$ ■

Example 2   Consider the polynomial in x and y: $4x^2y - 5xy^3$. Find the value of the polynomial when $x = 3$ and $y = -2$.

Solution   Substitute 3 for x and -2 for y in the polynomial and simplify:

$$4x^2y - 5xy^3 = 4(3)^2(-2) - 5(3)(-2)^3$$
$$= 4(9)(-2) - 5(3)(-8)$$
$$= -72 + 120$$
$$= 48$$ ■

Adding and Subtracting Polynomials

If two terms have the same variables with the same exponents, they are called **like** or **similar terms**. Like terms can differ only in their numerical coefficients.

$3x^2$, $5x^2$, and $7x^2$ are like terms.

$5x^3y^2$, $17x^3y^2$, and $103x^3y^2$ are like terms.

$4x^4y^2$, $12xy^5$, and $98x^7y^9$ are unlike terms.

Recall that multiplication distributes over addition and that this fact is expressed by the formula

$$a(b + c) = ab + ac$$

Because multiplication is commutative, we can write the distributive property in the form

$$ba + ca = (b + c)a$$

This form of the distributive property enables us to combine like terms. For example,

$$3x + 7x = (3 + 7)x = 10x$$
$$5x^2y^3 + 22x^2y^3 = (5 + 22)x^2y^3 = 27x^2y^3$$
$$9xy^4 + 11xy^4 + 20xy^4 = (9 + 11 + 20)xy^4 = 40xy^4$$

However, the terms in the binomials

$$3x^2 - 5y^2, \qquad -2a^2 + 3a^3, \qquad \text{and} \qquad 5y^2 + 17xy$$

cannot be combined because they are not like terms.

The previous results suggest that to combine like terms we simply add their numerical coefficients and keep the same variables with the same exponents.

Example 3 **a.** $12x^2z + 13x^2z = 25x^2z$

b. $-28x^5y^2 + 11x^5y^2 = -17x^5y^2$

c. $22x^2y^3 - 7x^2y^3 = 15x^2y^3$ ∎

To subtract one monomial from another, we add the negative of the monomial that is to be subtracted.

Example 4 **a.** $8x^2 - 3x^2 = 8x^2 + (-3x^2) = 8x^2 + (-3)x^2 = 5x^2$

b. $3x^2y - 9x^2y = 3x^2y + (-9x^2y) = 3x^2y + (-9)x^2y = -6x^2y$

c. $-5x^5y^3z^2 - 3x^5y^3z^2 = -5x^5y^3z^2 + (-3x^5y^3z^2)$
$$= -8x^5y^3z^2$$ ∎

Because of the distributive property, we can remove parentheses enclosing several terms when the sign preceding the parentheses is a $+$ sign. We simply drop the parentheses:

$$+(a + b - c) = +1(a + b - c) = 1a + 1b - 1c = a + b - c$$

Polynomials are added by removing parentheses, if necessary, and combining any like terms that are contained within the polynomials.

Example 5

$$(3x^2 - 2x + 4) + (2x^2 + 4x - 3) = 3x^2 - 2x + 4 + 2x^2 + 4x - 3$$
$$= 3x^2 + 2x^2 - 2x + 4x + 4 - 3$$
$$= 5x^2 + 2x + 1 \qquad \blacksquare$$

For the sake of convenience, problems like the one in Example 5 are sometimes written with the terms aligned vertically to facilitate addition:

$$\begin{array}{r} 3x^2 - 2x + 4 \\ 2x^2 + 4x - 3 \\ \hline 5x^2 + 2x + 1 \end{array}$$

Because of the distributive property, we can also remove parentheses enclosing several terms when the sign preceding the parentheses is a $-$ sign. We simply drop the $-$ sign and the parentheses and *change the sign of each term within the parentheses.*

$$-(a + b - c) = -\mathbf{1}(a + b - c)$$
$$= -\mathbf{1}a + (-\mathbf{1})b - (-\mathbf{1})c$$
$$= -a - b + c$$

This suggests that the way to subtract polynomials is to remove parentheses and combine like terms.

Example 6   **a.** $(8x^3y + 2x^2y) - (2x^3y - 3x^2y) = 8x^3y + 2x^2y - 2x^3y + 3x^2y$
$$= 6x^3y + 5x^2y$$

b. $(3rt^2 + 4r^2t^2) - (8rt^2 - 4r^2t^2 + r^3t^2) = 3rt^2 + 4r^2t^2 - 8rt^2 + 4r^2t^2 - r^3t^2$
$$= -5rt^2 + 8r^2t^2 - r^3t^2 \qquad \blacksquare$$

To subtract polynomials in vertical form, we add the negative of the **subtrahend** (the bottom polynomial) to the **minuend** (the top polynomial).

$$\begin{array}{r} 8x^3y + 2x^2y \\ - \ 2x^3y - 3x^2y \\ \hline \end{array} \qquad \Rightarrow \qquad \begin{array}{r} 8x^3y + 2x^2y \\ + \ -2x^3y + 3x^2y \\ \hline 6x^3y + 5x^2y \end{array}$$

Example 7   Subtract $8rt^2 - 4r^2t^2 + r^3t^2$ from $3rt^2 + 4r^2t^2$.

Solution

$$\begin{array}{r} 3rt^2 + 4r^2t^2 \\ - \ 8rt^2 - 4r^2t^2 + r^3t^2 \\ \hline \end{array} \qquad \Rightarrow \qquad \begin{array}{r} 3rt^2 + 4r^2t^2 \\ + \ -8rt^2 + 4r^2t^2 - r^3t^2 \\ \hline -5rt^2 + 8r^2t^2 - r^3t^2 \end{array} \qquad \blacksquare$$

Because of the distributive property, we can remove parentheses enclosing several terms that are multiplied by a constant. We simply multiply each term

within the parentheses by the constant. For example,
$$3(2x^2 + 4x - 7) = 3(2x^2) + 3(4x) + 3(-7)$$
$$= 6x^2 + 12x - 21$$

Thus, to add multiples of one polynomial to another, or to subtract multiples of one polynomial from another, we proceed as in Example 8.

Example 8   Simplify $3(2x^2 + 4x - 7) - 2(3x^2 - 4x - 5)$.

Solution $3(2x^2 + 4x - 7) - 2(3x^2 - 4x - 5) = 6x^2 + 12x - 21 - 6x^2 + 8x + 10$
$$= 20x - 11 \qquad \blacksquare$$

■ EXERCISE 2.3

In Exercises 1–8, classify each polynomial as a monomial, binomial, trinomial, or none of these.

1. $3x^2$
2. $2y^3 + 4y^2$
3. $3x^2y - 2x + 3y$
4. $a^2 + b^2$

5. $x^2 - y^2$
6. $\dfrac{17}{2}x^3 + 3x^2 - x - 4$
7. 5
8. $8x^3y^5$

In Exercises 9–20, give the degree of each polynomial.

9. $3x^2 + 2$
10. x^{17}
11. $4x^8 + 3x^2y^4$
12. $19x^2y^4 - y^{10} + x^4$

13. $4x^2 - 5y^3z^3t^4$
14. $7x$
15. $121y$
16. $x^2y^3z^4 + z^{12}$

17. 77
18. 43
19. $x + y + xy$
20. $5xy - x$

In Exercises 21–26, rewrite each polynomial in descending powers of x.

21. $2x + 3x^3 - 4x^2 + 7$
22. $3x^3 + 5x - 3x^2 - 8$

23. $5xy^3 - 3x^2y^2 + 2x^3y - x^4 + y^4$
24. $x^2y + y^2x^{10} - x^{13}y + x^5 - y$

25. $3x^3z - 4x^6y + 3 - 4x$
26. $-6x^2yz + 7x^3y^2z - 8x^4yz^2 - 10$

In Exercises 27–30, consider the polynomial $P(x) = 2x^2 + x + 2$. Find the indicated value.

27. $P(0)$
28. $P(1)$
29. $P(4)$
30. $P(-3)$

In Exercises 31–44, consider the polynomial $P(x) = -3x^2 + 4x - 3$. Find the indicated value.

31. $P(1)$
32. $P(0)$
33. $P(-2)$
34. $P(3)$

35. $P(t)$
36. $P(z)$
37. $P(-x)$
38. $P(-r)$

39. $P(2x)$
40. $P(3x)$
41. $P(P(0))$
42. $P(P(2))$

43. $P(P(-1))$
44. $P(P(-2))$

In Exercises 45–58, find the value of the given expression if $x = 2$ and $y = -3$.

45. $2x^3 - 3x^2 - 4x + 2$
46. $3y^3 + 4y^2 - 2y - 4$

47. $x^2 + y^2$
48. $x^3 + y^3$
49. $x^3 - y^3$
50. $x^2 - y^2$

51. $3x^2y + xy^3$
52. $8xy - xy^2$
53. $\dfrac{9x^3}{y} - \dfrac{8y^3}{x}$
54. $\dfrac{27x^2}{y} + \dfrac{16y^4}{x}$

55. $\dfrac{3x^3 - 2y^2}{2x^2 + y^3}$
56. $\dfrac{2x^4 + 3y^3}{2x^3 - y}$
57. $\dfrac{3x^3 + 6y^2}{-2x - 3y^3}$
58. $\dfrac{4x^4 - 3y}{-2x^2 - y}$

In Exercises 59–64, use a calculator to find the value of each expression given that $x = 3.7$, $y = -2.5$, and $z = 8.9$.

59. x^2y **60.** xyz^2 **61.** $\dfrac{x^2}{z^2}$ **62.** $\dfrac{z^3}{y^2}$

63. $\dfrac{x + y + z}{xyz}$ **64.** $\dfrac{x + yz}{xy + z}$

In Exercises 65–72, simplify each expression, if necessary. Tell whether the terms are like or unlike terms. If they are like terms, find their sum.

65. $3x$, $7x$ **66.** $-8x$, $3y$ **67.** $7x$, $7y$ **68.** $3r^2t^3$, $-8r^2t^3$

69. 9, $3x^0$ **70.** $9u^2v$, x^0u^2v **71.** $(3x)^2$, $3x^2$ **72.** $(3x^2)^3$, $(2x^2)^3$

In Exercises 73–80, simplify each expression.

73. $8x + 4x$ **74.** $-2y + 16y$ **75.** $5x^3y^2z - 3x^3y^2z$ **76.** $8wxy - 12wxy$

77. $-2x^2y^3 + 3xy^4 - 5x^2y^3$ **78.** $3ab^4 - 4a^2b^2 - 2ab^4 + 2a^2b^2$

79. $(3x^2y)^2 + 2x^4y^2 - x^4y^2$ **80.** $(5x^2y^4)^3 - (5x^3y^6)^2$

In Exercises 81–100, perform the indicated operations.

81. $(3x^2 + 2x + 1) + (-2x^2 - 7x + 5)$ **82.** $(-2a^2 - 5a - 7) + (-3a^2 + 7a + 1)$

83. $(-a^2 + 2a + 3) - (4a^2 - 2a - 1)$ **84.** $(x^2 - 3x + 8) - (3x^2 + x + 3)$

85. $(7y^3 + 4y^2 + y + 3) + (-8y^3 - y + 3)$ **86.** $(6x^3 + 3x - 2) - (2x^3 + 3x^2 + 5)$

87. $(3x^2 + 4x - 3) + (2x^2 - 3x - 1) - (x^2 + x + 7)$

88. $(-2x^2 + 6x + 5) - (-4x^2 - 7x + 2) - (4x^2 + 10x + 5)$

89. $(3x^3 - 2x + 3) + (4x^3 + 3x^2 - 2) + (-4x^3 - 3x^2 + x + 12)$

90. $(x^4 - 3x^2 + 4) + (-2x^4 - x^3 + 3x^2) + (3x^2 + 2x + 1)$

91. $(3y^2 - 2y + 4) + [(2y^2 - 3y + 2) - (y^2 + 4y + 3)]$

92. $(-t^2 - t - 1) - [(t^2 + 3t - 1) - (-2t^2 + 4)]$

93. Add: $\begin{array}{r} 3x^3 - 2x^2 + 4x - 3 \\ -2x^3 + 3x^2 + 3x - 2 \\ \hline 5x^3 - 7x^2 + 7x - 12 \end{array}$ **94.** Add: $\begin{array}{r} 7a^3 + 3a + 7 \\ -2a^3 + 4a^2 - 13 \\ \hline 3a^3 - 3a^2 + 4a + 5 \end{array}$

95. Add: $\begin{array}{r} -2y^4 - 2y^3 + 4y^2 - 3y + 10 \\ -3y^4 + 7y^3 - y^2 + 14y - 3 \\ - 3y^3 - 5y^2 - 5y + 7 \\ -4y^4 + y^3 - 13y^2 + 14y - 2 \end{array}$ **96.** Add: $\begin{array}{r} 17t^4 + 3t^3 - 2t^2 - 3t + 4 \\ -12t^4 - 2t^3 + 3t^2 - 5t - 17 \\ -2t^4 - 7t^3 + 4t^2 + 12t - 5 \\ 5t^4 + t^3 + 5t^2 - 13t + 12 \end{array}$

97. Subtract: $\begin{array}{r} 3x^2 - 4x + 17 \\ 2x^2 + 4x - 5 \\ \hline \end{array}$ **98.** Subtract: $\begin{array}{r} -2y^2 - 4y + 3 \\ 3y^2 + 10y - 5 \\ \hline \end{array}$

99. Subtract: $\begin{array}{r} -5y^3 + 4y^2 - 11y + 3 \\ -2y^3 - 14y^2 + 17y - 32 \\ \hline \end{array}$ **100.** Subtract: $\begin{array}{r} 17x^4 - 3x^2 - 65x - 12 \\ 23x^4 + 14x^2 + 3x - 23 \\ \hline \end{array}$

In Exercises 101–106, simplify each expression.

101. $2(x^3 + x^2) + 3(2x^3 - x^2)$ **102.** $3(y^2 + 2y) - 4(y^2 - 4)$

103. $-5(2x^3 + 7x^2 + 4x) - 2(3x^3 - 4x^2 - 4x)$ **104.** $-3(3a^2 + 4b^3 + 7) + 4(5a^2 - 2b^3 + 3)$

105. $4(3z^2 - 4z + 5) + 6(-2z^2 - 3z + 4) - 2(4z^2 + 3z - 5)$

106. $-3(4x^3 - 2x^2 + 4) - 4(3x^3 + 4x^2 + 3x) + 5(3x - 4)$

107. Find the difference when $3x^2 + 4x - 3$ is subtracted from the sum of $-2x^2 - x + 7$ and $5x^2 + 3x - 1$.

108. Find the difference when $8x^3 + 2x^2 - 1$ is subtracted from the sum of $x^2 + x + 2$ and $2x^3 - x + 9$.

109. Find the sum when $2x^2 - 4x + 3$ minus $8x^2 + 5x - 3$ is added to $-2x^2 + 7x - 4$.

110. Find the sum when $7x^3 - 4x$ minus $x^2 + 2$ is added to $5 + 3x$.

2.4 MULTIPLYING POLYNOMIALS

We first consider multiplying a monomial by a monomial. In the examples, the commutative and associative properties of multiplication enable us to rearrange the factors and the parentheses.

Example 1   **a.** $(3x^2)(6x^3) = 3 \cdot x^2 \cdot 6 \cdot x^3$
$$= (3 \cdot 6)(x^2 \cdot x^3)$$
$$= 18x^5$$

b. $(-8x)(2y)(xy) = -8 \cdot x \cdot 2 \cdot y \cdot x \cdot y$
$$= (-8 \cdot 2) \cdot x \cdot x \cdot y \cdot y$$
$$= -16x^2 y^2$$

c. $(2a^3 b)(-7b^2 c)(-12ac^4) = 2 \cdot a^3 \cdot b \cdot (-7) \cdot b^2 \cdot c \cdot (-12) \cdot a \cdot c^4$
$$= 2(-7)(-12) \cdot a^3 \cdot a \cdot b \cdot b^2 \cdot c \cdot c^4$$
$$= 168a^4 b^3 c^5 \qquad \blacksquare$$

The results in Example 1 suggest that to multiply monomials we first multiply the numerical factors and then multiply the variable factors.

To find the product of a monomial and a polynomial, we use the distributive property or the extended distributive property.

$$a(b + c + d + \cdots) = ab + ac + ad + \cdots$$

Example 2   **a.** $3x^2(6xy + 3y^2) = 3x^2 \cdot 6xy + 3x^2 \cdot 3y^2$
$$= 18x^3 y + 9x^2 y^2$$

b. $5x^3 y^2(xy^3 - 2x^2 y) = 5x^3 y^2 \cdot xy^3 - 5x^3 y^2 \cdot 2x^2 y$
$$= 5x^4 y^5 - 10x^5 y^3$$

c. $-2ab^2(3bz - 2az + 4z^3) = -2ab^2 \cdot 3bz - (-2ab^2) \cdot 2az + (-2ab^2) \cdot 4z^3$
$$= -6ab^3 z + 4a^2 b^2 z - 8ab^2 z^3 \qquad \blacksquare$$

The results in Example 2 suggest that, to multiply a polynomial by a monomial, we multiply each term of the polynomial by the monomial.

To multiply a polynomial by another polynomial, we use the distributive property repeatedly.

Example 3 **a.** $(3x + 2)(4x + 9) = (3x + 2) \cdot 4x + (3x + 2) \cdot 9$

$$= 12x^2 + 8x + 27x + 18$$
$$= 12x^2 + 35x + 18$$

b. $(2a - b)(3a^2 - 4ab + b^2) = (2a - b)3a^2 - (2a - b)4ab + (2a - b)b^2$

$$= 6a^3 - 3a^2b - 8a^2b + 4ab^2 + 2ab^2 - b^3$$
$$= 6a^3 - 11a^2b + 6ab^2 - b^3 \qquad \blacksquare$$

The results of Example 3 suggest that, to multiply one polynomial by another, we multiply each term of one polynomial by each term of the other polynomial. It is often convenient to organize the work vertically, as in the following example.

Example 4 **a.** Multiply:

$$3x + 2$$
$$4x + 9$$

$4x(3x + 2) \longrightarrow 12x^2 + 8x$

$9(3x + 2) \longrightarrow \qquad + 27x + 18$

$$12x^2 + 35x + 18$$

b. Multiply:

$$3a^2 - 4ab + b^2$$
$$2a - b$$

$2a(3a^2 - 4ab + b^2) \longrightarrow 6a^3 - 8a^2b + 2ab^2$

$-b(3a^2 - 4ab + b^2) \longrightarrow \qquad - 3a^2b + 4ab^2 - b^3$

$$6a^3 - 11a^2b + 6ab^2 - b^3$$

c. Multiply:

$$2x^2 + 3xy + y^3$$
$$x - 2y$$

$x(2x^2 + 3xy + y^3) \longrightarrow 2x^3 + 3x^2y + xy^3$

$-2y(2x^2 + 3xy + y^3) \longrightarrow \qquad - 4x^2y \qquad - 6xy^2 - 2y^4$

$$2x^3 - x^2y + xy^3 - 6xy^2 - 2y^4 \qquad \blacksquare$$

Multiplying one binomial by another requires that each term of one binomial be multiplied by each term of the other binomial. This fact can be emphasized by drawing arrows to show the indicated products. For example, to multiply the binomials $3x + 2$ and $x + 4$, we can write

First terms   Last terms

$$(3x + 2)(x + 4) = 3x \cdot x + 3x \cdot 4 + 2 \cdot x + 2 \cdot 4$$
$$= 3x^2 + 12x + 2x + 8$$
$$= 3x^2 + 14x + 8$$

Inner terms

Outer terms

Note that the product of the first terms is $3x^2$, the product of the outer terms is $12x$, the product of the inner terms is $2x$, and the product of the last terms is 8.

This scheme is often called the **FOIL method of multiplying two binomials**. FOIL is an acronym for **F**irst terms, **O**uter terms, **I**nner terms, and **L**ast terms. Of course, the resulting terms of the product must be combined, if possible.

Example 5   Find the products:

a. $(x + 3)(x + 3)$,   b. $(y - 4)(y - 4)$, and   c. $(a + 6)(a - 6)$.

Solution   Multiply each term of one binomial by each term of the other binomial and simplify.

a. $(x + 3)(x + 3) = x^2 + 3x + 3x + 3^2$

$$= x^2 + 6x + 9$$

b. $(y - 4)(y - 4) = y^2 - 4y - 4y + 4^2$

$$= y^2 - 8y + 16$$

c. $(a + 6)(a - 6) = a^2 - 6a + 6a - 6^2$

$$= a^2 - 36$$ ∎

The products discussed in Example 5 are called **special products**. Because they occur so often, it is worthwhile to learn their forms. In the exercises, you will be asked to verify the following product formulas:

Special Product Formulas.

$$(x + y)^2 = (x + y)(x + y) = x^2 + 2xy + y^2$$
$$(x - y)^2 = (x - y)(x - y) = x^2 - 2xy + y^2$$
$$(x + y)(x - y) = x^2 - y^2$$

Because $x^2 + 2xy + y^2 = (x + y)^2$ and $x^2 - 2xy + y^2 = (x - y)^2$, the two trinomials are called **perfect square trinomials**.

The expressions $(x + y)^2$ and $(x - y)^2$ have trinomials for their products. It is common for students to forget to write the middle terms in these products. Remember that $(x + y)^2 \neq x^2 + y^2$ and that $(x - y)^2 \neq x^2 - y^2$. The product $(x + y)(x - y)$, however, is the binomial $x^2 - y^2$.

It is easy to multiply binomials by sight if we use the FOIL method. We first find the product of the first terms, then find the products of the outer terms and the inner terms and add them, if possible, and finally find the product of the last terms.

Example 6   Find the products: **a.** $(2x - 3)(3x + 2)$ and   **b.** $(3x + 1)(3x + 4)$ by sight.

Solution   **a.** $(2x - 3)(3x + 2) = 6x^2 - 5x - 6$

$6x^2$ -6

$-9x$

$4x$

Note that the middle term in the trinomial $6x^2 - 5x - 6$ comes from combining the products $-9x$ and $+4x$:

$$-9x + 4x = -5x$$

b. $(3x + 1)(3x + 4) = 9x^2 + 15x + 4$

$9x^2$ $+4$

$3x$

$12x$

Note that the middle term in the trinomial $9x^2 + 15x + 4$ comes from combining the products $+3x$ and $+12x$:

$$+3x + 12x = 15x$$ ∎

At first glance, the expression $3[x^2 - 2(x + 3)]$ does not look like a polynomial. But if we simplify the expression by removing the parentheses and the brackets, the expression takes the form of a polynomial:

$$3[x^2 - 2(x + 3)] = 3[x^2 - 2x - 6]$$
$$= 3x^2 - 6x - 18$$

If an expression has one set of grouping symbols enclosed within another set, it is usually wise to eliminate the inner set first.

Example 7   Find the product of $-2[y^3 + 3(y^2 - 2)]$ and $5[y^2 - 2(y + 1)]$.

Solution   First change each expression to polynomial form:

$$-2[y^3 + 3(y^2 - 2)] \qquad 5[y^2 - 2(y + 1)]$$
$$-2[y^3 + 3y^2 - 6] \qquad 5[y^2 - 2y - 2]$$
$$-2y^3 - 6y^2 + 12 \qquad 5y^2 - 10y - 10$$

Then, do the multiplication:

$$
\begin{array}{r}
-2y^3 - 6y^2 + 12 \\
5y^2 - 10y - 10 \\
\hline
-10y^5 - 30y^4 \qquad\qquad + 60y^2 \\
+ 20y^4 + 60y^3 \qquad\qquad - 120y \\
+ 20y^3 + 60y^2 \qquad\qquad - 120 \\
\hline
-10y^5 - 10y^4 + 80y^3 + 120y^2 - 120y - 120
\end{array}
$$

■

The following two examples show how to use the methods previously discussed to multiply expressions that are not polynomials.

Example 8   Find the product of $x^{-2} + y$ and $x^2 - y^{-2}$.

Solution   Multiply each term of the second expression by each term of the first expression, and simplify:

$$(x^{-2} + y)(x^2 - y^{-2}) = x^{-2}x^2 - x^{-2}y^{-2} + yx^2 - yy^{-2}$$
$$= x^0 - x^{-2}y^{-2} + yx^2 - y^{1+(-2)}$$
$$= 1 - x^{-2}y^{-2} + yx^2 - y^{-1}$$

■

Example 9   Find the product of $x^n + 2x$ and $x^n + 3x^{-n}$.

Solution   Multiply each term of the second expression by each term of the first expression, and simplify:

$$(x^n + 2x)(x^n + 3x^{-n}) = x^n x^n + x^n(3x^{-n}) + 2x(x^n) + 2x(3x^{-n})$$
$$= x^{2n} + 3x^n x^{-n} + 2x^{1+n} + 6xx^{-n}$$
$$= x^{2n} + 3x^0 + 2x^{n+1} + 6x^{1+(-n)}$$
$$= x^{2n} + 3 + 2x^{n+1} + 6x^{1-n}$$

■

■ **EXERCISE 2.4**

In Exercises 1–30, find each product.

1. $(2a^2)(-3ab)$
2. $(-3x^2y)(3xy)$
3. $(-3ab^2c)(5ac^2)$
4. $(-2m^2n)(-4mn^3)$
5. $(4a^2b)(-5a^3b^2)(6a^4)$
6. $(2x^2y^3)(4xy^5)(-5y^6)$
7. $(3x^3y^5)(2xy^2)^2$
8. $(a^3b^2c)^3(ab^2c^3)$
9. $(5x^3y^2)^4\left(\dfrac{1}{5}x^{-2}\right)^2$
10. $(4a^{-2}b^{-1})^2(2a^3b^4)^4$
11. $(-5xx^2)(-3xy)^4$
12. $(-2a^2ab^2)^3(-3ab^2b^2)$

13. $[(-2x^3y)(5x^2y^2)]^2$

14. $[(3x^2y^3)(4xy^5)]^3$

15. $3(x + 2)$

16. $-5(a + b)$

17. $-a(a - b)$

18. $y^2(y - 1)$

19. $3x(x^2 + 3x)$

20. $-2x(3x^2 - 2)$

21. $-2x(3x^2 - 3x + 2)$

22. $3a(4a^2 + 3a - 4)$

23. $5a^2b^3(2a^4b - 5a^0b^3)$

24. $-2a^3b(3a^0b^4 - 2a^2b^3)$

25. $7rst(r^2 + s^2 - t^2)$

26. $3x^2yz(x^2 - 2y + 3z^2)$

27. $-4x^2y^3(3x^2 - 4xy + y^2)$

28. $-2x^2(3x^4 - 2x^2 - 7)$

29. $4m^2n(-3mn)(m + n)$

30. $-3a^2b^3c(2bc^4)(3a + b - c)$

In Exercises 31–64, find each product. If possible, find the product by sight.

31. $(x + 2)(x + 2)$

32. $(x - 3)(x - 3)$

33. $(a - 4)(a - 4)$

34. $(y + 5)(y + 5)$

35. $(a + b)(a + b)$

36. $(a - 2b)(a - 2b)$

37. $(2x - y)(2x - y)$

38. $(3m + 4n)(3m + 4n)$

39. $(x + 2)(x - 2)$

40. $(z + 3)(z - 3)$

41. $(a + b)(a - b)$

42. $(2x + 3y)(2x - 3y)$

43. $(x + 2)(x + 3)$

44. $(y - 3)(y + 4)$

45. $(z - 7)(z - 2)$

46. $(x + 3)(x - 5)$

47. $(2a + 1)(a - 2)$

48. $(3b - 1)(2b - 1)$

49. $(3y - z)(2y - z)$

50. $(2m + n)(3m + n)$

51. $(2x - 3y)(x + 2y)$

52. $(3y + 2z)(y - 3z)$

53. $(3 - 2x)(3 + 4x)$

54. $(2x - 5)(2x + 5)$

55. $(3x + y)(3x - 3y)$

56. $(2x - 1)(3x + 2)$

57. $(4a - 3)(2a + 5)$

58. $(3a + 2)(2a - 7)$

59. $(u - v)^2$

60. $(u + v)^2$

61. $(2x + 1)^2$

62. $(3y - 2)^2$

63. $(3x + 2y)^2$

64. $(3x - 2y)^2$

In Exercises 65–80, find each product.

65. $(3y + 1)(2y^2 + 3y + 2)$

66. $(a + 2)(3a^2 + 4a - 2)$

67. $(2a - b)(3a^2 - 2ab + 2b^2)$

68. $(4x - 3y)(x^2 - 2xy + y^2)$

69. $(a + b + c)(2a - b - 2c)$

70. $(x - 2y - 3z)(3x + 2y + z)$

71. $(x + 2y + 3z)^2$

72. $(3x - 2y - z)^2$

73. $(r + s)^2(r - s)^2$

74. $r(r + s)(r - s)^2$

75. $(2x - 1)[2x^2 - 3(x + 2)]$

76. $(x + 1)^2[x^2 - 2(x + 2)]$

77. $[2x - 3(x^2 - x)]^3$

78. $-[y - 2(y + y^2)]^3$

79. $(a + b)(a - b)(a - 3b)$

80. $(x - y)(x + 2y)(x - 2y)$

In Exercises 81–90, find each product. Write all answers without negative exponents.

81. $x^3(2x^2 + x^{-2})$

82. $x^{-4}(2x^{-3} - 5x^2)$

83. $x^3y^{-6}z^{-2}(3x^{-2}y^2z - x^3y^{-4})$

84. $ab^{-2}c^{-3}(a^{-4}bc^3 + a^{-3}b^4c^3)$

85. $(x^{-1} + y)(x^{-1} - y)$

86. $(x^{-1} - y)(x^{-1} - y)$

87. $(2x^{-3} + y^3)(2x^3 - y^{-3})$

88. $(5x^{-4} - 4y^2)(5x^2 - 4y^{-4})$

89. $(2x^2 - 3y^{-2})(2x^2 + 3y^2)^2$

90. $(-3x^{-4} + 2y^{-1})(x + y^{-2})^2$

In Exercises 91–102, find each indicated product. Consider n to be a whole number.

91. $x^n(x^{2n} - x^n)$

92. $a^{2n}(a^n + a^{2n})$

93. $(x^n + 1)(x^n - 1)$

94. $(x^n - a^n)(x^n + a^n)$

95. $(x^n - y^n)(x^n - y^{-n})$

96. $(x^n + y^n)(x^n + y^{-n})$

97. $(x^{2n} + y^{2n})(x^{2n} - y^{2n})$

98. $(a^{3n} - b^{3n})(a^{3n} + b^{3n})$

99. $(2x^n - y^{2n})(3x^{-n} + y^{-2n})$

100. $(3x^{2n} + 2x^n - 1)^2$

101. $(x^n + y^n - 1)(x^n - y^n + 1)$

102. $(1 - x^n)(x^{-n} - 1)$

In Exercises 103–108, simplify each given expression.

103. $(3x - 4)^2 - (2x + 3)^2$

104. $(3y + 1)^2 + (2y - 4)^2$

105. $3(x - 3y)^2 + 2(3x + y)^2$

106. $2(x - y^2)^2 - 3(y^2 + 2x)^2$

107. $5(2y - z)^2 + 4(y + 2z)^2$

108. $3(x + 2z)^2 - 2(2x - z)^2$

109. Verify that $(x + y)^2 = x^2 + 2xy + y^2$.

110. Verify that $(x - y)^2 = x^2 - 2xy + y^2$.

111. Verify that $(x + y)(x - y) = x^2 - y^2$.

112. Verify that $(x + y + z)^2 = x^2 + y^2 + z^2 + 2xy + 2xz + 2yz$.

In Exercises 113–116, use a calculator to find each product.

113. $(3.21x - 7.85)(2.87x + 4.59)$

114. $(7.44y + 56.7)(-2.1y - 67.3)$

115. $(-17.3y + 4.35)^2$

116. $(-0.31x + 29.3)(-81x - 0.2)$

2.5   DIVIDING POLYNOMIALS

We begin by considering the quotient of two monomials.

Example 1   Simplify the expression $3a^2b^3 \div 2a^3b$.

Solution 1   Rewrite the expression as a fraction, rewrite both the numerator and the denominator, and divide out all common factors:

$$\frac{3a^2b^3}{2a^3b} = \frac{3aabbb}{2aaab}$$

$$= \frac{3aabbb}{2aaab}$$

$$= \frac{3b^2}{2a}$$

Solution 2 Rewrite the expression as a fraction and use the rules of exponents:

$$\frac{3a^2b^3}{2a^3b} = \frac{3}{2}a^{-1}b^2$$

$$= \frac{3}{2}\left(\frac{1}{a}\right)\frac{b^2}{1}$$

$$= \frac{3b^2}{2a}$$

∎

The same ideas are used to divide any polynomial by a monomial.

Example 2 Divide $4x^3y^2 + 3xy^5 - 12xy$ by $3x^2y^3$.

Solution Rewrite the expression as a fraction, and then as the sum of three separate fractions:

$$\frac{4x^3y^2 + 3xy^5 - 12xy}{3x^2y^3} = \frac{4x^3y^2}{3x^2y^3} + \frac{3xy^5}{3x^2y^3} + \frac{-12xy}{3x^2y^3}$$

Pick one of the methods used in the previous example and simplify each of the three fractions on the right-hand side of the equals sign:

$$\frac{4x^3y^2 + 3xy^5 - 12xy}{3x^2y^3} = \frac{4x}{3y} + \frac{y^2}{x} + \frac{-4}{xy^2}$$

$$= \frac{4x}{3y} + \frac{y^2}{x} - \frac{4}{xy^2}$$

∎

In the next example, we consider dividing a polynomial by another polynomial.

Example 3 Divide $x^2 + 7x + 12$ by $x + 4$.

Solution In Example 2, you divided a polynomial by a monomial. In this example, you must divide a polynomial by a binomial. There is an **algorithm** (a repeating series of steps) to use when the divisor is not a monomial. The algorithm follows closely the method of long division used when dividing numbers. The division of $x^2 + 7x + 12$ by $x + 4$ can be written in the form

$$x + 4 \overline{)\, x^2 + 7x + 12}$$

Here is how the division process works:

Step 1

$$x + 4 \overline{)\, x^2 + 7x + 12} \quad \overset{x}{}$$

How many times does x divide x^2? $x^2/x = x$. Place the x above the division symbol.

Step 2

$$x + 4 \overline{)\, x^2 + 7x + 12}$$
$$\underline{x^2 + 4x}$$

Multiply each term in the divisor by x. Place the product under $x^2 + 7x$ as indicated, and draw a line.

Step 3

$$x + 4 \overline{)\, x^2 + 7x + 12}$$
$$(-)$$
$$\underline{(-)\, x^2 + 4x}$$
$$3x + 12$$

Subtract $x^2 + 4x$ from $x^2 + 7x$ by adding the negative of $x^2 + 4x$ to $x^2 + 7x$. Bring down the next term.

Step 4

$$\begin{array}{r} x\ + 3 \\ x + 4 \overline{)\, x^2 + 7x + 12} \\ \underline{x^2 + 4x} \\ 3x + 12 \end{array}$$

How many times does x divide $3x$? $3x/x = +3$. Place the $+3$ above the division symbol.

Step 5

$$\begin{array}{r} x\ + 3 \\ x + 4 \overline{)\, x^2 + 7x + 12} \\ \underline{x^2 + 4x} \\ 3x + 12 \\ 3x + 12 \end{array}$$

Multiply each term in the divisor by 3. Place the product under $3x + 12$ as indicated, and draw a line.

Step 6

$$\begin{array}{r} x\ + 3 \\ x + 4 \overline{)\, x^2 + 7x + 12} \\ \underline{x^2 + 4x} \\ 3x + 12 \\ (-) \\ \underline{(-)\, 3x + 12} \\ 0 \end{array}$$

Subtract $3x + 12$ from $3x + 12$ by adding the negative of $3x + 12$.

The division process terminates when the result of the subtraction is either a constant or a polynomial with degree less than the degree of the divisor. Thus, the quotient is $x + 3$ and the remainder is 0.

It is always a good idea to check the quotient in a division problem. To do this, multiply the divisor (the number that you divided by) by the quotient (the answer). If the result is the dividend (the part under the division symbol), the answer is correct. Because

$$\underbrace{(x + 4)}_{\text{divisor}} \cdot \underbrace{(x + 3)}_{\text{quotient}} = \underbrace{x^2 + 7x + 12}_{\text{dividend}}$$

the answer checks. The quotient is $x + 3$.   ∎

Example 4 Divide $2a^3 + 9a^2 + 5a - 6$ by $2a + 3$.

Solution *Step 1*

$$\frac{a^2}{2a + 3 \overline{)\ 2a^3 + 9a^2 + 5a - 6}}$$

How many times does $2a$ divide $2a^3$? $2a^3/2a = a^2$. Place the a^2 in the quotient.

Step 2

$$\begin{array}{r} a^2 \\ 2a + 3 \overline{)\ 2a^3 + 9a^2 + 5a - 6} \\ 2a^3 + 3a^2 \end{array}$$

Multiply each term in the divisor by a^2. Place the product under $2a^3 + 9a^2$, and draw a line.

Step 3

$$\begin{array}{r} a^2 \\ 2a + 3 \overline{)\ 2a^3 + 9a^2 + 5a - 6} \\ (-) \\ (-)\ \ 2a^3 + 3a^2 \\ \hline 6a^2 + 5a \end{array}$$

Subtract $2a^3 + 3a^2$ by adding its negative. Bring down the next term.

Step 4

$$\begin{array}{r} a^2 + 3a \\ 2a + 3 \overline{)\ 2a^3 + 9a^2 + 5a - 6} \\ 2a^3 + 3a^2 \\ \hline 6a^2 + 5a \end{array}$$

How many times does $2a$ divide $6a^2$? $6a^2/2a = +3a$. Place the $+3a$ in the quotient.

Step 5

$$\begin{array}{r} a^2 + 3a \\ 2a + 3 \overline{)\ 2a^3 + 9a^2 + 5a - 6} \\ 2a^3 + 3a^2 \\ \hline 6a^2 + 5a \\ 6a^2 + 9a \end{array}$$

Multiply each term in the divisor by $+3a$. Place the product under $6a^2 + 5a$, and draw a line.

Step 6

$$\begin{array}{r} a^2 + 3a \\ 2a + 3 \overline{)\ 2a^3 + 9a^2 + 5a - 6} \\ 2a^3 + 3a^2 \\ \hline 6a^2 + 5a \\ (-) \\ (-)\ 6a^2 + 9a \\ \hline -4a - 6 \end{array}$$

Subtract $6a^2 + 9a$ by adding its negative. Bring down the next term.

Step 7

$$\begin{array}{r} a^2 + 3a\ - 2 \\ 2a + 3 \overline{)\ 2a^3 + 9a^2 + 5a - 6} \\ 2a^3 + 3a^2 \\ \hline 6a^2 + 5a \\ 6a^2 + 9a \\ \hline -4a - 6 \end{array}$$

How many times does $2a$ divide $-4a$? $-4a/2a = -2$. Place the -2 in the quotient.

Step 8

$$\begin{array}{r} a^2 + 3a - 2 \\ 2a + 3 \overline{)\ 2a^3 + 9a^2 + 5a - 6} \\ 2a^3 + 3a^2 \\ \hline 6a^2 + 5a \\ 6a^2 + 9a \\ \hline -4a - 6 \\ -4a - 6 \\ \hline \end{array}$$

Multiply each term in the divisor by -2. Place the product under $-4a - 6$, and draw a line.

Step 9

$$\begin{array}{r} a^2 + 3a - 2 \\ 2a + 3 \overline{)\ 2a^3 + 9a^2 + 5a - 6} \\ 2a^3 + 3a^2 \\ \hline 6a^2 + 5a \\ 6a^2 + 9a \\ \hline -4a - 6 \\ (+)(+) \\ \hline -4a - 6 \\ \hline 0 \end{array}$$

Subtract $-4a - 6$ by adding its negative.

Because the remainder is 0, the quotient is $a^2 + 3a - 2$.
This work can be checked by verifying that

$$\underbrace{(2a + 3)}_{\text{divisor}} \cdot \underbrace{(a^2 + 3a - 2)}_{\text{quotient}} = \underbrace{2a^3 + 9a^2 + 5a - 6}_{\text{dividend}}$$

■

Example 5   Divide $3x^3 + 2x^2 - 3x + 8$ by $x - 2$.

Solution

$$\begin{array}{r} 3x^2 + 8x + 13 \\ x - 2 \overline{)\ 3x^3 + 2x^2 - 3x + 8} \\ 3x^3 - 6x^2 \\ \hline 8x^2 - 3x \\ 8x^2 - 16x \\ \hline 13x + 8 \\ 13x - 26 \\ \hline 34 \end{array}$$

This division gives a quotient of $3x^2 + 8x + 13$ and a remainder of 34. It is common to form a fraction with the remainder as numerator and the divisor as denominator, and to write the answer as

$$3x^2 + 8x + 13 + \frac{34}{x - 2}$$

To check this answer, verify that

$$(x - 2)\left(3x^2 + 8x + 13 + \frac{34}{x - 2}\right) = 3x^3 + 2x^2 - 3x + 8$$ ∎

Example 6 Divide $-9x + 10x^2 + 8x^3 - 9$ by $3 + 2x$.

Solution The division algorithm works most efficiently when the polynomials in both the dividend and the divisor are written in descending powers of x. Use the commutative property of addition to rearrange the terms. Then, do the division:

$$
\begin{array}{r}
4x^2 - x - 3 \\
2x + 3 \overline{\smash{)}8x^3 + 10x^2 - 9x - 9} \\
\underline{8x^3 + 12x^2} \\
-2x^2 - 9x \\
\underline{-2x^2 - 3x} \\
-6x - 9 \\
\underline{-6x - 9} \\
0
\end{array}
$$

Hence,

$$\frac{-9x + 10x^2 + 8x^3 - 9}{3 + 2x} = 4x^2 - x - 3$$

Check this answer. ∎

Example 7 Divide $8x^3 + 1$ by $2x + 1$.

Solution Note that the terms involving x^2 and x are missing in the dividend of $8x^3 + 1$. You must either include the terms $0x^2$ and $0x$ in the dividend or leave spaces for them. After this adjustment, the division is routine.

$$
\begin{array}{r}
4x^2 - 2x + 1 \\
2x + 1 \overline{\smash{)}8x^3 + 0x^2 + 0x + 1} \\
\underline{8x^3 + 4x^2} \\
-4x^2 + 0x \\
\underline{-4x^2 - 2x} \\
+2x + 1 \\
\underline{+2x + 1} \\
0
\end{array}
$$

Hence,

$$\frac{8x^3 + 1}{2x + 1} = 4x^2 - 2x + 1$$

Check this answer. ∎

Example 8   Divide $-17x^2 + 5x + x^4 + 2$ by $x^2 - 1 + 4x$.

Solution   Rewrite the problem with both the divisor and the dividend in descending powers of x. Leave spaces for the missing terms in the dividend. Then perform the division as follows:

$$
\begin{array}{r}
x^2 - 4x \\
x^2 + 4x - 1 \overline{)\, x^4 - 17x^2 + 5x + 2} \\
\underline{x^4 + 4x^3 - x^2 } \\
-4x^3 - 16x^2 + 5x \\
\underline{-4x^3 - 16x^2 + 4x } \\
x + 2
\end{array}
$$

This division gives a quotient of $x^2 - 4x$ and a remainder of $x + 2$. Hence,

$$
\frac{-17x^2 + 5x + x^4 + 2}{x^2 - 1 + 4x} = x^2 - 4x + \frac{x + 2}{x^2 + 4x - 1}
$$

Check this answer.   ■

■ EXERCISE 2.5

In Exercises 1–18, perform each indicated operation. Express all answers without using negative exponents.

1. $4x^2y^3 \div 8x^5y^2$

2. $25x^4y^7 \div 5xy^9$

3. $\dfrac{33a^{-2}b^2}{44a^2b^{-2}}$

4. $\dfrac{-63a^4b^{-3}}{81a^{-3}b^3}$

5. $\dfrac{45x^{-2}y^{-3}t^0}{-63x^{-1}y^4t^2}$

6. $\dfrac{112a^0b^2c^{-3}}{48a^4b^0c^4}$

7. $\dfrac{-65a^{2n}b^nc^{3n}}{-15a^nb^{-n}c}$

8. $\dfrac{-32x^{-3n}y^{-2n}z}{40x^{-2}y^{-n}z^{n+1}}$

9. $(4x^2 - x^3) \div 6x$

10. $(5y^4 + 45y^3) \div 15y^2$

11. $\dfrac{4x^2y^3 + 2x^3y^2}{6xy}$

12. $\dfrac{9a^3y^2 - 18a^4y^3}{27a^2y^2}$

13. $\dfrac{24x^6y^7 - 12x^5y^{12} + 36xy}{48x^2y^3}$

14. $\dfrac{9x^4y^3 + 18x^2y - 27xy^4}{9x^3y^3}$

15. $\dfrac{3a^{-2}b^3 - 6a^2b^{-3} + 9a^{-2}}{12a^{-1}b}$

16. $\dfrac{4x^3y^{-2} + 8x^{-2}y^2 - 12y^4}{12x^{-1}y^{-1}}$

17. $\dfrac{x^ny^n - 3x^{2n}y^{2n} + 6x^{3n}y^{3n}}{x^ny^n}$

18. $\dfrac{2a^n - 3a^nb^{2n} - 6b^{4n}}{a^nb^{n-1}}$

In Exercises 19–54, use the division algorithm to find each quotient.

19. $\dfrac{x^2 + 5x + 6}{x + 3}$

20. $\dfrac{x^2 - 5x + 6}{x - 3}$

21. $(x^2 + 10x + 21) \div (x + 3)$

22. $(x^2 + 10x + 21) \div (x + 7)$

23. $\dfrac{6x^2 - x - 12}{2x + 3}$

24. $\dfrac{6x^2 - x - 12}{2x - 3}$

25. $\dfrac{3x^3 - 2x^2 + x + 6}{x - 1}$

26. $\dfrac{4a^3 + a^2 - 3a + 7}{a + 1}$

27. $\dfrac{6x^3 + 11x^2 - x - 2}{3x - 2}$

28. $\dfrac{6x^3 + 11x^2 - x + 10}{2x + 3}$

29. $\dfrac{6x^3 - x^2 - 6x - 9}{2x - 3}$

30. $\dfrac{16x^3 + 16x^2 - 9x - 5}{4x + 5}$

31. $(2a + 1 + a^2) \div (a + 1)$

32. $(a - 15 + 6a^2) \div (2a - 3)$

33. $(6y - 4 + 10y^2) \div (5y - 2)$

34. $(-10xy + x^2 + 16y^2) \div (x - 2y)$

35. $\dfrac{-18x + 12 + 6x^2}{x - 1}$

36. $\dfrac{27x + 23x^2 + 6x^3}{2x + 3}$

37. $\dfrac{-9x^2 + 8x + 9x^3 - 4}{3x - 2}$

38. $\dfrac{6x^2 + 8x^3 - 13x + 3}{4x - 3}$

39. $\dfrac{13x + 16x^4 + 3x^2 + 3}{4x + 3}$

40. $\dfrac{3x^2 + 9x^3 + 4x + 4}{3x + 2}$

41. $(a^3 + 1) \div (a - 1)$

42. $(27a^3 - 8b^3) \div (3a - 2b)$

43. $\dfrac{15a^3 - 29a^2 + 16}{3a - 4}$

44. $\dfrac{4x^3 - 12x^2 + 17x - 12}{2x - 3}$

45. $y - 2 \overline{) -24y + 24 + 6y^2}$

46. $3 - a \overline{) 21a - a^2 - 54}$

47. $2x + y \overline{) 32x^5 + y^5}$

48. $3x - y \overline{) 81x^4 - y^4}$

49. $x^2 - 2 \overline{) x^6 - x^4 + 2x^2 - 8}$

50. $x^2 + 3 \overline{) x^6 + 2x^4 - 6x^2 - 9}$

51. $(x^4 + 2x^3 + 4x^2 + 3x + 2) \div (x^2 + x + 2)$

52. $(2x^4 + 3x^3 + 3x^2 - 5x - 3) \div (2x^2 - x - 1)$

53. $x + x^2 + 2 \overline{) x^3 + 3x + 5x^2 + 6 + x^4}$

54. $x^3 + 1 + 2x \overline{) x^5 + 3x + 2}$

In Exercises 55–56, use a calculator to find each quotient.

55. $x - 2 \overline{) 9.8x^2 - 3.2x - 69.3}$

56. $2.5x - 3.7 \overline{) -22.25x^2 - 38.9x - 16.65}$

2.6   SYNTHETIC DIVISION

There is a shortcut method, called **synthetic division**, that we can use to divide a polynomial by a binomial of the form $x - r$. To see how this method works, we consider the division of $4x^3 - 5x^2 - 11x + 20$ by $x - 2$.

$$
\begin{array}{r}
4x^2 + 3x \;\; - \;\; 5 \\
x - 2 \overline{) 4x^3 - 5x^2 - 11x + 20} \\
\underline{4x^3 - 8x^2} \\
3x^2 - 11x \\
\underline{3x^2 - \;\; 6x} \\
-5x + 20 \\
\underline{-5x + 10} \\
10 \;\; \text{(remainder)}
\end{array}
$$

$$
\begin{array}{r}
4 \quad\quad 3 \quad - 5 \\
1 - 2 \overline{) 4 \quad -5 \quad -11 \quad 20} \\
\underline{4 \quad -8} \\
3 \quad -11 \\
\underline{3 \quad -\;6} \\
-5 \quad 20 \\
\underline{-5 \quad 10} \\
10 \;\; \text{(remainder)}
\end{array}
$$

On the left is the familiar long-division process, and on the right is the skeleton form of that division. All references to the variable x have been removed. The various powers of x can be remembered without actually writing them because the exponents of the terms in the divisor, dividend, and quotient were written in descending order.

We can further shorten the version on the right. The numbers printed in color need not be written because they are duplicates of the numbers immediately above them. Thus, we can write the division in the following form:

$$
\begin{array}{r}
4 \quad 3 \quad -5 \\
1-2\,\overline{)\,4 \quad -5 \quad -11 \quad 20\,} \\
-8 \\
\overline{3 } \\
-6 \\
\overline{-5 } \\
10 \\
\overline{10}
\end{array}
$$

We can shorten the process still further by compressing the work vertically, and eliminating the 1 (the coefficient of x in the divisor):

$$
\begin{array}{r}
4 \quad 3 \quad -5 \\
-2\,\overline{)\,4 \quad -5 \quad -11 \quad 20\,} \\
-8 \quad -6 \quad 10 \\
\overline{3 \quad -5 \quad 10}
\end{array}
$$

There is no reason why the quotient, represented by the numbers 4 3 -5, must appear *above* the long division. If we write the 4 on the bottom line, the bottom line gives the coefficients of the quotient, and it also gives the remainder. The entire top line can be eliminated. The division now appears as follows:

$$
\begin{array}{r}
-2\,\underline{|\quad 4 \quad -5 \quad -11 \quad 20} \\
-8 \quad -6 \quad 10 \\
\overline{4 \quad 3 \quad -5 \quad 10}
\end{array}
$$

The bottom line was obtained by subtracting the middle line from the top line. If we were to replace the -2 in the divisor by a $+2$, the division process would reverse the signs of every entry in the middle line. Then, the bottom line could be obtained by addition. Thus, we have this final form of the synthetic division.

$$
\begin{array}{r}
+2\,\underline{|\quad 4 \quad -5 \quad -11 \quad 20} \\
8 \quad 6 \quad -10 \\
\overline{4 \quad 3 \quad -5 \;|\; 10}
\end{array}
$$

The coefficients of the dividend

The coefficients of the quotient, and the remainder to the right of the vertical bar

Thus,

$$
\frac{4x^3 - 5x^2 - 11x + 20}{x - 2} = 4x^2 + 3x - 5 + \frac{10}{x - 2}
$$

Example 1   Use synthetic division to divide $6x^2 + 5x - 2$ by $x - 5$.

Solution   Begin by writing the coefficients of the dividend, and the 5 from the divisor, in the following form:

$$\underline{5}|\quad 6\quad 5\quad -2$$

Then follow these steps:

$$\underline{5}|\quad 6\quad 5\quad -2$$
$$6$$

Begin by bringing down the 6.

$$\underline{5}|\quad 6\quad 5\quad -2$$
$$\qquad\qquad 30$$
$$6$$

Multiply 5 and 6, to get 30.

$$\underline{5}|\quad 6\quad 5\quad -2$$
$$\qquad\qquad 30$$
$$6\quad 35$$

Add 5 and 30, to get 35.

$$\underline{5}|\quad 6\quad 5\quad -2$$
$$\qquad\qquad 30\quad 175$$
$$6\quad 35$$

Multiply 5 and 35, to get 175.

$$\underline{5}|\quad 6\quad 5\qquad -2$$
$$\qquad\quad 30\qquad 175$$
$$6\quad 35\ |\ 173$$

Add -2 and 175, to get 173.

The numbers 6 and 35 represent the quotient: $6x + 35$. The number 173 is the remainder. Thus,

$$\frac{6x^2 + 5x - 2}{x - 5} = 6x + 35 + \frac{173}{x - 5}$$

Check this answer.   ∎

Example 2   Use synthetic division to divide $5x^3 + x^2 - 3$ by $x - 2$.

Solution   Begin by writing

$$\underline{2}|\quad 5\quad 1\quad \mathbf{0}\quad -3$$

Write 0 for the coefficient of x, the missing term.

Then complete the division as follows:

$$\underline{2}|\quad 5\quad 1\quad 0\quad -3 \qquad \underline{2}|\quad 5\quad 1\quad 0\quad -3 \qquad \underline{2}|\quad 5\quad 1\quad 0\qquad -3$$
$$\qquad\qquad 10 \qquad\qquad\qquad\qquad\qquad 10\quad 22 \qquad\qquad\qquad\qquad 10\quad 22\quad 44$$
$$5\quad 11 \qquad\qquad\qquad\qquad 5\quad 11\quad 22 \qquad\qquad\qquad 5\quad 11\quad 22\ |\ 41$$

Thus,

$$\frac{5x^3 + x^2 - 3}{x - 2} = 5x^2 + 11x + 22 + \frac{41}{x - 2}$$

Check this answer.   ■

Example 3   Use synthetic division to divide $5x^2 + 6x^3 + 2 - 4x$ by $x + 2$.

Solution   First, rewrite the dividend with the exponents in descending order: $6x^3 + 5x^2 - 4x + 2$. Then rewrite the divisor in $x - r$ form: $x - (-2)$. Using synthetic division, begin by writing

$$\underline{-2\,|} \quad 6 \quad\quad 5 \quad -4 \quad\quad\quad 2$$

Then complete the division:

$$\begin{array}{r|rrrr} -2 & 6 & 5 & -4 & 2 \\ & & -12 & 14 & -20 \\ \hline & 6 & -7 & 10 & -18 \end{array}$$

Thus,

$$\frac{5x^2 + 6x^3 + 2 - 4x}{x + 2} = 6x^2 - 7x + 10 + \frac{-18}{x + 2}$$

Check this answer.   ■

Synthetic division is important in mathematics because of the following theorem, called the **Remainder Theorem**.

> **Remainder Theorem.**   If a polynomial $P(x)$ is divided by $x - r$, then the remainder is $P(r)$.

We will illustrate the Remainder Theorem in Example 4.

Example 4   If $P(x) = 2x^3 - 3x^2 - 2x + 1$, determine   **a.** $P(3)$ and   **b.** the remainder when $P(x)$ is divided by $x - 3$.

Solution   **a.** $P(3) = 2(3)^3 - 3(3)^2 - 2(3) + 1$

$= 2(27) - 3(9) - 6 + 1$

$= 54 - 27 - 5$

$= \mathbf{22}$

b. Use synthetic division to find the remainder when $P(x) = 2x^3 - 3x^2 - 2x + 1$ is divided by $x - 3$.

$$
\begin{array}{r|rrrr}
3 & 2 & -3 & -2 & 1 \\
  &   & 6 & 9 & 21 \\
\hline
  & 2 & 3 & 7 & 22 \\
\end{array}
$$

The remainder is 22.

The results of parts a and b show that, when $P(x)$ is divided by $x - 3$, the remainder is $P(3)$. ∎

It is often easier to calculate $P(r)$ by using synthetic division than by substituting r for x in $P(x)$. This is especially true if r is a number such as 2.3, 0.06, or 3.698.

■ EXERCISE 2.6

In Exercises 1–14, use synthetic division to perform each division.

1. $(x^2 + x - 2) \div (x - 1)$

2. $(x^2 + x - 6) \div (x - 2)$

3. $x - 4\overline{)\,x^2 - 7x + 12}$

4. $x - 5\overline{)\,x^2 - 6x + 5}$

5. $(x^2 + 8 + 6x) \div (x + 4)$

6. $(x^2 - 15 - 2x) \div (x + 3)$

7. $x + 2\overline{)\,x^2 - 5x + 14}$

8. $x + 6\overline{)\,x^2 + 13x + 42}$

9. $(3x^3 - 10x^2 + 5x - 6) \div (x - 3)$

10. $(2x^3 - 9x^2 + 10x - 3) \div (x - 3)$

11. $(2x^3 - 5x - 6) \div (x - 2)$

12. $(4x^3 + 5x^2 - 1) \div (x + 2)$

13. $x + 1\overline{)\,5x^2 + 6x^3 + 4}$

14. $x - 4\overline{)\,4 - 3x^2 + x}$

In Exercises 15–20, use a calculator and synthetic division to perform each division.

15. $x - 0.2\overline{)\,7.2x^2 - 2.1x + 0.5}$

16. $x - 0.4\overline{)\,8.1x^2 + 3.2x - 5.7}$

17. $x + 1.7\overline{)\,2.7x^2 + x - 5.2}$

18. $x + 2.5\overline{)\,1.3x^2 - 0.5x - 2.3}$

19. $x + 57\overline{)\,9x^3 - 25}$

20. $x - 2.3\overline{)\,0.5x^3 + x}$

In Exercises 21–28, let $P(x) = 2x^3 - 4x^2 + 2x - 1$. Evaluate the polynomial by substituting the given value of x into the polynomial and simplifying. Then evaluate the polynomial by using the Remainder Theorem and synthetic division.

21. $P(1)$

22. $P(2)$

23. $P(-2)$

24. $P(-1)$

25. $P(3)$

26. $P(-4)$

27. $P(0)$

28. $P(4)$

In Exercises 29–36, let $Q(x) = x^4 - 3x^3 + 2x^2 + x - 3$. Evaluate the polynomial by substituting the given value of x into the polynomial and simplifying. Then evaluate the polynomial by using the Remainder Theorem and synthetic division.

29. $Q(-1)$

30. $Q(1)$

31. $Q(2)$

32. $Q(-2)$

33. $Q(3)$

34. $Q(0)$

35. $Q(-3)$

36. $Q(-4)$

In Exercises 37–44, use the Remainder Theorem and synthetic division to find $P(r)$.

37. $P(x) = x^3 - 4x^2 + x - 2$; $r = 2$ **38.** $P(x) = x^3 - 3x^2 + x + 1$; $r = 1$

39. $P(x) = 2x^3 + x + 2$; $r = 3$ **40.** $P(x) = x^3 + x^2 + 1$; $r = -2$

41. $P(x) = x^4 - 2x^3 + x^2 - 3x + 2$; $r = -2$ **42.** $P(x) = x^5 + 3x^4 - x^2 + 1$; $r = -1$

43. $P(x) = 3x^5 + 1$; $r = -\frac{1}{2}$ **44.** $P(x) = 5x^7 - 7x^4 + x^2 + 1$; $r = 2$

45. Calculate 2^6 by using synthetic division to evaluate the polynomial $P(x) = x^6$ at $x = 2$.

46. Calculate $(-3)^5$ by using synthetic division to evaluate the polynomial $P(x) = x^5$ at $x = -3$.

CHAPTER SUMMARY

Key Words

algorithm (2.5)

base of an exponential
  expression (2.1)

binomial (2.3)

coefficient (2.1)

degree of a polynomial (2.3)

exponent (2.1)

FOIL method for multiplying
  binomials (2.4)

like terms (2.3)

monomial (2.3)

polynomial (2.3)

power of x (2.1)

similar terms (2.3)

trinomial (2.3)

Key Ideas

$$\overbrace{x^n = x \cdot x \cdot x \cdot \cdots \cdot x}^{n \text{ factors of } x}$$

(2.1)   For any natural n,

If m and n are integers and there are no divisions by zero, then

a. $x^m x^n = x^{m+n}$ **b.** $(x^m)^n = x^{mn}$

c. $(xy)^n = x^n y^n$ **d.** $\left(\dfrac{y}{x}\right)^n = \dfrac{y^n}{x^n}$

e. $x^0 = 1$ **f.** $x^{-n} = \dfrac{1}{x^n}$

g. $\dfrac{x^m}{x^n} = x^{m-n}$ **h.** $\left(\dfrac{y}{x}\right)^{-n} = \left(\dfrac{x}{y}\right)^n$

(2.2)   A number is written in scientific notation if it is expressed as a number between 1 and 10 multiplied by an appropriate power of 10.

(2.3)   A polynomial in x is the sum of one or more terms of the form ax^n, where a is a real number and n is a whole number.

A polynomial in several variables, say x, y, and z, is a sum of one or more terms of the form $ax^m y^n z^p$, where a is a real number and m, n, and p are whole numbers.

The **degree of a polynomial** is the degree of the term with highest degree contained within the polynomial.

If $P(x)$ is a polynomial in x, then $P(r)$ is the value of the polynomial at $x = r$.

To add like terms, add their numerical coefficients and use the same variables with the same exponents.

To add polynomials, add their like terms.

To subtract polynomials, add the negative of the subtrahend to the other polynomial.

(2.4)   To multiply monomials, multiply their numerical factors and multiply their variable factors.

To multiply a polynomial by a monomial, multiply each term of the polynomial by the monomial.

To multiply polynomials, multiply each term of one polynomial by each term of the other polynomial.

If one set of grouping symbols is contained within another set, remove the inner set first.

(2.5)   To find the quotient of two monomials, express the quotient as a fraction and use the rules of exponents to simplify.

(2.6)   Synthetic division can be used to divide polynomials by binomials of the form $x - r$.

If a polynomial $P(x)$ is divided by $x - r$, then the remainder is $P(r)$.

REVIEW EXERCISES

In Review Exercises 1–28, use the rules of exponents to simplify each quantity. Write all answers without using negative exponents.

1. 3^6

2. -2^6

3. $(-4)^3$

4. $-(-5)^4$

5. $(3x^4)(-2x^2)$

6. $(-x^5)(3x^3)$

7. $x^{-4}x^3$

8. $x^{-10}x^{12}$

9. $(3x^2)^3$

10. $(4x^4)^4$

11. $(-2x^2)^5$

12. $-(-3x^3)^5$

13. $(x^2)^{-5}$ **14.** $(x^{-4})^{-5}$ **15.** $(3x^{-3})^{-2}$ **16.** $(2x^{-4})^4$

17. $\dfrac{x^6}{x^4}$ **18.** $\dfrac{x^{12}}{x^7}$ **19.** $\dfrac{a^7}{a^{12}}$ **20.** $\dfrac{a^4}{a^7}$

21. $\dfrac{y^{-3}}{y^4}$ **22.** $\dfrac{y^5}{y^{-4}}$ **23.** $\dfrac{x^{-5}}{x^{-4}}$ **24.** $\dfrac{x^{-6}}{x^{-9}}$

25. $(3x^2y^3)^2$ **26.** $(-4a^3b^2)^{-4}$ **27.** $\left(\dfrac{3x^2}{4y^3}\right)^{-3}$ **28.** $\left(\dfrac{4y^{-2}}{5y^{-3}}\right)^3$

In Review Exercises 29–30, write each numeral in scientific notation.

29. 19,300,000,000   **30.** 0.0000000273

In Review Exercises 31–32, write each numeral in standard notation.

31. 7.2×10^7 **32.** 8.3×10^{-9}

In Review Exercises 33–36, find the required value if $P(x) = -x^2 + 4x + 6$.

33. $P(0)$ **34.** $P(1)$ **35.** $P(-t)$ **36.** $P(z)$

37. Give the degree of $P(x) = 3x^5 + 4x^3 + 2$.   **38.** Give the degree of $9x^2y + 13x^3y^2 + 8x^4y^4$.

In Review Exercises 39–42, simplify each expression.

39. $(3x^2 + 4x + 9) - (2x^2 - 2x + 7) + (4x^2 - 3x - 2)$
40. $(4x^3 + 4x^2 + 7) - (-2x^3 - x - 2) + (-5x^3 - 3x^2)$
41. $(2x^2 - 5x + 9) - (x^2 - 3) - (-3x^2 + 4x - 7)$
42. $(7x^3 - 6x^2 + 4x - 3) - (7x^3 + 6x^2 + 4x - 3)$

In Review Exercises 43–50, find each product.

43. $(8a^2b^2)(-2abc)$ **44.** $(-3xy^2z)(2xz^3)$
45. $2xy^2(x^3y - 4xy^5)$ **46.** $a^2b(a^2 + 2ab + b^2)$
47. $(8x - 5)(2x + 3)$ **48.** $(3x^2 + 2)(2x - 4)$
49. $(5x^2 - 4x + 5)(3x^2 - 2x + 10)$ **50.** $(3x^2 + x - 2)(x^2 - x + 2)$

In Review Exercises 51–58, perform each division.

51. Divide $(3x^3 - 4x^2 + 3x + 2)$ by $(x + 3)$.   **52.** Divide $(64x^3 + 125y^3)$ by $(4x + 5y)$.
53. $x - 1 \overline{)\, x^5 - 1}$ **54.** $x + 2 \overline{)\, x^5 + 32}$
55. $3x - 2 \overline{)\, 6x^3 + 5x^2 - 3x + 8}$ **56.** $x^2 - 1 \overline{)\, x^4 + x^2 - 2}$
57. $x^2 + 2x + 3 \overline{)\, x^4 - x^2 - 3}$ **58.** $3x + x^3 + 1 \overline{)\, 3x^3 - x^2 + 5}$

In Review Exercises 59–60, use synthetic division to perform each division.

59. $x - 4 \overline{)\, x^3 - 13x - 12}$ **60.** $x + 1 \overline{)\, x^4 + x^2 + 1}$

In Review Exercises 61–62, let $P(x) = 3x^2 - 2x + 3$. Use synthetic division and the Remainder Theorem to find each value.

61. $P(2)$ **62.** $P(-1)$

CHAPTER TWO TEST

In Problems 1–6, simplify each expression. Write all answers without using negative exponents. Assume that no denominators are zero.

1. x^3x^5

2. $(x^2y^3)^3$

3. $(m^{-4})^2$

4. $\left(\dfrac{a^3}{b^2}\right)^4$

5. $3x^0$

6. $\left(\dfrac{m^2n^3}{m^4n^{-2}}\right)^{-2}$

In Problems 7–8, write each number in scientific notation.

7. 4,700,000

8. 0.00000023

In Problems 9–10, write each number in standard notation.

9. 6.53×10^5

10. 24.5×10^{-3}

11. The moon is approximately 235,000 miles from the earth. Use scientific notation to express this distance in kilometers. (Hint: 1 mile $\approx$ 1.6 kilometers.)

12. Give the degree of the polynomial $3x^2y^3 + 4x^3y^7 - 7x^4y^5$.

In Problems 13–14, let $P(x) = -3x^2 + 2x - 1$ and find each value.

13. $P(2)$

14. $P(-1)$

In Problems 15–16, $x = 3$ and $y = -2$. Find the value of each expression.

15. $x^2 - y^2$

16. $\dfrac{4x^2 + y^2}{-xy^2}$

In Problems 17–28, perform the indicated operations.

17. $(2y^2 + 4y + 3) + (3y^2 - 3y - 4)$

18. $(-3u^2 + 2u - 7) - (u^2 + 7)$

19. $3(2a^2 - 4a + 2) - 4(-a^2 - 3a - 4)$

20. Add: $\begin{array}{r} 8x^2 + 4x - 9 \\ -2x^2 - 6x + 8 \end{array}$

21. $(3x^3y^2z)(-2xy^{-1}z^3)$

22. $-5a^2b(3ab^3 - 2ab^4)$

23. $(z + 4)(z - 4)$

24. $(3x - 2)(4x + 3)$

25. $(2x + 1)(x^2 - x - 3)$

26. $(x^n + y^n)(2x^n - y^n)$

27. $\dfrac{18x^2y^3 - 12x^3y^2 + 9xy}{-3xy^4}$

28. $2x - 1 \overline{)6x^3 + 5x^2 - 2}$

29. Find the remainder in the division

$$\dfrac{x^3 - 4x^2 + 5x + 3}{x + 1}$$

30. Find the remainder when $4x^3 + 3x^2 + 2x - 1$ is divided by $x - 2$ by completing the synthetic division

$$\begin{array}{r|rrrr} 2 & 4 & 3 & 2 & -1 \\ & & & & \\ \hline \end{array}$$

3 Factoring Polynomials

In the previous chapter we discussed how to multiply polynomials by polynomials. We now reverse that procedure and discuss how to split products apart and undo multiplications. The process of finding the individual factors of a known product is called **factoring**.

3.1 THE GREATEST COMMON FACTOR

If a natural number a divides a natural number b (without a remainder), then a is called a **factor** of b. The natural number factors of 6, for example, are 6, 3, 2, and 1 because each of these numbers divides 6. Recall that, if the only natural number factors of a natural number p (where $p > 1$) are 1 and p, then p is called a **prime number**. The set of prime numbers is the set

$$\mathbf{P} = \{2, 3, 5, 7, 11, 13, 17, 19, 23, 29, \ldots\}$$

To factor a natural number means to write the number as a product of other natural numbers. If each of the factors in the product is prime, we say that the natural number is written in **prime-factored form**. The statements

$$60 = 6 \cdot 10 = 2 \cdot 3 \cdot 2 \cdot 5 = 2^2 \cdot 3 \cdot 5$$
$$84 = 4 \cdot 21 = 2 \cdot 2 \cdot 3 \cdot 7 = 2^2 \cdot 3 \cdot 7$$

and

$$180 = 10 \cdot 18 = 2 \cdot 5 \cdot 3 \cdot 6 = 2 \cdot 5 \cdot 3 \cdot 3 \cdot 2 = 2^2 \cdot 3^2 \cdot 5$$

show the prime-factored forms of 60, 84, and 180. If a quantity is written in prime-factored form, we say it is in **completely factored form**.

The largest natural number that divides 60, 84, and 180 is called the **greatest common factor** or **greatest common divisor** of these three numbers. Because 60, 84, and 180 all have at least two factors of 2 and one factor of 3, the greatest common factor of these three numbers is $2^2 \cdot 3 = \mathbf{12}$. We note that

$$\frac{60}{12} = 5, \qquad \frac{84}{12} = 7, \qquad \text{and} \qquad \frac{180}{12} = 15$$

There is no natural number greater than 12 that divides 60, 84, and 180.

Likewise, algebraic monomials have greatest common factors. We consider three monomials with their prime factorizations:

$$6a^2b^3c = 3 \cdot 2 \cdot a \cdot a \cdot b \cdot b \cdot b \cdot c$$
$$9a^3b^2c = 3^2 \cdot a \cdot a \cdot a \cdot b \cdot b \cdot c$$
$$18a^4c^3 = 2 \cdot 3^2 \cdot a \cdot a \cdot a \cdot a \cdot c \cdot c \cdot c$$

Because each monomial has at least one factor of 3, two factors of a, and one factor of c in common, their greatest common factor is

$$3^1 \cdot a^2 \cdot c^1 = 3a^2c$$

To find the greatest common factor of several monomials, we follow these steps:

---

1. Completely factor each monomial.
2. Use each common factor the least number of times it appears in any one monomial.
3. Find the product of the factors found in step 2 to obtain the greatest common factor.

Recall that the distributive property provides a method for multiplying a polynomial by a monomial. For example,

$$2x^3y^3(3x^2 - 4y^3) = 2x^3y^3 \cdot 3x^2 - 2x^3y^3 \cdot 4y^3$$
$$= 6x^5y^3 - 8x^3y^6$$

If the product of a multiplication is $6x^5y^3 - 8x^3y^6$, we can use the distributive property backwards to find the individual factors.

$$6x^5y^3 - 8x^3y^6 = 2x^3y^3 \cdot 3x^2 - 2x^3y^3 \cdot 4y^3$$
$$= 2x^3y^3(3x^2 - 4y^3)$$

Because $2x^3y^3$ is the greatest common factor of the terms of $6x^5y^3 - 8x^3y^6$, this process is called **factoring out the greatest common factor**.

Example 1   Factor $25a^3b + 15ab^3$.

Solution   First factor each monomial:

$$25a^3b = 5 \cdot 5 \cdot a \cdot a \cdot a \cdot b$$
$$15ab^3 = 5 \cdot 3 \cdot a \cdot b \cdot b \cdot b$$

Because each term has at least one factor of 5, one factor of a, and one factor of b, and because there are no other common factors, $5ab$ is the greatest common factor of the two terms. Use the distributive property to factor out the $5ab$:

$$25a^3b + 15ab^3 = 5ab \cdot 5a^2 + 5ab \cdot 3b^2$$
$$= 5ab(5a^2 + 3b^2)$$

■

Example 2   Factor $3xy^2z^3 + 6xz^2 - 9xyz^4$.

Solution   First factor each monomial:

$$3xy^2z^3 = 3 \cdot x \cdot y \cdot y \cdot z \cdot z \cdot z$$
$$6xz^2 = 3 \cdot 2 \cdot x \cdot z \cdot z$$
$$-9xyz^4 = -3 \cdot 3 \cdot x \cdot y \cdot z \cdot z \cdot z \cdot z$$

Because each term has at least one factor of 3, one factor of x, and two factors of z, and because there are no other common factors, $3xz^2$ is the greatest common factor of the three terms. Use the distributive property to factor out the $3xz^2$:

$$3xy^2z^3 + 6xz^2 - 9xyz^4 = 3xz^2 \cdot y^2z + 3xz^2 \cdot 2 - 3xz^2 \cdot 3yz^2$$
$$= 3xz^2(y^2z + 2 - 3yz^2)$$

Example 3   Factor $x^3y^3z^3 + xyz$.

Solution   Because each term has at least one factor of x, one factor of y, and one factor of z, and because there are no other common factors, the greatest common factor of $x^3y^3z^3$ and xyz is xyz. Thus, the expression $x^3y^3z^3 + xyz$ can be factored as follows:

$$x^3y^3z^3 + xyz = xyz \cdot x^2y^2z^2 + xyz \cdot 1$$
$$= xyz(x^2y^2z^2 + 1)$$

It is important to understand where the "1" comes from. The last term, xyz, of the given binomial has an understood coefficient of 1. When the xyz is factored out, the 1 must be made explicit.

Example 4   Factor out the negative of the greatest common factor of $-6u^2v^3 + 8u^3v^2$.

Solution   The greatest common factor of the two terms is $2u^2v^2$. Thus, the negative of the greatest common factor is $-2u^2v^2$. To factor out $-2u^2v^2$, proceed as follows:

$$-6u^2v^3 + 8u^3v^2 = -2u^2v^2 \cdot 3v + 2u^2v^2 \cdot 4u$$
$$= -2u^2v^2 \cdot 3v - (-2u^2v^2) \cdot 4u$$
$$= -2u^2v^2(3v - 4u)$$

If a polynomial cannot be factored, we call the polynomial a **prime polynomial** or an **irreducible polynomial**.

Example 5   Factor $3x^2 + 4y + 7$.

Solution   Factor each monomial:

$$3x^2 = 3 \cdot x \cdot x$$
$$4y = 2 \cdot 2 \cdot y$$
$$7 = 7$$

Because there are no common factors other than 1, the given polynomial cannot be factored. It is an example of a prime polynomial. ∎

Sometimes the common factor in an expression is a polynomial with more than one term. For example, in the expression

$$x(a + b) + y(a + b)$$

the binomial $a + b$ is a factor of both terms. Hence the expression factors as

$$x(a + b) + y(a + b) = (a + b) \cdot x + (a + b) \cdot y$$
$$= (a + b)(x + y)$$

Example 6   Factor $a(x - y + z) - b(x - y + z) + 3(x - y + z)$.

Solution   Determine that $x - y + z$ is the greatest common factor, and use the distributive property to factor it out:

$$a(x - y + z) - b(x - y + z) + 3(x - y + z)$$
$$= (x - y + z) \cdot a - (x - y + z) \cdot b + (x - y + z) \cdot 3$$
$$= (x - y + z)(a - b + 3)$$ ∎

In advanced courses we must sometimes factor out an exponential expression with a variable exponent. For example, to factor x^{2n} from $x^{4n} + x^{3n} + x^{2n}$, we write the trinomial in the form

$$x^{2n} \cdot x^{2n} + x^{2n} \cdot x^n + x^{2n} \cdot 1$$

and factor out the x^{2n}:

$$x^{4n} + x^{3n} + x^{2n} = x^{2n} \cdot x^{2n} + x^{2n} \cdot x^n + x^{2n} \cdot 1$$
$$= x^{2n}(x^{2n} + x^n + 1)$$

Example 7   Factor $a^{-2}b^{-2}$ from $a^{-2}b - a^3b^{-2}$.

Solution   Write the expression $a^{-2}b - a^3b^{-2}$ in the form

$$a^{-2}b^{-2} \cdot b^3 - a^{-2}b^{-2} \cdot a^5$$

and factor out the $a^{-2}b^{-2}$:

$$a^{-2}b - a^3b^{-2} = a^{-2}b^{-2} \cdot b^3 - a^{-2}b^{-2} \cdot a^5$$
$$= a^{-2}b^{-2}(b^3 - a^5)$$ ∎

▬ EXERCISE 3.1 ▬▬▬▬▬▬▬▬▬▬▬▬▬▬▬▬▬▬▬▬▬▬▬▬▬▬▬▬▬

In Exercises 1–8, find the prime factorization of each number.

1.	6	**2.**	10	**3.**	135	**4.**	98
5.	128	**6.**	357	**7.**	325	**8.**	288

In Exercises 9–16, find the greatest common factor of each set of quantities.

9. $36, 48$ **10.** $45, 75$ **11.** $42, 36, 98$ **12.** $16, 40, 60$

13. $4a^2b, 8a^3c$ **14.** $6x^3y^2z, 9xyz^2$

15. $18x^4y^3z^2, -12xy^2z^3$ **16.** $6x^2y^3, 24xy^3, 40x^2y^2z^3$

In Exercises 17–46, factor each expression completely. If a polynomial is prime, so indicate.

17. $2x + 8$ **18.** $3y - 9$ **19.** $2x^2 - 6x$ **20.** $3y^3 + 6y^2$

21. $5xy + 10xy^2$ **22.** $7x^2 + 14x$ **23.** $15x^2y - 10x^2y^2$ **24.** $9x^3y^2 - 12x^2y$

25. $12r^2s^3t^4 + 15rt^6$ **26.** $13ab^2c^3 - 26a^3b^2c$

27. $24r^2s^3 - 12r^3s^2t + 6rst^2$ **28.** $18x^2y^2z^2 + 12xy^2z^2 - 24x^4y^4z^3$

29. $45x^{10}y^3 - 63x^7y^7 + 81x^{10}y^{10}$ **30.** $48u^6v^6 - 16u^4v^4 - 3u^6v^3$

31. $25x^3 - 14y^3 + 36x^3y^3$ **32.** $9m^4n^3p^2 + 18m^2n^3p^4 - 27m^3n^4p$

33. $24a^3b^5 + 32a^5b^3 - 64a^5b^5c^5$ **34.** $32a^4 + 9b^2 + 5a^4b^2$

35. $4(x + y) + t(x + y)$ **36.** $5(a - b) - t(a - b)$

37. $(a - b)r - (a - b)s$ **38.** $(x + y)u + (x + y)v$

39. $3(m + n + p) + x(m + n + p)$ **40.** $x^2(x - y - z) + y(x - y - z) - z(x - y - z)$

41. $(a + b)x - a(x + b)$ **42.** $a(x - b) + b(x + a)$

43. $(x + y)(x + y) + z(x + y)$ **44.** $(a - b)^2 + (a - b)$

45. $(u + v) - (u + v)^2$ **46.** $a(x - y) - (x - y)(x - y)$

In Exercises 47–56, factor out the negative of the greatest common factor.

47. $-x + y$ **48.** $-x^2 - x$ **49.** $-18a^2b - 12ab^2$ **50.** $-15y^3 + 25y^2$

51. $-63u^3v^6z^9 + 28u^2v^7z^2 - 21u^3v^3z^4$ **52.** $-56x^4y^3z^2 - 72x^3y^4z^5 + 80xy^2z^3$

53. $-a(x + y) + b(x + y)$ **54.** $-bx(a - b) - cx(a - b)$

55. $-32x^3(m - n + p) - 40x^2(m - n + p) + 16x^4(m - n + p)$

56. $-45a^2b^3(x + y - z) + 81a^3b^2(x + y - z) - 90a^4b^2(x + y - z)$

57. Factor x^2 from $x^{n+2} + x^{n+3}$.   **58.** Factor y^3 from $y^{n+3} + y^{n+5}$.

59. Factor y^n from $y^{n+2} - y^{n+3}$.   **60.** Factor x^n from $x^{n+3} - x^{n+5}$.

61. Factor x^{-2} from $x^4 - 5x^6$.   **62.** Factor y^{-4} from $7y^4 + y$.

63. Factor y^{-2n} from $y^{2n} + 1 + y^{-2n}$.   **64.** Factor x^{-3n} from $x^{6n} + x^{3n} + 1$.

In Exercises 65–68, use long division.

65. Show that $x + y$ is a factor of $x^4 - y^4$.   **66.** Show that $x - y$ is a factor of $x^5 - y^5$.

67. Show that $x + y$ is a factor of $x^7 + y^7$.   **68.** Show that $x^2 + y^2$ is a factor of $x^8 - y^8$.

*If the greatest common factor of several terms is 1, the terms are called **relatively prime**. In Exercises 69–76, tell whether the terms in each set are relatively prime.*

69. $14, 45$ **70.** $24, 63, 112$ **71.** $60, 28, 36$ **72.** $55, 49, 78$

73. $12x^2y, 5ab^3, 35x^2b^3$ **74.** $18uv, 25rs, 12rsuv$

75. $9(a - b), 16(a + b), 25(a + b + c)$ **76.** $44(x + y - z), 99(x - y + z), 121(x + y + z)$

3.2   THE DIFFERENCE OF TWO SQUARES; THE SUM AND DIFFERENCE OF TWO CUBES

There are special product formulas that lead to factoring formulas for the difference of two squares and the sum and difference of two cubes. We begin this section by using a special product formula discussed in Section 2.4 to factor the difference of two squares.

The Difference of Two Squares

If we multiply a binomial of the form $x + y$ by a binomial of the form $x - y$, we obtain another binomial:

$$\textbf{1.} \quad (x + y)(x - y) = x^2 - y^2$$

The binomial $x^2 - y^2$ is called the **difference of two squares** because x^2 represents the square of x, y^2 represents the square of y, and the binomial $x^2 - y^2$ represents the difference of these squares. Because of the symmetric property of equality, Equation 1 can be written in reverse order to give a formula for factoring the difference of two squares.

> **Formula for Factoring the Difference of Two Squares.**
> $$x^2 - y^2 = (x + y)(x - y)$$

This formula points out that the difference of the squares of two quantities such as x and y always factors into the sum of these quantities multiplied by the difference of these quantities.

To factor $49x^2 - 16$, for example, we write $49x^2 - 16$ in the form $(7x)^2 - 4^2$ and apply the formula for factoring the difference of two squares:

$$49x^2 - 16 = (7x)^2 - 4^2$$
$$= (7x + 4)(7x - 4)$$

This result can be verified by multiplying $7x + 4$ by $7x - 4$ and obtaining the product $49x^2 - 16$:

$$(7x + 4)(7x - 4) = 49x^2 - 28x + 28x - 16$$
$$= 49x^2 - 16$$

We note that, if $49x^2 - 16$ is divided by $7x + 4$, the quotient is $7x - 4$, and, if $49x^2 - 16$ is divided by $7x - 4$, the quotient is $7x + 4$.

Expressions such as $(7x)^2 + 4^2$ that represent the sum of two squares cannot be factored by using integer coefficients only. Thus, the binomial $49x^2 + 16$ is a prime binomial.

Example 1   Factor $64x^4 - 25y^2$.

Solution   Because $64x^4$ is the square of $8x^2$, and $25y^2$ is the square of $5y$, the binomial represents the difference of two squares. Its two factors are the sum of $8x^2$ and $5y$, and the difference of $8x^2$ and $5y$.

$$64x^4 - 25y^2 = (8x^2)^2 - (5y)^2$$
$$= (8x^2 + 5y)(8x^2 - 5y)$$

Verify by multiplication that $(8x^2 + 5y)(8x^2 - 5y) = 64x^4 - 25y^2$.   ∎

Example 2   Factor $a^4 - 1$.

Solution   Because the binomial represents the difference of the squares of a^2 and 1, it factors into the sum of a^2 and 1, and the difference of a^2 and 1:

$$a^4 - 1 = (a^2)^2 - 1^2$$
$$= (a^2 + 1)(a^2 - 1)$$

The factor $a^2 + 1$ represents the sum of two squares and cannot be factored. However, the factor $a^2 - 1$ represents the difference of two squares and can be factored as $(a + 1)(a - 1)$. Thus,

$$a^4 - 1 = (a^2 + 1)(a^2 - 1)$$
$$= (a^2 + 1)(a + 1)(a - 1)$$ ∎

Example 3   Factor $(x + y)^4 - z^4$.

Solution   This expression represents the difference of two squares and can be factored as follows:

$$(x + y)^4 - z^4 = [(x + y)^2]^2 - (z^2)^2$$
$$= [(x + y)^2 + z^2][(x + y)^2 - z^2]$$

The factor $(x + y)^2 + z^2$ represents the sum of two squares and cannot be factored. However, the factor $(x + y)^2 - z^2$ represents the difference of two squares and can be factored as $(x + y + z)(x + y - z)$. Thus,

$$(x + y)^4 - z^4 = [(x + y)^2 + z^2][(x + y)^2 - z^2]$$
$$= [(x + y)^2 + z^2](x + y + z)(x + y - z)$$ ∎

If it is possible to factor out a common factor before factoring the difference of two squares, we shall always do so. The factoring process is easier if all common factors are factored out first.

Example 4   Factor $2x^4y - 32y$.

Solution   Proceed as follows:

$$2x^4y - 32y = 2y(x^4 - 16) \qquad \text{Factor out } 2y.$$
$$= 2y(x^2 + 4)(x^2 - 4) \qquad \text{Factor } x^4 - 16.$$
$$= 2y(x^2 + 4)(x + 2)(x - 2) \qquad \text{Factor } x^2 - 4.$$ ∎

The Sum and Difference of Two Cubes

Two other special product formulas are

$$(x + y)(x^2 - xy + y^2) = x^3 + y^3$$

and

$$(x - y)(x^2 + xy + y^2) = x^3 - y^3$$

To verify the first formula, we multiply $x^2 - xy + y^2$ by $x + y$:

$$\begin{aligned}(x + y)(x^2 - xy + y^2) &= x \cdot x^2 - x \cdot xy + x \cdot y^2 + y \cdot x^2 - y \cdot xy + y \cdot y^2 \\ &= x^3 - x^2y + xy^2 + x^2y - xy^2 + y^3 \\ &= x^3 + y^3\end{aligned}$$

Likewise, the second formula can be verified by multiplication.

If we use the symmetric property of equality to write the previous special product formulas in reverse order, we have formulas for factoring the **sum of two cubes** and the **difference of two cubes.**

Formulas for Factoring the Sum and Difference of Two Cubes.

$$x^3 + y^3 = (x + y)(x^2 - xy + y^2)$$
$$x^3 - y^3 = (x - y)(x^2 + xy + y^2)$$

Note that the first factor in the factorization of $x^3 + y^3$ is $x + y$; the second factor is x^2 *minus* xy plus y^2. The first factor in the factorization of $x^3 - y^3$ is $x - y$; the second factor is x^2 *plus* xy plus y^2.

Example 5   Factor $a^3 + 8$.

Solution   Use the formula $x^3 + y^3 = (x + y)(x^2 - xy + y^2)$ with a in place of x and 2 in place of y:

$$\begin{aligned}a^3 + 8 &= a^3 + 2^3 \\ &= (a + 2)(a^2 - a2 + 2^2) \\ &= (a + 2)(a^2 - 2a + 4)\end{aligned}$$

Verify this result by multiplication.   ■

Example 6   Factor $27a^3 - 64b^3$.

Solution   Use the formula $x^3 - y^3 = (x - y)(x^2 + xy + y^2)$ with $3a$ in place of x and $4b$ in place of y:

$$\begin{aligned}27a^3 - 64b^3 &= (3a)^3 - (4b)^3 \\ &= (3a - 4b)[(3a)^2 + (3a)(4b) + (4b)^2] \\ &= (3a - 4b)(9a^2 + 12ab + 16b^2)\end{aligned}$$ ■

Example 7   Factor $a^3 - (c + d)^3$.

Solution
$$a^3 - (c + d)^3 = [a - (c + d)][a^2 + a(c + d) + (c + d)^2]$$
$$= (a - c - d)(a^2 + ac + ad + c^2 + 2cd + d^2) \qquad \blacksquare$$

Example 8   Factor $x^6 - 64$.

Solution   This expression is the difference of two squares and factors into the product of a sum and a difference:
$$x^6 - 64 = (x^3)^2 - 8^2$$
$$= (x^3 + 8)(x^3 - 8)$$

Each of these factors further, however, for one is the sum of two cubes and the other is the difference of two cubes:
$$x^6 - 64 = (x + 2)(x^2 - 2x + 4)(x - 2)(x^2 + 2x + 4) \qquad \blacksquare$$

Example 9   Factor $2a^5 + 128a^2$.

Solution   First factor out the common monomial factor of $2a^2$ to obtain
$$2a^5 + 128a^2 = 2a^2(a^3 + 64)$$

Then factor $a^3 + 64$ as the sum of two cubes to obtain
$$2a^5 + 128a^2 = 2a^2(a + 4)(a^2 - 4a + 16) \qquad \blacksquare$$

Example 10   Factor $16r^{6m} - 54t^{3n}$.

Solution   Proceed as follows:
$$16r^{6m} - 54t^{3n} = 2(8r^{6m} - 27t^{3n}) \qquad \text{Factor out a 2.}$$
$$= 2[(2r^{2m})^3 - (3t^n)^3] \qquad \begin{array}{l}\text{Write } 8r^{6m} \text{ as } (2r^{2m})^3 \\ \text{and write } 27t^{3n} \text{ as } (3t^n)^3.\end{array}$$
$$= 2(2r^{2m} - 3t^n)(4r^{4m} + 6r^{2m}t^n + 9t^{2n}) \qquad \text{Factor } (2r^{2m})^3 - (3t^n)^3. \qquad \blacksquare$$

■ EXERCISE 3.2

In Exercises 1–20, factor each expression completely. If a polynomial is prime, so indicate.

1. $x^2 - 4$

2. $y^2 - 9$

3. $9y^2 - 64$

4. $16x^4 - 81y^2$

5. $x^2 + 25$

6. $144a^2 - b^4$

7. $625a^2 - 169b^4$

8. $4y^2 + 9z^4$

9. $81a^4 - 49b^2$

10. $64r^6 - 121s^2$

11. $36x^4y^2 - 49z^4$

12. $100a^2b^4c^6 - 225d^8$

13. $(x + y)^2 - z^2$

14. $a^2 - (b - c)^2$

15. $(a - b)^2 - (c + d)^2$

16. $(m + n)^4 - (p - q)^2$

17. $x^4 - y^4$

18. $16a^4 - 81b^4$

19. $256x^4y^4 - z^8$

20. $225a^4 - 196b^8c^{12}$

In Exercises 21–30, factor each expression completely. Factor out all common monomial factors first.

21. $2x^2 - 288$
22. $8x^2 - 72$
23. $2x^3 - 32x$
24. $3x^2 - 243$
25. $5x^3 - 125x$
26. $6x^4 - 216x^2$
27. $r^2s^2t^2 - t^2x^4y^2$
28. $16a^4b^3c^4 - 64a^2bc^6$
29. $2(c - d)x^2 - 18(c - d)$
30. $3a^3(x + y) - 27a(x + y)$

In Exercises 31–42, factor each expression completely.

31. $r^3 + s^3$
32. $t^3 - v^3$
33. $x^3 - 8y^3$
34. $27a^3 + b^3$
35. $64a^3 - 125b^6$
36. $8x^6 + 125y^3$
37. $27x^3y^6 + 216z^9$
38. $1000a^6 - 343b^3c^6$
39. $27a^3 + (x + y)^6$
40. $64(x - y)^3 - 125z^6$
41. $x^6 + y^6$
42. $x^9 + y^9$

In Exercises 43–52, factor each expression completely. Factor out all common monomials first.

43. $5x^3 + 625$
44. $2x^3 - 128$
45. $4x^5 - 256x^2$
46. $2x^6 + 54x^3$
47. $128u^2v^3 - 2t^3u^2$
48. $56rs^2t^3 + 7rs^2v^6$
49. $(a + b)x^3 + 27(a + b)$
50. $rs^2(c - d)^3 + 27rs^2$
51. $6(a + b)^3 - 6z^3$
52. $18(x - y)^3 + 144(c - d)^3$

In Exercises 53–62, factor each expression completely. Assume that m and n are natural numbers.

53. $x^{2m} - y^{4n}$
54. $a^{4m} - b^{8n}$
55. $100a^{4m} - 81b^{2n}$
56. $25x^{8m} - 36y^{4n}$
57. $x^{3n} - 8$
58. $a^{3m} + 64$
59. $a^{3m} + b^{3n}$
60. $x^{6m} - y^{3n}$
61. $2x^{6m} + 16y^{3m}$
62. $24 + 3c^{3n}$

3.3 FACTORING TRINOMIALS

Many trinomials can be factored by using two special product formulas discussed in Section 2.4.

1. $(x + y)(x + y) = x^2 + 2xy + y^2$
2. $(x - y)(x - y) = x^2 - 2xy + y^2$

Recall that $x^2 + 2xy + y^2$ and $x^2 - 2xy + y^2$ are called **perfect square trinomials**. To factor the perfect square trinomial $z^2 + 6z + 9$, for example, we note that the trinomial can be written in the form $z^2 + 2(3)z + 3^2$. If $x = z$ and $y = 3$, this form matches the right-hand side of Formula 1. Thus, $z^2 + 6z + 9$ factors as

$$z^2 + 6z + 9 = z^2 + 2(3)z + 3^2$$
$$= (z + 3)(z + 3)$$

This result can be verified by multiplication:

$$(z + 3)(z + 3) = z^2 + 3z + 3z + 9$$
$$= z^2 + 6z + 9$$

Likewise, the perfect square trinomial $a^2 - 4ab + 4b^2$ can be written in the form

$$a^2 - 2(2b)a + (2b)^2$$

If $x = a$ and $y = 2b$, this form matches the right-hand side of Formula 2. Thus, $a^2 - 4ab + 4b^2$ factors as

$$a^2 - 4ab + 4b^2 = a^2 - 2(2b)a + (2b)^2$$
$$= (a - 2b)(a - 2b)$$

This result also can be verified by multiplication.

Many second-degree trinomials cannot be factored by using special product formulas. We begin our discussion of these **general trinomials** by considering trinomials whose lead coefficient (the coefficient of the squared term) is 1.

Factoring Trinomials with a Lead Coefficient of 1

To develop a strategy for factoring trinomials with a lead coefficient of 1, we recall that multiplying two binomials requires that each term of one binomial be multiplied by each term of the other binomial. For example,

$$(x + 3)(x + 1) = x^2 + x + 3x + 3$$
$$= x^2 + 4x + 3$$

In general, multiplying two binomials of the form $x + a$ and $x + b$ gives the following result:

$$(x + a)(x + b) = x^2 + bx + ax + ab$$
$$= x^2 + (b + a)x + ab \qquad \text{Factor out } x.$$

In the product, the coefficient of x^2 is 1, the coefficient of x is the sum of a and b, and the constant term is the product of a and b.

To factor the trinomial $x^2 + 7x + 12$, for example, we must find two binomials $x + a$ and $x + b$ such that

$$x^2 + 7x + 12 = (x + a)(x + b)$$

where the product of a and b is 12, and the sum of a and b is 7.

$$ab = 12 \qquad \text{and} \qquad a + b = 7$$

To find such numbers a and b, we list the possible factorizations of 12:

The one to choose

$$12(1) \qquad 6(2) \qquad 4(3) \qquad -12(-1) \qquad -6(-2) \qquad -4(-3)$$

Only in the factorization 4(3) do the factors have a sum of 7. Hence, $a = 4$, $b = 3$, and

$$x^2 + 7x + 12 = (x + a)(x + b)$$
$$\textbf{3.} \quad x^2 + 7x + 12 = (x + 4)(x + 3)$$

This factorization can be verified by multiplying $x + 4$ by $x + 3$ and observing that the product is $x^2 + 7x + 12$:

$$(x + 4)(x + 3) = x^2 + 3x + 4x + 12$$
$$= x^2 + 7x + 12$$

Because of the commutative property of multiplication, the order of the factors in Equation 3 is not important. Equation 3 can also be written as

$$x^2 + 7x + 12 = (x + 3)(x + 4)$$

In general, to factor trinomials with lead coefficients of 1, we follow these steps:

---

1.   Write the trinomial in descending powers of one variable.
2.   List the factorizations of the third term of the trinomial.
3.   Pick the factorization in which the sum of the factors is the coefficient of the middle term.

Example 1   Factor $x^2 - 6x + 8$.

Solution   Because this trinomial is already written in descending powers of x, you can proceed to step 2 and list the possible factorizations of the third term, 8.

The one to choose
$$8(1) \qquad 4(2) \qquad -8(-1) \qquad -4(-2)$$

The factorization in which the sum of the factors is -6 (the coefficient of the middle term of $x^2 - 6x + 8$) is $-4(-2)$. Hence, $a = -4$, $b = -2$, and

$$x^2 - 6x + 8 = (x + a)(x + b)$$
$$= (x - 4)(x - 2)$$

This result can be verified by multiplication:

$$(x - 4)(x - 2) = x^2 - 2x - 4x + 8$$
$$= x^2 - 6x + 8$$

■

Example 2   Factor $-x + x^2 - 12$.

Solution   Begin by writing the trinomial in descending powers of x:

$$-x + x^2 - 12 = x^2 - x - 12$$

Because the coefficient of the first term is 1, you can proceed to step 2 and list the possible factorizations of the third term:

The one to choose
↓

$$12(-1) \qquad 6(-2) \qquad 4(-3) \qquad 1(-12) \qquad 2(-6) \qquad 3(-4)$$

The factorization in which the sum of the factors is -1 (the coefficient of the middle term of $x^2 - x - 12$) is $3(-4)$. Hence, $a = 3$, $b = -4$, and

$$-x + x^2 - 12 = (x + a)(x + b)$$
$$= (x + 3)(x - 4)$$

Verify the result by multiplication.   ∎

Example 3   Factor $30x - 4xy - 2xy^2$.

Solution   Begin by writing the trinomial in descending powers of y:

$$30x - 4xy - 2xy^2 = -2xy^2 - 4xy + 30x$$

Each term in this trinomial shares a common monomial factor of $-2x$, which can be factored out:

$$30x - 4xy - 2xy^2 = -2x(y^2 + 2y - 15)$$

Because the lead coefficient of $y^2 + 2y - 15$ is 1, you can find the factorization of this trinomial by finding two factors of -15 whose sum is 2:

The one to choose
↓

$$15(-1) \qquad 5(-3) \qquad 1(-15) \qquad 3(-5)$$

Thus,

$$30x - 4xy - 2xy^2 = -2x(y^2 + 2y - 15)$$
$$= -2x(y + 5)(y - 3)$$

It is important to write the factor $-2x$ in each factorization. Verify this result by multiplication.   ∎

Factoring Trinomials with a Lead Coefficient other than 1

There are more combinations of factors to consider when factoring trinomials with a lead coefficient other than 1. To factor $5x^2 + 7x + 2$, for example, we must find two binomials of the form $ax + b$ and $cx + d$ such that

$$5x^2 + 7x + 2 = (ax + b)(cx + d)$$

Because the first term of the trinomial $5x^2 + 7x + 2$ is $5x^2$, the first terms of the binomial factors must be $5x$ and x:

$5x^2$

$$5x^2 + 7x + 2 = (5x + b)(x + d)$$

Because the product of the last terms must be 2, and because the sum of the products of the outer and inner terms must be $7x$, we must find two numbers whose product is 2 that will give a middle term of $7x$:

$$5x^2 + 7x + 2 = (5x + b)(x + d)$$
$$O + I = 7x$$

Because both $2(1)$ and $(-2)(-1)$ give a product of 2, there are four possible combinations to consider:

$$(5x + 2)(x + 1) \qquad (5x - 2)(x - 1)$$
$$(5x + 1)(x + 2) \qquad (5x - 1)(x - 2)$$

Of these possibilities, only the first one gives the proper middle term of $7x$. Thus,

$$5x^2 + 7x + 2 = (5x + 2)(x + 1)$$

Verify this result by multiplication:

$$(5x + 2)(x + 1) = 5x^2 + 5x + 2x + 2$$
$$= 5x^2 + 7x + 2$$

Example 4   Factor $3a^2 - 4a - 4$.

Solution   Because the first term of the trinomial is $3a^2$, the first terms of the binomial factors must be $3a$ and a:

$$3a^2$$
$$3a^2 - 4a - 4 = (3a + ?)(a + ?)$$

The product of the last terms must be -4, and the sum of the products of the outer terms and the inner terms must be $-4a$:

$$-4$$
$$3a^2 - 4a - 4 = (3a + ?)(a + ?)$$
$$O + I = -4a$$

Because $1(-4)$, $-1(4)$, and $-2(2)$ all give a product of -4, there are six possible combinations to consider:

$$(3a + 1)(a - 4) \qquad (3a - 4)(a + 1)$$
$$(3a - 1)(a + 4) \qquad (3a + 4)(a - 1)$$
$$(3a - 2)(a + 2) \qquad (3a + 2)(a - 2)$$

Of these possibilities, only the last gives the required middle term of $-4a$. Thus,

$$3a^2 - 4a - 4 = (3a + 2)(a - 2)$$

Verify this result by multiplication.   ■

It is not easy to give specific rules for factoring general trinomials because some guesswork is often necessary. However, the following hints are helpful:

To factor a general trinomial, follow these steps:

1. Write the trinomial in descending powers of one variable.
2. Factor out any greatest common factor (including -1 if that is necessary to make the coefficient of the first term positive).
3. When the sign of the first term of a trinomial is $+$ and the sign of the third term is $+$, the signs between the terms of each binomial factor are the same as the sign of the middle term of the trinomial. When the sign of the first term is $+$ and the sign of the third term is $-$, one of the signs between the terms of the binomial factors is $+$ and one is $-$.
4. Mentally try various combinations of first terms and last terms until you find one that works. If you exhaust all the possibilities, the trinomial does not factor using only integer coefficients.
5. Check the factorization by multiplication.

Example 5   Factor $24y + 10xy - 6x^2y$.

Solution   Begin by writing the trinomial in descending powers of x and factoring out the common factor of $-2y$:

$$24y + 10xy - 6x^2y = -6x^2y + 10xy + 24y$$
$$= -2y(3x^2 - 5x - 12)$$

Because the sign of the third term of $3x^2 - 5x - 12$ is $-$, the signs between the binomial factors will be opposite. Because the first term is $3x^2$, the first terms of the binomial factors must be $3x$ and x:

$$24y + 10xy - 6x^2y = -2y(3x \quad)(x \quad)$$

with $3x^2$ indicated above.

The product of the last terms must be -12, and the sum of the outer terms and the inner terms must be $-5x$:

$$24y + 10xy - 6x^2y = -2y(3x \quad ?)(x \quad ?)$$

with -12 indicated above and $O + I = -5x$ indicated below.

Because $1(-12)$, $2(-6)$, $3(-4)$, $12(-1)$, $6(-2)$, and $4(-3)$ all give a product of -12, there are 12 possible combinations to consider:

$$(3x + 1)(x - 12) \qquad (3x - 12)(x + 1)$$
$$(3x + 2)(x - 6) \qquad (3x - 6)(x + 2)$$
$$(3x + 3)(x - 4) \qquad (3x - 4)(x + 3)$$
$$(3x + 12)(x - 1) \qquad (3x - 1)(x + 12)$$
$$(3x + 6)(x - 2) \qquad (3x - 2)(x + 6)$$

The one to choose $\longrightarrow (3x + 4)(x - 3) \qquad (3x - 3)(x + 4)$

After mentally trying these combinations, you will find that only $(3x + 4)(x - 3)$ gives the proper middle term of $-5x$. Thus,

$$24y + 10xy - 6x^2y = -2y(3x^2 - 5x - 12)$$
$$= -2y(3x + 4)(x - 3)$$

Verify this result by multiplication.   ∎

Example 6   Factor $6y + 13x^2y + 6x^4y$.

Solution   Write the trinomial in descending powers of x and factor out the common factor of y to obtain

$$6y + 13x^2y + 6x^4y = 6x^4y + 13x^2y + 6y$$
$$= y(6x^4 + 13x^2 + 6)$$

Because the coefficients of the first and last terms of the trinomial $6x^4 + 13x^2 + 6$ are positive, the signs between the terms of each binomial will be $+$. The first term of the trinomial is $6x^4$, so the first terms of the binomial factors must be either $2x^2$ and $3x^2$, or perhaps x^2 and $6x^2$. Because the product of the last terms of the binomial factors must be 6, you must find two numbers whose product is 6 that will lead to a middle term of $13x^2$. After mentally trying some combinations, you will find the one that works.

$$6y + 13x^2y + 6x^4y = y(6x^4 + 13x^2 + 6)$$
$$= y(2x^2 + 3)(3x^2 + 2)$$

Verify this result by multiplication.   ∎

Example 7   Factor the trinomial $(x + y)^2 + 7(x + y) + 12$.

Solution   Note that the trinomial $(x + y)^2 + 7(x + y) + 12$ can be written as $z^2 + 7z + 12$, where $z = x + y$. The trinomial $z^2 + 7z + 12$ factors as $(z + 4)(z + 3)$. To find the factorization of $(x + y)^2 + 7(x + y) + 12$, substitute $x + y$ for z in the expression $(z + 4)(z + 3)$ to obtain

$$(x + y)^2 + 7(x + y) + 12 = (x + y + 4)(x + y + 3)$$ ∎

Example 8   Factor $x^{2n} + x^n - 2$.

Solution   Because the first term is x^{2n}, the first terms of the binomial factors must be x^n and x^n:

$$x^{2n} + x^n - 2 = (\overset{\overset{\displaystyle x^{2n}}{\frown}}{x^n}\quad)(x^n\quad)$$

Because the third term of the trinomial is -2, the last terms of the binomial factors must have opposite signs, have a product of -2, and lead to a middle term of x^n. The only combination that works is

$$x^{2n} + x^n - 2 = (x^n + 2)(x^n - 1)$$

Verify this result by multiplication.   ∎

The Key Number Method

The **key number method** of factoring trinomials eliminates much of the guesswork associated with the trial-and-error method. We illustrate the key number method by considering a trinomial of the form $ax^2 + bx + c$, whose factorization will be of the form $(mx + n)(px + q)$.

To factor the trinomial $6x^2 + 7x - 3$, where $a = 6$, $b = 7$, and $c = -3$, we follow these steps:

1. Find the product of a and c. This is the *key number*. In this example,

$$ac = 6(-3)$$
$$= -18$$

2. Find two factors of the key number whose sum is b. In this example, $b = 7$ and the key number, -18, factors as

$$18(-1), \quad 9(-2), \quad 6(-3), \quad 3(-6), \quad 2(-9), \quad \text{or} \quad 1(-18)$$

The only pair of factors whose sum is 7 is $9(-2)$:

$$9 + (-2) = 7$$

3. The numbers 9 and -2 will be the coefficients of the products of the outer and inner terms of the trinomial's factors:

To obtain the coefficient 9 of the outer product $9x$, we must use one of the following factorizations for values of m and q:

$$9(1), \quad 3(3), \quad \text{or} \quad 1(9)$$

But if $m = 9$, we cannot obtain a first term of $6x^2$, and if $q = 9$, we cannot obtain a last term of -3. Hence, the factorizations 9(1) and 1(9) can be eliminated, and the factors leading to the outer product must be 3(3):

Substitute 3 for m and 3 for q.

The other numbers are now determined. The number n must be -1 to give -3 as the product of the last terms, and the number p must be 2 to give $6x^2$ as the product of the first terms. Thus, the factorization of $6x^2 + 7x - 3$ is

$$(3x - 1)(2x + 3)$$

Check this result by multiplication.

Example 9   Use the key number method to factor $4x^2 - 16x + 15$.

Solution   In this example, $a = 4$, $b = -16$, and $c = 15$. The key number is $ac = 4(15) = 60$. Two factors of 60 that have a sum of -16 are -10 and -6:

$$(-10)(-6) = 60 \qquad \text{and} \qquad -10 + (-6) = b = -16$$

Thus, if the product of the outer terms is $-10x$, the product of the inner terms is $-6x$. (We could just as well have made the product of the outer terms $-6x$ and the product of the inner terms $-10x$.)

To obtain the coefficient -10 of the outer product, $-10x$, we must use one of the following factorizations for m and q:

$$10(-1), \quad 5(-2), \quad 2(-5), \quad \text{or} \quad 1(-10)$$

However, values of 10 or 5 for m cannot give a first term of $4x^2$, and a value of -10 for q cannot give a last term of 15. Thus, the factors leading to the outer product must be $2(-5)$:

Substitute 2 for m and -5 for q.

The other numbers are now determined. The number n must be -3 to give 15 as the product of the last terms, and the number p must be 2 to give $4x^2$ as the product of the first terms. Thus, the factorization of $4x^2 - 16x + 15$ is

$$(2x - 3)(2x - 5)$$

Check this result by multiplication.   ∎

■ EXERCISE 3.3

In Exercises 1–10, use a special product formula to factor each perfect square trinomial.

1.	$x^2 + 2x + 1$	**2.**	$y^2 - 2y + 1$	**3.**	$a^2 - 18a + 81$	**4.**	$b^2 + 12b + 36$
5.	$4y^2 + 4y + 1$	**6.**	$9x^2 + 6x + 1$	**7.**	$9b^2 - 12b + 4$	**8.**	$4a^2 - 12a + 9$
9.	$9z^2 + 24z + 16$			**10.**	$16z^2 - 24z + 9$		

In Exercises 11–22, factor each trinomial. If a trinomial is prime, so indicate.

11.	$x^2 + 5x + 6$	**12.**	$y^2 + 7y + 6$	**13.**	$x^2 - 4x + 4$	**14.**	$c^2 - 6c + 9$
15.	$b^2 + 8b + 18$	**16.**	$x^2 - 14x + 49$	**17.**	$x^2 - x - 30$	**18.**	$a^2 + 4a - 45$
19.	$a^2 + 5a - 50$	**20.**	$b^2 + 9b - 36$	**21.**	$y^2 - 4y - 21$	**22.**	$x^2 + 4x - 28$

In Exercises 23–34, factor each trinomial. Factor out all common monomials first. If the coefficient of the first term is negative, begin by factoring out -1.

23.	$3x^2 + 12x - 63$			**24.**	$2y^2 + 4y - 48$		
25.	$a^2b^2 - 13ab^2 + 22b^2$			**26.**	$a^2b^2x^2 - 18a^2b^2x + 81a^2b^2$		
27.	$b^2x^2 - 12bx^2 + 35x^2$	**28.**	$c^3x^2 + 11c^3x - 42c^3$	**29.**	$-a^2 + 4a + 32$	**30.**	$-x^2 - 2x + 15$
31.	$-3x^2 + 15x - 18$	**32.**	$-2y^2 - 16y + 40$	**33.**	$-4x^2 + 4x + 80$	**34.**	$-5a^2 + 40a - 75$

In Exercises 35–72, factor each trinomial. Factor out all common monomials first, including -1 if the first term is negative. If a trinomial is prime, so indicate.

35.	$6y^2 + 7y + 2$	**36.**	$6x^2 - 11x + 3$	**37.**	$8a^2 + 6a - 9$	**38.**	$15b^2 + 4b - 4$
39.	$6x^2 - 5x - 4$	**40.**	$18y^2 - 3y - 10$	**41.**	$5x^2 + 4x + 1$	**42.**	$6z^2 + 17z + 12$
43.	$8x^2 - 10x + 3$	**44.**	$4a^2 + 20a + 3$	**45.**	$6z^2 + 7z - 20$	**46.**	$7x^2 - 23x + 6$
47.	$a^2 - 3ab - 4b^2$	**48.**	$b^2 + 2bc - 80c^2$	**49.**	$2y^2 + yt - 6t^2$	**50.**	$3x^2 - 10xy - 8y^2$
51.	$3x^3 - 10x^2 + 3x$	**52.**	$6y^2 + 7y + 2$	**53.**	$-3a^2 + ab + 2b^2$	**54.**	$-2x^2 + 3xy + 5y^2$
55.	$9t^2 + 3t - 2$	**56.**	$3t^3 - 3t^2 + t$	**57.**	$9x^2 - 12x + 4$	**58.**	$4a^2 + 28a + 49$
59.	$-4x^2 - 9 + 12x$	**60.**	$6x + 4 + 9x^2$	**61.**	$15x^2 + 2 - 13x$	**62.**	$-90x^2 + 2 - 8x$
63.	$5a^2 + 45b^2 - 30ab$	**64.**	$x^2 + 324y^2 - 36xy$	**65.**	$8x^2z + 6xyz + 9y^2z$	**66.**	$x^3 - 60xy^2 + 7x^2y$
67.	$15x^2 + 74x - 5$	**68.**	$15x^2 - 7x - 30$	**69.**	$21x^4 - 10x^3 - 16x^2$	**70.**	$16x^3 - 50x^2 + 36x$
71.	$6x^2y^2 - 17xyz + 12z^2$			**72.**	$6u^2v^2 - uvz + 12z^2$		

In Exercises 73–84, factor each trinomial.

73. $x^4 + 8x^2 + 15$ **74.** $x^4 + 11x^2 + 24$ **75.** $y^4 - 13y^2 + 30$ **76.** $y^4 - 13y^2 + 42$

77. $a^4 - 13a^2 + 36$ **78.** $b^4 - 17b^2 + 16$ **79.** $z^4 - z^2 - 12$ **80.** $c^4 - 8c^2 - 9$

81. $x^6 + 4x^3 + 3$ **82.** $a^6 + a^3 - 2$ **83.** $y^6 - 9y^3 + 8$ **84.** $x^6 + 9x^3 + 8$

In Exercises 85–94, factor each expression.

85. $(x + 1)^2 + 2(x + 1) + 1$ **86.** $(a + b)^2 - 2(a + b) + 1$

87. $(a + b)^2 - 2(a + b) - 24$ **88.** $(x - y)^2 + 3(x - y) - 10$

89. $6(x + y)^2 - 7(x + y) - 20$ **90.** $2(x - z)^2 + 9(x - z) + 4$

91. $5(x^2 - 4x + 4) - 4(x - 2) - 1$ **92.** $6(x^2 + 2x + 1) + 5(x + 1) + 1$

93. $(4x^2 - 8x + 4) + (-5x + 5) + 1$ **94.** $(5x^2 + 30x + 45) + (6x + 18) + 1$

In Exercises 95–102, factor each expression. Assume that n is a natural number.

95. $x^{2n} + 2x^n + 1$ **96.** $x^{4n} - 2x^{2n} + 1$ **97.** $2a^{6n} - 3a^{3n} - 2$ **98.** $b^{2n} - b^n - 6$

99. $x^{4n} + 2x^{2n}y^{2n} + y^{4n}$ **100.** $y^{6n} + 2y^{3n}z + z^2$ **101.** $6x^{2n} + 7x^n - 3$ **102.** $12y^{4n} + 10y^{2n} + 2$

3.4   FACTORING BY GROUPING

Suppose we wish to factor an expression such as

$$ac + ad + bc + bd$$

Although there is no factor common to all four terms, there is a common factor of a in $ac + ad$ and a common factor of b in $bc + bd$. If we factor out these common factors, we obtain

$$ac + ad + bc + bd = a(c + d) + b(c + d)$$

Because each term in the expression $a(c + d) + b(c + d)$ has a common factor of $c + d$, it is not completely factored. To write the expression in completely factored form, we factor out the common factor of $c + d$ and obtain

$$ac + ad + bc + bd = a(c + d) + b(c + d)$$
$$= (c + d)(a + b)$$

The grouping in this type of problem is not always unique. For example, if we write the expression $ac + ad + bc + bd$ in the form

$$ac + bc + ad + bd$$

and factor c from the first two terms and d from the last two terms, we obtain

$$ac + bc + ad + bd = c(a + b) + d(a + b)$$

We can then factor out the common factor of $a + b$ to obtain the same result:

$$ac + bc + ad + bd = (a + b)(c + d)$$

The method used in the previous examples is called **factoring by grouping**.

Example 1   Factor $3ax^2 + 3bx^2 + a + 5bx + 5ax + b$.

Solution   Although there is no factor common to all six terms, $3x^2$ can be factored out of the first two terms, and $5x$ can be factored out of the fourth and fifth terms. Hence,

$$3ax^2 + 3bx^2 + a + 5bx + 5ax + b = 3x^2(a + b) + a + 5x(b + a) + b$$

This result can be written in the form

$$= 3x^2(a + b) + 5x(a + b) + (a + b)$$

The binomial $a + b$ is common to all three terms of the preceding expression and can be factored out. Thus,

$$3ax^2 + 3bx^2 + a + 5bx + 5ax + b = (a + b)(3x^2 + 5x + 1)$$

Because $3x^2 + 5x + 1$ is a prime polynomial, the factorization is complete.

∎

To factor an expression completely, it is often necessary to factor more than once, as the following example illustrates.

Example 2   Factor $3x^3y - 4x^2y^2 - 6x^2y + 8xy^2$.

Solution   Begin by factoring out the common factor of xy:

$$3x^3y - 4x^2y^2 - 6x^2y + 8xy^2 = xy(3x^2 - 4xy - 6x + 8y)$$

It would be incorrect to stop here because the expression is not in completely factored form. You can factor $3x^2 - 4xy - 6x + 8y$ by grouping:

$$
\begin{aligned}
3x^3y - 4x^2y^2 &- 6x^2y + 8xy^2 \\
&= xy(3x^2 - 4xy - 6x + 8y) \\
&= xy[x(3x - 4y) - 2(3x - 4y)] \qquad \text{Factor } x \text{ from } 3x^2 - 4xy \text{ and} \\
&\qquad\qquad\qquad\qquad\qquad\qquad\qquad\;\; -2 \text{ from } -6x + 8y. \\
&= xy(3x - 4y)(x - 2) \qquad\qquad\;\; \text{Factor out } 3x - 4y.
\end{aligned}
$$

Because no more factoring can be done, the factorization is complete.

∎

Example 3   Factor $x^3 + 5x^2 + 6x + x^2y + 5xy + 6y$.

Solution   Factor x from the first three terms and y from the last three and proceed as follows:

$$
\begin{aligned}
x^3 + 5x^2 &+ 6x + x^2y + 5xy + 6y \\
&= x(x^2 + 5x + 6) + y(x^2 + 5x + 6) \\
&= (x^2 + 5x + 6)(x + y) \qquad \text{Factor out } x^2 + 5x + 6. \\
&= (x + 3)(x + 2)(x + y) \qquad \text{Factor } x^2 + 5x + 6.
\end{aligned}
$$

∎

Example 4   Factor $x^4 + 2x^3 + x^2 + x + 1$.

Solution   Factor x^2 from the first three terms and proceed as follows:

$$x^4 + 2x^3 + x^2 + x + 1 = x^2(x^2 + 2x + 1) + (x + 1)$$
$$= x^2(x + 1)(x + 1) + (x + 1) \qquad \text{Factor } x^2 + 2x + 1.$$
$$= (x + 1)[x^2(x + 1) + 1] \qquad \text{Factor out } x + 1.$$
$$= (x + 1)(x^3 + x^2 + 1) \qquad\qquad ■$$

Example 5   Factor $x^2 + 12x + 36 - y^2$.

Solution   The first three terms factor as $(x + 6)(x + 6)$. Thus,

$$x^2 + 12x + 36 - y^2 = (x + 6)^2 - y^2$$

The expression $(x + 6)^2 - y^2$ is the difference of two squares and can be factored accordingly:

$$x^2 + 12x + 36 - y^2 = (x + 6)^2 - y^2$$
$$= [(x + 6) + y][(x + 6) - y]$$
$$= (x + 6 + y)(x + 6 - y) \qquad\qquad ■$$

The next examples use the technique of adding and subtracting the same quantity from an expression to make it factor as the difference of two squares.

Example 6   Factor $x^4 + x^2 + 1$.

Solution   This trinomial cannot be factored as the product of two binomials because there is no combination that will give a middle term of $1x^2$. However, if the middle term were $2x^2$, the factorization would be easy. You can make the middle term $2x^2$ by adding x^2 to the trinomial. To ensure that adding x^2 does not change the value of the trinomial, you must also subtract x^2:

$$x^4 + x^2 + 1 = x^4 + x^2 + x^2 + 1 - x^2$$
$$= x^4 + 2x^2 + 1 - x^2$$

Because the first three terms of the previous expression factor as $(x^2 + 1)(x^2 + 1)$, you can proceed as follows:

$$x^4 + x^2 + 1 = x^4 + 2x^2 + 1 - x^2$$
$$= (x^2 + 1)^2 - x^2$$
$$= [(x^2 + 1) + x][(x^2 + 1) - x] \qquad \text{Factor the difference of two squares.}$$
$$= (x^2 + x + 1)(x^2 - x + 1) \qquad \text{Write each factor in descending}$$
$$\text{powers of } x. \qquad\qquad ■$$

Example 7   Factor $x^6 - 1$.

Solution   The expression $x^6 - 1$ is the difference of two cubes and factors accordingly:

$$x^6 - 1 = (x^2)^3 - 1^3 = (x^2 - 1)(x^4 + x^2 + 1)$$

The first factor is the difference of two squares and can be factored as follows:

$$x^6 - 1 = (x + 1)(x - 1)(x^4 + x^2 + 1)$$

The last factor is the trinomial of Example 6 and can be factored as

$$(x^2 + x + 1)(x^2 - x + 1)$$

Thus,

$$x^6 - 1 = (x + 1)(x - 1)(x^2 + x + 1)(x^2 - x + 1)$$

Note that this problem could have been factored as the difference of two squares first, and then as the sum and difference of two cubes:

$$\begin{aligned} x^6 - 1 &= (x^3 + 1)(x^3 - 1) \\ &= (x + 1)(x^2 - x + 1)(x - 1)(x^2 + x + 1) \end{aligned}$$ ■

The method of factoring by grouping can be used to help factor trinomials of the form $ax^2 + bx + c$. For example, to factor the trinomial $6x^2 + 7x - 3$, we proceed as follows:

1. First determine the product ac: $6(-3) = -18$. This number is often called the **key number**.
2. Find two factors of the key number -18 whose sum is $b = 7$:

$$9(-2) = -18 \qquad \text{and} \qquad 9 + (-2) = 7$$

3. Use the factors 9 and -2 as coefficients of the terms to be placed between $6x^2$ and -3:

$$6x^2 + 7x - 3 = 6x^2 + 9x - 2x - 3$$

4. Factor by grouping:

$$\begin{aligned} 6x^2 + 9x - 2x - 3 &= 3x(2x + 3) - (2x + 3) \\ &= (2x + 3)(3x - 1) \qquad \text{Factor out } 2x + 3. \end{aligned}$$

We can verify this factorization by multiplication.

▬ EXERCISE 3.4

In Exercises 1–24, factor each expression by grouping. You may have to rearrange some terms first.

1. $ax + bx + ay + by$	2. $ar - br + as - bs$	3. $x^2 + yx + 2x + 2y$	4. $2c + 2d - cd - d^2$
5. $3c - cd + 3d - c^2$	6. $x^2 + 4y - xy - 4x$	7. $a^2 - 4b + ab - 4a$	8. $7u + v^2 - 7v - uv$
9. $ax + bx - a - b$		10. $x^2y - ax - xy + a$	
11. $x^2 + xy + xz + xy + y^2 + zy$		12. $ab - b^2 - bc + ac - bc - c^2$	

13. $x^2y + xy^2 + 2xyz + xy^2 + y^3 + 2y^2z$

14. $a^3 - 2a^2b + a^2c - a^2b + 2ab^2 - abc$

15. $2n^4p - 2n^2 - n^3p^2 + np + 2mn^3p - 2mn$

16. $a^2c^3 + ac^2 + a^3c^2 - 2a^2bc^2 - 2bc^2 + c^3$

17. $x^4 - 2x^3 + x^2 + x - 1$

18. $a^4 + 4a^3 + 4a^2 + 2a + 4$

19. $a^2 - b^2 + 2a - 2b$

20. $m^2 + 3m + 3n - n^2$

21. $y + 4 + ay + y + 4a + 4$

22. $bx + 2x - 3b - 6 + x - 3$

23. $x^2 - 1 + 3x^5 + 6x^4 + 3x^3$

24. $3y^2 + 6y + 3y^6 + 12y^5 + 12y^4$

In Exercises 25–34, factor a trinomial and then factor the difference of two squares. You may have to rearrange some terms first.

25. $x^2 + 4x + 4 - y^2$

26. $x^2 - 6x + 9 - 4y^2$

27. $x^2 + 2x + 1 - 9z^2$

28. $x^2 + 10x + 25 - 16z^2$

29. $4a^2 - 4ab + b^2 - c^2$

30. $a^2 - 6ab + 9b^2 - 25c^2$

31. $a^2 - b^2 + 8a + 16$

32. $a^2 + 14a - 25b^2 + 49$

33. $4x^2 - z^2 + 4xy + y^2$

34. $x^2 - 4xy - 4z^2 + 4y^2$

In Exercises 35–42, add and subtract some term and then factor as the difference of two squares.

35. $x^4 + 5x^2 + 9$

36. $x^4 + 7x^2 + 16$

37. $4a^4 + 1 + 3a^2$

38. $a^4 + 6a^2 + 25$

39. $a^4 + 4b^4$

40. $4a^4 + b^4$

41. $x^4 - 7x^2 + 1$

42. $x^4 - 12x^2 + 4$

43.   Factor $x^6 - 64$

44.   Factor $x^6 - y^6$.

In Exercises 45–50, use factoring by grouping to help factor each trinomial.

45. $a^2 - 17a + 16$

46. $b^2 - 4b - 21$

47. $2u^2 + 5u + 3$

48. $6y^2 + 5y - 6$

49. $20r^2 - 7rs - 6s^2$

50. $20u^2 + 19uv + 3v^2$

3.5   SUMMARY OF FACTORING TECHNIQUES

In this section we discuss ways to approach a randomly chosen factoring problem. For example, suppose we wish to factor the trinomial

$$x^2y^2z^3 + 7xy^2z^3 + 6y^2z^3$$

We begin by attempting to identify the problem type. The first type to look for is **factoring out a common monomial**. Because the trinomial has a common monomial factor of y^2z^3, we factor it out:

$$x^2y^2z^3 + 7xy^2z^3 + 6y^2z^3 = y^2z^3(x^2 + 7x + 6)$$

We then note that $x^2 + 7x + 6$ is a trinomial that can be factored as $(x + 6)(x + 1)$. Thus,

$$x^2y^2z^3 + 7xy^2z^3 + 6y^2z^3 = y^2z^3(x^2 + 7x + 6)$$
$$= y^2z^3(x + 6)(x + 1)$$

To identify the type of a factoring problem, follow these steps:

---

1. Factor out all common monomial factors.
2. If an expression has two terms, check to see if the problem type is
    a. the **difference of two squares**: $x^2 - y^2 = (x + y)(x - y)$
    b. the **sum of two cubes**: $x^3 + y^3 = (x + y)(x^2 - xy + y^2)$
    c. the **difference of two cubes**: $x^3 - y^3 = (x - y)(x^2 + xy + y^2)$
3. If an expression has three terms, check to see if the problem type is
    a **perfect trinomial square**: $x^2 + 2xy + y^2 = (x + y)(x + y)$
    $$x^2 - 2xy + y^2 = (x - y)(x - y)$$
    If the trinomial is not a perfect trinomial square, attempt to factor
    the trinomial as a **general trinomial**.
4. If an expression has four or more terms, try to **factor the expression
    by grouping**.
5. Continue until each individual factor is prime.
6. Check the results by multiplying.

Example 1   Factor $48a^4c^3 - 3b^4c^3$.

Solution   Begin by factoring out the common monomial factor of $3c^3$:

$$48a^4c^3 - 3b^4c^3 = 3c^3(16a^4 - b^4)$$

Because the expression $16a^4 - b^4$ has two terms, check to see if it is the difference of two squares, which it is. As the difference of two squares, it factors as
$(4a^2 + b^2)(4a^2 - b^2)$. Thus,

$$48a^4c^3 - 3b^4c^3 = 3c^3(16a^4 - b^4)$$
$$= 3c^3(4a^2 + b^2)(4a^2 - b^2)$$

The binomial $4a^2 + b^2$ is the sum of two squares and cannot be factored.
However, the binomial $4a^2 - b^2$ is again the difference of two squares and
factors as $(2a + b)(2a - b)$. Thus,

$$48a^4c^3 - 3b^4c^3 = 3c^3(16a^4 - b^4)$$
$$= 3c^3(4a^2 + b^2)(4a^2 - b^2)$$
$$= 3c^3(4a^2 + b^2)(2a + b)(2a - b)$$

Because each of the individual factors is prime, the given expression is in completely factored form.   ■

Example 2   Factor $x^5y + x^2y^4 - x^3y^3 - y^6$.

Solution   Begin by factoring out the common monomial factor of y:

$$x^5y + x^2y^4 - x^3y^3 - y^6 = y(x^5 + x^2y^3 - x^3y^2 - y^5)$$

Because the expression $x^5 + x^2y^3 - x^3y^2 - y^5$ has four terms, try factoring by grouping to obtain

$$x^5y + x^2y^4 - x^3y^3 - y^6 = y(x^5 + x^2y^3 - x^3y^2 - y^5)$$
$$= y[x^2(x^3 + y^3) - y^2(x^3 + y^3)]$$
$$= y(x^3 + y^3)(x^2 - y^2) \quad \text{Factor out } x^3 + y^3.$$

Finally, factor $x^3 + y^3$ (the sum of two cubes) and $x^2 - y^2$ (the difference of two squares) to obtain

$$x^5y + x^2y^4 - x^3y^3 - y^6 = y(x + y)(x^2 - xy + y^2)(x + y)(x - y)$$

Because each of the individual factors is prime, the given expression is in completely factored form.   ■

■ EXERCISE 3.5

In Exercises 1–44, factor each polynomial completely. If the polynomial is prime, so indicate.

1. $x^2 + 8x + 16$

2. $20 + 11x - 3x^2$

3. $8x^3y^3 - 27$

4. $3x^2y + 6xy^2 - 12xy$

5. $xy - ty + xs - ts$

6. $bc + b + cd + d$

7. $25x^2 - 16y^2$

8. $27x^9 - y^3$

9. $12x^2 + 52x + 35$

10. $12x^2 + 14x - 6$

11. $6x^2 - 14x + 8$

12. $12x^2 - 12$

13. $56x^2 - 15x + 1$

14. $7x^2 - 57x + 8$

15. $4x^2y^2 + 4xy^2 + y^2$

16. $100z^2 - 81t^2$

17. $x^3 + (a^2y)^3$

18. $4x^2y^2z^2 - 26x^2y^2z^3$

19. $2x^3 - 54$

20. $4(xy)^3 + 256$

21. $ae + bf + af + be$

22. $a^2x^2 + b^2y^2 + b^2x^2 + a^2y^2$

23. $2(x + y)^2 + (x + y) - 3$

24. $(x - y)^3 + 125$

25. $625x^4 - 256y^4$

26. $2(a - b)^2 + 5(a - b) + 3$

27. $36x^4 - 36$

28. $6x^2 - 63 - 13x$

29. $2x^6 + 2y^6$

30. $x^4 - x^4y^4$

31. $a^4 - 13a^2 + 36$

32. $x^4 - 17x^2 + 16$

33. $x^2 + 6x + 9 - y^2$

34. $x^2 + 10x + 25 - y^8$

35. $4x^2 + 4x + 1 - 4y^2$

36. $9x^2 - 6x + 1 - 25y^2$

37. $z^4 + 7z^2 + 16$

38. $x^4 + 9x^2 + 25$

39. $x^5 + x^2 - x^3 - 1$

40. $x^5 - x^2 - 4x^3 + 4$

41. $x^5 - 9x^3 + 8x^2 - 72$

42. $x^5 - 4x^3 - 8x^2 + 32$

43. $2x^5z - 2x^2y^3z - 2x^3y^2z + 2y^5z$

44. $x^2y^3 - 4x^2y - 9y^3 + 36y$

CHAPTER SUMMARY

Key Words

completely factored form   (3.1)

difference of two cubes   (3.2)

difference of two squares   (3.2)

greatest common divisor   (3.1)

greatest common factor   (3.1)

irreducible polynomial   (3.1)

prime-factored form   (3.1)

prime polynomial   (3.1)

relatively prime terms   (3.1)

sum of two cubes   (3.2)

Key Ideas

(3.1) Always factor out all common monomial factors as your first step in a factoring problem.

Use the distributive property to factor out common monomial factors.

(3.2) The **difference of the squares** of two quantities factors into the product of the sum and difference of those quantities: $x^2 - y^2 = (x + y)(x - y)$.

The **sum of two cubes** factors as $x^3 + y^3 = (x + y)(x^2 - xy + y^2)$.

The **difference of two cubes** factors as $x^3 - y^3 = (x - y)(x^2 + xy + y^2)$.

(3.3) Use the special product formulas

$$x^2 + 2xy + y^2 = (x + y)(x + y)$$
$$x^2 - 2xy + y^2 = (x - y)(x - y)$$

to factor perfect trinomial squares. If a polynomial is not a perfect trinomial square, use the methods for factoring general trinomials.

(3.4) If an expression has four or more terms, try to factor the expression by grouping.

If a trinomial cannot be factored directly, consider adding to and subtracting from the trinomial some appropriate quantity to form the difference of two squares.

REVIEW EXERCISES

In Review Exercises 1–50, factor each polynomial completely. Factor out all common monomials first, including -1 if the coefficient of the first term is negative. If a polynomial is prime, so indicate.

1. $4x + 8$ **2.** $3x^2 - 6x$ **3.** $5x^2y^3 - 10xy^2$ **4.** $7a^4b^2 + 49a^3b$

5. $-8x^2y^3z^4 - 12x^4y^3z^2$ **6.** $12a^6b^4c^2 + 15a^2b^4c^6$

7. $27x^3y^3z^3 + 81x^4y^5z^2 - 90x^2y^3z^7$ **8.** $-36a^5b^4c^2 + 60a^7b^5c^3 - 24a^2b^3c^7$

9. $5x^2(x + y)^3 - 15x^3(x + y)^4$ **10.** $-49a^3b^2(a - b)^4 + 63a^2b^4(a - b)^3$

11. $z^2 - 16$ **12.** $y^2 - 121$ **13.** $x^2y^4 - 64z^6$ **14.** $a^2b^2 + c^2$

15. $(x + z)^2 - t^2$ **16.** $(a + b)^4 - c^2$ **17.** $2x^4 - 98$ **18.** $3x^6 - 300x^2$

19. $x^3 + 343$ **20.** $a^3 - 125$ **21.** $8y^3 - 512$ **22.** $4x^3y + 108yz^3$

23. $y^2 + 21y + 20$ **24.** $z^2 - 11z + 30$ **25.** $-x^2 - 3x + 28$ **26.** $y^2 - 5y - 24$

27. $4a^2 - 5a + 1$ **28.** $3b^2 + 2b + 1$ **29.** $7x^2 + x + 2$ **30.** $-15x^2 + 14x + 8$

31. $y^3 + y^2 - 2y$ **32.** $2a^4 + 4a^3 - 6a^2$ **33.** $-3x^2 - 9x - 6$ **34.** $8x^2 - 4x - 24$

35. $15x^2 - 57xy - 12y^2$ **36.** $30x^2 + 65xy + 10y^2$

37. $24x^2 - 23xy - 12y^2$ **38.** $14x^2 + 13xy - 12y^2$ **39.** $x^4 + 13x^2 + 49$ **40.** $x^4 + 17x^2 + 81$

41. $xy + 2y + 4x + 8$ **42.** $ac + bc + 3a + 3b$

43. $x^4 + 4y + 4x^2 + x^2y$ **44.** $a^5 + b^2c + a^2c + a^3b^2$ **45.** $z^2 - 4 + zx - 2x$ **46.** $x^2 + 2x + 1 - p^2$

47. $x^2 + 4x + 4 - 4p^4$ **48.** $y^2 + 3y + 2 + 2x + xy$ **49.** $a^4 + 4a^2 + 16$ **50.** $z^4 + 64$

CHAPTER THREE TEST

1. Find the prime factorization of 228.

2. Which of the following polynomials is prime?

$$2x + 4 \qquad 3x^2 + 2x \qquad 3x^2 + 2$$

In Problems 3–6, factor each expression completely.

3. $3xy^2 + 6x^2y$

4. $12a^3b^2c - 3a^2b^2c^2 + 6abc^3$

5. $(u - v)r + (u - v)s$

6. $-2x^2y(r + s) + 4xy^2(r + s)$

7. Factor y^n from $x^2y^{n+2} + y^n$.

8. Factor b^n from $a^nb^n - ab^{-n}$.

In Problems 9–16, factor each expression completely.

9. $x^2 - 49$ **10.** $2x^2 - 32$ **11.** $4y^4 - 64$ **12.** $b^3 + 125$

13. $b^3 - 27$ **14.** $3u^3 - 24$ **15.** $9z^2 - 16t^4$ **16.** $8x^3 + 27y^3$

In Problems 17–26, factor each trinomial completely. Assume that n is a natural number.

17. $x^2 + 8x + 15$ **18.** $x^2 - 3x - 18$ **19.** $2a^2 - 5a - 12$ **20.** $6b^2 + b - 2$

21. $6u^2 + 9u - 6$ **22.** $20r^2 - 15r - 5$ **23.** $6x^2 + xy - y^2$ **24.** $5x^2 + 3xy - 2y^2$

25. $x^{2n} + 2x^n + 1$ **26.** $2x^{2n} + 3x^n - 2$

In Problems 27–32, factor each expression completely.

27. $ax - xy + ay - y^2$

28. $ax + ay + bx + by - cx - cy$

29. $x^2 + 6x + 9 - y^2$

30. $x^4 + 3x^2 + 4$

31. $x^4 - 20x^2 + 64$

32. $x^4 + 2x^3 - 2x - 1$

CUMULATIVE REVIEW EXERCISES (CHAPTERS 1–3)

In Exercises 1–2, classify each number as a natural number, a whole number, an integer, a rational number, an irrational number, a real number, a positive number, or a negative number. Each number will be in many classifications.

1. $\dfrac{5}{3}$

2. $-\sqrt{11}$

In Exercises 3–4, simplify each expression and classify each result as an even integer, an odd integer, a prime number, or a composite number. Each result will be in more than one category.

3. $\dfrac{27}{9}$

4. $\dfrac{15 + 5}{5}$

In Exercises 5–6, write each expression without using absolute value symbols, and simplify.

5. $-(|5| - |3|)$

6. $\dfrac{|-5| + |-3|}{-|4|}$

7. Write the terminating decimal 0.875 in fractional form.

8. Draw a number line and graph the prime numbers from 50 to 60.

In Exercises 9–12, indicate which property of equality or property of real numbers justifies each statement.

9. If $3 = x$ and $x = y$, then $3 = y$.

10. $3(x + y) = 3x + 3y$

11. $(a + b) + c = c + (a + b)$

12. $(ab)c = a(bc)$

13. Find the additive inverse of -5.

14. Find the multiplicative inverse of $-\frac{2}{3}$.

In Exercises 15–18, perform the indicated operations.

15. $2 + 4 \cdot 5$

16. $\dfrac{8 - 4}{2 - 4}$

17. $20 \div (-10 \div 2)$

18. $\dfrac{6 + 3(6 + 4)}{2(3 - 9)}$

In Exercises 19–22, perform the indicated operations. Simplify each answer, if possible.

19. $-\dfrac{5}{6} \cdot \dfrac{3}{20}$

20. $\dfrac{2}{3}\left(-\dfrac{4}{5} \div \dfrac{28}{35}\right)$

21. $-\left(\dfrac{1}{3} + \dfrac{3}{4}\right)\left(\dfrac{5}{3} + \dfrac{1}{2}\right)$

22. $\dfrac{1}{2} + \left(\dfrac{2}{3} - \dfrac{3}{4}\right)$

In Exercises 23–26, simplify each expression and write all answers without using negative exponents. Assume that no denominators are 0.

23. $(x^2 y^3)^4$

24. $\dfrac{c^4 c^8}{(c^5)^2}$

25. $\left(-\dfrac{a^3 b^{-2}}{ab}\right)^{-1}$

26. $\left(\dfrac{-3a^3 b^{-2}}{6a^{-2} b^3}\right)^0$

27. Write the number 0.00000497 using scientific notation.

28. Write the number 9.32×10^8 using standard notation.

29. Classify the polynomial $3 + x + 4x^2$ as a monomial, binomial, or trinomial.

30. Give the degree of the polynomial $3 + x^2 y + 17x^3 y^4$.

31. If $P(x) = -3x^3 + x - 4$, find $P(-2)$.

32. Evaluate $\dfrac{x^2 - y^2}{2x + y}$ if $x = 2$ and $y = -3$.

In Exercises 33–38, perform the indicated operations and simplify.

33. $(3x^2 - 2x + 7) + (-2x^2 + 2x + 5) + (3x^2 - 4x + 2)$

34. $(-5x^2 + 3x + 4) - (-2x^2 + 3x + 7)$

35. $(3x + 4)(2x - 5)$

36. $(2x^n - 1)(x^n + 2)$

37. $(x^2 + 9x + 20) \div (x + 5)$

38. $(2x^2 + 4x - x^3 + 3) \div (x - 1)$

In Exercises 39–50, factor each expression.

39. $3r^2 s^3 - 6rs^4$

40. $5(x - y) - a(x - y)$

41. $xu + yv + xv + yu$

42. $81x^4 - 16y^4$

43. $8x^3 - 27y^6$

44. $6x^2 + 5x - 6$

45. $9x^2 - 30x + 25$

46. $15x^2 - x - 6$

47. $27a^3 + 8b^3$

48. $6x^2 + x - 35$

49. $x^2 + 10x + 25 - y^4$

50. $x^4 + 8x^2 + 36$

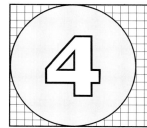

4 Equations and Inequalities

In this chapter we consider equations and inequalities, two of the most basic ideas in algebra. Equations and inequalities are used in almost every academic and vocational field, especially in science, business, economics, and electronics.

4.1 LINEAR EQUATIONS AND THEIR SOLUTIONS

An **equation** is a statement indicating that two mathematical expressions are equal. The equation $2 + 4 = 6$ is an example of a true equation, and $2 + 4 = 7$ is an example of a false equation. An equation such as

$$7x - 3 = 4$$

is either true or false depending on the value of x, called a **variable**. If $x = 1$, the equation is true because the value 1 satisfies the equation:

$$7(1) - 3 = 4$$
$$7 - 3 = 4$$
$$4 = 4$$

However, the equation is false for all other values of x.

The set of all numbers that are permissible replacements for a variable is called the **domain** of the variable. The numbers in the domain of the variable that satisfy the equation make up the **solution set** of the equation. The elements of the solution set are called **roots** or **solutions** of the equation. Finding the solution set or the roots of an equation is called **solving the equation**.

Example 1 Determine the domain of x and the solution set for the equation $2x + 4 = 10$.

Solution Because any number can be substituted for x, the domain of x is the set of real numbers:

The domain of $x = \{x : x$ is a real number.$\}$

The solution set of the equation is $\{3\}$, because 3 is the only real number that satisfies the equation:

$$2x + 4 = 10$$
$$2(3) + 4 \overset{?}{=} 10$$
$$6 + 4 \overset{?}{=} 10$$
$$10 = 10$$

∎

Example 2   Determine the domain of x and the solution set for the equation $\dfrac{8}{x} = 4$.

Solution   The domain of x is the set of all real numbers except 0. If 0 is substituted for x, the equation is neither true nor false. In fact, the equation is nonsense because division by 0 is undefined.

The domain of $x = \{x : x \text{ is a nonzero real number.}\}$

The solution set of the equation is $\{2\}$, because 2 is the only number that satisfies the equation:

$$\frac{8}{x} = 4$$

$$\frac{8}{2} \overset{?}{=} 4$$

$$4 = 4$$ ■

When every number in the domain of the variable is a solution of the equation, we call the equation an **identity**. If only some of the numbers in the domain are solutions, the equation is called a **conditional equation**. If no numbers in the domain are solutions, the equation is called an **impossible equation** or a **contradiction**. For example, if x is a real number, then

$x + 2 = x + 2$ is an identity because every number in the domain of x is a solution.

$2x + 4 = 10$ is a conditional equation because only the number 3 in the domain of x is a solution.

$x + 2 = x + 1$ is an impossible equation because no number in the domain of x is a solution.

Solving Equations

The method used for finding the solution set of a conditional equation involves replacing the equation with simpler ones having the same solution set. Such equations are called **equivalent equations**.

> **Definition.**   Two equations are called **equivalent equations** if they have the same solution set.

The process of replacing conditional equations with simpler but equivalent ones continues until a trivial equation appears with solutions that are obvious. This method requires the following properties of equality along with the properties of equality listed in Section 1.2.

The Addition and Subtraction Properties of Equality.   If any quantity is added to or subtracted from both sides of an equation, a new equation is formed that is equivalent to the original equation.

In symbols, if a, b, and c are real numbers and $a = b$, then

$$a + c = b + c \qquad \text{and} \qquad a - c = b - c$$

The Multiplication and Division Properties of Equality.   If both sides of an equation are multiplied or divided by the same nonzero constant, a new equation is formed that is equivalent to the original equation.

In symbols, if a, b, and c are real numbers, $a = b$, and $c \neq 0$, then

$$ac = bc \qquad \text{and} \qquad \frac{a}{c} = \frac{b}{c}$$

The easiest equations to solve are the **first-degree** or **linear equations**.

Definition.   A **linear equation in one variable**, say x, is any equation that can be written in the form

$$ax + c = 0 \qquad (a \text{ and } c \text{ are real numbers and } a \neq 0)$$

To solve the linear equation $2x + 8 = 0$, for example, we first add -8 to both sides of the equation and then combine terms:

$$2x + 8 = 0$$
$$2x + 8 + (-8) = 0 + (-8)$$
$$2x = -8$$

We then divide both sides of the equation by 2 and simplify:

$$\frac{2x}{2} = \frac{-8}{2}$$
$$x = -4$$

To show that -4 is a solution, we substitute -4 for x in the original equation and simplify:

$$2x + 8 = 0$$
$$2(-4) + 8 \stackrel{?}{=} 0$$
$$-8 + 8 \stackrel{?}{=} 0$$
$$0 = 0$$

Because -4 satisfies the equation, it is a solution. Furthermore, -4 is the only number that satisfies the equation. Thus, the solution set is $\{-4\}$. In general, every linear equation has exactly one solution.

The next examples involve linear equations.

Example 3   Solve the equation $3x + 6 = 24$.

Solution   You must find a number x that satisfies the equation. This goal is achieved by writing a series of simplified equations, all of which are equivalent to the original equation:

$$3x + 6 = 24$$
$$3x + 6 + (-6) = 24 + (-6) \qquad \text{Add } -6 \text{ to both sides.}$$
$$3x = 18 \qquad \text{Combine terms.}$$
$$\frac{3x}{3} = \frac{18}{3} \qquad \text{Divide both sides by 3.}$$
$$x = 6 \qquad \text{Simplify.}$$

To check this result, substitute 6 for x in the original equation and show that it satisfies the equation:

$$3x + 6 = 24$$
$$3(6) + 6 \overset{?}{=} 24$$
$$18 + 6 \overset{?}{=} 24$$
$$24 = 24$$

Because 6 satisfies the equation, it is a solution, and the solution set of the original equation is $\{6\}$.   ∎

Example 4   Solve $3(2x - 1) = 2x + 9$ for x.

Solution   Use the distributive property to remove parentheses, and proceed as follows:

$$3(2x - 1) = 2x + 9$$
$$6x - 3 = 2x + 9 \qquad \text{Remove parentheses.}$$
$$6x - 3 + 3 = 2x + 9 + 3 \qquad \text{Add 3 to both sides.}$$
$$6x = 2x + 12 \qquad \text{Combine terms.}$$
$$6x + (-2x) = 2x + (-2x) + 12 \qquad \text{Add } -2x \text{ to both sides.}$$
$$4x = 12 \qquad \text{Combine terms.}$$
$$\frac{4x}{4} = \frac{12}{4} \qquad \text{Divide both sides by 4.}$$
$$x = 3 \qquad \text{Simplify.}$$

To check this result, substitute 3 for x in the original equation and verify that 3 makes the equation a true statement:

$$3(2x - 1) = 2x + 9$$
$$3(2 \cdot 3 - 1) \overset{?}{=} 2 \cdot 3 + 9$$
$$3(5) \overset{?}{=} 6 + 9$$
$$15 = 15$$

Because 3 satisfies the equation, it is a solution, and the solution set of the original equation is {3}.   ∎

To solve a linear equation, it is helpful to follow these steps:

1. If the equation contains fractions, multiply both sides of the equation by a suitable number to eliminate the fractions.
2. Use the distributive property to remove all sets of parentheses and combine like terms.
3. Undo all indicated additions and subtractions to get all variables on one side of the equation and all numbers on the other side. Combine terms, if necessary.
4. Undo all indicated multiplications and divisions to cause the coefficient of the variable to be 1.
5. Check the result by replacing the variable with the possible solution and verifying that the number satisfies the equation.

Example 5   Solve the equation $\frac{5}{3}(x - 3) = \frac{3}{2}(x - 2) + 2$.

Solution   *Step 1*

Because 6 is the smallest number that can be divided by both 2 and 3, multiply both sides of the equation by 6 to eliminate the fractions:

$$\frac{5}{3}(x - 3) = \frac{3}{2}(x - 2) + 2$$
$$6\left[\frac{5}{3}(x - 3)\right] = 6\left[\frac{3}{2}(x - 2) + 2\right]$$
$$10(x - 3) = 9(x - 2) + 12$$

Step 2

Remove parentheses and combine terms:

$$10x - 30 = 9x - 18 + 12$$
$$10x - 30 = 9x - 6$$

Step 3

Undo all additions and subtractions by adding $-9x$ and 30 to both sides to get the variables and numbers on opposite sides of the equals sign. Then, combine terms.

$$10x - 30 + (-9x) + 30 = 9x - 6 + (-9x) + 30$$
$$x = 24$$

Because the coefficient of x in the above equation is 1, *Step 4* is unnecessary.

Step 5

Check the result by substituting **24** for x in the original equation and simplifying:

$$\frac{5}{3}(x - 3) = \frac{3}{2}(x - 2) + 2$$
$$\frac{5}{3}(24 - 3) \overset{?}{=} \frac{3}{2}(24 - 2) + 2$$
$$\frac{5}{3}(21) \overset{?}{=} \frac{3}{2}(22) + 2$$
$$5(7) \overset{?}{=} 33 + 2$$
$$35 = 35$$

Because 24 satisfies the equation, it is a solution, and the solution set of the original equation is $\{24\}$. ∎

Example 6 Solve the equation $\dfrac{x + 2}{5} - 4x = \dfrac{8}{5} - \dfrac{x + 9}{2}$.

Solution

$$\frac{x + 2}{5} - 4x = \frac{8}{5} - \frac{x + 9}{2}$$

$$10\left(\frac{x + 2}{5} - 4x\right) = 10\left(\frac{8}{5} - \frac{x + 9}{2}\right) \qquad \text{Multiply both sides by 10.}$$

$$2(x + 2) - 40x = 2(8) - 5(x + 9) \qquad \text{Remove parentheses and simplify.}$$

$$2x + 4 - 40x = 16 - 5x - 45 \qquad \text{Remove parentheses.}$$

$$-38x + 4 = -5x - 29 \qquad \text{Combine terms.}$$

$$-33x = -33 \qquad \text{Add } 5x \text{ and } -4 \text{ to both sides.}$$

$$\frac{-33x}{-33} = \frac{-33}{-33} \qquad \text{Divide both sides by } -33.$$

$$x = 1 \qquad \text{Simplify.}$$

Check:

$$\frac{x + 2}{5} - 4x = \frac{8}{5} - \frac{x + 9}{2}$$

$$\frac{1 + 2}{5} - 4(1) \stackrel{?}{=} \frac{8}{5} - \frac{1 + 9}{2} \qquad \text{Substitute 1 for } x \text{ in the original equation.}$$

$$\frac{3}{5} - 4 \stackrel{?}{=} \frac{8}{5} - 5$$

$$\frac{3}{5} - \frac{20}{5} \stackrel{?}{=} \frac{8}{5} - \frac{25}{5}$$

$$-\frac{17}{5} = -\frac{17}{5}$$

Because 1 satisfies the equation, it is a solution, and the solution set of the original equation is $\{1\}$. ∎

Example 7 Solve the equation $\dfrac{x - 1}{3} + 4x = \dfrac{3}{2} + \dfrac{13x - 2}{3}$.

Solution

$$\frac{x - 1}{3} + 4x = \frac{3}{2} + \frac{13x - 2}{3}$$

$$6\left(\frac{x - 1}{3} + 4x\right) = 6\left(\frac{3}{2} + \frac{13x - 2}{3}\right) \qquad \text{Multiply both sides by 6.}$$

$$2(x - 1) + 6(4x) = 9 + 2(13x - 2) \qquad \text{Use the distributive property.}$$

$$2x - 2 + 24x = 9 + 26x - 4 \qquad \text{Remove parentheses.}$$

$$26x - 2 = 26x + 5 \qquad \text{Combine terms.}$$

$$-2 = 5 \qquad \text{Add } -26x \text{ to both sides.}$$

Because $-2 \neq 5$, the original equation has no solutions. Its solution set is $\varnothing$.

If the final equation in this example had been an identity such as $-2 = -2$ or $5 = 5$, the original equation would be an identity also. ∎

Repeating Decimals

In Section 1.1 we claimed that every repeating decimal can be written as a rational number in fractional form. We now show that this statement is true by demonstrating a process that uses linear equations, by which we can convert any repeating decimal to fractional form. For example, to write the decimal $0.2\,54\,54\,\overline{54}$ as a rational number in fractional form, we first note that the decimal has a repeating block of two digits. We then form an equation by setting x equal to the decimal:

1. $x = 0.2\,54\,54\,54\ldots$

We then form another equation by multiplying both sides of Equation 1 by 10^2, which is 100:

2. $100x = 25.4\,54\,54\,54\ldots$

We then subtract each side of Equation 1 from the corresponding side of Equation 2 to obtain

$$
\begin{aligned}
100x &= 25.4\,54\,54\,54\ldots \\
x &= 0.2\,54\,54\,54\ldots \\
\hline
99x &= 25.2
\end{aligned}
$$

Finally, we solve the linear equation $99x = 25.2$ for x and simplify the fraction:

$$x = \frac{25.2}{99} = \frac{252}{990} = \frac{\cancel{18} \cdot 14}{\cancel{18} \cdot 55} = \frac{14}{55}$$

We can use a calculator to verify that the decimal representation of $\frac{14}{55}$ is

$0.2\,54\,54\,\overline{54}$

The key step in the process was multiplying both sides of Equation 1 by 10^2. If there had been n digits in the repeating block of the decimal, we would have multiplied both sides of Equation 1 by 10^n.

Word Problems

The solution of word problems often leads to linear equations. In this section we consider two integer problems and a perimeter problem.

Example 8   If the sum of three consecutive odd integers is 213, what are the integers?

Analysis: Recall that consecutive odd integers are odd integers that differ by 2; numbers such as 11, 13, 15, and 17 are consecutive odd integers. Thus, if x is an odd integer, the algebraic expressions

$x,\quad x + 2,\quad \text{and}\quad x + 4$

represent three consecutive odd integers. The sum of these integers can be expressed in two ways, as either

$x + (x + 2) + (x + 4)\qquad \text{or}\qquad 213$

Solution   Let x represent the first odd integer.
Then $x + 2$ represents the second odd integer.
Then $x + 4$ represents the third odd integer.

The first odd integer	+	the second odd integer	+	the third odd integer	=	the sum of the integers.
x	$+$	$x + 2$	$+$	$x + 4$	$=$	213

$$3x + 6 = 213 \qquad \text{Combine terms.}$$
$$3x = 207 \qquad \text{Add } -6 \text{ to both sides.}$$
$$x = 69 \qquad \text{Divide both sides by 3.}$$
$$x + 2 = 71$$
$$x + 4 = 73$$

The three consecutive odd integers are 69, 71, and 73.

Check: The numbers 69, 71, and 73 are consecutive odd integers that do have a sum of 213.   ■

Example 9   A man wants to cut a 27-foot rope into three pieces. He wants the longest piece to be 2 feet longer than twice the shortest and the middle-sized piece to be twice as long as the shortest. How long will each piece be?

Analysis: The information is given in terms of the length of the shortest piece of rope. Thus, pick a variable to represent the length of the shortest piece. Then express the lengths of the other pieces in terms of the variable.

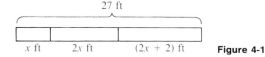

x ft $2x$ ft $(2x + 2)$ ft   **Figure 4-1**

Solution   Let x represent the length of the shortest piece of rope.
Then $2x$ represents the length of the middle-sized piece, and $2x + 2$ represents the length of the longest piece.

Sketch the facts described in the problem as in Figure 4-1. From the figure you can see that the sum of the individual lengths must equal the total length of the rope:

The length of the shortest piece	+	the length of the middle-sized piece	+	the length of the longest piece	=	the total length.
x	$+$	$2x$	$+$	$2x + 2$	$=$	27

$$5x + 2 = 27 \qquad \text{Combine terms.}$$
$$5x = 25 \qquad \text{Add } -2 \text{ to both sides.}$$
$$x = 5 \qquad \text{Divide both sides by 5.}$$

Thus, the shortest piece is 5 feet long, the middle-sized piece is 2(5) or 10 feet long, and the longest piece is 2(5) + 2 or 12 feet long.

Check: Because 5 feet, 10 feet, and 12 feet total 27 feet, because the middle piece is twice as long as the shortest, and because the longest piece is 2 feet longer than twice the shortest, the solution checks.   ∎

Example 10   A rectangle is 6 meters longer than it is wide. If the perimeter of the rectangle is 28 meters, find the dimensions of the rectangle.

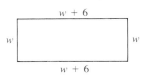

Figure 4-2

Analysis: The perimeter of a rectangle is the distance around it. If w is chosen to represent the width of the rectangle, then its length is $w + 6$. Making a sketch such as Figure 4-2 is helpful. The perimeter can be expressed either as $w + (w + 6) + w + (w + 6)$ or as 28.

Solution   Let w represent the width of the rectangle.
Then $w + 6$ represents the length of the rectangle.
Then you have

One width	+	one length	+	another width	+	another length	=	the perimeter.

$$w \quad + \quad w + 6 \quad + \quad w \quad + \quad w + 6 \quad = \quad 28$$

$$4w + 12 = 28 \quad \text{Combine terms.}$$
$$4w = 16 \quad \text{Add } -12 \text{ to both sides.}$$
$$w = 4 \quad \text{Divide both sides by 4.}$$
$$w + 6 = 10$$

The dimensions of the rectangle are 4 meters by 10 meters.

Check: If a rectangle has a width of 4 meters and a length of 10 meters, the length is 6 meters greater than the width, and the perimeter is $4 + 10 + 4 + 10 = 28$ meters.   ∎

▬ EXERCISE 4.1 ▬▬▬▬▬▬▬▬▬▬▬▬▬▬▬▬▬▬▬▬▬▬▬▬▬

In Exercises 1–8, find the domain of the variable. **Do not solve the equation.**

1. $3x + 2 = 7$

2. $7x - 2 = 2$

3. $\dfrac{1}{x - 2} = 3$

4. $\dfrac{x + 2}{x - 3} = 3$

5. $\dfrac{3x - 2}{(x + 3)(x - 2)} = 4$

6. $\dfrac{8x + 5}{(x + 12)(x + 1)} = 5$

7. $\dfrac{3x^2 - 15}{x(x + 10)(x - 10)} = 32$

8. $\dfrac{3x}{x + 9} = \dfrac{x}{x^2 + 4}$

In Exercises 9–60, solve each equation and check the result.

9. $x + 6 = 8$ **10.** $y - 7 = 3$ **11.** $10 = z - 4$ **12.** $12 = 7 + t$

13. $2u = 6$ **14.** $3v = 12$ **15.** $\dfrac{x}{4} = 7$ **16.** $\dfrac{x}{6} = 8$

17. $\dfrac{3}{4}x = \dfrac{1}{2}$ **18.** $\dfrac{2}{3}x = \dfrac{5}{4}$ **19.** $2x + 1 = 13$ **20.** $2x - 4 = 16$

21. $\dfrac{3}{4}x - 3 = -9$ **22.** $\dfrac{4}{5}x + 5 = 17$ **23.** $2r - 5 = 1 - r$ **24.** $5s - 13 = s - 1$

25. $\dfrac{1}{2}a - 4 = -1 + 2a$ **26.** $2x + 3 = \dfrac{2}{3}x - 1$ **27.** $3a - 22 = -2a - 7$ **28.** $a + 18 = 6a - 3$

29. $3(x + 1) = 15$ **30.** $-2(x + 5) = 30$ **31.** $5(5 - a) = 37 - 2a$ **32.** $4a + 17 = 7(a + 2)$

33. $4(y + 1) = -2(4 - y)$ **34.** $5x + 4 = x + 24$ **35.** $3(y - 4) - 6 = 0$ **36.** $2x + (2x - 3) = 5$

37. $3(y - 5) + 10 = 2(y + 4)$ **38.** $2(5x + 2) = 3(3x - 2)$

39. $9(x + 2) = -6(4 - x) + 18$ **40.** $3(x + 2) - 2 = -(5 + x) + x$

41. $3(x - 4) + 6 = -2(x + 4) + 5x$ **42.** $8(3a - 5) - 4(2a + 3) = 12$

43. $\dfrac{x}{2} - \dfrac{x}{3} = 4$ **44.** $\dfrac{x}{2} + \dfrac{x}{3} = 10$ **45.** $\dfrac{x}{6} + 1 = \dfrac{x}{3}$ **46.** $\dfrac{3}{2}(y + 4) = \dfrac{20 - y}{2}$

47. $5 - \dfrac{x + 2}{3} = 7 - x$ **48.** $3x - \dfrac{2(x + 3)}{3} = 16 - \dfrac{x + 2}{2}$

49. $\dfrac{4x - 2}{2} = \dfrac{3x + 6}{3}$ **50.** $2(x - 3) = \dfrac{3}{2}(x - 4) + \dfrac{x}{2}$

51. $\dfrac{a + 1}{3} + \dfrac{a - 1}{5} = \dfrac{2}{15}$ **52.** $\dfrac{2z + 3}{3} + \dfrac{3z - 4}{6} = \dfrac{z - 2}{2}$

53. $\dfrac{5a}{2} - 12 = \dfrac{a}{3} + 1$ **54.** $\dfrac{5a}{6} - \dfrac{5}{2} = -\dfrac{1}{2} - \dfrac{a}{6}$

55. $y(y + 2) = (y + 1)^2 - 1$ **56.** $x(x - 3) = (x - 1)^2 - (5 + x)$

57. $0.05x + 0.04(5000 - x) = 220$ (*Hint:*   Multiply both sides by 100.)

58. $0.06x + 0.08(20,000 - x) = 1,500$

59. $0.05x + 0.1x + 0.25(100 - x) = 24.5$ **60.** $0.09y + 0.14(10,000 - y) = 1,275$

In Exercises 61–64, write each repeating decimal number as a fraction. Simplify the answer, if necessary.

61. $0.33\overline{3}$ **62.** $0.29\ 29\ \overline{29}$ **63.** $-0.34\ 89\ 89\ \overline{89}$ **64.** $-2.3\ 47\ 47\ \overline{47}$

In Exercises 65–80, solve each word problem.

65. If the sum of two consecutive integers is 75, what are the integers?

66. If the sum of three consecutive integers is 318, what are the integers?

67. The sum of three integers is 114. If the first integer is 24 larger than the second, and the second integer is 6 larger than the third, what is the second integer?

68. The sum of three consecutive even integers is 384. What are the integers?

69. The sum of the first and third integers of three consecutive odd integers is 58. What is the middle integer?

70. The sum of the second and fourth integers of four consecutive integers is 46. What is the sum of all the integers?

71. Jim wants to saw a 17-foot board into three pieces. The longest piece is to be three times as long as the shortest, and the middle-sized piece is to be 2 feet longer than the shortest. How long should each piece be?

72. A 30-foot steel beam is to be cut into two pieces. The longer piece is to be 2 feet more than three times as long as the shorter. How long will each piece be?

73. A 60-foot rope is cut into four pieces with each successive piece being twice as long as the previous one. How long is the longest piece?

74. A 185-foot cable is cut into three pieces: two pieces of equal length and a third piece that is 5 feet longer than the sum of the equal pieces. How long is the longer piece?

75. The length of a rectangle is twice the width. If the perimeter is 72 centimeters, what are the dimensions of the rectangle?

76. The width of a rectangle is one-third its length. The perimeter of the rectangle is 96 meters. What are the dimensions of the rectangle?

77. The length of a rectangle is 6 feet greater than its width. The perimeter of the rectangle is 72 feet. Find its area. (*Hint:*   The area of a rectangle is the product of its length and its width: $A = lw$.)

78. A man has 624 feet of fencing to enclose a small pasture. Because a river runs along one side, he will have to use fencing only on three sides. What will be the dimensions of the enclosed pasture if the length runs along the river and is to be double the width?

79. A man has 150 feet of fencing to build a rectangular, two-section pen as shown in Illustration 1. If one end is to be square, what are the outside dimensions of the entire pen?

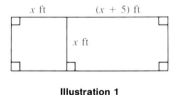

Illustration 1

80. A woman wants to fence in a 20-foot by 30-foot swimming pool and have a walkway of uniform width all the way around. How wide will the walkway be if the woman uses 180 feet of fencing?

4.2 APPLICATIONS

In this section we continue the discussion of word problems. In a broader sense, it is our purpose to discuss problem-solving techniques that can be used in many different situations. The following steps provide a strategy for solving a variety of problems:

1.   Read the problem several times to analyze the facts given. What information is given? What are you asked to find? Often a sketch or diagram will help you visualize the facts of the problem.

2. Pick a variable to indicate a quantity that must be found and write a sentence telling what the variable represents. Express all other quantities mentioned in the problem as expressions involving this single variable.
3. Organize the data and find a way to express a quantity in two different ways.
4. Write an equation showing that the two quantities found in step 3 are equal.
5. Solve the equation.
6. Check the result in the words of the problem.

Although this list is helpful, it does not apply to all situations totally. You may have to modify these steps slightly.

The word problems discussed in this section fall into several categories.

Area Problems

Example 1   The width of a rectangle is 4 centimeters less than its length. If the width is increased by 2 centimeters and the length is increased by 8 centimeters, the area is increased by 84 square centimeters. Find the dimensions of the original rectangle.

Analysis: Recall that the area of a rectangle is given by the formula $A = lw$. If the length of the original rectangle is l, then the width is $l - 4$, and the area is $l(l - 4)$. See Figure 4-3. If the width were increased by 2 centimeters and the length by 8 centimeters, the width and length of the larger rectangle would be $l - 2$ and $l + 8$. Hence, the area of the larger rectangle would be $(l - 2)(l + 8)$. If 84 square centimeters is added to the area of the original rectangle, the result is the same as the area of the larger rectangle.

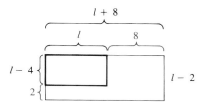

Figure 4-3

Solution   Let l represent the length of the original rectangle.
Then $l - 4$ represents the width of the original rectangle.
Then $l - 2$ represents the width of the larger rectangle.
Then $l + 8$ represents the length of the larger rectangle.

| The area of the original rectangle | $+$ | 84 | $=$ | the area of the larger rectangle. |

$$l(l - 4) \quad + \quad 84 \quad = \quad (l - 2)(l + 8)$$

$$l^2 - 4l + 84 = l^2 + 6l - 16 \qquad \text{Remove parentheses.}$$
$$-4l + 84 = 6l - 16 \qquad \text{Add } -l^2 \text{ to both sides.}$$
$$100 = 10l \qquad \text{Add } 4l + 16 \text{ to both sides.}$$
$$10 = l \qquad \text{Divide both sides by 10.}$$
$$6 = l - 4$$

The dimensions of the original rectangle are 6 centimeters by 10 centimeters.

Check: The area of the original rectangle is $6 \cdot 10 = 60$ square centimeters. The area of the larger rectangle is $8 \cdot 18 = 144$ square centimeters. The larger rectangle is 84 square centimeters greater than the original rectangle.   ■

Lever Problems

Example 2   Sarah, David, and Heidi are positioned on a balanced seesaw as in Figure 4-4. If Sarah weighs 35 pounds and Heidi weighs 95 pounds, how much does David weigh?

Analysis: The key to this problem is a fact from physics. If the seesaw is to remain in balance, Sarah's weight times her distance from the fulcrum plus David's weight times his distance from the fulcrum must equal Heidi's weight times her distance from the fulcrum.

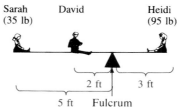

Figure 4-4

Solution   Let w represent David's weight in pounds.

| Sarah's weight times distance | $+$ | David's weight times distance | $=$ | Heidi's weight times distance. |

$$35 \cdot 5 \quad + \quad w \cdot 2 \quad = \quad 95 \cdot 3$$

$$175 + 2w = 285 \qquad \text{Simplify.}$$
$$2w = 110 \qquad \text{Add } -175 \text{ to both sides.}$$
$$w = 55 \qquad \text{Divide both sides by 2.}$$

David weighs 55 pounds.

Check: $35 \cdot 5 + 55 \cdot 2 = 175 + 110 = 285$

$95 \cdot 3 = 285$ ■

Coin Problems

Example 3   Judy has a certain number of quarters. She has four times as many dimes. She also has five times as many nickels as dimes. Altogether she has $11.55. How many quarters, dimes, and nickels does she have?

Analysis: The key to this problem is to set the value of the quarters plus the value of the dimes plus the value of the nickels equal to the value $11.55. If q is the number of quarters, $0.25q$ is the value of the quarters. Because there are $4q$ dimes, the value of the dimes is $0.10(4q)$. Because there are $5(4q) = 20q$ nickels, the value of the nickels is $0.05(20q)$. Set the sum of these values equal to $11.55.

Solution   Let q represent the number of quarters.
Then $4q$ represents the number of dimes.
Then $5(4q) = 20q$ represents the number of nickels.

The value of the quarters		the value of the dimes		the value of the nickels		the total value.
	+		+		=	

$$0.25q \quad + \quad 0.10(4q) \quad + \quad 0.05(20q) \quad = \quad 11.55$$

Multiply both sides by 100. $25q + 10(4q) + 5(20q) = 1155$

Simplify. $25q + 40q + 100q = 1155$

Combine terms. $165q = 1155$

Divide both sides by 165. $q = 7$

$$4q = 28$$
$$20q = 140$$

Judy has 7 quarters, 28 dimes, and 140 nickels.

Check: The value of the 7 quarters is $1.75, the value of the 28 dimes is $2.80, and the value of the 140 nickels is $7.00. The total value is $11.55.   ■

Investment Problems

Example 4   Steven has $15,000 to invest for one year. He invests some of it at 9% and the rest at 8%. If his total income from these investments is $1260, how much did he invest at each rate?

Analysis: The key to this problem is to add the interest from the 9% investment to the interest from the 8% investment, and set that sum equal to the total interest earned. For simple interest, the interest earned is computed by the formula $i = prt$, where i is the interest, p is the principal, r is the rate of interest, and t is the length of time (in this case, $t = 1$). Hence, if x dollars are invested at 9%, the interest earned is $0.09x$. If x dollars are invested at 9%, then the remaining money $(15000 - x)$ is invested at 8%. The amount of interest earned on that money is $0.08(15000 - x)$. The sum of these two amounts of money equals $1260.

Solution   Let x be the number of dollars invested at 9%.
Then $15000 - x$ is the number of dollars invested at 8%.

The interest earned at 9%	+	the interest earned at 8%	=	the total interest.

$$0.09x \quad + \quad 0.08(15000 - x) \quad = \quad 1260.00$$

Multiply both sides by 100. $9x + 8(15000 - x) = 126000$

Remove parentheses. $9x + 120000 - 8x = 126000$

Combine terms. $x + 120000 = 126000$

Add -120000 to both sides. $x = 6000$

$$15000 - x = 9000$$

Steven invested $6000 at 9% and $9000 at 8%.

Check: The interest on $6000 is $0.09(\$6000) = \$540$. The interest on $9000 is $0.08(\$9000) = \$720$. The total interest is $1260. ■

Uniform Motion Problems

Example 5   A car leaves city A traveling toward city B at the rate of 55 miles per hour. At the same time, another car leaves city B traveling toward city A at the rate of 50 miles per hour. How long will it take them to meet if the cities are 157.5 miles apart?

Analysis: Uniform motion problems are based on the formula $d = rt$, where d is distance, r is rate, and t is time. It is often helpful to organize the information of a uniform motion problem in a chart like Figure 4-5. You know that the faster car is traveling at 55 miles per hour and that the slower car is traveling at 50 miles per hour. You also know that they travel for the same amount of time, say t hours. The distance that the faster car travels is $55t$ miles and the

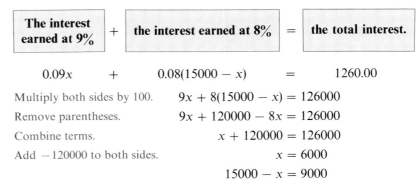

	r	$\cdot$	t	=	d
(1) Faster car	55		t		$55t$
(2) Slower car	50		t		$50t$

Figure 4-5

distance that the slower car travels is 50*t* miles. The sum of these distances equals 157.5 miles, the distance between the cities.

Solution   Let *t* represent the time that each car travels.
Then 55*t* represents the distance traveled by the faster car.
Then 50*t* represents the distance traveled by the slower car.

The distance the faster car goes	+	the distance the slower car goes	=	the distance between cities.
55*t*	+	50*t*	=	157.5

$$\text{Combine terms.} \quad 105t = 157.5$$
$$\text{Divide both sides by 105.} \quad t = 1.5$$

The two cars will meet in 1.5 hours.

Check: Car 1 travels 1.5(55) = 82.5 miles. Car 2 travels 1.5(50) = 75 miles. The total distance traveled is 157.5 miles.   ■

Mixture Problems

Example 6   A candy store owner notices that he has 20 pounds of cashews that are getting stale. They are not selling because they cost a high price of $6 per pound. In order to sell the cashews, the store owner decides to mix peanuts with them to lower the price per pound. If peanuts sell for $1.50 per pound, how many pounds of peanuts must be mixed with the cashews to make a mixture that he could sell for $3 per pound?

Analysis: This problem is very similar to the previous uniform motion problem, except that it is based on the formula $V = pn$, where V represents value, p represents price per pound, and n represents the number of pounds. Let x represent the number of pounds of peanuts to be used. Then $20 + x$ represents the total pounds in the mixture. Enter the known information in the chart of Figure 4-6. Note that the value of the cashews plus the value of the peanuts is equal to the value of the mixture.

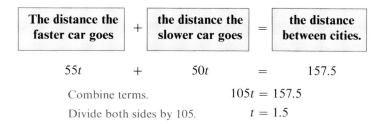

	p ·	n =	V
Cashews	6.00	20	120.00
Peanuts	1.50	x	1.5x
Mixture	3.00	$20 + x$	$3(20 + x)$

Figure 4-6

Solution   Let x represent the number of pounds of peanuts to be used. Then $20 + x$ represents the number of pounds in the mixture.

The value of the cashews	+	the value of the peanuts	=	the value of the mixture.
120	+	$1.5x$	=	$3(20 + x)$

Multiply both sides by 10.	$1200 + 15x = 30(20 + x)$
Remove parentheses.	$1200 + 15x = 600 + 30x$
Add $-15x - 600$ to both sides.	$600 = 15x$
Divide both sides by 15.	$40 = x$

The store owner should mix 40 pounds of peanuts with the 20 pounds of cashews.

Check: The cashews are valued at $6(20) = $120. The peanuts are valued at $1.50(40) = $60. The mixture is valued at $3(60) = $180. The value of the cashews added to the value of the peanuts does equal the value of the mixture.   ∎

Example 7   A car radiator has a capacity of 15 quarts and is filled with a mixture of 80% water and 20% antifreeze. How many quarts of solution must be drained and replaced with pure antifreeze to bring the mixture in the radiator up to a 50% antifreeze solution?

Analysis: The key to this problem is to note that whatever pure antifreeze finally ends up in the radiator could have come from one of two sources—either from what was left in the partially drained radiator, or from the pure antifreeze that was added. If x represents the amount of solution to be drained (and, therefore, the amount to be replaced with pure antifreeze), then the amount of pure antifreeze remaining in the radiator after draining is the amount present originally minus the amount drained. This is 20% of 15 (the amount originally present) minus 20% of x (the amount drained). The amount of pure antifreeze added is x, and the amount needed when you are done is 50% of 15.

Solution   Let x represent the number of quarts to be drained and then replaced.

The amount of pure antifreeze in original solution	−	the amount of pure antifreeze to be drained	+	the amount of pure antifreeze to be added	=	the amount of pure antifreeze in final solution.
$0.20(15)$	−	$0.20(x)$	+	$1.00x$	=	$0.50(15)$

Multiply both sides by 10. $2(15) - 2x + 10x = 5(15)$

Simplify and combine terms. $30 + 8x = 75$

Add -30 to both sides. $8x = 45$

Divide both sides by 8. $x = \dfrac{45}{8}$

You must drain $\frac{45}{8}$, or $5\frac{5}{8}$, quarts.

Check: You begin with $0.20(15) = 3$ quarts of antifreeze. You drain $0.20(\frac{45}{8}) = \frac{9}{8}$ quarts of antifreeze. You add $1.00(\frac{45}{8}) = 5\frac{5}{8}$ quarts of antifreeze. The total is $3 - \frac{9}{8} + \frac{45}{8} = 7\frac{1}{2}$ quarts of antifreeze, which is half the capacity of the radiator.

■

■ EXERCISE 4.2

Solve and check each word problem.

1.   A rectangle has a length of 9 centimeters and an area of 54 square centimeters. Find its width.

2.   A rectangle is 6 feet longer than it is wide, and its area is 30 square feet more than the square of its width. Find the dimensions of the rectangle.

3.   The width of a rectangle is 2 inches shorter than its length. If both the length and the width are increased by 5 inches, the area is increased by 75 square inches. What are the dimensions of the original rectangle?

4. ◄   A rectangle is 1 foot longer than it is wide. If the length is increased by 2 feet and the width is decreased by 6 feet, the area is decreased by 50 square feet. What are the dimensions of the original rectangle?

5.   A rectangle is 11 meters longer than it is wide. If the length is decreased by 12 meters and the width is increased by 10 meters, the area is decreased by 24 square meters. What is the perimeter of the original rectangle?

6. ◄   If the height of a triangle with a base of 8 inches is tripled, its area is increased by 96 square inches. Find the height of the triangle. (*Hint:*   The area is given by the formula $A = \frac{1}{2}bh$, where A is the area, b is the base, and h is the height.)

7.   A seesaw is 20 feet long and the fulcrum is in the center. If an 80-pound boy sits at one end, how far will the boy's 160-pound father have to sit from the fulcrum to balance the seesaw?

8.   Two girls, one weighing 110 pounds and the other 88 pounds, sit on opposite ends of an 18-foot seesaw. Where must the fulcrum be placed so that the seesaw balances?

9.   A lady uses a 10-foot bar to lift a 210-pound stone. If she places another rock 3 feet from the stone to act as the fulcrum, how much force must she exert to move the stone?

10.   Two men wish to lift a 2500-pound car. To do so, they use a 12-foot steel bar and a fulcrum placed 3 feet from the car. If one of the two men weighs 200 pounds and pushes on the far end of the bar, and the other man, who weighs 150 pounds, pushes also, can they lift the car?

11.   Sally and Sue, each weighing 110 pounds, sit at opposite ends of a 14-foot seesaw, and Sue's brother Jim, who weighs twice as much, sits 3 feet in front of Sue. Where should the fulcrum be placed to balance the seesaw?

12.   Jim and Bob sit at opposite ends of an 18-foot seesaw, with the fulcrum at its center. Jim weighs 160 pounds, and Bob weighs 200 pounds. Kimberly sits 4 feet in front of Jim, and the seesaw balances. How much less does Kimberly weigh than Bob?

13.   A person has a certain number of nickels, twice as many dimes, and four times as many pennies. How many does the person have of each if their total value is $2.90?

14. Sarah has the same number of quarters and dimes. She also has some nickels. If the value of her 68 coins is $8.15, how many quarters does she have?

15. A collection of 24 coins, only quarters and nickels, has a value of $3.40. How many quarters and nickels are there?

16. A collection of nickels, dimes, and quarters has a value of $11.10. There are three times as many dimes as nickels, and twice as many quarters as dimes. How many are there of each?

17. A handful of dimes and nickels, eight coins in all, would be worth 10¢ less if all the dimes were nickels and all the nickels were dimes. How many dimes and nickels are there?

18. Fred has some dimes and some quarters, ten coins in all. If his dimes were quarters and his quarters were dimes, he would have 30¢ less. How much money does he have?

19. Heidi invested $12,000, some at 8% and some at 9%. How much is invested at each rate if her income from the two investments is $1060 each year?

20. Sam invested $14,000, some at 7% and some at 10%. His annual income from these investments is $1280. How much did he invest at each rate?

21. A teacher wishes to earn $1500 per year in supplemental income from a cash gift of $16,000. She puts $6000 in a credit union that pays 7%. What rate must she earn on the remainder to achieve her goal?

22. Paul split an inheritance between two investments, one paying 7% and the other paying 10%. Paul invested twice as much in the 10% investment as in the 7% investment. His combined annual income from these two investments was $4050. How much did Paul inherit?

23. George has some money to invest. If George could invest an extra $3000, he would be eligible for a 21% special account. Otherwise, he could invest his money at 18% interest. The 21% account would yield twice as much income annually as the 18% investment. If George cannot find the extra money, how much does he have available to invest?

24. A bus driver wishes to earn $3500 per year in supplemental income from an inheritance of $40,000. The driver puts $10,000 in a bank paying 8%. What rate must he earn on the remainder to achieve his goal?

25. For a certain movie, student tickets were $2 each and adult tickets were $4 each. If 200 tickets were sold and the total receipts were $750, how many student and how many adult tickets were sold?

26. At a school play 140 tickets were sold. Adult tickets cost $2.50 each and student tickets cost $1.50 each. How many of each were sold if the receipts were $290?

27. Some college students take a bus to an airport to catch a plane. Their bus traveled at 55 miles per hour for 2 hours. Their plane cruised at 450 miles per hour. How long were they in the air if the total distance traveled was 1460 miles?

28. A cyclist leaves a city riding at the rate of 18 miles per hour. One hour later, a car leaves the same city going at the rate of 44 miles per hour and in the same direction. How long will it take the car to overtake the cyclist?

29. A boat can go 12 miles per hour in still water. If it goes upstream for 3 hours against a current of 4 miles per hour, how long will it take the boat to return?

30. Sarah walked north at the rate of 3 miles per hour and returned at the rate of 4 miles per hour. How many miles did she walk if the round trip took 3.5 hours?

31. Grant traveled a distance of 400 miles in a time of 8 hours. Part of the time the rate of speed was 45 miles per hour, and part of the time the rate of speed was 55 miles per hour. How long did Grant travel at each rate?

32. A motorboat can go 18 miles per hour in still water. If it can go 80 miles downstream in 4 hours and return in 5 hours, what is the speed of the current?

33. The owner of a candy store wishes to make 30 pounds of a mixture of two candies to sell for $1.00 per pound. If one candy sells for $0.95 per pound and the other candy sells for $1.10 per pound, how many pounds of each should he use?

34. A mixture of candy is made to sell for $0.89 per pound. If 32 pounds of a cheaper candy, selling for $0.80 per pound, are used along with 12 pounds of a more expensive candy, what is the price per pound of the better candy?

35. How much water should be added to 20 ounces of a 15% solution of alcohol to dilute it to a 10% solution?

36. How much water must be boiled away to increase the concentration of 300 gallons of a salt solution from 2% to 3%?

37. Cream is approximately 22% butterfat. How many gallons of cream must be mixed with milk testing at 2% butterfat to give 20 gallons of milk containing 4% butterfat?

38. How much acid must be added to 60 grams of a solution that is 65% acid to obtain a new solution that is 75% acid?

4.3 LITERAL EQUATIONS

Equations that contain many variables are called **literal equations**. Often, these equations are **formulas** such as $A = \frac{1}{2}bh$, the formula for finding the area of a triangle with a base of b units and a height of h units. Suppose we wish to use this formula to find the heights of several triangles whose areas and bases are known. It would be very tedious to substitute values of A and b into the formula and then repeatedly solve the formula $A = \frac{1}{2}bh$ for h. It would be better to solve the formula for h first, and then substitute values for A and b, and compute h directly.

To solve a formula for a variable means to isolate that variable on one side of an equation and isolate all other quantities on the other side of the equation. The first example shows how to solve the formula $A = \frac{1}{2}bh$ for h.

Example 1 Solve the formula $A = \dfrac{1}{2} bh$ for h.

Solution

$$A = \frac{1}{2} bh$$

$$2A = bh \qquad \text{Multiply both sides by 2.}$$

$$\frac{2A}{b} = h \qquad \text{Divide both sides by } b.$$

$$h = \frac{2A}{b} \qquad \text{Use the symmetric property of equality.} \qquad \blacksquare$$

Example 2 The formula $A = p + prt$ gives the amount of money in a savings account at the end of a specific time. A represents the amount, p the principal, r the rate, and t the time. Solve the formula for t.

Solution

$$A = p + prt$$

$$A - p = prt \qquad \text{Add } -p \text{ to both sides.}$$

$$\frac{A - p}{pr} = t \qquad \text{Divide both sides by } pr.$$

$$t = \frac{A - p}{pr}$$

∎

Example 3 Solve the formula $A = p + prt$ for p.

Solution In this example, you must factor the p out of the two terms on the right-hand side of the equation. Then, you can solve for p.

$$A = p + prt$$

$$A = p(1 + rt) \qquad \text{Factor } p \text{ out of } p + prt.$$

$$\frac{A}{1 + rt} = p \qquad \text{Divide both sides by } 1 + rt.$$

$$p = \frac{A}{1 + rt}$$

∎

Example 4 Solve the formula $\dfrac{1}{r} = \dfrac{1}{r_1} + \dfrac{1}{r_2}$ for r.

Solution This formula contains three variables: r, r_1, and r_2. The variables r_1 and r_2 contain subscripts of 1 and 2, respectively. The purpose of the subscripts is to identify two variables that represent similar quantities. The given formula is used in electronics to calculate the combined resistance r of two resistors in parallel. The variable r_1 represents the resistance of the first resistor, and the variable r_2 represents the resistance of the second resistor. Solve for r as follows:

$$\frac{1}{r} = \frac{1}{r_1} + \frac{1}{r_2}$$

$$\frac{rr_1r_2}{r} = \frac{rr_1r_2}{r_1} + \frac{rr_1r_2}{r_2} \qquad \text{Multiply both sides by } rr_1r_2.$$

$$r_1r_2 = rr_2 + rr_1 \qquad \text{Simplify each fraction.}$$

$$r_1r_2 = r(r_2 + r_1) \qquad \text{Factor out } r \text{ on the right-hand side.}$$

$$\frac{r_1r_2}{r_2 + r_1} = r \qquad \text{Divide both sides by } r_2 + r_1.$$

$$r = \frac{r_1r_2}{r_2 + r_1}$$

∎

Example 5 A saleslady in a high-fashion dress shop earns \$200 per week plus a 5% commission on the value of the merchandise she sells. What dollar volume must she sell each week to earn $250, $300, and $350 in three successive weeks?

Solution   The saleslady's weekly earnings e are computed with the formula

$$e = 200 + 0.05v$$

where v represents the value of the merchandise she sells. Begin by solving the formula for v:

$$e = 200 + 0.05v$$
$$e - 200 = 0.05v$$
$$v = \frac{e - 200}{0.05}$$

Then substitute $250, $300, and $350 for e and solve for v:

$$v = \frac{e - 200}{0.05} \qquad v = \frac{e - 200}{0.05} \qquad v = \frac{e - 200}{0.05}$$

$$v = \frac{250 - 200}{0.05} \qquad v = \frac{300 - 200}{0.05} \qquad v = \frac{350 - 200}{0.05}$$

$$= 1000 \qquad\qquad = 2000 \qquad\qquad = 3000$$

She must sell $1000 worth of merchandise the first week, $2000 worth the second week, and $3000 worth the third week.   ■

EXERCISE 4.3

In Exercises 1–40, solve each equation for the variable indicated.

1. $A = lw$ for w

2. $p = 4s$ for s

3. $A = \pi r^2$ for r^2

4. $A = \frac{1}{2}bh$ for b

5. $V = \frac{1}{3}Bh$ for B

6. $V = \pi r^2 h$ for h

7. $I = prt$ for t

8. $I = prt$ for r

9. $p = 2l + 2w$ for w

10. $p = 2l + 2w$ for l

11. $A = \frac{1}{2}h(b_1 + b_2)$ for b_1

12. $A = \frac{1}{2}h(b_1 + b_2)$ for b_2

13. $z = \frac{x - \mu}{\sigma}$ for x

14. $z = \frac{x - \mu}{\sigma}$ for μ

15. $y = mx + b$ for x

16. $y = mx + b$ for m

17. $l = a + (n - 1)d$ for n

18. $l = a + (n - 1)d$ for d

19. $r_1 r_2 = rr_2 + rr_1$ for r_1

20. $r_1 r_2 = rr_2 + rr_1$ for r

21. $\sigma^2 = \frac{\Sigma x^2}{n} - \mu^2$ for Σx^2

22. $\sigma^2 = \frac{\Sigma x^2}{n} - \mu^2$ for n

23. $S = \dfrac{a - lr}{1 - r}$ for r

24. $S = \dfrac{a - lr}{1 - r}$ for l

25. $a = \dfrac{(n - 2)180}{n}$ for n

26. $C = \dfrac{5}{9}(F - 32)$ for F

27. $P = L + \dfrac{s}{f}i$ for s

28. $P = L + \dfrac{s}{f}i$ for f

29. $\dfrac{1}{r} = \dfrac{1}{r_1} + \dfrac{1}{r_2}$ for r_2

30. $S = \dfrac{n(a + l)}{2}$ for n

31. $y - y_1 = m(x - x_1)$ for x

32. $y - y_1 = m(x - x_1)$ for x_1

33. $H = \dfrac{2ab}{a + b}$ for a

34. $H = \dfrac{2ab}{a + b}$ for b

35. $\dfrac{x^2}{a^2} + \dfrac{y^2}{b^2} = 1$ for a^2

36. $\dfrac{x^2}{a^2} - \dfrac{y^2}{b^2} = 1$ for y^2

37. $y = a(x^2 - h) + k$ for h

38. $y = a(x^2 - h) + k$ for x^2

39. $V = \dfrac{1}{3}h(B_1 + B_2 + \sqrt{B_1 B_2})$ for h

40. $V = \pi h^2\left(r - \dfrac{h}{3}\right)$ for r

41. Solve the formula $F = \frac{9}{5}C + 32$ for C and find the Celsius temperatures that correspond to Fahrenheit temperatures of 32°, 70°, and 212°.

42. A man intends to invest \$1000. Solve the formula $A = p + prt$ for t and find the time required to double his money at the rates of 5%, 7%, and 10%.

43. The cost of electricity in a certain city is given by the formula

$$C = 0.07n + 6.50$$

where C is the cost and n is the number of kilowatt hours used. Solve the formula for n and find the number of kilowatt hours used for costs of \$49.90, \$75.10, and \$125.50.

44. A monthly water bill in a certain city is calculated by using the formula

$$n = \frac{5{,}000C - 17{,}500}{6}$$

where n is the number of gallons used and C is the monthly cost. Solve the formula for C and compute the bill for quantities used of 500, 1200, and 2500 gallons.

45. While waiting for his car to be repaired, John rents a car for \$12 per day plus 10¢ per mile. If John keeps the car for 2 days, how many miles can he drive for a total cost of \$30? How many miles can he drive for a total cost of \$40?

46. Jill earns \$17 per day delivering pizzas. She is paid \$5 per day plus 60¢ for each pizza delivered. How many more deliveries must she make each day to increase her earnings to \$23 per day?

47. Bob's father will pay him \$1750 and give him a used car if Bob agrees to work 5 months. When Bob quit after 3 months, his father paid him \$810 and the car. How much was the car worth?

48. The landlord of a duplex apartment collected \$8730 rent in one year by renting both units. One apartment rents for \$60 more per month than the other, but was vacant for 3 months. What is the monthly rent of the more expensive apartment?

4.4   SOLVING EQUATIONS BY FACTORING

An equation such as $3x^2 + 4x - 7 = 0$ or $-5y^2 + 3y + 8 = 0$ is called a **quadratic** or **second-degree equation**.

> **Definition.**   A **quadratic equation** is an equation that can be written in the form $ax^2 + bx + c = 0$, where a, b, and c are real numbers and $a \neq 0$.

Many quadratic equations can be solved by factoring. To do so, we use the **zero-factor theorem**.

> **The Zero-Factor Theorem.**   If a and b are real numbers, and
> $$\text{if } ab = 0, \quad \text{then} \quad a = 0 \text{ or } b = 0.$$

This theorem points out that, if the product of two or more numbers is 0, then at least one of them must be 0.

For example, to use the zero-factor theorem to solve the equation

$$\textbf{1.} \quad x^2 + 5x + 6 = 0$$

we factor the left-hand side to obtain

$$(x + 3)(x + 2) = 0$$

Because the product of the factors $x + 3$ and $x + 2$ is 0, then (by the zero-factor theorem) at least one of the factors is 0. Thus, we can set each factor equal to 0 and solve each resulting equation for x:

$$x + 3 = 0 \qquad \text{or} \qquad x + 2 = 0$$
$$x = -3 \qquad \qquad \qquad x = -2$$

To check the work we substitute -3 and -2 for x in Equation 1 and verify that each number satisfies it.

$$x^2 + 5x + 6 = 0 \qquad\qquad x^2 + 5x + 6 = 0$$
$$(-3)^2 + 5(-3) + 6 \stackrel{?}{=} 0 \qquad (-2)^2 + 5(-2) + 6 \stackrel{?}{=} 0$$
$$9 - 15 + 6 \stackrel{?}{=} 0 \qquad\qquad 4 - 10 + 6 \stackrel{?}{=} 0$$
$$0 = 0 \qquad\qquad\qquad\qquad 0 = 0$$

Because both -3 and -2 satisfy the equation, both numbers are solutions.

If either b or c is 0 in an equation of the form $ax^2 + bx + c = 0$, the equation is called an **incomplete quadratic equation**.

Example 1   Solve the equation $3x^2 + 6x = 0$.

Solution   This equation is an incomplete quadratic equation with c (the constant term) equal to 0. To solve this equation, factor the left-hand side, set each factor equal to 0, and solve each resulting equation for x.

$$3x^2 + 6x = 0$$
$$3x(x + 2) = 0$$
$$3x = 0 \quad \text{or} \quad x + 2 = 0$$
$$x = 0 \qquad\qquad x = -2$$

Verify that both solutions check.   ∎

Example 2   Solve the equation $x^2 - 16 = 0$.

Solution   This equation is an incomplete quadratic equation with b (the coefficient of x) equal to 0. To solve this equation, factor the difference of two squares on the left-hand side, set each factor equal to 0, and solve each resulting equation.

$$x^2 - 16 = 0$$
$$(x + 4)(x - 4) = 0$$
$$x + 4 = 0 \quad \text{or} \quad x - 4 = 0$$
$$x = -4 \qquad\qquad x = 4$$

Verify that both solutions check.   ∎

Many equations that do not appear to be quadratic can be put into quadratic form and then solved by factoring.

Example 3   Solve the equation $x = \dfrac{6}{5} - \dfrac{6}{5}x^2$.

Solution

$$x = \frac{6}{5} - \frac{6}{5}x^2$$

$$5x = 6 - 6x^2 \qquad\qquad \text{Multiply both sides by 5.}$$

$$6x^2 + 5x - 6 = 0 \qquad\qquad \text{Add } 6x^2 - 6 \text{ to both sides.}$$

$$(3x - 2)(2x + 3) = 0 \qquad\qquad \text{Factor } 6x^2 + 5x - 6.$$

$$3x - 2 = 0 \quad \text{or} \quad 2x + 3 = 0 \qquad \text{Set each factor equal to zero.}$$

$$3x = 2 \qquad\qquad 2x = -3$$

$$x = \frac{2}{3} \qquad\qquad x = -\frac{3}{2}$$

Check: $x = \dfrac{6}{5} - \dfrac{6}{5}x^2$ $\bigg|$ $x = \dfrac{6}{5} - \dfrac{6}{5}x^2$

$\dfrac{2}{3} \overset{?}{=} \dfrac{6}{5} - \dfrac{6}{5}\left(\dfrac{2}{3}\right)^2$ $\bigg|$ $-\dfrac{3}{2} \overset{?}{=} \dfrac{6}{5} - \dfrac{6}{5}\left(-\dfrac{3}{2}\right)^2$

$\dfrac{2}{3} \overset{?}{=} \dfrac{6}{5} - \dfrac{6}{5}\left(\dfrac{4}{9}\right)$ $\bigg|$ $-\dfrac{3}{2} \overset{?}{=} \dfrac{6}{5} - \dfrac{6}{5}\left(\dfrac{9}{4}\right)$

$\dfrac{2}{3} \overset{?}{=} \dfrac{6}{5} - \dfrac{8}{15}$ $\bigg|$ $-\dfrac{3}{2} \overset{?}{=} \dfrac{6}{5} - \dfrac{27}{10}$

$\dfrac{2}{3} \overset{?}{=} \dfrac{18}{15} - \dfrac{8}{15}$ $\bigg|$ $-\dfrac{3}{2} \overset{?}{=} \dfrac{12}{10} - \dfrac{27}{10}$

$\dfrac{2}{3} \overset{?}{=} \dfrac{10}{15}$ $\bigg|$ $-\dfrac{3}{2} \overset{?}{=} -\dfrac{15}{10}$

$\dfrac{2}{3} = \dfrac{2}{3}$ $\bigg|$ $-\dfrac{3}{2} = -\dfrac{3}{2}$

Both solutions check.   ■

Often the factoring method can be used to solve equations that contain polynomials with degree greater than two.

Example 4   Solve the equation $6x^3 - x^2 - 2x = 0$.

Solution   Because x is a common factor, factor an x from the third-degree polynomial on the left-hand side and proceed as follows:

$6x^3 - x^2 - 2x = 0$

$x(6x^2 - x - 2) = 0$

$x(3x - 2)(2x + 1) = 0$ Factor $6x^2 - x - 2$.

$x = 0 \quad \text{or} \quad 3x - 2 = 0 \quad \text{or} \quad 2x + 1 = 0$ Set each factor equal to 0.

$$x = \frac{2}{3} \qquad x = -\frac{1}{2}$$

Verify that all three solutions check.   ■

Example 5   Solve the equation $x^4 - 5x^2 + 4 = 0$.

Solution   Factor the trinomial on the left-hand side and proceed as follows:

$x^4 - 5x^2 + 4 = 0$

$(x^2 - 1)(x^2 - 4) = 0$

$(x + 1)(x - 1)(x + 2)(x - 2) = 0$ Factor $x^2 - 1$ and $x^2 - 4$.

$x + 1 = 0$ or $x - 1 = 0$ or $x + 2 = 0$ or $x - 2 = 0$ Set each factor
$\quad x = -1$ $\qquad\qquad x = 1$ $\qquad\qquad x = -2$ $\qquad\qquad x = 2$ equal to 0.

Verify that all four solutions check.   ■

Example 6   The height of a triangle is 3 times its base. The area of the triangle is 96 square meters. Find its base and height.

Solution   Let x be the positive number that represents the length of the base of the triangle. Then $3x$ represents the height of the triangle. Substitute x for b, $3x$ for h, and 96 for A in the formula for the area of a triangle, and solve for x.

$$A = \frac{1}{2}\, bh$$

$$96 = \frac{1}{2}\, x(3x)$$

$$192 = 3x^2 \qquad\qquad \text{Multiply both sides by 2.}$$

$$64 = x^2 \qquad\qquad \text{Divide both sides by 3.}$$

$$0 = x^2 - 64 \qquad\qquad \text{Add } -64 \text{ to both sides.}$$

$$0 = (x + 8)(x - 8) \qquad \text{Factor } x^2 - 64.$$

$$x + 8 = 0 \quad \text{or} \quad x - 8 = 0 \qquad \text{Set each factor equal to 0.}$$
$$x = -8 \qquad\quad x = 8$$

A triangle cannot have a base of -8 meters. Thus, the base of the triangle is 8 meters, and the height is 3(8) meters, or 24 meters.

Check: The area of a triangle with a base of 8 meters and a height of 24 meters is 96 square meters:

$$A = \frac{1}{2}\, bh$$

$$= \frac{1}{2}\, (8)(24)$$

$$= 4(24)$$

$$= 96$$

The solution checks.   ■

▬ EXERCISE 4.4

In Exercises 1–24, solve each equation by factoring.

1. $4x^2 + 8x = 0$
2. $x^2 - 9 = 0$
3. $y^2 - 16 = 0$
4. $5y^2 - 10y = 0$
5. $x^2 + x = 0$
6. $x^2 - 3x = 0$
7. $5y^2 - 25y = 0$
8. $y^2 - 36 = 0$
9. $z^2 + 8z + 15 = 0$
10. $w^2 + 7w + 12 = 0$
11. $y^2 - 7y + 6 = 0$
12. $n^2 - 5n + 6 = 0$

13. $y^2 - 7y + 12 = 0$ **14.** $x^2 - 3x + 2 = 0$ **15.** $x^2 + 6x + 8 = 0$ **16.** $x^2 + 9x + 20 = 0$

17. $3m^2 + 10m + 3 = 0$ **18.** $2r^2 + 5r + 3 = 0$ **19.** $2y^2 - 5y + 2 = 0$ **20.** $2x^2 - 3x + 1 = 0$

21. $2x^2 - x - 1 = 0$ **22.** $2x^2 - 3x - 5 = 0$ **23.** $3s^2 - 5s - 2 = 0$ **24.** $8t^2 + 10t - 3 = 0$

In Exercises 25–36, write each equation in quadratic form and solve it by factoring.

25. $x(x - 6) + 9 = 0$ **26.** $x^2 + 8(x + 2) = 0$ **27.** $8a^2 = 3 - 10a$ **28.** $5z^2 = 6 - 13z$

29. $b(6b - 7) = 10$ **30.** $2y(4y + 3) = 9$ **31.** $\dfrac{3a^2}{2} = \dfrac{1}{2} - a$ **32.** $x^2 = \dfrac{1}{2}(x + 1)$

33. $x^2 + 1 = \dfrac{5}{2}x$ **34.** $\dfrac{3}{5}(x^2 - 4) = -\dfrac{9}{5}x$ **35.** $x\left(3x + \dfrac{22}{5}\right) = 1$ **36.** $x\left(\dfrac{x}{11} - \dfrac{1}{7}\right) = \dfrac{6}{77}$

In Exercises 37–48, solve each equation by factoring.

37. $x^3 + x^2 = 0$ **38.** $2x^4 + 8x^3 = 0$ **39.** $y^3 - 49y = 0$ **40.** $2z^3 - 200z = 0$

41. $x^3 - 4x^2 - 21x = 0$ **42.** $x^3 + 8x^2 - 9x = 0$ **43.** $z^4 - 13z^2 + 36 = 0$ **44.** $y^4 - 10y^2 + 9 = 0$

45. $3a(a^2 + 5a) = -18a$ **46.** $7t^3 = 2t\left(t + \dfrac{5}{2}\right)$ **47.** $\dfrac{x^2(6x + 37)}{35} = x$ **48.** $x^2 = -\dfrac{4x^3(3x + 5)}{3}$

In Exercises 49–54, solve each equation by factoring by grouping.

49. $x^3 + 3x^2 - x - 3 = 0$ **50.** $x^3 - x^2 - 4x + 4 = 0$

51. $2r^3 + 3r^2 - 18r - 27 = 0$ **52.** $3s^3 - 2s^2 - 3s + 2 = 0$

53. $3y^3 + y^2 = 4(3y + 1)$ **54.** $w^3 + 16 = w(w + 16)$

In Exercises 55–66, solve each word problem.

55. The product of two consecutive even integers is 288. Find the integers.

56. The product of two consecutive odd integers is 143. Find the integers.

57. The sum of the squares of two consecutive positive integers is 85. Find the integers.

58. The sum of the squares of three consecutive positive integers is 77. Find the integers.

59. A rectangle with an area of 96 square meters is 4 meters longer than it is wide. Find its perimeter.

60. One side of a rectangle is three times longer than another. If its area is 147 square centimeters, what are its dimensions?

61. The area of a square is numerically equal to its perimeter. How long is one side of the square?

62. A rectangle is 2 inches longer than it is wide. Numerically, its area exceeds its perimeter by 11. What is the perimeter of the rectangle?

63. An artist intends to paint a 60-square-foot mural on a wall that is 18 feet long and 11 feet high. What will be the dimensions of the mural if the artist leaves a border of uniform width around it?

64. A woman plans to use one-fourth of her 48-foot by 100-foot rectangular backyard as a garden. What will be the perimeter of the garden if the length is to be 40 feet greater than the width?

65. A rectangular room is twice as long as it is wide. It is divided into two rectangular parts by a partition that is 12 feet from one end of the room. If the other part of the room contains 560 square feet, find the dimensions of the room.

66. If the length of one side of a square is increased by 4 inches, the area of the square becomes nine times greater. What was the perimeter of the original square?

(continued)

67. Find a quadratic equation whose roots are 3 and 5.

68. Find a quadratic equation whose roots are -2 and 6.

69. Find a quadratic equation whose roots are   0 and -5.

70. Find a quadratic equation whose roots are $\frac{1}{2}$ and $\frac{1}{3}$.

4.5   ABSOLUTE VALUE EQUATIONS

In this section we will discuss how to solve equations that involve absolute values. We begin by reviewing the definition of the absolute value of x.

Definition.   If x is a positive number or 0, then $|x| = x$.
If x is a negative number, then $|x| = -x$.

The definition of the absolute value of any real number describes a method for associating a nonnegative real number with a real number. If a number x is positive or 0, then the number is its own absolute value. On the other hand, if a number x is negative, then the negative of x (which is positive) is the absolute value of x. In either case, $|x|$ is nonnegative (positive or 0):

$$|x| \geq 0 \qquad \text{for all real numbers } x$$

Example 1   Find   **a.** $|9|$,   **b.** $|-5|$,   **c.** $|0|$,   and   **d.** $|2 - \pi|$.

Solution   **a.**   Because 9 is positive, 9 is its own absolute value:

$$|9| = 9$$

b.   Because -5 is negative, the negative of -5 is the absolute value:

$$|-5| = -(-5) = 5$$

c.   Part one of the definition states that

$$|0| = 0$$

d.   Because π is approximately 3.14, it follows that $2 - \pi$ is negative. Thus,

$$|2 - \pi| = -(2 - \pi) = \pi - 2 \qquad ■$$

The placement of a $-$ sign in an expression containing an absolute value symbol is important. For example, $|-19| = 19$, but $-|19| = -(19) = -19$.

Example 2   Find   **a.** $-|-10|$,   **b.** $-|13|$,   and   **c.** $-(-|-3|)$.

Solution   **a.** $-|-10| = -(10) = -10$

b. $-|13| = -(13) = -13$

c. $-(-|-3|) = -(-(3)) = 3 \qquad ■$

Consider the equation $|x| = 5$. If x is positive or 0, then $|x| = x$ and $x = 5$. On the other hand, if x negative, then $|x| = -x$ and $-x = 5$ or $x = -5$. Hence, we have $x = 5$ or $x = -5$.

We generalize this idea in the following theorem.

> **Theorem.**   If k is a positive constant, then
>
> $$|x| = k \quad \text{is equivalent to} \quad x = k \text{ or } x = -k$$

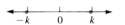

Figure 4-7

The absolute value of x can be interpreted as the distance on a number line that a point is from the origin. The solutions of the equation $|x| = k$ are represented by the two points that lie exactly k units from the origin. See Figure 4-7.

The expression $|x - 3|$ in the equation $|x - 3| = 7$ can be interpreted as a distance also. The equation $|x - 3| = 7$ indicates that a point on a number line with a coordinate of $x - 3$ is 7 units from the origin. Thus, $x - 3$ can be either 7 or -7. This gives two equations, and each can be solved separately:

$$x - 3 = 7 \quad \text{or} \quad x - 3 = -7$$
$$x = 10 \qquad\qquad x = -4$$

The solutions to the equation $|x - 3| = 7$ are $x = 10$ and $x = -4$. Note that, if either 10 or -4 is substituted for x in the expression $|x - 3|$, the result is 7. Hence, both values check.

Example 3   Solve the equation $|3x - 2| = 5$.

Solution   Write $|3x - 2| = 5$ as

$$3x - 2 = 5 \quad \text{or} \quad 3x - 2 = -5$$

and solve each possibility for x:

$$3x - 2 = 5 \quad \text{or} \quad 3x - 2 = -5$$
$$3x = 7 \qquad\qquad 3x = -3$$
$$x = \frac{7}{3} \qquad\qquad x = -1$$

Verify that both solutions check.   ■

Example 4   Solve the equation $\left|7x + \dfrac{1}{2}\right| = -4$.

Solution   Because the absolute value of any number cannot be negative, the expression $|7x + \frac{1}{2}|$ cannot equal -4. This equation is an impossible equation and has no solutions.   ■

Example 5   Solve the equation $|5x + 3| = |3x + 25|$.

Solution   This equation is true if $5x + 3$ and $3x + 25$ are equal or if they are negatives of each other. Write an equation for each condition and solve each one for x.

$$5x + 3 = 3x + 25 \quad \text{or} \quad 5x + 3 = -(3x + 25)$$
$$2x = 22 \qquad\qquad\quad 5x + 3 = -3x - 25$$
$$x = 11 \qquad\qquad\qquad 8x = -28$$
$$x = -\frac{28}{8}$$
$$x = -\frac{7}{2}$$

Verify that both solutions check.   ■

■ EXERCISE 4.5

In Exercises 1–12, find the value of each expression.

1. $|8|$
2. $|-18|$
3. $|-12|$
4. $|15|$

5. $-|2|$
6. $-|-20|$
7. $-|-30|$
8. $-|5|^2$

9. $-(-|50|)$
10. $-(-|-60|)$
11. $|\pi - 4|$
12. $|2\pi - 4|$

In Exercises 13–24, select the smaller of the two numbers.

13. $|2|, \ \ |5|$
14. $|-6|, \ \ |2|$
15. $|5|, \ \ |-8|$
16. $|6|, \ \ |3|$

17. $|-2|, \ \ |10|$
18. $|-6|, \ \ -|6|$
19. $|-3|, \ \ -|-4|$
20. $|-3|, \ \ |-2|$

21. $-|-5|, \ \ -|-7|$
22. $-|-8|, \ \ -|20|$

23. $-x, \ \ |x + 1|$ (x is a negative integer)
24. $y, \ \ |y - 1|$ (y is a positive integer)

In Exercises 25–50, solve each equation, if possible, and check the answers.

25. $|x| = 8$
26. $|x| = 9$
27. $|x - 3| = 6$
28. $|x + 4| = 8$

29. $|2x - 3| = 5$
30. $|4x - 4| = 20$
31. $|3x + 2| = 16$
32. $|5x - 3| = 22$

33. $\left|\frac{7}{2}x + 3\right| = -5$
34. $|2x + 10| = 0$
35. $\left|\frac{x}{2} - 1\right| = 3$
36. $\left|\frac{4x - 64}{4}\right| = 32$

37. $|3x + 24| = 0$
38. $|x - 21| = -8$
39. $\left|\frac{3x + 48}{3}\right| = 12$
40. $\left|\frac{x}{2} + 2\right| = 4$

41. $|2x + 1| = |3x + 3|$
42. $|5x - 7| = |4x + 1|$
43. $|3x - 1| = |x + 5|$
44. $|3x + 1| = |x - 5|$

45. $\left|\frac{x}{2} + 2\right| = \left|\frac{x}{2} - 2\right|$
46. $|7x + 12| = |x - 6|$
47. $\left|x + \frac{1}{3}\right| = |x - 3|$
48. $\left|x - \frac{1}{4}\right| = |x + 4|$

49. $|3x + 7| = -|8x - 2|$
50. $-|17x + 13| = |3x - 14|$

51. Construct several examples to illustrate that $|a \cdot b| = |a| \cdot |b|$.

52.   Construct several examples to illustrate that $\left|\dfrac{a}{b}\right| = \dfrac{|a|}{|b|}$.

53.   Construct several examples to illustrate that $|a + b|$ does not always equal $|a| + |b|$.

54.   Construct several examples to illustrate that $|a - b|$ does not always equal $|a| - |b|$.

4.6   LINEAR INEQUALITIES

So far, we have discussed statements indicating that quantities are equal. We now turn our attention to statements indicating that two quantities are not equal. Such statements are called **inequalities**. Recall the following symbols and their meanings.

$a < b$	means	"a is less than b."
$a > b$	means	"a is greater than b."
$a \leq b$	means	"a is less than or equal to b."
$a \geq b$	means	"a is greater than or equal to b."

Because 2 is less than 3, we write $2 < 3$. To indicate that a number x is greater than 4 or equal to 4, we write $x \geq 4$. By definition, the symbol $a < b$ means that "a is less than b," but it also means that "b is greater than a." Note that, if $a < b$, then a lies to the left of b on a number line.

Statements such as $x^2 + 1 > 0$ that are true for all values of x are called **absolute inequalities**. Statements such as $3x + 2 < 8$ that are true for some x, but not all x, are called **conditional inequalities**. We begin the discussion on solving conditional inequalities by listing the fundamental properties of inequalities.

The Trichotomy Property for Real Numbers.   For two real numbers a and b, exactly one of the following three statements is true:

$$a < b, \qquad a = b, \qquad \text{or} \qquad a > b$$

The trichotomy property indicates that one and only one of three statements is true about any two real numbers. Either the first number is less than the second, the first number is equal to the second, or the first number is greater than the second.

If a, b, and c are real numbers with $a < b$ and $b < c$, then $a < c$.

> If a, b, and c are real numbers with $a > b$ and $b > c$, then $a > c$.

The previous two statements cite the **transitive property** for $<$ and $>$. The relationships $\leq$ and $\geq$ are also transitive.

Property 1 of Inequalities.   Any real number can be added to (or subtracted from) both sides of an inequality to produce another inequality with the *same* order (direction).

Consider the true inequality $3 < 12$. If any number x is added to both sides of this inequality, another true inequality results, $3 + x < 12 + x$, and the "is less than" symbol remains an "is less than" symbol. Adding x to both sides does not change the order (direction) of the inequality.

Likewise, subtracting x from both sides of an inequality does not change the order (direction) of the inequality. Thus, we have $3 - x < 12 - x$.

Property 2 of Inequalities.   If both sides of an inequality are multiplied (or divided) by a positive number, another inequality results that has the *same* order (direction) as the original inequality.

Consider the true inequality $-4 < 6$. If both sides of this inequality are multiplied by any positive number such as $+7$, another true inequality results that has the *same* order:

$$-4 < 6$$
$$7(-4) < 7(6) \qquad \text{Multiply both sides by 7.}$$
$$-28 < 42 \qquad \text{Simplify.}$$

Likewise, if both sides of $-4 < 6$ are divided by any positive number such as $+2$, another true inequality results that has the *same* order:

$$-4 < 6$$
$$\frac{-4}{2} < \frac{6}{2} \qquad \text{Divide both sides by 2.}$$
$$-2 < 3 \qquad \text{Simplify.}$$

Property 3 of Inequalities.   If both sides of an inequality are multiplied (or divided) by a negative number, another inequality results, but with the *opposite* order (direction) of the original inequality.

Consider the true inequality $-4 < 6$. If both sides of this inequality are multiplied by any negative number such as -7, another inequality results that has the *opposite* order.

$$-4 < 6$$
$$-7(-4) > -7(6) \qquad \text{Multiply both sides by } -7 \text{ and}$$
$$\qquad\qquad\qquad\qquad \text{reverse the order of the inequality.}$$
$$28 > -42 \qquad \text{Simplify.}$$

Likewise, if both sides of $-4 < 6$ are divided by a negative number such as -2, another true inequality results that has the *opposite* order.

$$-4 < 6$$
$$\frac{-4}{-2} > \frac{6}{-2} \qquad \text{Divide both sides by } -2 \text{ and reverse the order of the inequality.}$$
$$2 > -3 \qquad \text{Simplify.}$$

If an inequality can be expressed in either the form $ax + c < 0$ or $ax + c > 0$ with $a \neq 0$, then it is called a **linear inequality**. Solve linear inequalities as if they were linear equations, but with one exception. If you multiply or divide both sides by a *negative* number, remember to reverse the order of the inequality.

Example 1   Solve the linear inequality $3(2x - 9) < 9$.

Solution   Solve the inequality as if it were an equation:

$$3(2x - 9) < 9$$
$$6x - 27 < 9 \qquad \text{Remove parentheses.}$$
$$6x < 36 \qquad \text{Add 27 to both sides.}$$
$$x < 6 \qquad \text{Divide both sides by 6.}$$

It is common to show the solution set as a graph on a number line. All values of x that are less than 6 can be shown by the arrow in Figure 4-8. The open circle at 6 indicates that 6 is not included in the solution set.

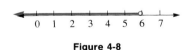

Figure 4-8   ■

Example 2   Solve the linear inequality $-4(3x + 2) \leq 16$.

Solution   Solve the inequality as if it were an equation:

$$-4(3x + 2) \leq 16$$
$$-12x - 8 \leq 16 \qquad \text{Remove parentheses.}$$
$$-12x \leq 24 \qquad \text{Add 8 to both sides.}$$
$$x \geq -2 \qquad \text{Divide both sides by } -12 \text{ and reverse the } \leq \text{ symbol.}$$

Note that the order of the inequality is reversed when both sides are divided by -12. The graph of the solution set is shown in Figure 4-9. The closed circle at -2 indicates that -2 is included in the solution set.

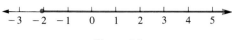

Figure 4-9   ■

Example 3   Solve the inequality $\frac{2}{3}(x + 2) > \frac{4}{5}(x - 3)$.

Solution

$$\frac{2}{3}(x + 2) > \frac{4}{5}(x - 3)$$

$$15 \cdot \frac{2}{3}(x + 2) > 15 \cdot \frac{4}{5}(x - 3) \qquad \text{Multiply both sides by 15.}$$

$$10(x + 2) > 12(x - 3) \qquad \text{Simplify.}$$

$$10x + 20 > 12x - 36 \qquad \text{Remove parentheses.}$$

$$-2x + 20 > -36 \qquad \text{Add } -12x \text{ to both sides.}$$

$$-2x > -56 \qquad \text{Add } -20 \text{ to both sides.}$$

$$x < 28 \qquad \text{Divide both sides by } -2 \\ \text{and reverse the } > \text{ symbol.}$$

The graph of the solution set is shown in Figure 4-10.

Figure 4-10   ■

Double Inequalities

There are times when it is convenient to say that x is between two numbers—for example, that x is between -3 and 8. This can be expressed by the *double inequality*

$$-3 < x < 8$$

This double inequality is understood to contain two distinct linear inequalities:

$$-3 < x \quad \text{and} \quad x < 8$$

These two inequalities mean that "x is greater than -3 *and* x is less than 8." The word *and* indicates that the two inequalities must hold true simultaneously. This result is generalized in the following statement.

> The double inequality $c < x < d$ is equivalent to $c < x$ *and* $x < d$.

Example 4   Solve the inequality $-3 \le 2x + 5 < 7$.

Solution   This inequality can be solved by isolating x between the inequality symbols in the double inequality:

$$-3 \le 2x + 5 < 7$$
$$-8 \le 2x < 2 \qquad \text{Add } -5 \text{ to all three sides.}$$
$$-4 \le x < 1 \qquad \text{Divide all three sides by 2.}$$

The graph of the solution set is shown in Figure 4-11.

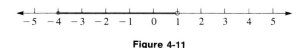

Figure 4-11

Example 5   Solve the inequality $x + 3 < 2x - 1 < 4x - 3$.

Solution   Because it is impossible to isolate x between the "is less than" symbols, it is necessary to convert this double inequality into two linear inequalities, and solve each one separately.

$$\begin{array}{ccc} x + 3 < 2x - 1 & \text{and} & 2x - 1 < 4x - 3 \\ 4 < x & & 2 < 2x \\ & & 1 < x \end{array}$$

Only those values of x that are greater than 4 and also greater than 1 are in the solution set. Because all numbers that are greater than 4 are also greater than 1, the solutions are all numbers x, where $x > 4$. The graph of the solution set is shown in Figure 4-12.

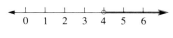

Figure 4-12

To indicate that x is *not* between two numbers such as -3 and 8 requires the following two separate inequalities:

$$x \le -3 \quad \text{or} \quad x \ge 8$$

This statement indicates that x must be less than or equal to -3 *or* x must be greater than or equal to 8. It is incorrect to string the inequalities together as $8 \le x \le -3$ because that would imply that $8 \le -3$, which is impossible. Consequently, these two inequalities *cannot* be written as a double inequality. The graph of the statement $x \le -3$ or $x \ge 8$ appears in Figure 4-13.

Note that the word *or* in the statement $x \le -3$ or $x \ge 8$ indicates that only one of the inequalities needs to be true.

Figure 4-13

■ EXERCISE 4.6

In Exercises 1–42, solve each inequality and graph its solution set.

1. $x + 4 < 5$ **2.** $x - 5 > 2$ **3.** $-3x - 1 \le 5$ **4.** $-2x + 6 \ge 16$

5. $5x - 3 > 7$ **6.** $7x - 9 < 5$ **7.** $8 - 9y \ge -y$ **8.** $4 - 3x \le x$

9. $-3(a + 2) > 2(a + 1)$ **10.** $-4(y - 1) < y + 8$

11. $3(z - 2) \le 2(z + 7)$ **12.** $5(3 + z) > -3(z + 3)$

13. $-11(2 - b) < 4(2b + 2)$ **14.** $-9(h - 3) + 2h \le 8(4 - h)$

15. $\frac{1}{2}y + 2 \ge \frac{1}{3}y - 4$ **16.** $\frac{1}{4}x - \frac{1}{3} \le x + 2$ **17.** $\frac{3}{4}x - 4 < \frac{4}{5}x + 1$ **18.** $\frac{7}{8}(a - 3) < \frac{3}{4}(a + 3)$

19. $\frac{2}{3}x + \frac{3}{2}(x - 5) \le x$ **20.** $\frac{5}{9}(x + 3) - \frac{4}{3}(x - 3) \ge x - 1$

21. $-2 < -b + 3 < 5$ **22.** $4 < -t - 2 < 9$ **23.** $15 > 2x - 7 > 9$ **24.** $25 > 3x - 2 > 7$

25. $-6 < -3(x - 4) \le 24$ **26.** $-4 \le -2(x + 8) < 8$

27. $0 \ge \frac{1}{2}x - 4 > 6$ **28.** $-6 \le \frac{1}{3}a + 1 < 0$ **29.** $0 \le \frac{4 - x}{3} \le 2$ **30.** $-2 \le \frac{5 - 3x}{2} \le 2$

31. $x + 3 < 3x - 1 < 2x + 2$ **32.** $x - 1 \le 2x + 4 \le 3x - 1$

33. $4x \ge -x + 5 \ge 3x - 4$ **34.** $\frac{1}{2}x > -\frac{1}{3}x > x + 2$

35. $5(x + 1) \le 4(x + 3) < 3(x - 1)$ **36.** $-5(2 + x) < 4x + 1 < 3x$

37. $3x + 2 < 8$ or $2x - 3 > 11$ **38.** $3x + 4 < -2$ or $3x + 4 > 10$

39. $-4(x + 2) \ge 12$ or $3x + 8 < 11$ **40.** $5(x - 2) \ge 0$ and $-3x < 9$

41. $x < -3$ and $x > 3$ **42.** $x < 3$ or $x > -3$

43. Construct examples to illustrate that $|x| + |y| \ge |x + y|$.

44. Under what conditions is $|x| + |y| = |x + y|$?

45. Under what conditions is $|x| + |y| > |x + y|$?   **46.** Are the relations "$\le$" and "$\ge$" reflexive?

47. Are the relations "$<$" and "$>$" reflexive?   **48.** Are the relations "$<$" and "$>$" symmetric?

49. Are the relations "$\le$" and "$\ge$" symmetric?   **50.** If $x < 3$, must it be true that $x^2 < 9$?

51. The $27 wholesale cost of a clock radio added to the profit must be no more than $42 or the radio will not sell. What are the possible profits?

52. A train can travel 80 miles per hour for no more than 3 hours. How far might the train travel in that time?

53. One side of a regular pentagon (a figure with five equal sides) must be at least 37 inches but cannot exceed 52 inches. What is the range of values for the perimeter?

54. Jim can afford to spend no more than $330 on a record player and some records. If the record player costs $175 and records are $8.50 each, what is the greatest number of records he can buy?

55. A student has exam scores of 70, 77, and 85. What score on a fourth exam would give him an average of 80 or better?

56. The length of a rectangle is 3 feet greater than its width. If the perimeter must be at least 34 feet but not more than 54 feet, what is the possible range of values of the width?

4.7   INEQUALITIES CONTAINING ABSOLUTE VALUES

Consider the inequality $|x| < 5$. If $x \geq 0$, then $|x| = x$ and $|x| < 5$ is equivalent to $x < 5$. If $x < 0$, then $|x| = -x$ and $-x < 5$, which is equivalent to $x > -5$. Thus, if x is positive or 0, then x must be less than 5, and if x is negative, then x must be greater than -5. This implies that x must be between -5 and 5. The two inequalities $x < 5$ and $x > -5$ are equivalent to the double inequality $-5 < x < 5$. We generalize the results of this example in the following theorem.

Theorem.   If k is a positive constant, then

$$|x| < k \quad \text{is equivalent to} \quad -k < x < k$$

The solutions to the inequality $|x| < k$ are the coordinates of the points on a number line that are less than k units from the origin. See Figure 4-14.

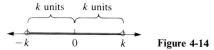

Figure 4-14

Example 1   Solve the inequality $|2x - 3| < 9$.

Solution   Rewrite the inequality as a double inequality and solve for x:

$$|2x - 3| < 9 \quad \text{is equivalent to} \quad -9 < 2x - 3 < 9$$

$$-9 < 2x - 3 < 9$$
$$-6 < 2x < 12 \qquad \text{Add 3 to all sides.}$$
$$-3 < x < 6 \qquad \text{Divide all sides by 2.}$$

Figure 4-15

Any number between -3 and 6, not including either -3 or 6, is in the solution set for this inequality. The graph appears in Figure 4-15. ∎

The previous theorem is also true if the "$<$" symbol is replaced by the "$\leq$" symbol. Thus,

$$|x| \leq k \quad \text{is equivalent to} \quad -k \leq x \leq k$$

Example 2   Solve the inequality $|3x + 2| \leq 5$.

Solution   Rewrite the expression as a double inequality and solve for x:

$$|3x + 2| \leq 5 \quad \text{is equivalent to} \quad -5 \leq 3x + 2 \leq 5$$

$$-5 \leq 3x + 2 \leq 5$$
$$-7 \leq 3x \leq 3 \qquad \text{Add } -2 \text{ to all sides.}$$
$$-\frac{7}{3} \leq x \leq 1 \qquad \text{Divide all sides by 3.}$$

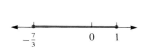

Figure 4-16

Figure 4-16 is the graph of the solution set. ∎

We have considered the relationships $|x| = k$ and $|x| < k$. We now consider the inequality $|x| > k$, where k is a positive constant. If $x \geq 0$, then $|x| = x$ and $|x| > k$ is equivalent to $x > k$. If $x < 0$, then $|x| = -x$ and $-x > k$, which is equivalent to $x < -k$. Thus, if x is positive or 0, then x is greater than k; if x is negative, then x is less than $-k$. This implies that we can write the solutions to the inequality $|x| > k$ as

$$x < -k \quad \text{or} \quad x > k$$

The solutions to the inequality $|x| > k$ are the coordinates of the points on the number line that are greater than k units from the origin. See Figure 4-17.

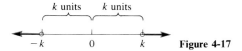

Figure 4-17

The solutions of the inequality $|x| > k$ are $x < -k$ or $x > k$. The *or* indicates an either/or situation. It is necessary for x to satisfy only one of the two conditions to be in the solution set.

Theorem.   If k is a nonnegative constant, then

$$|x| > k \quad \text{is equivalent to} \quad x < -k \text{ or } x > k$$

Example 3   Solve the inequality $|5x - 10| > 20$.

Solution   Write the inequality as two separate inequalities and solve each one for x:

$$|5x - 10| > 20 \quad \text{is equivalent to} \quad 5x - 10 < -20 \text{ or } 5x - 10 > 20$$

$$
\begin{array}{lll}
5x - 10 < -20 & \quad \text{or} \quad & 5x - 10 > 20 \\
5x < -10 & & 5x > 30 \qquad \text{Add 10 to both sides.} \\
x < -2 & & x > 6 \qquad \text{Divide both sides by 5.}
\end{array}
$$

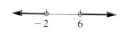

Figure 4-18

Thus, x is either less than -2 or greater than 6: $x < -2$ or $x > 6$. Figure 4-18 is the graph of the solution set.   ■

The previous theorem is also true if the ">" and "<" symbols are replaced by "≥" and "≤" symbols, respectively. Thus,

$$|x| \geq k \quad \text{is equivalent to} \quad x \leq -k \text{ or } x \geq k$$

Figure 4-19

Example 4   Solve the inequality $|3x - 5| \geq -2$.

Solution   Because the absolute value of any number is nonnegative and because any nonnegative number is larger than -2, the inequality is true for all x. Figure 4-19 is the graph of the solution set for this absolute inequality.   ■

Example 5   Solve the inequality $\left|\dfrac{x-3}{5}\right| \geq 6$.

Solution   Rewrite the inequality as two separate inequalities and solve each one for x:

$$\left|\frac{x-3}{5}\right| \geq 6 \quad \text{is equivalent to} \quad \frac{x-3}{5} \leq -6 \quad \text{or} \quad \frac{x-3}{5} \geq 6$$

$\dfrac{x-3}{5} \leq -6$ $\quad$ or	$\dfrac{x-3}{5} \geq 6$
$x - 3 \leq -30$	$x - 3 \geq 30$ $\qquad$ Multiply both sides by 5.
$x \leq -27$	$x \geq 33$ $\qquad$ Add 3 to both sides.

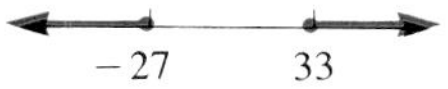

Figure 4-20

Figure 4-20 is the graph of the solution set.   ■

Example 6   Solve the inequality $\left|\dfrac{2}{3}x - 2\right| - 3 > 6$.

Solution

$$\left|\frac{2}{3}x - 2\right| - 3 > 6$$

$$\left|\frac{2}{3}x - 2\right| > 9 \qquad\qquad \text{Add 3 to both sides.}$$

$\dfrac{2}{3}x - 2 < -9$ $\quad$ or	$\dfrac{2}{3}x - 2 > 9$ $\qquad$ Rewrite as two separate inequalities.
$\dfrac{2}{3}x < -7$	$\dfrac{2}{3}x > 11$ $\qquad$ Add 2 to both sides.
$2x < -21$	$2x > 33$ $\qquad$ Multiply both sides by 3.
$x < -\dfrac{21}{2}$	$x > \dfrac{33}{2}$ $\qquad$ Divide both sides by 2.

Figure 4-21

Figure 4-21 is the graph of the solution set.   ■

■ EXERCISE 4.7

In Exercises 1–40, solve each inequality and graph its solution set.

1. $|2x| < 8$ $\qquad$ **2.** $|3x| < 27$ $\qquad$ **3.** $|x + 9| \leq 12$ $\qquad$ **4.** $|x - 8| \leq 12$

5. $|3x + 2| < -3$ $\qquad$ **6.** $|3x - 2| < 10$ $\qquad$ **7.** $|4x - 1| \leq 7$ $\qquad$ **8.** $|5x - 12| < -5$

9. $|5x| > 5$ $\qquad$ **10.** $|7x| > 7$ $\qquad$ **11.** $|x - 12| \geq 24$ $\qquad$ **12.** $|x + 5| \geq 7$

13. $|3x + 2| > 14$ $\qquad$ **14.** $|2x - 5| > 25$ $\qquad$ **15.** $|4x + 3| > -5$ $\qquad$ **16.** $|4x + 3| > 0$

17. $-|2x - 3| < -7$ $\qquad$ **18.** $-|3x + 1| < -8$ $\qquad$ **19.** $|8x - 3| > 0$ $\qquad$ **20.** $|7x + 2| > -8$

21. $\left|\dfrac{x-2}{3}\right| \leq 4$ $\qquad$ **22.** $\left|\dfrac{x-2}{3}\right| > 4$ $\qquad$ **23.** $|3x + 1| + 2 < 6$ $\qquad$ **24.** $|3x - 2| + 2 \geq 0$

25. $3|2x + 5| \geq 9$ **26.** $-2|3x - 4| < 16$ **27.** $|5x - 1| + 4 \leq 0$ **28.** $-|5x - 1| + 2 < 0$

29. $\left|\frac{1}{3}x + 7\right| + 5 > 6$ **30.** $\left|\frac{1}{2}x - 3\right| - 4 < 2$ **31.** $\left|\frac{1}{5}x - 5\right| + 4 > 4$ **32.** $\left|\frac{1}{6}x + 6\right| + 2 < 2$

33. $\left|\frac{3}{5}x + \frac{7}{3}\right| < 2$ **34.** $\left|\frac{7}{3}x - \frac{3}{5}\right| \geq 1$ **35.** $\left|3\left(\frac{x + 4}{4}\right)\right| > 0$ **36.** $3\left|\frac{1}{3}(x - 2)\right| + 2 \leq 3$

37. $\left|\frac{1}{7}x + 1\right| \leq 0$ **38.** $|2x + 1| + 2 \leq 2$ **39.** $\left|\frac{x - 5}{10}\right| \leq 0$ **40.** $\left|\frac{3}{5}x - 2\right| + 3 \leq 3$

CHAPTER SUMMARY

Key Words

absolute inequalities (4.6)	*incomplete quadratic equation* (4.4)
conditional equation (4.1)	*linear equation* (4.1)
conditional inequalities (4.6)	*linear inequality* (4.6)
contradiction (4.1)	*literal equation* (4.3)
domain (4.1)	*quadratic equation* (4.4)
equation (4.1)	*roots of an equation* (4.1)
equivalent equations (4.1)	*second-degree equation* (4.4)
first-degree equation (4.1)	*solution of an equation* (4.1)
formula (4.3)	*solution set* (4.1)
identity (4.1)	*variable* (4.1)
impossible equation (4.1)	

Key Ideas

(4.1)   An **equation** is a statement indicating that two quantities are equal.

An **identity** is an equation that is true for all values of its variable.

A **conditional equation** is true for some but not all values of its variable.

An **impossible equation** is true for no values of its variable.

The **domain** of a variable is the set of numbers that, when substituted for the variable, give statements that are defined and can be judged as true or false.

The numbers in the domain of a variable that make an equation true are called **solutions** or **roots** of the equation.

If a and b are real numbers and $a = b$, then

$$a + c = b + c \qquad a - c = b - c \qquad ac = bc \qquad \frac{a}{c} = \frac{b}{c} \quad (c \neq 0)$$

Every repeating decimal can be written as a rational number in fractional form.

(4.2)   To solve a word problem, try to express a quantity in two ways and, thereby, form an equation. Then solve the equation.

(4.3)   **Literal equations** are equations that contain several variables. Many literal equations are formulas.

Use the methods for solving equations to solve literal equations for an indicated variable.

(4.4)   To solve a **quadratic equation** by factoring, write the equation in quadratic form, factor the polynomial, and use the zero-factor theorem.

(4.5) $\begin{cases} \text{If } x \geq 0, \text{ then } |x| = x. \\ \text{If } x < 0, \text{ then } |x| = -x. \end{cases}$

If k is a positive constant,

$$|x| = k \quad \text{is equivalent to} \quad x = k \text{ or } x = -k.$$

(4.6)   The **trichotomy property** states that, if a and b are two real numbers, then $a < b$, $a = b$, or $a > b$.

The relationships $<$, $>$, $\leq$, and $\geq$ obey the transitive property.

Solve a **linear inequality** in the same way as a linear equation. However, remember to change the order of the inequality if both sides are multiplied or divided by a negative number.

Solve a **double inequality** by isolating the variable between the inequality symbols, or by solving each inequality separately.

(4.7)   If k is a positive constant, then

$$|x| < k \quad \text{is equivalent to} \quad -k < x < k$$
$$|x| > k \quad \text{is equivalent to} \quad x < -k \text{ or } x > k$$

REVIEW EXERCISES

In Review Exercises 1–8, solve and check each equation.

1. $5x + 12 = 37$

2. $-3x - 7 = 20$

3. $4(y - 1) = 28$

4. $3(x + 7) = 42$

5. $13(x - 9) - 2 = 7x - 5$

6. $\dfrac{8(x - 5)}{3} = 2(x - 4)$

7. $\dfrac{3y}{4} - 13 = -\dfrac{y}{3}$

8. $\dfrac{2y}{5} + 5 = \dfrac{14y}{10}$

In Review Exercises 9–12, solve and check each word problem.

9. The sum of three consecutive even integers is 270. What are the integers?

10. A rectangle is 4 meters longer than it is wide. If the perimeter of the rectangle is 28 meters, find its area.

11. Sally has $25,000 to invest. She invests some money at 10% interest and the rest at 9%. If her total annual income from these two investments is $2430, how much did she invest at each rate?

12. How much water must be added to 20 liters of a 12% alcohol solution to dilute it to an 8% solution?

In Review Exercises 13–16, solve for the variable indicated.

13. $V = \dfrac{4}{3}\pi r^3$ for r^3

14. $V = \dfrac{1}{3}\pi r^2 h$ for h

15. $V = \dfrac{1}{6}H(S_0 + 4S_1 + S_2)$ for S_0

16. $V = \pi h^2\left(r - \dfrac{h}{3}\right)$ for r

In Review Exercises 17–20, solve each equation by factoring. Check each solution.

17. $12x^2 + 4x - 5 = 0$

18. $7y^2 - 37y + 10 = 0$

19. $t^2(15t - 2) = 8t$

20. $3u^3 = u(19u + 14)$

In Review Exercises 21–24, solve and check each equation.

21. $|3x + 1| = 10$

22. $\left|\dfrac{3}{2}x - 4\right| = 9$

23. $|3x + 2| = |2x - 3|$

24. $|5x - 4| = |4x - 5|$

In Review Exercises 25–28, solve each inequality and graph its solution set.

25. $\dfrac{1}{3}y - 2 \geq \dfrac{1}{2}y + 2$

26. $\dfrac{7}{4}(x + 3) < \dfrac{3}{8}(x - 3)$

27. $3 < 3x + 4 < 10$

28. $4x > 3x + 2 > x - 3$

In Review Exercises 29–32, solve each inequality and graph its solution set.

29. $|2x + 7| < 3$

30. $|3x - 8| \geq 4$

31. $\left|\dfrac{3}{2}x - 14\right| \geq 0$

32. $\left|\dfrac{2}{3}x + 14\right| < 0$

CHAPTER FOUR TEST

1. Find the domain of x in the following equation. **Do not solve the equation.**

$$\frac{x - 2}{(x + 2)(x - 3)} = 7$$

In Problems 2–3, solve each equation.

2. $9(x + 4) + 4 = 4(x - 5)$

3. $\dfrac{y - 1}{5} + 2 = \dfrac{2y - 3}{3}$

4. A 20-foot pipe is to be cut into three pieces. One piece is to be twice as long as another, and the third piece is to be six times as long as the shortest. What will be the length of the longest piece?

5. A rectangle with a perimeter of 26 centimeters is 5 centimeters longer than it is wide. What is its area?

6. Bob invests part of $10,000 at 9% annual interest and the rest at 8%. His annual income from these investments is $860. How much does he invest at 8%?

7. Two students drive separate cars from one city to another. One student drives at 50 mph and the other at 55 mph. How far apart are the cities if the slower driver needs an extra 36 minutes to complete the trip?

8.   How many liters of water are needed to dilute 20 liters of a 5% salt solution to a 1% solution?

9.   Solve $P = L + \dfrac{s}{f} i$ for i.   **10.**   Solve $r_1 r_2 = r_2 r + r_1 r$ for r.

In Problems 11–12, solve each equation.

11. $x^2 - 5x - 6 = 0$ **12.** $t^2(1 + t) - 2t = 10t$

13.   The area of a square is numerically three times as great as its perimeter. Find its perimeter.

14.   The sum of the squares of two consecutive integers is 61. Find the product of the integers.

In Problems 15–16, write each expression without using absolute value symbols.

15. $|5 - 8|$ **16.** $|4\pi - 4|$

In Problems 17–22, solve each equation or inequality. Graph each solution set on the number line.

17. $|2x + 3| = 11$ **18.** $|3x + 4| = |x + 12|$

19. $-2(2x + 3) \geq 14$ **20.** $-2 < \dfrac{x - 4}{3} < 4$

21. $|x + 3| \leq 4$ **22.** $|2x - 4| > 2$

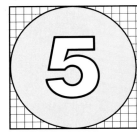

Rational Expressions

Expressions such as $\frac{3}{5}$ and $-\frac{7}{4}$ that indicate the quotient of two numbers are called **arithmetic fractions**. Algebraic fractions such as

$$\frac{x^2 + 2}{x - 3} \quad \text{and} \quad \frac{a^3 + 2a^2 + 7}{2a^2 - 5a + 4}$$

that indicate the quotient of two polynomials are called **rational expressions**. Because division by 0 is undefined, the value of a polynomial occurring in the denominator of a rational expression can never be 0. For example, x cannot be 7 in the fraction

$$\frac{3x}{x - 7}$$

because this value would cause the denominator of the fraction to be 0. Likewise, the number -2 cannot be substituted for m in the fraction

$$\frac{5m + n}{8m + 16}$$

because the denominator would be 0: $8(-2) + 16 = 0$.

The factoring skills learned in Chapter 3 will be of extreme value as we develop the properties of rational expressions.

5.1 SIMPLIFYING RATIONAL EXPRESSIONS

Rational expressions—algebraic fractions with polynomial numerators and polynomial denominators—behave exactly like arithmetic fractions. They can be simplified, multiplied, divided, added, and subtracted using the same rules that govern arithmetic fractions.

To simplify a fraction means to reduce it to lowest terms. To do so, we use Property 3 of fractions, first introduced in Section 1.4. This property enables us to divide out all factors that are common to both the numerator and the denominator of a fraction.

Property 3 of Fractions. If $b \neq 0$ and $k \neq 0$, then

$$\frac{a}{b} = \frac{ak}{bk}$$

Example 1 Simplify the following rational expressions by reducing them to lowest terms:

a. $\dfrac{10k}{25k^2}$ and **b.** $\dfrac{-8y^3z^5}{6y^4z^3}$

Solution Factor each numerator and denominator, and use Property 3 of fractions to divide out all common factors:

a. $\dfrac{10k}{25k^2} = \dfrac{5 \cdot 2 \cdot k}{5 \cdot 5 \cdot k \cdot k}$

$\qquad\quad = \dfrac{\cancel{5} \cdot 2 \cdot \cancel{k}}{\cancel{5} \cdot 5 \cdot \cancel{k} \cdot k}$

$\qquad\quad = \dfrac{2}{5k}$

b. $\dfrac{-8y^3z^5}{6y^4z^3} = \dfrac{-2 \cdot 4 \cdot y \cdot y \cdot y \cdot z \cdot z \cdot z \cdot z \cdot z}{2 \cdot 3 \cdot y \cdot y \cdot y \cdot y \cdot z \cdot z \cdot z}$

$\qquad\qquad = \dfrac{-\cancel{2} \cdot 4 \cdot \cancel{y} \cdot \cancel{y} \cdot \cancel{y} \cdot \cancel{z} \cdot \cancel{z} \cdot \cancel{z} \cdot z \cdot z}{\cancel{2} \cdot 3 \cdot \cancel{y} \cdot \cancel{y} \cdot \cancel{y} \cdot y \cdot \cancel{z} \cdot \cancel{z} \cdot \cancel{z}}$

$\qquad\qquad = -\dfrac{4z^2}{3y}$ ∎

Example 2 Simplify the rational expression $\dfrac{x^2 - 16}{x + 4}$.

Solution Factor the numerator and divide out all common factors:

$$\frac{x^2 - 16}{x + 4} = \frac{\cancel{(x + 4)}(x - 4)}{1\cancel{(x + 4)}} = \frac{x - 4}{1} = x - 4$$ ∎

Example 3 Simplify the fraction $\dfrac{2x^2 + 11x + 12}{3x^2 + 11x - 4}$.

Solution Factor both the numerator and the denominator and divide out all common factors:

$$\frac{2x^2 + 11x + 12}{3x^2 + 11x - 4} = \frac{(2x + 3)\cancel{(x + 4)}}{(3x - 1)\cancel{(x + 4)}} = \frac{2x + 3}{3x - 1}$$

CAUTION! Do not divide out the x's in this result. The x in the numerator is a factor of the first *term* only and not a factor of the entire numerator. Likewise, the x in the denominator is not a factor of the entire denominator.   ■

To simplify the fraction $\dfrac{b-a}{a-b}$, we can factor -1 from the numerator and divide out any factors common to both the numerator and the denominator:

$$\frac{b-a}{a-b} = \frac{-(-b+a)}{a-b} = \frac{-\overset{1}{(a-b)}}{\underset{1}{a-b}} = \frac{-1}{1} = -1$$

In general, we have the following theorem:

Theorem.   The quotient of any nonzero quantity and its negative is -1.

Example 4   Simplify the fraction $\dfrac{3x^2 - 10xy - 8y^2}{4y^2 - xy}$.

Solution   Factor both the numerator and the denominator and apply the previous theorem:

$$\frac{3x^2 - 10xy - 8y^2}{4y^2 - xy} = \frac{(3x + 2y)\overset{-1}{(x-4y)}}{y\underset{1}{(4y-x)}}$$

Because $x - 4y$ and $4y - x$ are negatives, their quotient is -1.

$$= \frac{-(3x + 2y)}{y}$$

$$= \frac{-3x - 2y}{y}$$
    ■

Many fractions we shall encounter are already in simplified form. For example, to attempt to simplify the fraction

$$\frac{x^2 + xa + 2x + 2a}{x^2 + x - 6}$$

we factor both the numerator and the denominator and divide out any common factors that exist:

$$\frac{x^2 + xa + 2x + 2a}{x^2 + x - 6} = \frac{x(x + a) + 2(x + a)}{(x - 2)(x + 3)} = \frac{(x + a)(x + 2)}{(x - 2)(x + 3)}$$

Because there are no factors common to both the numerator and the denominator, this fraction cannot be simplified. It is already in lowest terms.

Example 5   Simplify the fraction $\dfrac{(x^2 + 2x)(x^2 + 2x - 3)}{(x^2 + x - 2)(x^2 + 3x)}$.

Solution   Factor the polynomials in both the numerator and the denominator and divide out all common factors:

$$\frac{(x^2 + 2x)(x^2 + 2x - 3)}{(x^2 + x - 2)(x^2 + 3x)} = \frac{x(x + 2)(x + 3)(x - 1)}{(x + 2)(x - 1)x(x + 3)}$$

$$= 1 \qquad\blacksquare$$

Remember that only *factors* that are common to the *entire* numerator and the *entire* denominator can be divided out. *Terms* that are common to both the numerator and denominator *cannot* be divided out. For example, consider this correct simplification:

$$\frac{3 + 7}{3} = \frac{10}{3}$$

It would be incorrect to divide out the common *term* of 3 in the above simplification. Note that doing so gives an incorrect answer:

$$\frac{3 + 7}{3} = \frac{\overset{1}{\cancel{3}} + 7}{\underset{1}{\cancel{3}}} = \frac{1 + 7}{1} = 8$$

The 3's in the fraction

$$\frac{5 + 3(2)}{3(4)}$$

cannot be divided out either. The 3 in the numerator is a factor of the second term only. To be divided out, it must be a factor of the entire numerator. It is not correct to divide out the y in the fraction

$$\frac{x^2 y + 6x}{y}$$

either. The y is not a factor of the entire numerator.

■ EXERCISE 5.1

In Exercises 1–58, simplify each fraction if possible. If a fraction is already in lowest terms, so indicate.

1. $\dfrac{12}{18}$

2. $\dfrac{25}{55}$

3. $-\dfrac{112}{36}$

4. $-\dfrac{49}{21}$

5. $\dfrac{288}{312}$

6. $\dfrac{144}{72}$

7. $-\dfrac{244}{74}$

8. $-\dfrac{512}{236}$

9. $\dfrac{12x^3}{3x}$

10. $-\dfrac{15a^2}{25a^3}$

11. $\dfrac{-24x^3y^4}{18x^4y^3}$

12. $\dfrac{15a^5b^4}{21b^3c^2}$

13. $\dfrac{(3x^3)^2}{9x^4}$

14. $\dfrac{8(x^2y^3)^3}{2(xy^2)^2}$

15. $-\dfrac{11x(x-y)}{22(x-y)}$

16. $\dfrac{x(x-2)^2}{(x-2)^3}$

17. $\dfrac{9y^2(y-z)}{21y(y-z)^2}$

18. $\dfrac{(a-b)(b-c)(c-d)}{(c-d)(b-c)(a-b)}$

19. $\dfrac{x+y}{x^2-y^2}$

20. $\dfrac{x-y}{x^2-y^2}$

21. $\dfrac{5x-10}{x^2-4x+4}$

22. $\dfrac{y-xy}{xy-x}$

23. $\dfrac{12-3x^2}{x^2-x-2}$

24. $\dfrac{x^2+2x-15}{x^2-25}$

25. $\dfrac{3x+6y}{x+2y}$

26. $\dfrac{x^2+y^2}{x+y}$

27. $\dfrac{x^3+8}{x^2-2x+4}$

28. $\dfrac{x^2+3x+9}{x^3-27}$

29. $\dfrac{x^2+2x+1}{x^2+4x+3}$

30. $\dfrac{6x^2+x-2}{8x^2+2x-3}$

31. $\dfrac{3m-6n}{3n-6m}$

32. $\dfrac{ax+by+ay+bx}{a^2-b^2}$

33. $\dfrac{4x^2+24x+32}{16x^2+8x-48}$

34. $\dfrac{a^2-4}{a^3-8}$

35. $\dfrac{3x^2-3y^2}{x^2+2y+2x+yx}$

36. $\dfrac{x^2+x-30}{x^2-x-20}$

37. $\dfrac{4x^2+8x+3}{6+x-2x^2}$

38. $\dfrac{6x^2+13x+6}{6-5x-6x^2}$

39. $\dfrac{a^3+27}{4a^2-36}$

40. $\dfrac{a-b}{b^2-a^2}$

41. $\dfrac{2x^2-3x-9}{2x^2+3x-9}$

42. $\dfrac{6x^2-7x-5}{2x^2+5x+2}$

43. $\dfrac{(m+n)^3}{m^2+2mn+n^2}$

44. $\dfrac{x^3-27}{3x^2-8x-3}$

45. $\dfrac{x^4-y^4}{(x^2+2xy+y^2)(x^2+y^2)}$

46. $\dfrac{-4x-4+3x^2}{4x^2-2-7x}$

47. $\dfrac{4a^2-9b^2}{2a^2-ab-6b^2}$

48. $\dfrac{x^2+2xy}{x+2y+x^2-4y^2}$

49. $\dfrac{x-y}{x^3-y^3-x+y}$

50. $\dfrac{2x^2+2x-12}{x^3+3x^2-4x-12}$

51. $\dfrac{x^6-y^6}{x^4+x^2y^2+y^4}$

52. $\dfrac{6xy-4x-9y+6}{6y^2-13y+6}$

53. $\dfrac{x^4+15x^2+64}{x^2+8-x}$

54. $\dfrac{x^2+9-x}{x^4+17x^2+81}$

55. $\dfrac{(x^2-1)(x+1)}{(x^2-2x+1)^2}$

56. $\dfrac{(x^2+2x+1)(x^2-2x+1)}{(x^2-1)^2}$

57. $\dfrac{(2x^2+3xy+y^2)(3a+b)}{(x+y)(2xy+2bx+y^2+by)}$

58. $\dfrac{(x-1)(6ax+9x+4a+6)}{(3x+2)(2ax-2a+3x-3)}$

5.2   MULTIPLYING AND DIVIDING RATIONAL EXPRESSIONS

Recall that Property 4 of fractions, first introduced in Section 1.4, asserted that fractions are multiplied and divided according to the following rules:

> **Property 4 of Fractions.**   If no denominators are 0, then
>
> $$\dfrac{a}{b}\cdot\dfrac{c}{d}=\dfrac{a\cdot c}{b\cdot d}=\dfrac{ac}{bd}\qquad\text{and}\qquad\dfrac{a}{b}\div\dfrac{c}{d}=\dfrac{a}{b}\cdot\dfrac{d}{c}=\dfrac{ad}{bc}$$

These rules were assumed to be true in Section 1.4. We now explain why they are reasonable. We begin with the multiplication rule.

Recall that the area of a rectangle is the product of its length and width. If the square in Figure 5-1 is divided into 5 equal parts vertically and 4 equal parts horizontally, the square is divided into 20 equal pieces. Each of the 20 pieces represents $\frac{1}{20}$ of the total area of the square. The shaded rectangle has a width of $\frac{3}{4}$ and a length of $\frac{4}{5}$. The area of the shaded rectangle is 12 of these 20 equal pieces. Hence, we have

$$A = l \cdot w$$

$$\frac{12}{20} = \frac{4}{5} \cdot \frac{3}{4}$$

This example justifies the procedure for multiplying fractions: multiply the numerators and multiply the denominators.

Figure 5-1

Example 1   Find the product of $\dfrac{x^2 - 6x + 9}{x}$ and $\dfrac{x^2}{x - 3}$.

Solution   Factor $x^2 - 6x + 9$ and x^2, find the product of the fractions by multiplying their numerators and multiplying their denominators. Then simplify the resulting fraction by dividing out any factors that are common to both the numerator and denominator.

$$\frac{x^2 - 6x + 9}{x} \cdot \frac{x^2}{x - 3} = \frac{(x - 3)(x - 3)}{x} \cdot \frac{xx}{x - 3}$$

$$= \frac{(x - 3)(x - 3)xx}{x(x - 3)}$$

$$= x(x - 3) \qquad\qquad\blacksquare$$

Example 2   Find the product of $\dfrac{x^2 - x - 6}{x^2 - 4}$ and $\dfrac{x^2 + x - 6}{x^2 - 9}$.

Solution   Factor each polynomial, find the product of the fractions, and simplify the resulting fraction.

$$\frac{x^2 - x - 6}{x^2 - 4} \cdot \frac{x^2 + x - 6}{x^2 - 9} = \frac{(x - 3)(x + 2)}{(x + 2)(x - 2)} \cdot \frac{(x + 3)(x - 2)}{(x + 3)(x - 3)}$$

$$= \frac{(x - 3)(x + 2)(x + 3)(x - 2)}{(x + 2)(x - 2)(x + 3)(x - 3)}$$

$$= \frac{(x - 3)(x + 2)(x + 3)(x - 2)}{(x + 2)(x - 2)(x + 3)(x - 3)}$$

$$= 1 \qquad\qquad\blacksquare$$

Note that in the previous examples the common factors could have been divided out before the multiplication was performed.

Example 3   Multiply: $\dfrac{6x^2 + 5x - 4}{2x^2 + 5x + 3} \cdot \dfrac{8x^2 + 6x - 9}{12x^2 + 7x - 12}$.

Solution   Factor first in order to divide out all factors common to both the numerator and the denominator in either fraction. Then multiply.

$$\frac{6x^2 + 5x - 4}{2x^2 + 5x + 3} \cdot \frac{8x^2 + 6x - 9}{12x^2 + 7x - 12} = \frac{(3x + 4)(2x - 1)}{(2x + 3)(x + 1)} \cdot \frac{(4x - 3)(2x + 3)}{(3x + 4)(4x - 3)}$$

$$= \frac{(3x + 4)(2x - 1)}{(2x + 3)(x + 1)} \cdot \frac{(4x - 3)(2x + 3)}{(3x + 4)(4x - 3)}$$

$$= \frac{2x - 1}{x + 1} \qquad \blacksquare$$

Example 4   Simplify: $(x^2 - 2x) \cdot \dfrac{x}{x^2 - 5x + 6}$.

Solution   Write the first factor as a fraction with a denominator of 1. Then proceed as in the previous examples.

$$(x^2 - 2x) \cdot \frac{x}{x^2 - 5x + 6} = \frac{x^2 - 2x}{1} \cdot \frac{x}{x^2 - 5x + 6}$$

$$= \frac{x(x - 2)}{1} \cdot \frac{x}{(x - 2)(x - 3)}$$

$$= \frac{x^2}{x - 3} \qquad \blacksquare$$

Recall that certain pairs of numbers such as 3 and $\frac{1}{3}$, $\frac{2}{5}$ and $\frac{5}{2}$, and $\frac{-7}{8}$ and $\frac{-8}{7}$ have products that are equal to 1. Such pairs of numbers are called **reciprocals** of each other.

Definition.   If the product of two numbers is 1, those numbers are called **multiplicative inverses** or **reciprocals** of each other.

Dividing by a number is the same as multiplying by its **multiplicative inverse** or **reciprocal**. For example, $6 \div 3$ and $6 \cdot \frac{1}{3}$ both give 2 for the answer. To divide by 3 is to multiply by $\frac{1}{3}$. Similarly, $56 \div \frac{8}{7}$ and $56 \cdot \frac{7}{8}$ give the same result. To divide by $\frac{8}{7}$ is to multiply by $\frac{7}{8}$. The rule for division of fractions assets that, if $b \neq 0$, $c \neq 0$, and $d \neq 0$, then

$$\frac{a}{b} \div \frac{c}{d} \quad \text{is equivalent to} \quad \frac{a}{b} \cdot \frac{d}{c}$$

This is true because c/d and d/c are reciprocals of each other. To divide by c/d is to multiply by d/c. The previous discussion justifies the procedure for dividing fractions: invert the divisor and multiply.

Example 5 Divide: $\dfrac{x^3 + 8}{x + 1} \div \dfrac{x^2 - 2x + 4}{2x^2 - 2}$.

Solution Using the rule for division of fractions, multiply by the reciprocal of the divisor. Then simplify.

$$\frac{x^3 + 8}{x + 1} \div \frac{x^2 - 2x + 4}{2x^2 - 2} = \frac{x^3 + 8}{x + 1} \cdot \frac{2x^2 - 2}{x^2 - 2x + 4}$$

$$= \frac{(x + 2)(x^2 - 2x + 4)}{(x + 1)} \cdot \frac{2(x + 1)(x - 1)}{(x^2 - 2x + 4)}$$

$$= 2(x + 2)(x - 1) \qquad \blacksquare$$

Example 6 Divide: $\dfrac{x^2 - 4}{x - 1} \div (x - 2)$.

Solution Write the divisor as a fraction with a denominator of 1. Then invert the divisor, multiply, factor, and divide out any common factors.

$$\frac{x^2 - 4}{x - 1} \div (x - 2) = \frac{x^2 - 4}{x - 1} \div \frac{x - 2}{1}$$

$$= \frac{x^2 - 4}{x - 1} \cdot \frac{1}{x - 2}$$

$$= \frac{(x + 2)(x - 2) \cdot 1}{(x - 1)(x - 2)}$$

$$= \frac{x + 2}{x - 1} \qquad \blacksquare$$

Example 7 Simplify: $\dfrac{x^2 + 2x - 3}{6x^2 + 5x + 1} \div \dfrac{2x^2 - 2}{2x^2 - 5x - 3} \cdot \dfrac{6x^2 + 4x - 2}{x^2 - 2x - 3}$.

Solution Factor everything you can, and change the division to a multiplication. It is understood that, in the absence of grouping symbols, multiplications and divisions are performed from left to right. Therefore, only the middle fraction is to be inverted. Finally, divide out any common factors and multiply.

$$\frac{x^2 + 2x - 3}{6x^2 + 5x + 1} \div \frac{2x^2 - 2}{2x^2 - 5x - 3} \cdot \frac{6x^2 + 4x - 2}{x^2 - 2x - 3}$$

$$= \frac{(x + 3)(x - 1)}{(3x + 1)(2x + 1)} \cdot \frac{(2x + 1)(x - 3)}{2(x + 1)(x - 1)} \cdot \frac{2(3x - 1)(x + 1)}{(x - 3)(x + 1)}$$

$$= \frac{(x + 3)(3x - 1)}{(3x + 1)(x + 1)} \qquad \blacksquare$$

EXERCISE 5.2

In Exercises 1–46, perform the indicated operations and simplify.

1. $\dfrac{3}{4} \cdot \dfrac{5}{3} \cdot \dfrac{8}{7}$

2. $-\dfrac{5}{6} \cdot \dfrac{3}{7} \cdot \dfrac{14}{25}$

3. $-\dfrac{6}{11} \div \dfrac{36}{55}$

4. $\dfrac{17}{12} \div \dfrac{34}{3}$

5. $\dfrac{x^2 y^2}{cd} \cdot \dfrac{c^{-2} d^2}{x}$

6. $\dfrac{a^{-2} b^2}{x^{-1} y} \cdot \dfrac{a^4 b^4}{x^2 y^3}$

7. $\dfrac{-x^2 y^{-2}}{x^{-1} y^{-3}} \div \dfrac{x^{-3} y^2}{x^4 y^{-1}}$

8. $\dfrac{(a^3)^2}{b^{-1}} \div \dfrac{(a^3)^{-2}}{b^{-1}}$

9. $\dfrac{x^2 + 2x + 1}{x} \cdot \dfrac{x^2 - x}{x^2 - 1}$

10. $\dfrac{a + 6}{a^2 - 16} \cdot \dfrac{3a - 12}{3a + 18}$

11. $\dfrac{2x^2 - x - 3}{x^2 - 1} \cdot \dfrac{x^2 + x - 2}{2x^2 + x - 6}$

12. $\dfrac{9x^2 + 3x - 20}{3x^2 - 7x + 4} \cdot \dfrac{3x^2 - 5x + 2}{9x^2 + 18x + 5}$

13. $\dfrac{x^2 - 16}{x^2 - 25} \div \dfrac{x + 4}{x - 5}$

14. $\dfrac{a^2 - 9}{a^2 - 49} \div \dfrac{a + 3}{a + 7}$

15. $\dfrac{a^2 + 2a - 35}{12x} \div \dfrac{x}{a^2 + 4a - 21}$

16. $\dfrac{x^2 - 4}{2b - bx} \div \dfrac{x^2 + 4x + 4}{2b + bx}$

17. $(x + 1) \cdot \dfrac{1}{x^2 + 2x + 1}$

18. $\dfrac{x^2 - 4}{x} \div (x + 2)$

19. $(x^2 - x - 2) \cdot \dfrac{x^2 + 3x + 2}{x^2 - 4}$

20. $(2x^2 - 9x - 5) \cdot \dfrac{x}{2x^2 + x}$

21. $(2x^2 - 15x + 25) \div \dfrac{(2x - 5)(x + 1)}{x + 1}$

22. $(x^2 - 6x + 9) \div \dfrac{x^2 - 9}{x + 3}$

23. $\dfrac{x^3 + y^3}{x^3 - y^3} \div \dfrac{x^2 - xy + y^2}{x^2 + xy + y^2}$

24. $\dfrac{x^2 - 6x + 9}{x^2 - 4} \div \dfrac{x^2 - 9}{x^2 - 8x + 12}$

25. $\dfrac{m^2 - n^2}{2x^2 + 3x - 2} \cdot \dfrac{2x^2 + 5x - 3}{n^2 - m^2}$

26. $\dfrac{x^2 - y^2}{2x^2 + 2xy + x + y} \cdot \dfrac{2x^2 - 5x - 3}{yx - 3y - x^2 + 3x}$

27. $\dfrac{ax + ay + bx + by}{x^3 - 27} \cdot \dfrac{x^2 + 3x + 9}{xc + xd + yc + yd}$

28. $\dfrac{x^2 + 3x + yx + 3y}{x^2 - 9} \cdot \dfrac{x - 3}{x + 3}$

29. $\dfrac{3x^2 y^2}{6x^3 y} \cdot \dfrac{-4x^7 y^{-2}}{18x^{-2} y} \div \dfrac{36x}{18y^{-2}}$

30. $\dfrac{9ab^3}{7xy} \cdot \dfrac{14xy^2}{27z^3} \div \dfrac{18a^2 b^2 x}{3z^2}$

31. $(4x + 12) \cdot \dfrac{x^2}{2x - 6} \div \dfrac{2}{x - 3}$

32. $(4x^2 - 9) \div \dfrac{2x^2 + 5x + 3}{x + 2} \div (2x - 3)$

33. $\dfrac{2x^2 - 2x - 4}{x^2 + 2x - 8} \cdot \dfrac{3x^2 + 15x}{x + 1} \div \dfrac{4x^2 - 100}{x^2 - x - 20}$

34. $\dfrac{6a^2 - 7a - 3}{a^2 - 1} \div \dfrac{4a^2 - 12a + 9}{a^2 - 1} \cdot \dfrac{2a^2 - a - 3}{3a^2 - 2a - 1}$

35. $\dfrac{2t^2 + 5t + 2}{t^2 - 4t + 16} \div \dfrac{t + 2}{t^3 + 64} \div \dfrac{2t^3 + 9t^2 + 4t}{t + 1}$

36. $\dfrac{a^6 - b^6}{a^4 - a^3 b} \cdot \dfrac{a^3}{a^4 + a^2 b^2 + b^4} \div \dfrac{1}{a}$

37. $\dfrac{x^4 + 7x^2 + 16}{x^6} \cdot \dfrac{x^3}{x^2 + 4 - x}$

38. $\dfrac{x^2 + 6 - 3x}{y^2 - 1} \cdot \dfrac{y^2 + 2y + 1}{x^4 + 3x^2 + 36}$

39. $(x^2 - x - 6) \div (x - 3) \div (x - 2)$

40. $(x^2 - x - 6) \div [(x - 3) \div (x - 2)]$

41. $\dfrac{3x^2 - 2x}{3x + 2} \div (3x - 2) \div \dfrac{3x}{3x - 3}$

42. $(2x^2 - 3x - 2) \div \dfrac{2x^2 - x - 1}{x - 2} \div (x - 1)$

43. $\dfrac{2x^2 + 5x - 3}{x^2 + 2x - 3} \div \left(\dfrac{x^2 + 2x - 35}{x^2 - 6x + 5} \div \dfrac{x^2 - 9x + 14}{2x^2 - 5x + 2} \right)$

44. $\dfrac{x^2 - 4}{x^2 - x - 6} \div \left(\dfrac{x^2 - x - 2}{x^2 - 8x + 15} \cdot \dfrac{x^2 - 3x - 10}{x^2 + 3x + 2} \right)$

45. $\dfrac{x^2 - x - 12}{x^2 + x - 2} \div \dfrac{x^2 - 6x + 8}{x^2 - 3x - 10} \cdot \dfrac{x^2 - 3x + 2}{x^2 - 2x - 15}$

46. $\dfrac{4x^2 - 10x + 6}{x^4 - 3x^3} \div \dfrac{2x - 3}{2x^3} \cdot \dfrac{x - 3}{2x - 2}$

5.3   ADDING AND SUBTRACTING RATIONAL EXPRESSIONS

Property 5 of fractions, first discussed in Section 1.4, asserted that fractions are added and subtracted according to the following rules:

Property 5 of Fractions.   If there are no divisions by 0, then

$$\frac{a}{b} + \frac{c}{b} = \frac{a + c}{b} \qquad \text{and} \qquad \frac{a}{b} - \frac{c}{b} = \frac{a - c}{b}$$

When we add or subtract two fractions with like denominators, these rules can be used directly: Simply add or subtract the numerators and use the same denominator.

To make these rules reasonable, think of problems such as

$$\frac{2}{7} + \frac{3}{7} = \frac{5}{7} \qquad \text{and} \qquad \frac{5}{9} - \frac{4}{9} = \frac{1}{9}$$

as problems in the form

2 sevenths + 3 sevenths = 5 sevenths

and

5 ninths − 4 ninths = 1 ninth

Example 1   Simplify: **a.** $\dfrac{17}{22} + \dfrac{13}{22}$,   **b.** $\dfrac{3}{2x} + \dfrac{7}{2x}$, and   **c.** $\dfrac{4x}{x + 2} - \dfrac{7x}{x + 2}$.

Solution   **a.** $\dfrac{17}{22} + \dfrac{13}{22} = \dfrac{17 + 13}{22} = \dfrac{30}{22} = \dfrac{15 \cdot 2}{11 \cdot 2} = \dfrac{15}{11}$

b. $\dfrac{3}{2x} + \dfrac{7}{2x} = \dfrac{3 + 7}{2x} = \dfrac{10}{2x} = \dfrac{5}{x}$

c. $\dfrac{4x}{x + 2} - \dfrac{7x}{x + 2} = \dfrac{4x - 7x}{x + 2} = \dfrac{-3x}{x + 2}$ ∎

If we add or subtract fractions with unlike denominators, we must convert them to fractions with the same denominator. To do so, we use Property 3 of fractions to insert whatever factors are required to form a common denominator.

Example 2   Simplify: **a.** $\dfrac{3}{x} + \dfrac{4}{y}$ and **b.** $\dfrac{4x}{x+2} - \dfrac{7x}{x-2}.$

Solution   **a.** $\dfrac{3}{x} + \dfrac{4}{y} = \dfrac{3y}{xy} + \dfrac{x4}{xy} = \dfrac{3y + 4x}{xy}$

b. $\dfrac{4x}{x+2} - \dfrac{7x}{x-2} = \dfrac{4x(x-2)}{(x+2)(x-2)} - \dfrac{(x+2)7x}{(x+2)(x-2)}$

$$= \dfrac{(4x^2 - 8x) - (7x^2 + 14x)}{(x+2)(x-2)}$$

$$= \dfrac{4x^2 - 8x - 7x^2 - 14x}{(x+2)(x-2)}$$

$$= \dfrac{-3x^2 - 22x}{(x+2)(x-2)}$$

Note that the minus sign between the fractions in part b influences *both* terms of the binomial $7x^2 + 14x$.   ■

To add fractions, a common denominator must be found. It is sensible to use the smallest and the least complicated denominator possible. That simplest denominator is called the **least** (or lowest) **common denominator** or, more simply, the **LCD**. We now consider how it can be found.

Suppose the unlike denominators of three fractions are 12, 20, and 35. First, we find the unique prime factorization of each number.

$$12 = 4 \cdot 3 = 2^2 \cdot 3$$
$$20 = 4 \cdot 5 = 2^2 \cdot 5$$
$$35 = 5 \cdot 7$$

Because the least common denominator is the smallest number that can be divided by 12, 20, and 35, it must contain factors of 2^2, 3, 5, and 7. Hence, the least common denominator is

$$\text{LCD} = 2^2 \cdot 3 \cdot 5 \cdot 7$$
$$= 420$$

That is, 420 is the smallest number that can be divided evenly by 12, 20, and 35.

When finding a least common denominator, always factor each denominator first and then create the LCD by using each factor the greatest number of times that it appears in any one denominator. The product of these factors is the LCD.

Example 3   The polynomial denominators of three fractions are $x^2 + 7x + 6$, $x^2 - 36$, and $x^2 + 12x + 36$. Find the LCD.

Solution Factor each polynomial:

$$x^2 + 7x + 6 = (x + 6)(x + 1)$$
$$x^2 - 36 = (x + 6)(x - 6)$$
$$x^2 + 12x + 36 = (x + 6)(x + 6) = (x + 6)^2$$

Use each factor the greatest number of times that it appears in any one denominator to find the LCD:

$$LCD = (x + 6)^2(x + 1)(x - 6)$$

There is no need to do any multiplication. Leave the LCD in factored form. ∎

Example 4 Add the fractions $\dfrac{x}{x^2 - 2x + 1}$ and $\dfrac{3}{x^2 - 1}$.

Solution Factor each denominator and find the LCD:

$$x^2 - 2x + 1 = (x - 1)(x - 1) = (x - 1)^2$$
$$x^2 - 1 = (x + 1)(x - 1)$$

The LCD is $(x - 1)^2(x + 1)$. Write each fraction with its denominator in factored form, convert all fractions to fractions with a denominator of $(x - 1)^2(x + 1)$, add the fractions, and simplify.

$$\frac{x}{x^2 - 2x + 1} + \frac{3}{x^2 - 1}$$

$$= \frac{x}{(x - 1)(x - 1)} + \frac{3}{(x + 1)(x - 1)}$$

$$= \frac{x(x + 1)}{(x - 1)(x - 1)(x + 1)} + \frac{3(x - 1)}{(x + 1)(x - 1)(x - 1)}$$

$$= \frac{x^2 + x + 3x - 3}{(x - 1)(x - 1)(x + 1)}$$

$$= \frac{x^2 + 4x - 3}{(x - 1)(x - 1)(x + 1)}$$

Always simplify the final result if possible. In this case, it cannot be simplified. ∎

Example 5 Simplify: $\dfrac{2x}{x^2 - 4} - \dfrac{1}{x^2 - 3x + 2} + \dfrac{x + 1}{x^2 + x - 2}$.

Solution Factor the denominators and determine that the LCD is $(x + 2)(x - 2)(x - 1)$. Write all of the fractions in a form bearing the least common denominator, remove the resulting parentheses in each numerator, perform the indicated subtraction and addition, and simplify.

$$\frac{2x}{x^2 - 4} - \frac{1}{x^2 - 3x + 2} + \frac{x + 1}{x^2 + x - 2}$$

$$= \frac{2x}{(x - 2)(x + 2)} - \frac{1}{(x - 2)(x - 1)} + \frac{(x + 1)}{(x - 1)(x + 2)}$$

$$= \frac{2x(x - 1)}{(x - 2)(x + 2)(x - 1)} - \frac{1(x + 2)}{(x - 2)(x - 1)(x + 2)} + \frac{(x + 1)(x - 2)}{(x - 1)(x + 2)(x - 2)}$$

$$= \frac{2x(x - 1) - 1(x + 2) + (x + 1)(x - 2)}{(x + 2)(x - 2)(x - 1)}$$

$$= \frac{2x^2 - 2x - x - 2 + x^2 - x - 2}{(x + 2)(x - 2)(x - 1)}$$

$$= \frac{3x^2 - 4x - 4}{(x + 2)(x - 2)(x - 1)}$$

Factor the numerator on the chance that the fraction will simplify:

$$= \frac{(3x + 2)(x - 2)}{(x + 2)(x - 2)(x - 1)}$$

In this example, the fraction does simplify. Hence,

$$\frac{2x}{x^2 - 4} - \frac{1}{x^2 - 3x + 2} + \frac{x + 1}{x^2 + x - 2} = \frac{3x + 2}{(x + 2)(x - 1)}$$ ■

Example 6   Simplify: $3 + \dfrac{7}{x - 2}$.

Solution   Because 3 can be written as $\frac{3}{1}$, you must find the sum of two fractions. The LCD is $x - 2$, and the first term (the constant 3) must be written as a fraction with that denominator. Then, add the fractions.

$$3 + \frac{7}{x - 2} = \frac{3}{1} + \frac{7}{x - 2}$$

$$= \frac{3(x - 2)}{1(x - 2)} + \frac{7}{x - 2}$$

$$= \frac{3x - 6 + 7}{x - 2}$$

$$= \frac{3x + 1}{x - 2}$$ ■

Example 7   Simplify: $\dfrac{3x}{x - 1} - \dfrac{2x^2 + 3x - 2}{(x + 1)(x - 1)}$.

Solution   Write each fraction in a form bearing the LCD of $(x + 1)(x - 1)$, remove the resulting parentheses in the first numerator, perform the indicated subtraction, and simplify.

$$\frac{3x}{x - 1} - \frac{2x^2 + 3x - 2}{(x + 1)(x - 1)} = \frac{(x + 1)3x}{(x + 1)(x - 1)} - \frac{2x^2 + 3x - 2}{(x + 1)(x - 1)}$$

$$= \frac{3x^2 + 3x}{(x + 1)(x - 1)} - \frac{2x^2 + 3x - 2}{(x + 1)(x - 1)}$$

$$= \frac{3x^2 + 3x - (2x^2 + 3x - 2)}{(x + 1)(x - 1)}$$

$$= \frac{3x^2 + 3x - 2x^2 - 3x + 2}{(x + 1)(x - 1)}$$

$$= \frac{x^2 + 2}{(x + 1)(x - 1)}$$

Note that the minus sign between the fractions influences all three terms of the trinomial $2x^2 + 3x - 2$. Whenever you subtract one fraction from another, remember to subtract each term of the numerator of the second fraction.   ■

Example 8   Simplify: $\left(\dfrac{x^2}{x - 2} + \dfrac{4}{2 - x}\right)^2$

Solution   Perform the addition of the fractions within the parentheses. To write them as fractions with a common denominator, multiply both the numerator and the denominator of the second fraction by -1. Combine these fractions, simplify, and square the result.

$$\left(\frac{x^2}{x - 2} + \frac{4}{2 - x}\right)^2 = \left[\frac{x^2}{x - 2} + \frac{(-1)4}{-1(2 - x)}\right]^2$$

$$= \left[\frac{x^2}{x - 2} + \frac{-4}{x - 2}\right]^2$$

$$= \left[\frac{x^2 - 4}{x - 2}\right]^2$$

$$= \left[\frac{(x + 2)(x - 2)}{x - 2}\right]^2$$

$$= (x + 2)^2$$

$$= x^2 + 4x + 4$$ ■

EXERCISE 5.3

In Exercises 1–16, perform the indicated operations and simplify, if necessary.

1. $\dfrac{3}{4} + \dfrac{7}{4}$ **2.** $\dfrac{5}{11} + \dfrac{2}{11}$ **3.** $\dfrac{10}{33} - \dfrac{21}{33}$ **4.** $\dfrac{8}{15} - \dfrac{2}{15}$

5. $\dfrac{3}{4y} + \dfrac{8}{4y}$

6. $\dfrac{5}{3z^2} - \dfrac{6}{3z^2}$

7. $\dfrac{3}{a+b} - \dfrac{a}{a+b}$

8. $\dfrac{x}{x+4} + \dfrac{5}{x+4}$

9. $\dfrac{3x}{2x+2} + \dfrac{x+8}{2x+2}$

10. $\dfrac{4y}{y-4} - \dfrac{16}{y-4}$

11. $\dfrac{3x}{x-3} - \dfrac{9}{x-3}$

12. $\dfrac{9x}{x-y} - \dfrac{9y}{x-y}$

13. $\dfrac{5x}{x+1} + \dfrac{3}{x+1} - \dfrac{2x}{x+1}$

14. $\dfrac{4}{a+4} - \dfrac{2a}{a+4} + \dfrac{3a}{a+4}$

15. $\dfrac{3(x^2+x)}{x^2-5x+6} + \dfrac{-3(x^2-x)}{x^2-5x+6}$

16. $\dfrac{2x+4}{x^2+13x+12} - \dfrac{x+3}{x^2+13x+12}$

In Exercises 17–24, the denominators of several fractions are given. Find the LCD.

17. 8, 12, 18

18. 10, 15, 28

19. $x^2 + 3x, \quad x^2 - 9$

20. $3y^2 - 6y, \quad 3y(y-4)$

21. $x^3 + 27, \quad x^2 + 6x + 9$

22. $x^3 - 8, \quad x^2 - 4x + 4$

23. $2x^2 + 5x + 3, \quad 4x^2 + 12x + 9, \quad x^2 + 2x + 1$

24. $2x^2 + 5x + 3, \quad 4x^2 + 12x + 9, \quad 4x + 6$

In Exercises 25–80, perform the indicated operations and simplify, if possible.

25. $\dfrac{1}{2} + \dfrac{1}{3}$

26. $\dfrac{5}{6} + \dfrac{2}{7}$

27. $\dfrac{7}{15} - \dfrac{17}{25}$

28. $\dfrac{8}{9} - \dfrac{5}{12}$

29. $\dfrac{a}{2} + \dfrac{2a}{5}$

30. $\dfrac{b}{6} + \dfrac{3a}{4}$

31. $\dfrac{3a}{2} - \dfrac{4b}{7}$

32. $\dfrac{2m}{3} - \dfrac{4n}{5}$

33. $\dfrac{3}{4x} + \dfrac{2}{3x}$

34. $\dfrac{2}{5a} + \dfrac{3}{2b}$

35. $\dfrac{3a}{2b} - \dfrac{2b}{3a}$

36. $\dfrac{5m}{2n} - \dfrac{3n}{4m}$

37. $\dfrac{a+b}{3} + \dfrac{a-b}{7}$

38. $\dfrac{x-y}{2} + \dfrac{x+y}{3}$

39. $\dfrac{3}{x+2} + \dfrac{5}{x-4}$

40. $\dfrac{2}{a+4} - \dfrac{6}{a+3}$

41. $\dfrac{x+2}{x+5} - \dfrac{x-3}{x+7}$

42. $\dfrac{7}{x+3} + \dfrac{4x}{x+6}$

43. $x + \dfrac{1}{x}$

44. $2 - \dfrac{1}{x+1}$

45. $\dfrac{x}{x^2+5x+6} + \dfrac{x}{x^2-4}$

46. $\dfrac{x}{3x^2-2x-1} + \dfrac{4}{3x^2+10x+3}$

47. $\dfrac{4}{x^2-2x-3} - \dfrac{x}{3x^2-7x-6}$

48. $\dfrac{2a}{a^2-2a-8} + \dfrac{3}{a^2-5a+4}$

49. $\dfrac{8}{x^2-9} + \dfrac{2}{x-3} - \dfrac{6}{x}$

50. $\dfrac{x}{x^2-4} - \dfrac{x}{x+2} + \dfrac{2}{x}$

51. $2x + 3 + \dfrac{1}{x+1}$

52. $x + 1 + \dfrac{1}{x-1}$

53. $1 + x - \dfrac{x}{x-5}$

54. $2 - x + \dfrac{3}{x-9}$

55. $\dfrac{3x}{x-1} - 2x - x^2$

56. $\dfrac{23}{x-1} + 4x - 5x^2$

57. $\dfrac{y+4}{y^2+7y+12} - \dfrac{y-4}{y+3} + \dfrac{47}{y+4}$

58. $\dfrac{x+3}{2x^2-5x+2} - \dfrac{3x-1}{x^2-x-2}$

59. $\dfrac{3}{x+1} - \dfrac{2}{x-1} + \dfrac{x+3}{x^2-1}$

60. $\dfrac{2}{x-2} + \dfrac{3}{x+2} - \dfrac{x-1}{x^2-4}$

61. $\dfrac{x-2}{x^2-3x}+\dfrac{2x-1}{x^2+3x}-\dfrac{2}{x^2-9}$

62. $\dfrac{2}{x-1}-\dfrac{2x}{x^2-1}-\dfrac{x}{x^2+2x+1}$

63. $\dfrac{5}{x^2-25}-\dfrac{3}{2x^2-9x-5}+1$

64. $\dfrac{3x}{2x-1}+\dfrac{x+1}{3x+2}+\dfrac{2x}{6x^3+x^2-2x}$

65. $\dfrac{3x}{x-3}+\dfrac{4}{x-2}-\dfrac{5x}{x^3-5x^2+6x}$

66. $\dfrac{2x-1}{x^2+x-6}-\dfrac{3x-5}{x^2-2x-15}+\dfrac{2x-3}{x^2-7x+10}$

67. $2+\dfrac{4a}{a^2-1}-\dfrac{2}{a+1}$

68. $\dfrac{a}{a-1}-\dfrac{a+1}{2a-2}+a$

69. $\dfrac{x+5}{2x^2-2}+\dfrac{x}{2x+2}-\dfrac{3}{x-1}$

70. $\dfrac{a}{2-a}+\dfrac{3}{a-2}-\dfrac{3a-2}{a^2-4}$

71. $\dfrac{a}{a-b}+\dfrac{b}{a+b}+\dfrac{a^2+b^2}{b^2-a^2}$

72. $\dfrac{7n^2}{m-n}+\dfrac{3m}{n-m}-\dfrac{3m^2-n}{m^2-2mn+n^2}$

73. $\dfrac{3b}{2a-b}+\dfrac{2a-1}{b-2a}-\dfrac{3a^2+b}{b^2-4ab+4a^2}$

74. $\dfrac{m+1}{m^2+2m+1}+\dfrac{m-1}{m^2-2m+1}+\dfrac{2}{m^2-1}$ (*Hint:* Think about this before finding the LCD.)

75. $\left(\dfrac{1}{x-1}+1\right)\left(\dfrac{x-1}{3}\right)$

76. $\left(\dfrac{1}{x-1}+\dfrac{1}{x+1}\right)\left(\dfrac{x+1}{2x+4}\right)$

77. $\left(\dfrac{x}{3}-\dfrac{3}{x}\right)\left(\dfrac{1}{x-3}-\dfrac{1}{x+3}\right)$

78. $\left(\dfrac{4}{y}-\dfrac{y}{4}\right)\left(\dfrac{y}{y+4}+\dfrac{y}{y-4}\right)$

79. $\left(1-\dfrac{3}{x}\right)^2$

80. $\left(\dfrac{3}{a-2}+\dfrac{a}{a+2}\right)^2$

81. Show that $\dfrac{a}{b}+\dfrac{c}{d}=\dfrac{ad+bc}{bd}$.

82. Show that $\dfrac{a}{b}-\dfrac{c}{d}=\dfrac{ad-bc}{bd}$.

5.4 COMPLEX FRACTIONS

A **complex fraction** is a rational expression that has a fraction in its numerator or in its denominator or both. Examples of complex fractions are

$$\dfrac{\dfrac{3}{5}}{\dfrac{6}{7}}\qquad \dfrac{\dfrac{x+2}{3}}{x-4}\quad\text{and}\quad \dfrac{\dfrac{3x^2-2}{2x}}{3x-\dfrac{2}{y}}$$

There are two methods used to simplify complex fractions. In one method we write the complex fraction in an equivalent form:

$$\dfrac{\dfrac{a}{b}}{\dfrac{c}{d}}=\dfrac{a}{b}\div\dfrac{c}{d}$$

and then use the division rule for fractions. In the other method we multiply both the numerator and the denominator of the complex fraction

$$\frac{\dfrac{a}{b}}{\dfrac{c}{d}}$$

by bd, the LCD of $\dfrac{a}{b}$ and $\dfrac{c}{d}$. The next three examples illustrate each method.

Example 1   Simplify the complex fraction $\dfrac{\dfrac{3a}{b}}{\dfrac{6ac}{b^2}}$.

Solution 1   Write the complex fraction in an equivalent form:

$$\frac{\dfrac{3a}{b}}{\dfrac{6ac}{b^2}} = \frac{3a}{b} \div \frac{6ac}{b^2}$$

Then the indicated division can be accomplished as follows:

$$\frac{\dfrac{3a}{b}}{\dfrac{6ac}{b^2}} = \frac{3a}{b} \div \frac{6ac}{b^2}$$

$$= \frac{3a}{b} \cdot \frac{b^2}{6ac}$$

$$= \frac{b}{2c}$$

Solution 2   Multiply both the numerator and the denominator of the complex fraction by b^2, the LCD of $3a/b$ and $6ac/b^2$, and simplify:

$$\frac{\dfrac{3a}{b}}{\dfrac{6ac}{b^2}} = \frac{\dfrac{3a}{b} \cdot b^2}{\dfrac{6ac}{b^2} \cdot b^2}$$

$$= \frac{3ab}{6ac}$$

$$= \frac{b}{2c}$$

Example 2   Simplify the complex fraction $\dfrac{\dfrac{1}{x} + \dfrac{1}{y}}{\dfrac{1}{x} - \dfrac{1}{y}}$.

Solution 1   Add the fractions in the numerator and in the denominator. Then simplify the fraction as in Solution 1 of Example 1.

$$\frac{\dfrac{1}{x} + \dfrac{1}{y}}{\dfrac{1}{x} - \dfrac{1}{y}} = \frac{\dfrac{1y}{xy} + \dfrac{x1}{xy}}{\dfrac{1y}{xy} - \dfrac{x1}{xy}}$$

$$= \frac{\dfrac{y + x}{xy}}{\dfrac{y - x}{xy}}$$

$$= \frac{y + x}{xy} \div \frac{y - x}{xy}$$

$$= \frac{y + x}{\cancel{xy}} \cdot \frac{\cancel{xy}}{y - x}$$

$$= \frac{y + x}{y - x}$$

Solution 2   Multiply both the numerator and the denominator by xy and simplify. Note that the product xy is the least common denominator of all the fractions that appear in the problem.

$$\frac{\dfrac{1}{x} + \dfrac{1}{y}}{\dfrac{1}{x} - \dfrac{1}{y}} = \frac{\left(\dfrac{1}{x} + \dfrac{1}{y}\right)xy}{\left(\dfrac{1}{x} - \dfrac{1}{y}\right)xy}$$

$$= \frac{\dfrac{xy}{x} + \dfrac{xy}{y}}{\dfrac{xy}{x} - \dfrac{xy}{y}}$$

$$= \frac{y + x}{y - x}$$ ∎

Example 3   Simplify $\dfrac{x^{-1} + y^{-1}}{x^{-2} - y^{-2}}$. If you recall that $a^{-n} = \dfrac{1}{a^n}$, then you will recognize that this problem is a disguised complex fraction.

Solution 1   Add the fractions in the numerator and the denominator. Then simplify as in Solution 1 of Example 1.

$$\frac{x^{-1} + y^{-1}}{x^{-2} - y^{-2}} = \frac{\dfrac{1}{x} + \dfrac{1}{y}}{\dfrac{1}{x^2} - \dfrac{1}{y^2}}$$

$$= \frac{\dfrac{y}{xy} + \dfrac{x}{xy}}{\dfrac{y^2}{x^2 y^2} - \dfrac{x^2}{x^2 y^2}}$$

$$= \frac{\dfrac{y + x}{xy}}{\dfrac{y^2 - x^2}{x^2 y^2}}$$

$$= \frac{y + x}{xy} \div \frac{y^2 - x^2}{x^2 y^2}$$

$$= \frac{y + x}{xy} \cdot \frac{x x y y}{(y - x)(y + x)}$$

$$= \frac{xy}{y - x}$$

Solution 2   Multiply both numerator and denominator by $x^2 y^2$, the LCD of all the fractions that appear in the problem, and simplify:

$$\frac{x^{-1} + y^{-1}}{x^{-2} - y^{-2}} = \frac{\dfrac{1}{x} + \dfrac{1}{y}}{\dfrac{1}{x^2} - \dfrac{1}{y^2}}$$

$$= \frac{\left(\dfrac{1}{x} + \dfrac{1}{y}\right) x^2 y^2}{\left(\dfrac{1}{x^2} - \dfrac{1}{y^2}\right) x^2 y^2}$$

$$= \frac{xy^2 + yx^2}{y^2 - x^2}$$

$$= \frac{xy(y + x)}{(y + x)(y - x)}$$

$$= \frac{xy}{y - x}$$

Note that $x^{-1} + y^{-1}$ means $1/x + 1/y$, and that $(x + y)^{-1}$ means $1/(x + y)$. Hence, $x^{-1} + y^{-1} \neq (x + y)^{-1}$.

Example 4 Simplify the fraction $\dfrac{\dfrac{2x}{1-\dfrac{1}{x}}+3}{3-\dfrac{2}{x}}$.

Solution Begin by multiplying both the numerator and denominator of the fraction

$$\frac{2x}{1-\dfrac{1}{x}}$$

by x. This will eliminate the complex fraction in the numerator of the original fraction.

$$\frac{\dfrac{2x}{1-\dfrac{1}{x}}+3}{3-\dfrac{2}{x}}=\frac{\dfrac{x\,2x}{x\left(1-\dfrac{1}{x}\right)}+3}{3-\dfrac{2}{x}}$$

$$=\frac{\dfrac{2x^2}{x-1}+3}{3-\dfrac{2}{x}}$$

Then multiply both the numerator and denominator by $x(x-1)$, the LCD of $2x^2/(x-1)$, 3, and $2/x$, and simplify:

$$\frac{\dfrac{2x}{1-\dfrac{1}{x}}+3}{3-\dfrac{2}{x}}=\frac{\left(\dfrac{2x^2}{x-1}+3\right)x(x-1)}{\left(3-\dfrac{2}{x}\right)x(x-1)}$$

$$=\frac{2x^3+3x(x-1)}{3x(x-1)-2(x-1)}$$

$$=\frac{2x^3+3x^2-3x}{3x^2-5x+2}$$

This result does not simplify. ∎

■ EXERCISE 5.4

Simplify each complex fraction.

1. $\dfrac{\dfrac{1}{2}}{\dfrac{3}{4}}$

2. $-\dfrac{\dfrac{3}{4}}{\dfrac{1}{2}}$

3. $\dfrac{-\dfrac{2}{3}}{\dfrac{6}{9}}$

4. $\dfrac{\dfrac{11}{18}}{\dfrac{22}{27}}$

5. $\dfrac{\dfrac{1}{2}+\dfrac{1}{3}}{\dfrac{1}{4}}$

6. $\dfrac{\dfrac{1}{4}-\dfrac{1}{5}}{\dfrac{1}{3}}$

7. $\dfrac{\dfrac{1}{6}-\dfrac{2}{7}}{\dfrac{1}{7}}$

8. $\dfrac{\dfrac{2}{3}+\dfrac{4}{5}}{\dfrac{1}{3}}$

9. $\dfrac{\dfrac{4x}{y}}{\dfrac{6xz}{y^2}}$

10. $\dfrac{\dfrac{5t^4}{9x}}{\dfrac{2t}{18x}}$

11. $\dfrac{5ab^2}{\dfrac{ab}{25}}$

12. $\dfrac{\dfrac{6a^2b}{4t}}{3a^2b^2}$

13. $\dfrac{\dfrac{x-y}{xy}}{\dfrac{y-x}{x}}$

14. $\dfrac{\dfrac{x^2+5x+6}{3xy}}{\dfrac{x^2-9}{6xy}}$

15. $\dfrac{\dfrac{1}{x}-\dfrac{1}{y}}{xy}$

16. $\dfrac{xy}{\dfrac{1}{x}-\dfrac{1}{y}}$

17. $\dfrac{\dfrac{1}{a}+\dfrac{1}{b}}{\dfrac{1}{a}}$

18. $\dfrac{\dfrac{1}{b}}{\dfrac{1}{a}-\dfrac{1}{b}}$

19. $\dfrac{1+\dfrac{x}{y}}{1-\dfrac{x}{y}}$

20. $\dfrac{\dfrac{x}{y}+1}{1-\dfrac{x}{y}}$

21. $\dfrac{x+1-\dfrac{6}{x}}{\dfrac{1}{x}}$

22. $\dfrac{x-1-\dfrac{2}{x}}{\dfrac{x}{3}}$

23. $\dfrac{5xy}{1+\dfrac{1}{xy}}$

24. $\dfrac{3a}{a+\dfrac{1}{a}}$

25. $\dfrac{a-4+\dfrac{1}{a}}{-\dfrac{1}{a}-a+4}$

26. $\dfrac{a+1+\dfrac{1}{a^2}}{\dfrac{1}{a^2}+a-1}$

27. $\dfrac{1+\dfrac{6}{x}+\dfrac{8}{x^2}}{1+\dfrac{1}{x}-\dfrac{12}{x^2}}$

28. $\dfrac{1-\dfrac{x^2}{x}-\dfrac{2}{x}}{\dfrac{6}{x^2}+\dfrac{1}{x}-1}$

29. $\dfrac{\dfrac{1}{a+1}+1}{\dfrac{3}{a-1}+1}$

30. $\dfrac{2+\dfrac{3}{x+1}}{\dfrac{1}{x}+x+x^2}$

31. $\dfrac{x^{-1}+y^{-1}}{x}$

32. $\dfrac{x^{-1}-y^{-1}}{y}$

33. $\dfrac{y}{x^{-1}-y^{-1}}$

34. $\dfrac{x}{x^{-1}+y^{-1}}$

35. $\dfrac{x^{-1}+y^{-1}}{x^{-1}-y^{-1}}$

36. $\dfrac{(x+y)^{-1}}{x^{-1}+y^{-1}}$

37. $\dfrac{x+y}{x^{-1}+y^{-1}}$

38. $\dfrac{x-y}{x^{-1}-y^{-1}}$

39. $\dfrac{x-y^{-2}}{y-x^{-2}}$

40. $\dfrac{x^{-2}-y^{-2}}{x^{-1}-y^{-1}}$

41. $\dfrac{1+\dfrac{a}{b}}{1-\dfrac{a}{1-\dfrac{a}{b}}}$

42. $\dfrac{1+\dfrac{2}{1-\dfrac{a}{b}}}{1-\dfrac{a}{b}}$

43. $\dfrac{x-\dfrac{1}{x}}{1+\dfrac{1}{\dfrac{1}{x}}}$

44. $\dfrac{\dfrac{a^2+3a+4}{ab}}{2+\dfrac{3+a}{\dfrac{2}{a}}}$

45. $\dfrac{b}{b + \dfrac{2}{2 + \dfrac{1}{2}}}$ **46.** $\dfrac{2y}{y - \dfrac{y}{3 - \dfrac{1}{2}}}$ **47.** $a + \dfrac{a}{1 + \dfrac{a}{a + 1}}$ **48.** $b + \dfrac{b}{1 - \dfrac{b + 1}{b}}$

49. $\dfrac{x - \dfrac{1}{1 - \dfrac{x}{2}}}{\dfrac{3}{x + \dfrac{2}{3}} - x}$ **50.** $\dfrac{\dfrac{2x}{x - \dfrac{1}{x}} - \dfrac{1}{x}}{2x + \dfrac{2x}{1 - \dfrac{1}{x}}}$

5.5   EQUATIONS CONTAINING RATIONAL EXPRESSIONS

Equations often contain fractions that have numerators and denominators that are polynomials. Such equations are called **rational equations**. To solve rational equations, it is usually best to begin by clearing the equation of fractions. To do so, we multiply both sides of the equation by the least common denominator of the fractions that appear in the equation. For example, to solve the equation

$$\frac{3}{5} + \frac{7}{x + 2} = 2$$

we first multiply both sides by $5(x + 2)$ and then simplify to obtain

$$5(x + 2)\left(\frac{3}{5} + \frac{7}{x + 2}\right) = 5(x + 2)2$$
$$3(x + 2) + 5(7) = 10(x + 2)$$
$$3x + 6 + 35 = 10x + 20$$
$$3x + 41 = 10x + 20$$
$$-7x = -21$$
$$x = 3$$

To verify that 3 satisfies the equation, we substitute 3 for x in the original equation and simplify:

$$\frac{3}{5} + \frac{7}{x + 2} = 2$$
$$\frac{3}{5} + \frac{7}{3 + 2} \overset{?}{=} 2$$
$$\frac{3}{5} + \frac{7}{5} \overset{?}{=} 2$$
$$2 = 2$$

Because 3 satisfies the equation, it is a solution, and the solution set is $\{3\}$.

Example 1 Solve the equation $\dfrac{-x^2 + 10}{x^2 - 1} + \dfrac{3x}{x - 1} = \dfrac{2x}{x + 1}$.

Solution Clear the fractions by multiplying both sides of the given equation by the LCD of the three fractions. Then proceed as follows:

$$\frac{-x^2 + 10}{x^2 - 1} + \frac{3x}{x - 1} = \frac{2x}{x + 1}$$

$$\frac{-x^2 + 10}{(x + 1)(x - 1)} + \frac{3x}{x - 1} = \frac{2x}{x + 1} \qquad \text{Factor } x^2 - 1.$$

$$\frac{(x + 1)(x - 1)(-x^2 + 10)}{(x + 1)(x - 1)} + \frac{3x(x + 1)(x - 1)}{x - 1} = \frac{2x(x + 1)(x - 1)}{x + 1} \qquad \begin{array}{l}\text{Multiply both sides}\\ \text{by } (x + 1)(x - 1).\end{array}$$

$$-x^2 + 10 + 3x(x + 1) = 2x(x - 1) \qquad \text{Simplify.}$$

$$-x^2 + 10 + 3x^2 + 3x = 2x^2 - 2x \qquad \text{Remove parentheses.}$$

$$2x^2 + 10 + 3x = 2x^2 - 2x \qquad \text{Combine terms.}$$

$$10 + 3x = -2x \qquad \text{Add } -2x^2 \text{ to both sides.}$$

$$10 + 5x = 0 \qquad \text{Add } 2x \text{ to both sides.}$$

$$5x = -10 \qquad \text{Add } -10 \text{ to both sides.}$$

$$x = -2 \qquad \text{Divide both sides by 5.}$$

Verify that -2 is a solution to the original equation. ∎

In the previous examples we multiplied both sides of an equation by a quantity that contained a variable, and we obtained the correct solution to the given equation. Sometimes, however, multiplying both sides of an equation by a quantity that contains a variable leads to false solutions called **extraneous solutions**. This happens when we inadvertently multiply both sides of an equation by 0 and obtain a solution that leads to a 0 in the denominator of a fraction. We must be careful to exclude from the solution set of an equation any value that makes the denominator of a fraction 0 and, thus, is not in the domain of the variable. The next example illustrates a rational equation that has an extraneous solution.

Example 2 Solve the equation $\dfrac{2(x + 1)}{x - 3} = \dfrac{x + 5}{x - 3}$.

Solution Clear the equation of fractions by multiplying both sides by $x - 3$. However, if $x = 3$, the quantity $x - 3$ is equal to 0, and a 0 will appear in the denominator of each fraction. Thus, if you obtain an apparent solution of 3, you must discard it.

$$\frac{2(x + 1)}{x - 3} = \frac{x + 5}{x - 3}$$

$$(x - 3)\frac{2(x + 1)}{x - 3} = (x - 3)\frac{x + 5}{x - 3} \qquad \text{Multiply both sides by } x - 3.$$

$$2(x + 1) = x + 5 \qquad \text{Simplify.}$$

$$2x + 2 = x + 5 \qquad \text{Remove parentheses.}$$

$$x + 2 = 5 \qquad \text{Add } -x \text{ to both sides.}$$

$$x = 3 \qquad \text{Add } -2 \text{ to both sides.}$$

Because a solution of 3 leads to a 0 in the denominator of a fraction, it is an extraneous root and must be discarded. This equation has no solutions. Its solution set is $\varnothing$, the empty set. ∎

Example 3 Solve the equation $\dfrac{x + 1}{5} - 2 = -\dfrac{4}{x}$.

Solution Clear the equation of fractions by multiplying both sides by $5x$ and proceed as follows:

$$\frac{x + 1}{5} - 2 = -\frac{4}{x}$$

$$5x\left(\frac{x + 1}{5} - 2\right) = 5x\left(-\frac{4}{x}\right) \qquad \text{Multiply both sides by } 5x.$$

$$x(x + 1) - 10x = -20 \qquad \text{Remove parentheses and simplify.}$$

$$x^2 + x - 10x = -20 \qquad \text{Remove parentheses.}$$

$$x^2 - 9x + 20 = 0 \qquad \text{Combine terms and add 20 to both sides.}$$

$$(x - 5)(x - 4) = 0 \qquad \text{Factor } x^2 - 9x + 20.$$

$$x - 5 = 0 \quad \text{or} \quad x - 4 = 0 \qquad \text{Set each factor equal to 0.}$$

$$x = 5 \qquad \qquad x = 4$$

Because each apparent solution is in the domain of x, both 4 and 5 are solutions of the original equation. The solution set is $\{4, 5\}$. Verify this result by showing that both 4 and 5 satisfy the original equation. ∎

Many applications, such as shared-work problems, lead to rational equations.

Example 4 A drain can empty a swimming pool in 3 days, and a second drain can empty the pool in 2 days. How many days will it take to empty the pool if both drains are used?

Analysis: The key is to note what each drain can do in 1 day. Then, if you add what the first drain can do in 1 day to what the second drain can do in 1 day, the sum is what they can do together in 1 day. Because the first drain can empty the pool in 3 days, it can do $\frac{1}{3}$ of the job in 1 day. Because the second drain can empty the pool in 2 days, it can do $\frac{1}{2}$ of the job in 1 day. If it takes x days for both drains to empty the pool, together they can do $1/x$ of the job in 1 day.

Solution   Let x represent the number of days that it takes both drains to empty the pool. Then form the equation

What drain 1 can do in one day		what drain 2 can do in one day		what they can do together in one day.
$\dfrac{1}{3}$	$+$	$\dfrac{1}{2}$	$=$	$\dfrac{1}{x}$

$$6x\left(\frac{1}{3} + \frac{1}{2}\right) = 6x\left(\frac{1}{x}\right)$$ Multiply both sides by $6x$.

$$2x + 3x = 6$$ Remove parentheses and simplify.

$$5x = 6$$ Combine terms.

$$x = \frac{6}{5}$$ Divide both sides by 5.

It will take both drains $1\frac{1}{5}$ days to drain the pool.

Check: In $\frac{6}{5}$ days the first drain does $\frac{1}{3}(\frac{6}{5})$ of the total job and the second drain does $\frac{1}{2}(\frac{6}{5})$ of the total job. The sum of their efforts, $\frac{2}{5} + \frac{3}{5}$, is equal to one complete job.   ∎

Example 5   A man drives 200 miles to a convention. Because of road construction his average speed on the return trip is 10 miles per hour less than his average speed going to the convention. If the return trip took 1 hour longer, how fast did he drive in each direction?

Analysis: Because the distance d traveled is given by the formula

$$d = rt$$

where r is the average rate of speed and t is the time, the time is given by the formula

$$t = \frac{d}{r}$$

Organize the information given in the problem in a chart such as Figure 5-2.

	d	$=$	r	$\cdot$	t
Going	200		r		$\dfrac{200}{r}$
Returning	200		$r - 10$		$\dfrac{200}{r - 10}$

Figure 5-2

Solution   Let r represent the average rate of speed going to the meeting.
Then $r - 10$ represents the average rate of speed on the return trip.

Because the return trip took 1 hour longer, you can form the following equation:

The time it took to travel to the convention	$+ 1 =$	**the time it took to return.**

$$\frac{200}{r} \qquad + 1 = \qquad \frac{200}{r - 10}$$

Solve the equation as follows:

$$r(r - 10)\left(\frac{200}{r} + 1\right) = r(r - 10)\frac{200}{r - 10} \qquad \text{Multiply both sides by } r(r - 10).$$

$$200(r - 10) + r(r - 10) = 200r \qquad \text{Remove parentheses and simplify.}$$

$$200r - 2000 + r^2 - 10r = 200r \qquad \text{Remove parentheses.}$$

$$r^2 - 10r - 2000 = 0 \qquad \text{Add } -200r \text{ to both sides.}$$

$$(r - 50)(r + 40) = 0 \qquad \text{Factor } r^2 - 10r - 2000.$$

$$r - 50 = 0 \qquad \text{or} \qquad r + 40 = 0 \qquad \text{Set each factor equal to 0.}$$

$$r = 50 \qquad \qquad r = -40$$

Because a speed cannot be negative, exclude the possible solution of -40. The man averaged 50 miles per hour going to the convention, thus he averaged $50 - 10$ or 40 miles per hour returning.

Check: At 50 miles per hour, the 200-mile trip took 4 hours. At 40 miles per hour, the return trip took 5 hours, which is 1 hour longer.   ■

▬ EXERCISE 5.5 ▬▬▬▬▬▬▬▬

In Exercises 1–30, solve each equation. If a solution is extraneous, so indicate.

1. $\dfrac{1}{4} + \dfrac{9}{x} = 1$

2. $\dfrac{1}{3} - \dfrac{10}{x} = -3$

3. $\dfrac{34}{x} - \dfrac{3}{2} = -\dfrac{13}{20}$

4. $\dfrac{1}{2} + \dfrac{7}{x} = 2 + \dfrac{1}{x}$

5. $\dfrac{3}{y} + \dfrac{7}{2y} = 13$

6. $\dfrac{2}{x} + \dfrac{1}{2} = \dfrac{7}{2x}$

7. $\dfrac{x + 1}{x} - \dfrac{x - 1}{x} = 0$

8. $\dfrac{2}{x} + \dfrac{1}{2} = \dfrac{9}{4x} - \dfrac{1}{2x}$

9. $\dfrac{7}{5x} - \dfrac{1}{2} = \dfrac{5}{6x} + \dfrac{1}{3}$

10. $\dfrac{x - 3}{x - 1} - \dfrac{2x - 4}{x - 1} = 0$

11. $\dfrac{3 - 5y}{2 + y} = \dfrac{3 + 5y}{2 - y}$

12. $\dfrac{x}{x - 2} = 1 + \dfrac{1}{x - 3}$

13. $\dfrac{a + 2}{a + 1} = \dfrac{a - 4}{a - 3}$

14. $\dfrac{z + 2}{z + 8} - \dfrac{z - 3}{z - 2} = 0$

15. $\dfrac{x + 2}{x + 3} - 1 = \dfrac{1}{3 - 2x - x^2}$

16. $\dfrac{x - 3}{x - 2} - \dfrac{1}{x} = \dfrac{x - 3}{x}$

17. $\dfrac{x}{x+2} = 1 - \dfrac{3x+2}{x^2+4x+4}$

18. $\dfrac{3+2a}{a^2+6+5a} + \dfrac{2-5a}{a^2-4} = \dfrac{2-3a}{a^2-6+a}$

19. $\dfrac{2}{x-2} + \dfrac{1}{x+1} = \dfrac{1}{x^2-x-2}$

20. $\dfrac{5}{y-1} + \dfrac{3}{y-3} = \dfrac{8}{y-2}$

21. $\dfrac{a-1}{a+3} - \dfrac{1-2a}{3-a} = \dfrac{2-a}{a-3}$

22. $\dfrac{5}{2z^2+z-3} - \dfrac{2}{2z+3} = \dfrac{z+1}{z-1} - 1$

23. $\dfrac{5}{x+4} + \dfrac{1}{x+4} = x - 1$

24. $\dfrac{2}{x-1} + \dfrac{x-2}{3} = \dfrac{4}{x-1}$

25. $\dfrac{3}{x+1} - \dfrac{x-2}{2} = \dfrac{x-2}{x+1}$

26. $\dfrac{x-4}{x-3} + \dfrac{x-2}{x-3} = x - 3$

27. $\dfrac{2}{x-3} + \dfrac{3}{4} = \dfrac{17}{2x}$

28. $\dfrac{30}{y-2} + \dfrac{24}{y-5} = 13$

29. $\dfrac{x+4}{x+7} - \dfrac{x}{x+3} = \dfrac{3}{8}$

30. $\dfrac{5}{x+4} - \dfrac{1}{3} = \dfrac{x-1}{x}$

In Exercises 31–44, solve each word problem.

31. If Laura can paint a house in 5 days and her brother Scott can paint the house in 3 days, how long will it take them to paint the house if they work together?

32. If Kristy can mow a lawn in 4 hours and her younger brother Steven can mow the same lawn in 3 hours, how long will it take if they work together?

33. A pipe can drain a pool in 9 hours. If a second pipe is also used, the pool can be drained in 3 hours. How long does it take the second pipe to drain the pool?

34. One pipe can fill a pond in 3 weeks, and a second pipe can fill the pond in 5 weeks. However, evaporation and seepage can empty the pond in 10 weeks. If both pipes are used, how long will it take to fill the pond?

35. Sally can clean the house in 6 hours, and her father can clean the house in 4 hours. Sally's younger brother, Dennis, can completely mess up the house in 8 hours. If Sally and her father clean and Dennis plays, how long will it take to clean the house?

36. Sam makes hamburgers at a fast food restaurant. He can make 600 burgers in 3 hours. If his manager helps him, together they can make 600 burgers in 2 hours. How long will it take the manager alone to make 400 burgers?

37. A boy can drive a motorboat 45 miles down a river in the same amount of time that he can drive 27 miles upstream. What is the speed of the current in the river if the speed of the boat in still water is 12 miles per hour?

38. If a plane that can fly 340 miles per hour in still air can travel 200 miles downwind in the same amount of time that it can travel 140 miles upwind, what is the velocity of the wind?

39. A train travels 120 miles and returns the same distance in a total time of 5 hours. If the speed of the train averaged 20 miles per hour slower on the return trip, how fast did the train travel in each direction?

40. A woman who can row 3 miles per hour in still water rows 10 miles downstream and returns upstream in a total of 12 hours. What is the speed of the current of the river?

41. If three times a certain integer is added to four times its reciprocal, the result is 8. Find the integer.

42. If three times a number is subtracted from four times its reciprocal, the result is 11. Find the number. (There are two possibilities.)

43. A repairman purchased several washing-machine motors for a total of $224. When the unit cost decreased by $4, he was able to buy one extra motor for the same total price. How many motors did he buy originally?

44. An appliance store manager bought several microwave ovens for a total of $8100 and sold them all at a profit of $90 each. With these total receipts she was able to buy 10 more microwaves than before. What was her per-unit cost on the second order?

CHAPTER SUMMARY

Key Words

complex fractions   (5.4)   *rational equations*   (5.5)
extraneous solutions   (5.5)   *rational expressions*   (5.1)
least common denominator   (5.3)   *reciprocals*   (5.2)
multiplicative inverses   (5.2)

Key Ideas

(5.1)   Division by 0 is undefined.

$$\frac{a}{b} = \frac{ak}{bk}, \quad \text{provided that } b \neq 0 \text{ and } k \neq 0.$$

To simplify a fraction, factor the numerator and denominator, and remove all factors common to both the numerator and denominator.

(5.2) $\dfrac{a}{b} \cdot \dfrac{c}{d} = \dfrac{ac}{bd}, \quad$ provided that $b \neq 0$ and $d \neq 0.$

$\dfrac{a}{b} \div \dfrac{c}{d} = \dfrac{a}{b} \cdot \dfrac{d}{c}, \quad$ provided that $b \neq 0,\ d \neq 0,$ and $c \neq 0.$

If the product of two numbers is 1, the numbers are called **reciprocals** or **multiplicative inverses** of each other.

If a number is to be divided by a fraction, multiply the number by the reciprocal of the fraction.

(5.3) $\dfrac{a}{b} + \dfrac{c}{b} = \dfrac{a + c}{b}, \quad$ provided that $b \neq 0.$

$\dfrac{a}{b} - \dfrac{c}{b} = \dfrac{a - c}{b}, \quad$ provided that $b \neq 0.$

Fractions must be written with common denominators before they can be combined by addition or subtraction.

To find the least common denominator (LCD) of two fractions, factor each denominator and use each factor the greatest number of times that it appears in any one denominator. The product of these factors is the LCD of the fractions.

(5.4)   If a fraction has a fractional numerator or denominator, it is called a **complex fraction**.

(5.5) Multiplying both sides of an equation by a quantity that contains a variable can lead to **extraneous solutions**.

REVIEW EXERCISES

In Review Exercises 1–6, simplify each fraction.

1. $\dfrac{248x^2y}{576xy^2}$

2. $\dfrac{212m^3n}{588m^2n^3}$

3. $\dfrac{x^2 - 49}{x^2 + 14x + 49}$

4. $\dfrac{x^2 + 6x + 36}{x^3 - 216}$

5. $\dfrac{x^2 - 2x + 4}{2x^3 + 16}$

6. $\dfrac{2m - 2n}{n - m}$

In Review Exercises 7–20, perform the indicated operations and simplify.

7. $\dfrac{x^2 + 4x + 4}{x^2 - x - 6} \cdot \dfrac{x^2 - 9}{x^2 + 5x + 6}$

8. $\dfrac{x^3 - 64}{x^2 + 4x + 16} \div \dfrac{x^2 - 16}{x + 4}$

9. $\dfrac{5y}{x - y} - \dfrac{3}{x - y}$

10. $\dfrac{3x - 1}{x^2 + 2} + \dfrac{3(x - 2)}{x^2 + 2}$

11. $\dfrac{3}{x + 2} + \dfrac{2}{x + 3}$

12. $\dfrac{4x}{x - 4} - \dfrac{3}{x + 3}$

13. $\dfrac{x^2 + 3x + 2}{x^2 - x - 6} \cdot \dfrac{3x^2 - 3x}{x^2 - 3x - 4} \div \dfrac{x^2 + 3x + 2}{x^2 - 2x - 8}$

14. $\dfrac{x^2 - x - 6}{x^2 - 3x - 10} \div \dfrac{x^2 - x}{x^2 - 5x} \cdot \dfrac{x^2 - 4x + 3}{x^2 - 6x + 9}$

15. $\dfrac{2x}{x + 1} + \dfrac{3x}{x + 2} + \dfrac{4x}{x^2 + 3x + 2}$

16. $\dfrac{5x}{x - 3} + \dfrac{5}{x^2 - 5x + 6} + \dfrac{x + 3}{x - 2}$

17. $\dfrac{3(x + 2)}{x^2 - 1} - \dfrac{2}{x + 1} + \dfrac{4(x + 3)}{x^2 - 2x + 1}$

18. $\dfrac{x}{x^2 + 4x + 4} + \dfrac{2x}{x^2 - 4} - \dfrac{x^2 - 4}{x - 2}$

19. $\dfrac{x + 2}{x^2 - 9} - \dfrac{x^2 + 6x + 9}{x^2 + 5x + 6} + \dfrac{3x}{x - 3}$

20. $\dfrac{-2(3 + x)}{x^2 + 6x + 9} + \dfrac{3(x + 2)}{x^2 - 6x + 9} - \dfrac{1}{x^2 - 9}$

In Review Exercise 21–30, simplify each complex fraction.

21. $\dfrac{\dfrac{3}{x} - \dfrac{2}{y}}{xy}$

22. $\dfrac{\dfrac{1}{x} + \dfrac{2}{y}}{\dfrac{2}{x} - \dfrac{1}{y}}$

23. $\dfrac{2x + 3 + \dfrac{1}{x}}{x + 2 + \dfrac{1}{x}}$

24. $\dfrac{6x + 13 + \dfrac{6}{x}}{6x + 5 - \dfrac{6}{x}}$

25. $\dfrac{1 + \dfrac{3}{x}}{x + 3}$

26. $\dfrac{1 - \dfrac{1}{x} - \dfrac{2}{x^2}}{1 + \dfrac{4}{x} + \dfrac{3}{x^2}}$

27. $\dfrac{(x - y)^{-2}}{x^{-2} - y^{-2}}$

28. $\dfrac{x^{-1} + 1}{x + 1}$

29. $\dfrac{x^{-1} + y}{x - y^{-1}}$

30. $\dfrac{x^{-2} + 1}{x^2 + 1}$

In Review Exercises 31–34, solve each equation, if possible.

31. $\dfrac{4}{x} - \dfrac{1}{10} = \dfrac{7}{2x}$

32. $\dfrac{2}{x + 5} - \dfrac{1}{6} = \dfrac{1}{x + 4}$

33. $\dfrac{2(x - 5)}{x - 2} = \dfrac{6x + 12}{4 - x^2}$

34. $\dfrac{7}{x + 9} - \dfrac{x + 2}{2} = \dfrac{x + 4}{x + 9}$

In Review Exercises 35–36, solve each word problem.

35. Traffic reduced Jim's usual speed by 10 miles per hour, which lengthened his 200-mile trip by 1 hour. What is his usual speed?

36. On a 600-mile trip, a pilot can save 30 minutes by increasing her usual speed by 40 miles per hour. What is her usual speed?

CHAPTER FIVE TEST

In Problems 1–4, simplify each fraction.

1. $\dfrac{-12x^2y^3z^2}{18x^3y^4z^2}$

2. $\dfrac{2x+4}{x^2-4}$

3. $\dfrac{3y-6z}{2z-y}$

4. $\dfrac{2x^2+7x+3}{4x+12}$

In Problems 5–14, perform the indicated operations and simplify, if necessary. **Write all answers without using negative exponents.**

5. $\dfrac{x^2y^{-2}}{x^3z^2}\cdot\dfrac{x^2z^4}{y^2z}$

6. $\dfrac{(x+1)(x+2)}{10}\cdot\dfrac{5}{x+2}$

7. $\dfrac{u^2+5u+6}{u^2-4}\cdot\dfrac{u^2-5u+6}{u^2-9}$

8. $\dfrac{x^3+y^3}{4}\div\dfrac{x^2-xy+y^2}{2x+2y}$

9. $\dfrac{xu+2u+3x+6}{u^2-9}\cdot\dfrac{2u-6}{x^2+3x+2}$

10. $\dfrac{a^2+7a+12}{a+3}\div\dfrac{16-a^2}{a-4}$

11. $\dfrac{3t}{t+3}+\dfrac{9}{t+3}$

12. $\dfrac{3w}{w-5}-\dfrac{w+10}{w-5}$

13. $\dfrac{2}{r}+\dfrac{r}{s}$

14. $\dfrac{x+2}{x+1}-\dfrac{x+1}{x+2}$

In Problems 15–16, simplify each complex fraction.

15. $\dfrac{\dfrac{2u^2w^3}{v^2}}{\dfrac{4uw^4}{uv}}$

16. $\dfrac{\dfrac{x}{y}+\dfrac{1}{2}}{\dfrac{x}{2}-\dfrac{1}{y}}$

In Problems 17–18, solve each equation.

17. $\dfrac{2}{x-1}+\dfrac{5}{x+2}=\dfrac{11}{x+2}$

18. $\dfrac{u-2}{u-3}+3=u-\dfrac{u-4}{u-3}$

In Problems 19–20, solve each word problem.

19. A boat sails a distance of 440 nautical miles. If the boat had averaged 11 nautical miles more each day, the trip would have required 2 fewer days. How long did the trip take?

20. A student can earn $300 interest annually by investing in a bank certificate of deposit at a certain interest rate. If she were to receive an annual interest rate that is 4% higher, she could receive the same annual interest by investing $2000 less. How much would she invest at each rate?

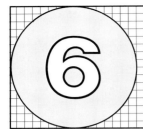

6 Rational Exponents and Radicals

In previous chapters we squared and cubed numbers and raised numbers to other integral powers. We now discuss how to raise numbers to nonintegral powers and how to find roots of numbers.

6.1 RATIONAL EXPONENTS

The rules of integral exponents discussed in Chapter 2 can be extended to include rational (fractional) exponents if we define the exponential expression $a^{1/n}$ in the following way:

Definition. If n is a natural number and $a \geq 0$, then $a^{1/n}$ is the nonnegative number whose nth power is a. In symbols,

$$(a^{1/n})^n = a$$

If n is a natural number and $a \geq 0$, the nonnegative number $a^{1/n}$ is called the **principal nth root** of a. The expression $a^{1/2}$ is called the **square root** of a, and the expression $a^{1/3}$ is called the **cube root** of a.

Example 1
a. $36^{1/2} = 6$ because $6^2 = 36$.

b. $9^{1/2} = 3$ because $3^2 = 9$.

c. $8^{1/3} = 2$ because $2^3 = 8$.

d. $625^{1/4} = 5$ because $5^4 = 625$.   Read $625^{1/4}$ as "the fourth root of 625."

e. $0^{1/7} = 0$ because $0^7 = 0$.

f. $-32^{1/5} = -(32^{1/5}) = -(2) = -2$.

g. $(-25)^{1/2}$ is not a real number because the square of no real number is -25. ∎

In the expression $a^{1/n}$, if n is an odd natural number, we can remove the restriction that $a \geq 0$.

Definition.   If n is an odd natural number and a is any real number, then $a^{1/n}$ is the real number whose nth power is a. In symbols,

$$(a^{1/n})^n = a$$

Example 2   **a.** $(-8)^{1/3} = -2$ because $(-2)^3 = -8$.

b. $(-32)^{1/5} = -2$ because $(-2)^5 = -32$.

c. $64^{1/3} = 4$ because $4^3 = 64$.

d. $3125^{1/5} = 5$ because $5^5 = 3125$.   ∎

The following chart summarizes the definitions concerning the exponential expression $a^{1/n}$:

If n is a natural number and a is a real number, then
If $a > 0$, then $a^{1/n}$ is the positive number such that $(a^{1/n})^n = a$.
If $a = 0$, then $a^{1/n} = 0$.
If $a < 0$ $\begin{cases} \text{and } n \text{ is odd, then } a^{1/n} \text{ is the real number such that } (a^{1/n})^n = a. \\ \text{and } n \text{ is even, then } a^{1/n} \text{ is not a real number.} \end{cases}$

The definition of $a^{1/n}$ can be extended to include rational exponents whose numerators are not 1. For example, $4^{3/2}$ can be written as either

$$(4^{1/2})^3 \qquad \text{or} \qquad (4^3)^{1/2}$$

because of a power rule of exponents. In general, we have the following rule:

If m and n are positive integers and the fraction $\dfrac{m}{n}$ has been simplified to lowest terms, then

$$a^{m/n} = (a^{1/n})^m = (a^m)^{1/n}$$

Because of the previous statement, we can look at the expression $a^{m/n}$ in two different ways:

1. $a^{m/n}$ means the mth power of the nth root of a.
2. $a^{m/n}$ means the nth root of the mth power of a.

For example $16^{3/4}$ and $(-27)^{2/3}$ can be interpreted as

$$16^{3/4} = (16^{1/4})^3 = (2)^3 = 8 \qquad (-27)^{2/3} = [(-27)^{1/3}]^2 = (-3)^2 = 9$$

or as

$$16^{3/4} = (16^3)^{1/4} = (4096)^{1/4} = 8 \qquad (-27)^{2/3} = [(-27)^2]^{1/3} = 729^{1/3} = 9$$

Either way, the answer is the same. As the previous examples suggest, however, it is usually easier to take the root of the base first in order to avoid large numbers.

To be consistent with the definition of negative exponents, we define $a^{-m/n}$ as follows:

Definition.   If m and n are positive integers, the fraction $\dfrac{m}{n}$ has been simplified to lowest terms, and $a \neq 0$, then

$$a^{-m/n} = \frac{1}{a^{m/n}} \qquad \text{and} \qquad \frac{1}{a^{-m/n}} = a^{m/n}$$

Example 3   **a.** $64^{-2/3} = \dfrac{1}{64^{2/3}} = \dfrac{1}{(64^{1/3})^2} = \dfrac{1}{4^2} = \dfrac{1}{16}$

b. $16^{-3/2} = \dfrac{1}{16^{3/2}} = \dfrac{1}{(16^{1/2})^3} = \dfrac{1}{4^3} = \dfrac{1}{64}$

c. $(-32)^{-2/5} = \dfrac{1}{(-32)^{2/5}} = \dfrac{1}{[(-32)^{1/5}]^2} = \dfrac{1}{(-2)^2} = \dfrac{1}{4}$

d. $(-16)^{-3/4}$ is not a real number because $(-16)^{1/4}$ is not a real number.   ■

The familiar rules of integral exponents also hold for rational exponents. The following example illustrates the use of each rule for expressions containing rational exponents.

Example 4   Assume that all variables represent positive numbers, and write all answers without using negative exponents.

a. $7^{2/5} \cdot 7^{1/5} = 7^{3/5}$ $a^m a^n = a^{m+n}$

b. $(4^{1/3})^5 = 4^{(1/3)5} = 4^{5/3}$ $(a^m)^n = a^{mn}$

c. $(5 \cdot 4)^{4/3} = 5^{4/3} \cdot 4^{4/3}$ $(ab)^n = a^n b^n$

d. $\dfrac{8^{3/7}}{8^{2/7}} = 8^{3/7 - 2/7} = 8^{1/7}$ $\dfrac{a^m}{a^n} = a^{m-n}$

e. $\left(\dfrac{2}{3}\right)^{2/5} = \dfrac{2^{2/5}}{3^{2/5}}$ $\left(\dfrac{a}{b}\right)^n = \dfrac{a^n}{b^n}$

f. $5^{-2/3} = \dfrac{1}{5^{2/3}}$ $\qquad\qquad\qquad$ $a^{-n} = \dfrac{1}{a^n}$

g. $\dfrac{1}{4^{-2/3}} = 4^{2/3}$ $\qquad\qquad\quad$ $\dfrac{1}{a^{-n}} = a^n$

h. $(2.5)^0 = 1$ $\qquad\qquad\qquad$ $a^0 = 1$ ∎

The next examples illustrate how to work with exponential expressions with variables in their bases.

Example 5   Assume all variables represent positive numbers. Write all answers without using negative exponents.

a. $(25x)^{1/2} = 25^{1/2}x^{1/2}$
$$= 5x^{1/2}$$

b. $\dfrac{(a^{2/3}b^{1/2})^6}{(y^2)^2} = \dfrac{a^{12/3}b^{6/2}}{y^4}$
$$= \dfrac{a^4 b^3}{y^4}$$

c. $\dfrac{a^{5/3}a^{1/4}}{a^{1/6}} = a^{5/3+1/4-1/6}$
$$= a^{20/12+3/12-2/12}$$
$$= a^{21/12}$$
$$= a^{7/4}$$

d. $\dfrac{(12ab^2)^{1/2}(12ab)^{1/2}}{ab^{3/2}}$
$$= \dfrac{12^{1/2}a^{1/2}b12^{1/2}a^{1/2}b^{1/2}}{ab^{3/2}}$$
$$= \dfrac{12^{1/2}12^{1/2}a^{1/2}a^{1/2}bb^{1/2}}{ab^{3/2}}$$
$$= \dfrac{12^{1/2+1/2}a^{1/2+1/2}b^{1+1/2}}{ab^{3/2}}$$
$$= \dfrac{12ab^{3/2}}{ab^{3/2}}$$
$$= 12$$

e. $\dfrac{a^{x/2}a^{x/3}}{a^{x/4}} = a^{x/2+x/3-x/4}$
$$= a^{6x/12+4x/12-3x/12}$$
$$= a^{7x/12}$$ ∎

Example 6   Assume all variables represent positive numbers. Perform the indicated operations and write all answers without using negative exponents.

a. $a^{4/5}(a^{1/5} + a^{5/4}) = a^{4/5}a^{1/5} + a^{4/5}a^{5/4}$ $\qquad$ Use the distributive property.
$$= a^{4/5+1/5} + a^{4/5+5/4} \qquad\qquad \text{Use the rule } a^m a^n = a^{m+n}.$$
$$= a^{5/5} + a^{16/20+25/20} \qquad\qquad \text{Add exponents.}$$
$$= a + a^{41/20} \qquad\qquad\qquad\quad \text{Simplify.}$$

b. $x^{1/2}(x^{-1/2} + x^{1/2}) = x^{1/2}x^{-1/2} + x^{1/2}x^{1/2}$ Use the distributive property.

$= x^{1/2 - 1/2} + x^{1/2 + 1/2}$ Use the rule $a^m a^n = a^{m+n}$

$= x^0 + x^1$ Simplify.

$= 1 + x$

c. $(x^{2/3} + 1)(x^{2/3} - 1) = x^{4/3} - x^{2/3} + x^{2/3} - 1$ Use the FOIL method.

$= x^{4/3} - 1$ Simplify.   ∎

■ **EXERCISE 6.1**

In Exercises 1–44, simplify each expression, if possible. **Write all answers without using negative exponents.**

1. $16^{1/2}$

2. $25^{1/2}$

3. $27^{1/3}$

4. $64^{1/3}$

5. $81^{1/4}$

6. $625^{1/4}$

7. $32^{1/5}$

8. $0^{1/5}$

9. $\left(\dfrac{1}{4}\right)^{1/2}$

10. $\left(\dfrac{1}{16}\right)^{1/2}$

11. $\left(\dfrac{1}{8}\right)^{1/3}$

12. $\left(\dfrac{1}{16}\right)^{1/4}$

13. $-16^{1/4}$

14. $-125^{1/3}$

15. $(-27)^{1/3}$

16. $(-125)^{1/3}$

17. $(-64)^{1/3}$

18. $(-216)^{1/3}$

19. $0^{1/3}$

20. $25^{3/2}$

21. $36^{3/2}$

22. $27^{2/3}$

23. $81^{3/4}$

24. $100^{3/2}$

25. $144^{3/2}$

26. $1000^{2/3}$

27. $\left(\dfrac{1}{8}\right)^{2/3}$

28. $\left(\dfrac{4}{9}\right)^{3/2}$

29. $\left(\dfrac{8}{27}\right)^{2/3}$

30. $\left(\dfrac{27}{64}\right)^{2/3}$

31. $4^{-3/2}$

32. $25^{-5/2}$

33. $16^{-3/2}$

34. $81^{-3/2}$

35. $(-27)^{-2/3}$

36. $(-8)^{-2/3}$

37. $(-32)^{-2/5}$

38. $(-16)^{-5/2}$

39. $\left(\dfrac{1}{4}\right)^{-3/2}$

40. $\left(\dfrac{4}{25}\right)^{-3/2}$

41. $\left(\dfrac{27}{8}\right)^{-4/3}$

42. $\left(\dfrac{25}{49}\right)^{-3/2}$

43. $\left(-\dfrac{8}{27}\right)^{-1/3}$

44. $\left(\dfrac{16}{81}\right)^{-3/4}$

In Exercises 45–56, perform the indicated operations. **Write all answers as a single expression without using negative exponents.**

45. $5^{3/7}5^{2/7}$

46. $4^{2/5}4^{2/5}$

47. $(4^{1/5})^3$

48. $(3^{1/3})^5$

49. $\dfrac{9^{4/5}}{9^{3/5}}$

50. $\dfrac{7^{2/3}}{7^{1/2}}$

51. $\dfrac{7^{1/2}}{7^0}$

52. $5^{1/3}5^{-5/3}$

53. $6^{-2/3}6^{-4/3}$

54. $\dfrac{3^{4/3}3^{1/3}}{3^{2/3}}$

55. $\dfrac{2^{5/6}2^{1/3}}{2^{1/2}}$

56. $\dfrac{5^{1/3}5^{1/2}}{5^{1/3}}$

In Exercises 57–76, simplify each expression. Assume that all variables represent positive numbers. **Write all answers without using negative exponents.**

57. $(8x)^{1/3}$

58. $(32x^3)^{1/5}$

59. $(27x^2y)^{2/3}$

60. $(81x^2y)^{3/4}$

61. $(25x^2y)^{3/2}$

62. $(125x^2y)^{4/3}$

63. $(4xy^3)^{-1/2}$

64. $(8x^2y)^{-1/3}$

65. $\dfrac{(4x^3y)^{1/2}}{(9xy)^{1/2}}$

66. $\dfrac{(27x^3y)^{1/3}}{(8xy^2)^{2/3}}$

67. $\dfrac{(8xy^2)^{1/2}(2xy)^{1/2}}{xy^{1/2}}$

68. $\dfrac{(4x^2y)^{1/3}(2xy^2)^{1/3}}{(xy^2)^{2/3}}$

69. $x^{a/3}x^{a/2}$

70. $x^{a/4}x^{a/3}$

71. $\dfrac{x^{a/4}}{x^{a/3}}$

72. $\dfrac{x^{a/2}}{x^{a/3}}$

73. $\dfrac{x^{a/5}x^{2a/5}}{x^{4a/5}}$

74. $\dfrac{x^{1/b}x^{2/b}}{x^{4/b}}$

75. $\left(\dfrac{x^{2/a}x^{3/a}}{x^{1/b}}\right)^{ab}$

76. $\left(\dfrac{x^b y^c}{z^b}\right)^{c/b}$

In Exercises 77–98, perform the indicated multiplications to remove parentheses. **Write all answers without using negative exponents.**

77. $y^{1/3}(y^{2/3} + y^{5/3})$

78. $y^{2/5}(y^{-2/5} + y^{3/5})$

79. $a^{2/3}(a^{4/3} + a^{-2/3})$

80. $a^{-2/3}(a^{5/3} + a^{2/3})$

81. $x^{3/5}(x^{7/5} - x^{2/5} + 1)$

82. $x^{4/3}(x^{2/3} + 3x^{5/3} - 4)$

83. $z^{1/3}y^{1/2}(z^{-1/3} + 1 - y^{-1/2})$

84. $z^{-2/3}x^{1/3}(z^{5/3}x^{2/3} - z^{-1/3}x^{-1/3})$

85. $(x^{1/2} + 2)(x^{1/2} - 2)$

86. $(x^{1/2} + y^{1/2})(x^{-1/2} + y^{-1/2})$

87. $(x^{2/3} - x)(x^{2/3} + x)$

88. $(x^{1/2} + y^{1/2})(x^{1/2} - y^{1/2})$

89. $(x^{-1/2} + y^{1/2})(x^{1/2} + y^{-1/2})$

90. $(x^{1/3} + x^2)(x^{1/3} - x^2)$

91. $(x^{2/3} + y^{2/3})^2$

92. $(a^{1/2} - b^{2/3})^2$

93. $(a^{3/2} - b^{3/2})^2$

94. $(x^{-1/2} - x^{1/2})^2$

95. $(x^{1/3} + 1)(x^{2/3} - x^{1/3} + 1)$

96. $(x^{1/3} - 2)(x^{2/3} + 2x^{1/3} + 4)$

97. $[(3 - x^{1/3})(9 + x^{2/3} + 3x^{1/3})]^2$

98. $[x^{-1/3}(x^{-2/3} + x^{1/3})]^2$

6.2   RADICAL EXPRESSIONS

In the previous section we defined the symbol $a^{1/n}$ to be the nth root of a. We now introduce a different symbol for the nth root of a.

Definition.   If n is a natural number greater than 1 and if $a^{1/n}$ is a real number, then

$$a^{1/n} = \sqrt[n]{a}$$

The symbol $\sqrt[n]{a}$ is called a **radical expression** (or radical). The symbol $\sqrt{}$ is called a **radical sign**, the number a is called the **radicand**, and n is called the **index** (or the **order**) of the radical. If the order of a radical is 2, the expression is called a **square root** and we do not write the index. Thus,

$$\sqrt{a} \qquad \text{means} \qquad \sqrt[2]{a}$$

If the index of a radical is 3, the radical is called a **cube root**.

We now restate the definition for the nth root of a number using radical notation:

Definition.   If n is a natural number greater than 1 and $a \geq 0$, then $\sqrt[n]{a}$ is the nonnegative number whose nth power is a. In symbols,

$$(\sqrt[n]{a})^n = a$$

The nonnegative number $\sqrt[n]{a}$ is called the **principal nth root** of a.

If 2 is substituted for n in the equation $(\sqrt[n]{a})^n = a$, we have

$$(\sqrt[2]{a})^2 = (\sqrt{a})^2 = \sqrt{a}\,\sqrt{a} = a$$

Thus, if a can be factored into two equal factors, then either of those factors is a square root of a.

In the expression $\sqrt[n]{a}$, if n is an odd natural number greater than 1, we can remove the restriction that $a \geq 0$.

Definition.   If n is an odd natural number greater than 1 and if a is any real number, then $\sqrt[n]{a}$ is the real number whose nth power is a. In symbols,

$$(\sqrt[n]{a})^n = a$$

Example 1

a. $\sqrt{36} = 6$ because $6^2 = 36$.   Read $\sqrt{36}$ as "the square root of 36."

b. $\sqrt[4]{81} = 3$ because $3^4 = 81$.   Read $\sqrt[4]{81}$ as "the fourth root of 81."

c. $\sqrt[3]{8} = 2$ because $2^3 = 8$.   Read $\sqrt[3]{8}$ as "the cube root of 8."

d. $\sqrt[3]{-8} = -2$ because $(-2)^3 = -8$.

e. $-\sqrt{16} = -(\sqrt{16}) = -(4) = -4$.

f. $\sqrt[7]{0} = 0$ because $0^7 = 0$.   Read $\sqrt[7]{0}$ as "the seventh root of 0."   ■

The following chart summarizes the definitions concerning the radical expression $\sqrt[n]{a}$:

If n is a natural number greater than 1 and a is a real number, then

If $a > 0$, then $\sqrt[n]{a}$ is the positive number such that $(\sqrt[n]{a})^n = a$.

If $a = 0$, then $\sqrt[n]{a} = 0$.

If $a < 0 \begin{cases} \text{and } n \text{ is odd, then } \sqrt[n]{a} \text{ is the real number such that } (\sqrt[n]{a})^n = a. \\ \text{and } n \text{ is even, then } \sqrt[n]{a} \text{ is not a real number.} \end{cases}$

In the previous section we saw that $x^{m/n} = (x^m)^{1/n} = (x^{1/n})^m$. The same fact stated in radical notation is

$$x^{m/n} = \sqrt[n]{x^m} = (\sqrt[n]{x})^m \qquad \text{provided } \sqrt[n]{x} \text{ is a real number.}$$

Thus, the nth root of x^m is the same as the mth power of the nth root of x.

Example 2   **a.** $\sqrt[3]{8^2} = \sqrt[3]{64} = 4$ or $\sqrt[3]{8^2} = (\sqrt[3]{8})^2 = 2^2 = 4$

b. $\sqrt{9^3} = \sqrt{729} = 27$ or $\sqrt{9^3} = (\sqrt{9})^3 = 3^3 = 27$ ∎

All positive numbers have two square roots. One of them is positive and one of them is negative. For example, a square root of 100 is any number whose square is 100. There are two such numbers: 10 and -10. *The symbol $\sqrt{100}$ represents the positive square root of* 100. Thus,

$$\sqrt{100} = 10$$

The negative square root of 100 is represented by the symbol $-\sqrt{100}$. Thus,

$$-\sqrt{100} = -10$$

In general, the number a^2 has two square roots. They are a and $-a$. One of these numbers is positive and the other is negative. If a might be negative, we cannot write $\sqrt{a^2} = a$. We must use absolute value symbols to guarantee that $\sqrt{a^2}$ is positive. Thus, if a is unrestricted,

$$\sqrt{a^2} = |a|$$

For example, if $a = -3$, we have

$$\sqrt{(-3)^2} = |-3| = 3.$$

A similar argument holds when the index n is any even natural number. The symbol $\sqrt[4]{16}$, for example, means the *positive* fourth root of 16. Thus,

$$\sqrt[4]{16} = 2 \qquad \text{Because } 2^4 = 16$$

The symbol $-\sqrt[4]{16}$ represents the negative fourth root of 16:

$$-\sqrt[4]{16} = -2$$

Example 3   **a.** $\sqrt[4]{256} = |4| = 4$ **b.** $\sqrt[6]{64} = |2| = 2$

c. $-\sqrt[4]{2^4} = -|2| = -2$ **d.** $\sqrt[4]{(-2)^4} = |-2| = 2$

e. $-\sqrt[4]{(-3)^4} = -|-3| = -3$ **f.** $-\sqrt[6]{729} = -|3| = -3$ ∎

When the index n of a radical is an odd natural number, there is only one real nth root of a and we do not use absolute value symbols. For example,

$$\sqrt[3]{8} = 2 \qquad \text{and} \qquad \sqrt[3]{-8} = -2$$

In general, we have the following rules:

> If n is an even natural number, then
>
> $$\sqrt[n]{a^n} = |a|$$
>
> If n is an odd natural number, then
>
> $$\sqrt[n]{a^n} = a$$

Example 4 **a.** $\sqrt{x^2} = |x|$ because $|x|^2 = x^2$ and $|x| \geq 0$.

b. $\sqrt[3]{x^3} = x$ because $x^3 = x^3$.

c. $\sqrt[4]{a^4} = |a|$ because $|a|^4 = a^4$ and $|a| \geq 0$.

d. $\sqrt[5]{-32x^5} = -2x$ because $(-2x)^5 = -32x^5$.

e. $\sqrt{x^4} = x^2$ because $(x^2)^2 = x^4$. No absolute value signs are needed because x^2 cannot be negative. ∎

Many properties of exponents have counterparts in radical notation. For example, because $a^{1/n}b^{1/n} = (ab)^{1/n}$, we have

$$\sqrt[n]{a}\,\sqrt[n]{b} = \sqrt[n]{ab}$$

Thus, as long as all expressions represent real numbers, the product of the nth roots of two numbers is equal to the nth root of their product. More formally, we have the following:

> **Property 1 of Radicals.** If $\sqrt[n]{a}$ and $\sqrt[n]{b}$ are real numbers, then
>
> $$\sqrt[n]{ab} = \sqrt[n]{a}\,\sqrt[n]{b}$$

Note that Property 1 of radicals involves the nth root of the product of two numbers. However, there is no such property for sums. For example,

$$\sqrt{9 + 4} \neq \sqrt{9} + \sqrt{4}$$

because

$$\sqrt{9 + 4} = \sqrt{13} \qquad \text{but} \qquad \sqrt{9} + \sqrt{4} = 3 + 2 = 5$$

Numbers such as 1, 4, 9, 16, 25, and 36 that are squares of integers are called **perfect squares**. Numbers such as 1, 8, 27, and 64 that are cubes of integers are called **perfect cubes**. In like fashion, there are perfect fourth powers, perfect fifth powers, and so on. We can use this concept of perfect powers and Property 1 of radicals to simplify many radical expressions.

Example 5   Simplify   **a.** $\sqrt{12}$,   **b.** $\sqrt{98}$, and   **c.** $\sqrt[3]{54}$.

Solution   **a.**   Factor 12 so that one factor is the largest perfect square that divides 12. In this case, the largest perfect square that divides 12 is 4. Rewrite 12 as $4 \cdot 3$, apply Property 1 of radicals, and simplify:

$$\sqrt{12} = \sqrt{4 \cdot 3} = \sqrt{4}\sqrt{3} = 2\sqrt{3}$$

b.   The largest perfect square factor of 98 is 49. Thus,

$$\sqrt{98} = \sqrt{49 \cdot 2} = \sqrt{49}\sqrt{2} = 7\sqrt{2}$$

c.   The largest perfect cube factor of 54 is 27. Thus,

$$\sqrt[3]{54} = \sqrt[3]{27 \cdot 2} = \sqrt[3]{27}\sqrt[3]{2} = 3\sqrt[3]{2}$$ ∎

Another property of radicals involves the quotient of two radicals. Because $\dfrac{a^{1/n}}{b^{1/n}} = \left(\dfrac{a}{b}\right)^{1/n}$, it follows that

$$\frac{\sqrt[n]{a}}{\sqrt[n]{b}} = \sqrt[n]{\frac{a}{b}} \qquad (b \neq 0)$$

Thus, as long as all expressions represent real numbers, the quotient of the nth roots of two numbers is equal to the nth root of their quotient. More formally, we have the following:

Property 2 of Radicals.   If $\sqrt[n]{a}$ and $\sqrt[n]{b}$ are real numbers and $b \neq 0$, then

$$\sqrt[n]{\frac{a}{b}} = \frac{\sqrt[n]{a}}{\sqrt[n]{b}}$$

Example 6   Simplify   **a.** $\dfrac{\sqrt{72}}{\sqrt{2}}$ and   **b.** $\sqrt[3]{\dfrac{9}{27}}$.

Solution   **a.**   Write the quotient of the square roots as the square root of a quotient and simplify.

$$\frac{\sqrt{72}}{\sqrt{2}} = \sqrt{\frac{72}{2}} \qquad \text{Use Property 2 of radicals.}$$
$$= \sqrt{36}$$
$$= 6$$

b. Write the cube root of the quotient as a quotient of two cube roots.

$$\sqrt[3]{\frac{9}{27}} = \frac{\sqrt[3]{9}}{\sqrt[3]{27}} \qquad \text{Use Property 2 of radicals.}$$

$$= \frac{\sqrt[3]{9}}{3}$$

■

We will use Properties 1 and 2 of radicals to simplify many radical expressions. A radical expression is said to be in simplest form only if each of the following statements is true:

A radical expression is in simplest form only if

1. No radical appears in the denominator of a fraction.
2. No fraction appears in a radicand.
3. No prime factor of the radicand occurs more times than the index of the radical.
4. There is no common factor (other than 1) between the index of the radical and all the exponents of the factors of the radicand.

Example 7   Simplify each of the following expressions. Assume that all variables represent positive numbers. Thus, no absolute value signs will be needed.

a. $\sqrt{128a^5}$,   **b.** $\sqrt[3]{24x^5}$,   **c.** $\dfrac{\sqrt{45xy^2}}{\sqrt{5x}}$, and   **d.** $\dfrac{\sqrt[3]{-432x^5}}{\sqrt[3]{8x}}$

Solution   **a.** Rewrite $128a^5$ as $64a^4 \cdot 2a$, where $64a^4$ is the largest perfect square that divides $128a^5$. Then apply Property 1 of radicals, and simplify.

$$\sqrt{128a^5} = \sqrt{64a^4 \cdot 2a} = \sqrt{64a^4}\sqrt{2a} = 8a^2\sqrt{2a}$$

b. Rewrite $24x^5$ as $8x^3 \cdot 3x^2$, where $8x^3$ is the largest perfect cube that divides $24x^5$. Then apply Property 1 of radicals, and simplify.

$$\sqrt[3]{24x^5} = \sqrt[3]{8x^3 \cdot 3x^2} = \sqrt[3]{8x^3}\sqrt[3]{3x^2} = 2x\sqrt[3]{3x^2}$$

c. Use Property 2 of radicals to rewrite the quotient of the square roots as the square root of a quotient. Then simplify.

$$\frac{\sqrt{45xy^2}}{\sqrt{5x}} = \sqrt{\frac{45xy^2}{5x}} = \sqrt{9y^2} = 3y$$

d. Use Property 2 of radicals to rewrite the quotient of the cube roots as the cube root of a quotient. Then simplify.

$$\frac{\sqrt[3]{-432x^5}}{\sqrt[3]{8x}} = \sqrt[3]{\frac{-432x^5}{8x}} = \sqrt[3]{-54x^4} = \sqrt[3]{-27x^3 \cdot 2x}$$

$$= \sqrt[3]{-27x^3}\sqrt[3]{2x} = -3x\sqrt[3]{2x}$$

■

To simplify a radical with a complicated radicand, we can use the prime factorization of the radicand to determine its perfect square factors. For example, to simplify $\sqrt{3168x^5y^7}$, we first find the prime factorization of $3168x^5y^7$:

$$3168x^5y^7 = 2^5 \cdot 3^2 \cdot 11 \cdot x^5 \cdot y^7$$

Thus, we have

$$
\begin{aligned}
\sqrt{3168x^5y^7} &= \sqrt{2^4 \cdot 3^2 \cdot x^4 \cdot y^6 \cdot 2 \cdot 11 \cdot x \cdot y} \\
&= \sqrt{2^4 \cdot 3^2 \cdot x^4 \cdot y^6} \sqrt{2 \cdot 11 \cdot x \cdot y} \\
&= 2^2 \cdot 3x^2y^3 \sqrt{22xy} \\
&= 12x^2y^3 \sqrt{22xy}
\end{aligned}
$$

Rationalizing the Denominator

The radical expression $\sqrt{70}/\sqrt{3}$ is not in simplest form because it contains a radical in its denominator. To simplify this expression we must use a process called **rationalizing the denominator**. To eliminate the radical in the denominator, we multiply both the numerator and the denominator of the fraction by $\sqrt{3}$ to obtain

$$\frac{\sqrt{70}}{\sqrt{3}} = \frac{\sqrt{70} \cdot \sqrt{3}}{\sqrt{3} \cdot \sqrt{3}} = \frac{\sqrt{210}}{3}$$

Because there is no radical in the denominator and because $\sqrt{210}$ cannot be simplified, the radical expression $\sqrt{210}/3$ is in simplest form.

Example 8 Use the process of rationalizing the denominator to simplify $\sqrt{\dfrac{20}{7}}$.

Solution First write the square root of the quotient as the quotient of two square roots:

$$\sqrt{\frac{20}{7}} = \frac{\sqrt{20}}{\sqrt{7}}$$

Then rationalize the denominator by multiplying both the numerator and the denominator by $\sqrt{7}$:

$$\frac{\sqrt{20}}{\sqrt{7}} = \frac{\sqrt{20} \cdot \sqrt{7}}{\sqrt{7} \cdot \sqrt{7}} = \frac{\sqrt{140}}{7}$$

However, the radical in the numerator of $\sqrt{140}/7$ can be simplified, and the fraction can be written as follows:

$$\frac{\sqrt{140}}{7} = \frac{\sqrt{4 \cdot 35}}{7} = \frac{\sqrt{4} \cdot \sqrt{35}}{7} = \frac{2\sqrt{35}}{7}$$

∎

Example 9   Rationalize the denominator of the fraction $\dfrac{1}{\sqrt[3]{2}}$.

Solution   To rationalize the denominator, multiply both the numerator and the denominator by a number that will result in a perfect cube under the radical sign. Because $2 \cdot 4 = 8$ is a perfect cube, $\sqrt[3]{4}$ is such a number. Proceed as follows:

$$\frac{1}{\sqrt[3]{2}} = \frac{1 \cdot \sqrt[3]{4}}{\sqrt[3]{2} \cdot \sqrt[3]{4}} = \frac{\sqrt[3]{4}}{\sqrt[3]{8}} = \frac{\sqrt[3]{4}}{2} \qquad \blacksquare$$

Example 10   Rationalize the denominator of the fraction $\dfrac{\sqrt[3]{5}}{\sqrt[3]{18}}$.

Solution   To rationalize the denominator, multiply both the numerator and the denominator by a number that will result in a perfect cube under the radical sign in the denominator. The first six perfect cubes are

$$1^3 = 1 \qquad 2^3 = 8 \qquad 3^3 = 27 \qquad 4^3 = 64 \qquad 5^3 = 125 \qquad \text{and} \qquad 6^3 = 216$$

and 216 is the smallest perfect cube that is divisible by 18: $216 \div 18 = 12$. Thus, multiplying both the numerator and the denominator by $\sqrt[3]{12}$ will give a perfect cube under the radical sign in the denominator:

$$\frac{\sqrt[3]{5}}{\sqrt[3]{18}} = \frac{\sqrt[3]{5} \cdot \sqrt[3]{12}}{\sqrt[3]{18} \cdot \sqrt[3]{12}} = \frac{\sqrt[3]{60}}{\sqrt[3]{216}} = \frac{\sqrt[3]{60}}{6} \qquad \blacksquare$$

Example 11   Rationalize the denominator of the fraction $\dfrac{\sqrt{5xy^2}}{\sqrt{xy^3}}$. Assume that x and y are positive numbers.

Solution 1 $\dfrac{\sqrt{5xy^2}}{\sqrt{xy^3}} = \sqrt{\dfrac{5xy^2}{xy^3}}$ **Solution 2** $\dfrac{\sqrt{5xy^2}}{\sqrt{xy^3}} = \sqrt{\dfrac{5xy^2}{xy^3}}$

$$= \sqrt{\frac{5}{y}} \qquad\qquad\qquad\qquad = \sqrt{\frac{5}{y}}$$

$$= \frac{\sqrt{5}}{\sqrt{y}} \qquad\qquad\qquad\qquad = \sqrt{\frac{5 \cdot y}{y \cdot y}}$$

$$= \frac{\sqrt{5} \cdot \sqrt{y}}{\sqrt{y} \cdot \sqrt{y}} \qquad\qquad\qquad = \frac{\sqrt{5y}}{\sqrt{y^2}}$$

$$= \frac{\sqrt{5y}}{y} \qquad\qquad\qquad\qquad = \frac{\sqrt{5y}}{y} \qquad \blacksquare$$

Example 12   Simplify $\sqrt{x^2 + 6x + 9}$. Assume that x is positive.

Solution   Note that the radical can be written in the form $\sqrt{(x+3)^2}$. Because $(x+3)(x+3) = (x+3)^2$ and $x+3$ is positive, it follows that $\sqrt{(x+3)^2} = x + 3$. Thus,

$$\sqrt{x^2 + 6x + 9} = \sqrt{(x+3)^2}$$
$$= x + 3$$

■ EXERCISE 6.2

In Exercises 1–24, simplify each radical.

1. $\sqrt{121}$ **2.** $\sqrt{144}$ **3.** $-\sqrt{64}$ **4.** $-\sqrt{1}$

5. $\sqrt[3]{1}$ **6.** $\sqrt[3]{-8}$ **7.** $\sqrt[3]{-125}$ **8.** $\sqrt[3]{512}$

9. $\sqrt[4]{81}$ **10.** $\sqrt[6]{64}$ **11.** $-\sqrt[5]{243}$ **12.** $-\sqrt[4]{625}$

13. $\sqrt[5]{-32}$ **14.** $\sqrt[3]{-512}$ **15.** $\sqrt{9^3}$ **16.** $\sqrt[3]{8^4}$

17. $\sqrt[4]{16^3}$ **18.** $\sqrt[3]{(-27)^2}$ **19.** $\sqrt[5]{-32^2}$ **20.** $\sqrt[4]{\left(\frac{1}{16}\right)^3}$

21. $\sqrt[3]{-\left(\frac{1}{8}\right)^2}$ **22.** $\sqrt[3]{\left(\frac{8}{27}\right)^2}$ **23.** $\sqrt[5]{243^{-2}}$ **24.** $\sqrt[5]{32^{-3}}$

In Exercises 25–36, simplify each radical. Use absolute value symbols where necessary.

25. $\sqrt{4x^2}$ **26.** $\sqrt{9a^2}$ **27.** $\sqrt[3]{8a^3}$ **28.** $\sqrt[3]{27x^6}$

29. $\sqrt[4]{x^4}$ **30.** $\sqrt[4]{x^8}$ **31.** $\sqrt[4]{x^{12}}$ **32.** $\sqrt{x^8}$

33. $\sqrt[5]{-x^5}$ **34.** $\sqrt[3]{-x^6}$ **35.** $\sqrt[3]{-27a^6}$ **36.** $\sqrt[5]{-32x^5}$

In Exercises 37–88, simplify each radical expression. Assume that all variables represent positive numbers. No absolute value symbols will be necessary.

37. $\sqrt{5}\sqrt{5}$ **38.** $\sqrt{11}\sqrt{11}$ **39.** $\sqrt[3]{2}\sqrt[3]{2}\sqrt[3]{2}$ **40.** $\sqrt[3]{4}\sqrt[3]{4}\sqrt[3]{4}$

41. $\sqrt{t}\sqrt{t}$ **42.** $-\sqrt{z}\sqrt{z}$ **43.** $\sqrt{20}$ **44.** $\sqrt{8}$

45. $\sqrt{24}$ **46.** $\sqrt{50}$ **47.** $\sqrt{200}$ **48.** $\sqrt{250}$

49. $-\sqrt{50x^2}$ **50.** $-\sqrt{75a^2}$ **51.** $\sqrt{32b}$ **52.** $-\sqrt{80c}$

53. $-\sqrt{112a^3}$ **54.** $\sqrt{147a^5}$ **55.** $\sqrt{175a^2b^3}$ **56.** $-\sqrt{128a^3b^5}$

57. $-\sqrt{300xy}$ **58.** $\sqrt{200x^2y}$ **59.** $\sqrt[3]{81}$ **60.** $\sqrt[3]{-72}$

61. $\sqrt[3]{-80}$ **62.** $\sqrt[3]{270}$ **63.** $\sqrt[3]{-54x^6}$ **64.** $-\sqrt[3]{-81a^3}$

65. $-\sqrt[3]{16x^{12}y^3}$ **66.** $\sqrt[3]{40a^3b^6}$ **67.** $\sqrt[4]{32x^{12}y^4}$ **68.** $-\sqrt[4]{243x^{20}y^8}$

69. $-\sqrt[5]{64x^{10}y^5}$ **70.** $\sqrt[5]{486a^{25}b^{20}}$ **71.** $-\dfrac{\sqrt{500}}{\sqrt{5}}$ **72.** $\dfrac{\sqrt{128}}{\sqrt{2}}$

73. $\dfrac{\sqrt{98}}{\sqrt{2}}$ **74.** $-\dfrac{\sqrt{75}}{\sqrt{3}}$ **75.** $\dfrac{\sqrt{180ab^4}}{\sqrt{5ab^2}}$ **76.** $\dfrac{\sqrt{112xy^2}}{\sqrt{7xy}}$

77. $\dfrac{\sqrt{128x^7}}{\sqrt{8x^2}}$ **78.** $\dfrac{\sqrt{245a^7}}{\sqrt{5a}}$ **79.** $\dfrac{\sqrt[3]{48}}{\sqrt[3]{6}}$ **80.** $\dfrac{\sqrt[3]{64}}{\sqrt[3]{8}}$

81. $\dfrac{\sqrt[3]{189a^4}}{\sqrt[3]{7a}}$ **82.** $\dfrac{\sqrt[3]{243x^2}}{\sqrt[3]{9x}}$ **83.** $\sqrt{\dfrac{7}{9}}$ **84.** $\sqrt{\dfrac{3}{4}}$

85. $\sqrt{\dfrac{3x}{48x^3}}$ **86.** $\sqrt{\dfrac{2a^3}{128a^5}}$ **87.** $\sqrt{\dfrac{10abc^2}{98a^3b^5}}$ **88.** $\sqrt{\dfrac{14tu^2}{128t^3}}$

In Exercises 89–94, you may have to simplify the fraction partially to make the radicand in the denominator a perfect square or a perfect cube.

89. $\sqrt{\dfrac{22x^3}{242x}}$ **90.** $\sqrt{\dfrac{100x^4}{288}}$ **91.** $\sqrt[3]{\dfrac{4a^3}{27a^6}}$ **92.** $\sqrt[3]{\dfrac{3x^9}{8x^{12}}}$

93. $\sqrt[3]{\dfrac{18a^9}{24}}$ **94.** $\sqrt[3]{\dfrac{20b^{12}}{54}}$

In Exercises 95–114, rationalize each denominator. Assume that all variables represent positive numbers.

95. $\dfrac{1}{\sqrt{7}}$ **96.** $\dfrac{2}{\sqrt{6}}$ **97.** $\dfrac{\sqrt{2}}{\sqrt{3}}$ **98.** $\dfrac{\sqrt{3}}{\sqrt{2}}$

99. $\dfrac{\sqrt{5}}{\sqrt{8}}$ **100.** $\dfrac{\sqrt{3}}{\sqrt{50}}$ **101.** $\dfrac{\sqrt{8}}{\sqrt{2}}$ **102.** $\dfrac{\sqrt{27}}{\sqrt{3}}$

103. $\dfrac{1}{\sqrt[3]{2}}$ **104.** $\dfrac{2}{\sqrt[3]{6}}$ **105.** $\dfrac{3}{\sqrt[3]{9}}$ **106.** $\dfrac{2}{\sqrt[3]{a}}$

107. $\dfrac{\sqrt[3]{2}}{\sqrt[3]{3}}$ **108.** $\dfrac{\sqrt[3]{9}}{\sqrt[3]{54}}$ **109.** $\dfrac{\sqrt{8x^2y}}{\sqrt{xy}}$ **110.** $\dfrac{\sqrt{9xy}}{\sqrt{3x^2y}}$

111. $\dfrac{\sqrt{10xy^2}}{\sqrt{2xy^3}}$ **112.** $\dfrac{\sqrt{5ab^2c}}{\sqrt{10abc}}$ **113.** $\dfrac{\sqrt[3]{4a^2}}{\sqrt[3]{2ab}}$ **114.** $\dfrac{\sqrt[3]{9x}}{\sqrt[3]{3xy}}$

In Exercises 115–124, simplify each expression. Assume that all variables represent positive numbers.

115. $\sqrt[4]{x^5y^3z^8}$ **116.** $\sqrt[4]{x^7y^5z^{13}}$ **117.** $\sqrt[3]{-16a^5b^3c^2}$ **118.** $\sqrt[3]{-54a^{11}b^{13}c^{16}}$

119. $\sqrt[5]{-64a^6b^6c^{11}}$ **120.** $\sqrt[5]{486x^7y^8z^9}$ **121.** $\sqrt{x^2+2x+1}$ **122.** $\sqrt{x^2+4x+4}$

123. $\sqrt{x^2+8x+16}$ **124.** $\sqrt{x^4+6x^2+9}$

6.3 ADDING AND SUBTRACTING RADICAL EXPRESSIONS

Two radical expressions with the same index and the same radicand are called **like** or **similar radicals**. Because of the distributive property, we can combine them. For example, to simplify the expression $3\sqrt{2} + 2\sqrt{2}$, we use the distributive property to factor out $\sqrt{2}$ and simplify:

$$3\sqrt{2} + 2\sqrt{2} = (3+2)\sqrt{2}$$
$$= 5\sqrt{2}$$

If two radical expressions have the same index, but different radicands, they often can be adjusted so they have the same radicand. Then they can be combined. For example, to simplify the expression $\sqrt{27} - \sqrt{12}$, we simplify both radicals and then combine the like radicals.

$$\begin{aligned} \sqrt{27} - \sqrt{12} &= \sqrt{9 \cdot 3} - \sqrt{4 \cdot 3} \\ &= \sqrt{9}\sqrt{3} - \sqrt{4}\sqrt{3} \\ &= 3\sqrt{3} - 2\sqrt{3} \\ &= (3 - 2)\sqrt{3} \\ &= \sqrt{3} \end{aligned}$$

As the previous examples suggest, we can use the following rule to add or subtract radicals:

To add or subtract radicals, simplify each radical and combine all like radicals. To combine like radicals, add their coefficients and keep the same radical.

Example 1   Simplify $2\sqrt{12} - 3\sqrt{48} + 3\sqrt{3}$.

Solution   Simplify each radical separately, factor out the common factor of $\sqrt{3}$, and simplify:

$$\begin{aligned} 2\sqrt{12} - 3\sqrt{48} + 3\sqrt{3} &= 2\sqrt{4 \cdot 3} - 3\sqrt{16 \cdot 3} + 3\sqrt{3} \\ &= 2\sqrt{4}\sqrt{3} - 3\sqrt{16}\sqrt{3} + 3\sqrt{3} \\ &= 2(2)\sqrt{3} - 3(4)\sqrt{3} + 3\sqrt{3} \\ &= (4 - 12 + 3)\sqrt{3} \\ &= -5\sqrt{3} \end{aligned}$$ ■

Example 2   Simplify $\sqrt[3]{16} - \sqrt[3]{54} + \sqrt[3]{24}$.

Solution   Simplify each radical separately and proceed as follows:

$$\begin{aligned} \sqrt[3]{16} - \sqrt[3]{54} + \sqrt[3]{24} &= \sqrt[3]{8 \cdot 2} - \sqrt[3]{27 \cdot 2} + \sqrt[3]{8 \cdot 3} \\ &= \sqrt[3]{8}\sqrt[3]{2} - \sqrt[3]{27}\sqrt[3]{2} + \sqrt[3]{8}\sqrt[3]{3} \\ &= 2\sqrt[3]{2} - 3\sqrt[3]{2} + 2\sqrt[3]{3} \\ &= (2 - 3)\sqrt[3]{2} + 2\sqrt[3]{3} \\ &= -\sqrt[3]{2} + 2\sqrt[3]{3} \end{aligned}$$

Note that you cannot combine $-\sqrt[3]{2}$ and $2\sqrt[3]{3}$ because the radicals have different radicands.   ■

Example 3   Simplify $\sqrt[3]{16x^4} + \sqrt[3]{54x^4} - \sqrt[3]{-128x^4}$. Assume that $x > 0$.

Solution Simplify each radical expression separately, factor out the common factor of $\sqrt[3]{2x}$, and simplify:

$$\sqrt[3]{16x^4} + \sqrt[3]{54x^4} - \sqrt[3]{-128x^4} = \sqrt[3]{8x^3}\sqrt[3]{2x} + \sqrt[3]{27x^3}\sqrt[3]{2x} - \sqrt[3]{-64x^3}\sqrt[3]{2x}$$
$$= 2x\sqrt[3]{2x} + 3x\sqrt[3]{2x} + 4x\sqrt[3]{2x}$$
$$= (2x + 3x + 4x)\sqrt[3]{2x}$$
$$= 9x\sqrt[3]{2x}$$

■

Example 4   Simplify $3\sqrt[3]{24} - 8\sqrt[3]{81} - 2\sqrt[3]{\dfrac{3}{27}}$.

Solution Simplify each radical expression separately, and combine terms:

$$3\sqrt[3]{24} - 8\sqrt[3]{81} - 2\sqrt[3]{\frac{3}{27}} = 3\sqrt[3]{8}\sqrt[3]{3} - 8\sqrt[3]{27}\sqrt[3]{3} - 2\frac{\sqrt[3]{3}}{\sqrt[3]{27}}$$
$$= 3(2)\sqrt[3]{3} - 8(3)\sqrt[3]{3} - 2\frac{\sqrt[3]{3}}{3}$$
$$= 6\sqrt[3]{3} - 24\sqrt[3]{3} - \frac{2}{3}\sqrt[3]{3}$$
$$= \frac{18}{3}\sqrt[3]{3} - \frac{72}{3}\sqrt[3]{3} - \frac{2}{3}\sqrt[3]{3}$$
$$= \left(\frac{18}{3} - \frac{72}{3} - \frac{2}{3}\right)\sqrt[3]{3}$$
$$= -\frac{56}{3}\sqrt[3]{3}$$

■

■ EXERCISE 6.3

In Exercises 1–52, simplify and combine like radicals, if possible. Assume that all variables represent positive numbers.

1. $4\sqrt{2} + 6\sqrt{2}$

2. $6\sqrt{5} + 3\sqrt{5}$

3. $8\sqrt[5]{7} - 7\sqrt[5]{7}$

4. $10\sqrt[6]{12} - \sqrt[6]{12}$

5. $8\sqrt{x} + 6\sqrt{x}$

6. $10\sqrt{xy} - 2\sqrt{xy}$

7. $\sqrt{3} + \sqrt{27}$

8. $\sqrt{8} + \sqrt{32}$

9. $\sqrt{2} - \sqrt{8}$

10. $\sqrt{20} - \sqrt{125}$

11. $\sqrt{98} - \sqrt{50}$

12. $\sqrt{72} - \sqrt{200}$

13. $3\sqrt{24} + \sqrt{54}$

14. $\sqrt{18} + 2\sqrt{50}$

15. $\sqrt[3]{24} + \sqrt[3]{3}$

16. $\sqrt[3]{16} + \sqrt[3]{128}$

17. $\sqrt[3]{32} - \sqrt[3]{108}$

18. $\sqrt[3]{80} - \sqrt[3]{10000}$

19. $2\sqrt[3]{125} - 5\sqrt[3]{64}$

20. $3\sqrt[3]{27} + 12\sqrt[3]{216}$

21. $3\sqrt[3]{-54} + 8\sqrt[3]{-128}$

22. $5\sqrt[3]{-81} - 7\sqrt[3]{-375}$

23. $14\sqrt[4]{32} - 15\sqrt[4]{162}$

24. $23\sqrt[4]{768} + \sqrt[4]{48}$

25. $\sqrt{98} - \sqrt{50} - \sqrt{72}$

26. $\sqrt{20} + \sqrt{125} - \sqrt{80}$

27. $\sqrt{18} + \sqrt{300} - \sqrt{243}$

28. $\sqrt{80} - \sqrt{128} + \sqrt{288}$

29. $2\sqrt[3]{16} - \sqrt[3]{54} - 3\sqrt[3]{128}$

30. $\sqrt[4]{48} - \sqrt[4]{243} - \sqrt[4]{768}$

31. $\sqrt{25y^2z} - \sqrt{16y^2z}$

32. $\sqrt{x^2y} + \sqrt{9y}$

33. $\sqrt{x^4y^3} - \sqrt{x^4y^5} - \sqrt{x^4y^7}$

34. $\sqrt{ay^3} + \sqrt{ay^5} - \sqrt{ay^7}$

35. $\sqrt[5]{x^6y^2} + \sqrt[5]{32x^6y^2} + \sqrt[5]{x^{11}y^2}$

36. $\sqrt[3]{x^4y^3} + \sqrt[3]{x^7y^6} - \sqrt[3]{x^{10}y^9}$

37. $\sqrt{x^2 + 4x + 4} + \sqrt{x^2 + 2x + 1}$

38. $\sqrt{4x^2 + 12x + 9} + \sqrt{9x^2 + 6x + 1}$

39. $\sqrt{3x^2 + 6x + 3} + \sqrt{3x^2}$

40. $\sqrt{5x^2 - 10x + 5} - \sqrt{5x^2 + 20x + 20}$

41. $\sqrt{8} + \dfrac{4}{\sqrt{2}} - \sqrt{32}$

42. $\sqrt{12} + \dfrac{6}{\sqrt{3}} - 3\sqrt{243}$

43. $\sqrt{16x} - \dfrac{x}{\sqrt{x}}$

44. $\sqrt{25a^3} + \dfrac{\sqrt{a^4}}{a}$

45. $\sqrt{18} - \sqrt{12} + \dfrac{\sqrt{12}}{6} - \dfrac{\sqrt{8}}{4}$

46. $\sqrt{80} + \sqrt{28} + \dfrac{\sqrt{20}}{5} + \dfrac{\sqrt{28}}{7}$

47. $\dfrac{\sqrt{48a}}{3a} - \dfrac{\sqrt{108a^3}}{9a^2} + \dfrac{\sqrt{12a}}{6a}$

48. $\dfrac{\sqrt{200y}}{4y} + \dfrac{\sqrt{98y}}{2y} - \dfrac{\sqrt{288y^3}}{6y^2}$

49. $\dfrac{\sqrt{108x^3}}{4x^2} + \dfrac{\sqrt{75x}}{x} - \dfrac{\sqrt{147x}}{2x}$

50. $\dfrac{\sqrt{50a^5}}{10a^4} + \dfrac{5\sqrt{2a^3}}{2a^3} - \dfrac{\sqrt{200a}}{10a^2}$

51. $\dfrac{3\sqrt{28x^5y}}{4x} + \dfrac{2x\sqrt{7xy^3}}{3y} - \dfrac{\sqrt{112x^5y^3}}{3xy}$

52. $\dfrac{y\sqrt{18x^5}}{2x^2} + \dfrac{7\sqrt{2xy^4}}{4y} - \dfrac{\sqrt{18xy^2}}{12}$

6.4 MULTIPLYING AND DIVIDING RADICAL EXPRESSIONS

If two radical expressions have the same index, they can be multiplied and divided. We begin by showing how to multiply a monomial by a monomial.

Example 1   Multiply $3\sqrt{6}$ by $2\sqrt{3}$.

Solution   Make use of the commutative and associative properties of multiplication to multiply the coefficients and the radicals separately. Remember to simplify any radicals in the product, if possible.

$$3\sqrt{6} \cdot 2\sqrt{3} = 3(2)\sqrt{6}\sqrt{3}$$
$$= 6\sqrt{18}$$
$$= 6\sqrt{9}\sqrt{2}$$
$$= 6(3)\sqrt{2}$$
$$= 18\sqrt{2}$$

■

To multiply a polynomial by a monomial, we use the distributive property to remove parentheses and then simplify each term.

Example 2   Simplify $3\sqrt{3}(4\sqrt{8} - 5\sqrt{27})$.

Solution
$$3\sqrt{3}(4\sqrt{8} - 5\sqrt{27}) = 3\sqrt{3} \cdot 4\sqrt{8} - 3\sqrt{3} \cdot 5\sqrt{27}$$
$$= 12\sqrt{24} - 15\sqrt{81}$$
$$= 12\sqrt{4}\sqrt{6} - 15(9)$$
$$= 12(2)\sqrt{6} - 135$$
$$= 24\sqrt{6} - 135$$

■

To multiply a binomial by a binomial, we use the FOIL method.

Example 3   Simplify $(\sqrt{7} + \sqrt{2})(\sqrt{7} - 3\sqrt{2})$.

Solution

$$(\sqrt{7} + \sqrt{2})(\sqrt{7} - 3\sqrt{2}) = (\sqrt{7})^2 - 3\sqrt{7}\sqrt{2} + \sqrt{2}\sqrt{7} - 3\sqrt{2}\sqrt{2}$$
$$= 7 - 3\sqrt{14} + \sqrt{14} - 3(2)$$
$$= 7 - 2\sqrt{14} - 6$$
$$= 1 - 2\sqrt{14}$$

∎

Example 4   Multiply $\sqrt{3}x - \sqrt{5}$ by $\sqrt{2}x + \sqrt{10}$.

Solution   Multiply the two binomials using the FOIL method. Then, simplify each of the four terms.

$$(\sqrt{3}x - \sqrt{5})(\sqrt{2}x + \sqrt{10}) = \sqrt{3}\sqrt{2}x^2 + \sqrt{3}\sqrt{10}x - \sqrt{5}\sqrt{2}x - \sqrt{5}\sqrt{10}$$
$$= \sqrt{6}x^2 + \sqrt{30}x - \sqrt{10}x - \sqrt{50}$$
$$= \sqrt{6}x^2 + \sqrt{30}x - \sqrt{10}x - \sqrt{25}\sqrt{2}$$
$$= \sqrt{6}x^2 + \sqrt{30}x - \sqrt{10}x - 5\sqrt{2}$$

∎

To divide radical expressions, we rationalize the denominators of all fractions containing radicals and then simplify. In Section 6.2 we considered rationalizing denominators that were monomials. We now consider rationalizing denominators that are binomials. Suppose we wish to rationalize the denominator of the fraction

$$\frac{1}{\sqrt{2} + 1}$$

It is not sufficient to multiply the numerator and the denominator by $\sqrt{2}$. (Try it and discover why.) Instead we shall multiply both the numerator and the denominator by $\sqrt{2} - 1$. Note that this binomial is the same binomial as the denominator, but with the opposite sign between its terms.

$$\frac{1}{\sqrt{2} + 1} = \frac{1(\sqrt{2} - 1)}{(\sqrt{2} + 1)(\sqrt{2} - 1)}$$
$$= \frac{\sqrt{2} - 1}{(\sqrt{2})^2 - 1} \qquad (\sqrt{2} + 1)(\sqrt{2} - 1) = (\sqrt{2})^2 - 1$$
$$= \frac{\sqrt{2} - 1}{2 - 1}$$
$$= \frac{\sqrt{2} - 1}{1}$$
$$= \sqrt{2} - 1$$

In the previous discussion, we began by multiplying both the numerator and the denominator of the given fraction by $\sqrt{2} - 1$. This binomial is the same as the denominator of the given fraction $\sqrt{2} + 1$, except for the signs between their terms. Such binomials are called **conjugates** of each other.

Definition.   **Conjugate binomials** are binomials that are the same except for the sign between their terms. The conjugate of $a + b$ is $a - b$, and the conjugate of $a - b$ is $a + b$.

Example 5   Rationalize the denominator of the fraction $\dfrac{\sqrt{x} - \sqrt{3}}{\sqrt{x} - \sqrt{2}}$. Assume that x is a positive number.

Solution   Multiply both the numerator and denominator of the fraction by $\sqrt{x} + \sqrt{2}$, which is the conjugate of $\sqrt{x} - \sqrt{2}$. Then simplify.

$$\frac{\sqrt{x} - \sqrt{3}}{\sqrt{x} - \sqrt{2}} = \frac{(\sqrt{x} - \sqrt{3})(\sqrt{x} + \sqrt{2})}{(\sqrt{x} - \sqrt{2})(\sqrt{x} + \sqrt{2})}$$
$$= \frac{x + \sqrt{2x} - \sqrt{3x} - \sqrt{6}}{x - 2}$$

∎

Example 6   Rationalize the denominator of the fraction $\dfrac{9x^2}{\sqrt{3x}(\sqrt{5} - \sqrt{2})}$. Assume that x represents a positive number.

Solution   Multiply numerator and denominator by $\sqrt{3x}(\sqrt{5} + \sqrt{2})$, and simplify.

$$\frac{9x^2}{\sqrt{3x}(\sqrt{5} - \sqrt{2})} = \frac{9x^2 \cdot \sqrt{3x}(\sqrt{5} + \sqrt{2})}{\sqrt{3x}(\sqrt{5} - \sqrt{2}) \cdot \sqrt{3x}(\sqrt{5} + \sqrt{2})}$$
$$= \frac{9x^2\sqrt{3x}(\sqrt{5} + \sqrt{2})}{\sqrt{3x}\sqrt{3x}(\sqrt{5} - \sqrt{2})(\sqrt{5} + \sqrt{2})}$$
$$= \frac{9x^2\sqrt{3x}(\sqrt{5} + \sqrt{2})}{3x(5 - 2)}$$
$$= \frac{9x^2\sqrt{3x}(\sqrt{5} + \sqrt{2})}{9x}$$
$$= x\sqrt{3x}(\sqrt{5} + \sqrt{2})$$

∎

■ **EXERCISE 6.4** ▬▬▬▬▬▬▬▬▬▬

In Exercises 1–24, perform each indicated multiplication and simplify. Assume that all variables represent positive numbers.

1. $\sqrt{2}\sqrt{8}$

2. $\sqrt{3}\sqrt{27}$

3. $\sqrt{5}\sqrt{10}$

4. $\sqrt{7}\sqrt{35}$

5. $\sqrt{3}\sqrt{6}$

6. $\sqrt{11}\sqrt{33}$

7. $\sqrt[3]{5}\sqrt[3]{25}$

8. $\sqrt[3]{7}\sqrt[3]{49}$

9. $\sqrt[3]{9}\sqrt[3]{3}$

10. $\sqrt[3]{16}\sqrt[3]{4}$

11. $\sqrt[3]{2}\sqrt[3]{12}$

12. $\sqrt[3]{3}\sqrt[3]{18}$

13. $\sqrt{ab^3}\sqrt{ab}$

14. $\sqrt{8x}\sqrt{2x^3y}$

15. $\sqrt{5ab}\sqrt{5a}$

16. $\sqrt{15rs^2}\sqrt{10r}$

17. $\sqrt[3]{5r^2s}\sqrt[3]{2r}$

18. $\sqrt[3]{3xy^2z^3}\sqrt[3]{9x^3z}$

19. $\sqrt[3]{a^5bc^2}\sqrt[3]{16ab^5}$

20. $\sqrt[3]{3x^4y}\sqrt[3]{18x}$

21. $\sqrt{x(x+3)}\sqrt{x^3(x+3)}$

22. $\sqrt{y^2(x+y)}\sqrt{(x+y)^3}$

23. $\sqrt[3]{6x^2(y+z)^2}\sqrt[3]{18x(y+z)}$

24. $\sqrt[3]{9x^2y(z+1)^2}\sqrt[3]{6xy^2(z+1)}$

In Exercises 25–44, perform each indicated multiplication and simplify. Assume that all variables represent positive numbers.

25. $3\sqrt{5}(4-\sqrt{5})$

26. $2\sqrt{7}(3\sqrt{7}-1)$

27. $3\sqrt{2}(4\sqrt{3}+2\sqrt{7})$

28. $-\sqrt{3}(\sqrt{7}-\sqrt{5})$

29. $-2\sqrt{5}(4\sqrt{2}-3\sqrt{3})$

30. $3\sqrt{7}(2\sqrt{7}+3\sqrt{3})$

31. $(\sqrt{2}+1)(\sqrt{2}-3)$

32. $(2\sqrt{3}+1)(\sqrt{3}-1)$

33. $(4\sqrt{3}+3)(2\sqrt{3}-5)$

34. $(7\sqrt{2}+2)(3\sqrt{2}-5)$

35. $(\sqrt{5}+\sqrt{3})(\sqrt{5}+\sqrt{3})$

36. $(\sqrt{2}-\sqrt{3})(\sqrt{3}-\sqrt{2})$

37. $(\sqrt{3}-\sqrt{2})(\sqrt{3}+\sqrt{2})$

38. $(\sqrt{3}+\sqrt{2})(\sqrt{3}+\sqrt{2})$

39. $(2\sqrt{3}-\sqrt{5})(\sqrt{3}+3\sqrt{5})$

40. $(5\sqrt{2}-\sqrt{3})(2\sqrt{2}+2\sqrt{3})$

41. $(3\sqrt{2}-2)^2$

42. $(2\sqrt{3}+5)^2$

43. $-2\sqrt{3}(\sqrt{7}+\sqrt{3})^2$

44. $\sqrt{2}(2\sqrt{5}+3\sqrt{3})^2$

In Exercises 45–72, perform each division by rationalizing the denominator and simplifying. Assume that all variables represent positive numbers.

45. $\dfrac{1}{\sqrt{2}-1}$

46. $\dfrac{2}{\sqrt{3}-1}$

47. $\dfrac{-6}{\sqrt{5}+4}$

48. $\dfrac{-10}{\sqrt{5}-1}$

49. $\dfrac{2}{\sqrt{3}+1}$

50. $\dfrac{2}{\sqrt{5}+1}$

51. $\dfrac{25}{\sqrt{6}+1}$

52. $\dfrac{50}{\sqrt{7}+1}$

53. $\dfrac{\sqrt{2}}{\sqrt{5}+3}$

54. $\dfrac{\sqrt{3}}{\sqrt{3}-2}$

55. $\dfrac{\sqrt{7}}{2-\sqrt{5}}$

56. $\dfrac{\sqrt{11}}{3+\sqrt{7}}$

57. $\dfrac{2}{\sqrt{7}-\sqrt{5}}$

58. $\dfrac{5}{\sqrt{7}-\sqrt{2}}$

59. $\dfrac{20}{\sqrt{3}+1}$

60. $\dfrac{36}{\sqrt{5}+2}$

61. $\dfrac{\sqrt{3}+1}{\sqrt{3}-1}$

62. $\dfrac{\sqrt{2}-1}{\sqrt{2}+1}$

63. $\dfrac{\sqrt{7}-2}{\sqrt{2}+\sqrt{7}}$

64. $\dfrac{\sqrt{5}+2}{\sqrt{3}-\sqrt{2}}$

65. $\dfrac{2}{\sqrt{x}+1}$

66. $\dfrac{3}{\sqrt{x}-2}$

67. $\dfrac{x}{\sqrt{x}-4}$

68. $\dfrac{2x}{\sqrt{x}+1}$

69. $\dfrac{2z-1}{\sqrt{2z}-1}$

70. $\dfrac{3t-1}{\sqrt{3t}+1}$

71. $\dfrac{\sqrt{x}-\sqrt{y}}{\sqrt{x}+\sqrt{y}}$

72. $\dfrac{\sqrt{x}+\sqrt{y}}{\sqrt{x}-\sqrt{y}}$

6.5   RADICALS WITH DIFFERENT ORDERS

We have discussed how to add, subtract, multiply, and divide radicals with the same order (radicals with the same index). Fractional exponents enable us to simplify certain expressions involving radicals with different orders. For example, to simplify the radical expression $\sqrt[4]{4}$, we note that $4 = 2^2$, write the expression in rational exponent form, and proceed as follows:

$$\sqrt[4]{4} = \sqrt[4]{2^2} = (2^2)^{1/4} = 2^{2(1/4)} = 2^{1/2} = \sqrt{2}$$

Example 1   Assume that x and y represent positive numbers and simplify: **a.** $\sqrt[6]{8}$, **b.** $\sqrt[6]{25}$,   **c.** $\sqrt[12]{x^4}$,   **d.** $\sqrt[20]{x^6y^2}$, and   **e.** $\sqrt[9]{8x^6}$.

Solution   **a.** $\sqrt[6]{8} = \sqrt[6]{2^3} = 2^{3/6} = 2^{1/2} = \sqrt{2}$

b. $\sqrt[6]{25} = \sqrt[6]{5^2} = 5^{2/6} = 5^{1/3} = \sqrt[3]{5}$

c. $\sqrt[12]{x^4} = x^{4/12} = x^{1/3} = \sqrt[3]{x}$

d. $\sqrt[20]{x^6y^2} = (x^6y^2)^{1/20} = x^{6/20}y^{2/20} = x^{3/10}y^{1/10} = (x^3y)^{1/10} = \sqrt[10]{x^3y}$

e. $\sqrt[9]{8x^6} = \sqrt[9]{2^3x^6} = (2^3x^6)^{1/9} = 2^{3/9}x^{6/9} = 2^{1/3}x^{2/3} = (2x^2)^{1/3} = \sqrt[3]{2x^2}$ ■

By using rational exponents we can add, subtract, multiply, and divide many radicals with different orders. For example, to add the radicals $\sqrt[4]{25}$ and $\sqrt{20}$, we proceed as follows:

$$\begin{aligned}
\sqrt[4]{25} + \sqrt{20} &= \sqrt[4]{5^2} + \sqrt{4 \cdot 5} \\
&= (5^2)^{1/4} + \sqrt{4}\sqrt{5} \\
&= 5^{2/4} + 2\sqrt{5} \\
&= 5^{1/2} + 2\sqrt{5} \\
&= \sqrt{5} + 2\sqrt{5} \\
&= 3\sqrt{5}
\end{aligned}$$

To multiply $\sqrt{2}$ by $\sqrt[3]{5}$, we first write each number as a sixth root. To do so, we write each radical as an expression with a rational exponent, change each exponent to a fraction with a denominator of 6, and change back to radical notation:

$$\sqrt{2} = 2^{1/2} = 2^{3/6} = (2^3)^{1/6} = \sqrt[6]{2^3} = \sqrt[6]{8}$$
$$\sqrt[3]{5} = 5^{1/3} = 5^{2/6} = (5^2)^{1/6} = \sqrt[6]{5^2} = \sqrt[6]{25}$$

We then multiply the sixth roots:

$$\sqrt{2}\sqrt[3]{5} = \sqrt[6]{8}\sqrt[6]{25} = \sqrt[6]{8 \cdot 25} = \sqrt[6]{200}$$

Example 2   Write $\dfrac{\sqrt{3}}{\sqrt[3]{4}}$ as an expression containing a single radical.

Solution   First, eliminate the radical in the denominator by multiplying numerator and denominator by $\sqrt[3]{2}$:

$$\frac{\sqrt{3}}{\sqrt[3]{4}} = \frac{\sqrt{3}\sqrt[3]{2}}{\sqrt[3]{4}\sqrt[3]{2}}$$

$$= \frac{\sqrt{3}\sqrt[3]{2}}{\sqrt[3]{8}}$$

$$= \frac{\sqrt{3}\sqrt[3]{2}}{2}$$

Because the numerator is the product of radicals of different orders, rewrite the radicals in forms with fractional exponents having a common denominator, and proceed as follows:

$$\frac{\sqrt{3}}{\sqrt[3]{4}} = \frac{3^{1/2}2^{1/3}}{2}$$

$$= \frac{3^{3/6}2^{2/6}}{2}$$

$$= \frac{\sqrt[6]{3^3}\sqrt[6]{2^2}}{2}$$

$$= \frac{\sqrt[6]{3^3 \cdot 2^2}}{2}$$

$$= \frac{\sqrt[6]{27 \cdot 4}}{2}$$

$$= \frac{\sqrt[6]{108}}{2}$$

∎

Example 3   Assume that all variables represent positive numbers, and write $\sqrt{8x^3y}\sqrt[3]{9xy^4}$ as an expression containing a single radical.

Solution   First, remove all perfect square factors from the radicand within the square root, and all perfect cube roots from the other radicand:

$$\sqrt{8x^3y}\sqrt[3]{9xy^4} = \sqrt{4 \cdot 2 \cdot x^2 \cdot xy}\sqrt[3]{9xy \cdot y^3}$$

$$= 2x\sqrt{2xy} \cdot y\sqrt[3]{9xy}$$

$$= 2xy\sqrt{2xy}\sqrt[3]{9xy}$$

Write each radical in fractional exponent form, and adjust the fractional exponents to have common denominators. Then, convert back to radical form and find the product of the sixth roots.

$$\sqrt{8x^3y}\sqrt[3]{9xy^4} = 2xy(2xy)^{1/2}(9xy)^{1/3}$$
$$= 2xy(2xy)^{3/6}(9xy)^{2/6}$$
$$= 2xy\sqrt[6]{(2xy)^3}\sqrt[6]{(9xy)^2}$$
$$= 2xy\sqrt[6]{(2xy)^3(9xy)^2}$$
$$= 2xy\sqrt[6]{8x^3y^3 \cdot 81x^2y^2}$$
$$= 2xy\sqrt[6]{648x^5y^5} \qquad\blacksquare$$

Example 4   Write $\sqrt[3]{3x}\sqrt[5]{2x^2}$ as an expression containing a single radical.

Solution   Convert each radical to a form with fractional exponents having the same denominator, convert back to radical form, and find the product of the fifteenth roots:

$$\sqrt[3]{3x}\sqrt[5]{2x^2} = (3x)^{1/3}(2x^2)^{1/5}$$
$$= (3x)^{5/15}(2x^2)^{3/15}$$
$$= \sqrt[15]{(3x)^5}\,\sqrt[15]{(2x^2)^3}$$
$$= \sqrt[15]{243x^5}\,\sqrt[15]{8x^6}$$
$$= \sqrt[15]{243 \cdot 8x^5x^6}$$
$$= \sqrt[15]{1944x^{11}} \qquad\blacksquare$$

■ EXERCISE 6.5

In Exercises 1–16, assume that all variables represent positive numbers and simplify each radical.

1. $\sqrt[4]{9}$ 2. $\sqrt[4]{64}$ 3. $\sqrt[18]{x^9}$ 4. $\sqrt[12]{x^6}$
5. $\sqrt[4]{x^8}$ 6. $\sqrt[5]{y^{10}}$ 7. $\sqrt[6]{y^{18}}$ 8. $\sqrt[8]{x^{32}}$
9. $\sqrt[4]{16x^{12}}$ 10. $\sqrt[6]{27x^3}$ 11. $\sqrt[8]{81x^4}$ 12. $\sqrt[10]{243x^{10}}$
13. $\sqrt[9]{-8x^9}$ 14. $\sqrt[9]{-27x^{18}}$ 15. $\sqrt[3]{-64a^{12}}$ 16. $\sqrt[3]{-125a^3b^6}$

In Exercises 17–26, simplify all radicals, if possible, and then combine like radicals, if possible. Assume that all variables represent positive numbers.

17. $\sqrt{12} + \sqrt[4]{9}$ 18. $\sqrt{8} - \sqrt[4]{4}$ 19. $\sqrt[4]{64} - \sqrt{32}$ 20. $\sqrt[4]{144} + \sqrt{12}$
21. $\sqrt[4]{x^6} - \sqrt[6]{x^9}$ 22. $\sqrt[3]{a^4} + \sqrt[6]{a^8}$ 23. $\sqrt[6]{x^6y^2} + 2x\sqrt[3]{y}$ 24. $\sqrt[3]{a^2b^3} + \sqrt[9]{a^6b^9}$
25. $5\sqrt[5]{x^6y^{11}z^{16}} + 12\sqrt[10]{x^{12}y^{22}z^{32}}$ 26. $13\sqrt[6]{a^8b^6c^{12}} - 4\sqrt[3]{a^4b^3c^6}$

In Exercises 27–42, write each radical as another radical of the order indicated. Assume that all variables represent positive numbers.

27. $\sqrt{3}$;   sixth order   28. $\sqrt{2}$;   sixth order
29. $\sqrt{5}$;   eighth order   30. $\sqrt{7}$;   eighth order
31. $\sqrt[3]{15}$;   sixth order   32. $\sqrt[3]{9}$;   sixth order

33. $\sqrt[3]{4}$;   ninth order

34. $\sqrt[3]{7}$;   ninth order

35. $\sqrt[6]{3^3}$;   second order

36. $\sqrt[8]{7^4}$;   fourth order

37. $\sqrt[9]{5^3}$;   third order

38. $\sqrt[9]{7^6}$;   third order

39. $\sqrt{2xy}$;   sixth order

40. $\sqrt{3x^3y}$;   sixth order

41. $\sqrt[3]{4x^2y}$;   sixth order

42. $\sqrt[3]{9xy^2}$;   sixth order

In Exercises 43–66, perform each indicated operation. Express each answer as an expression containing a single radical. Assume that all variables represent positive numbers.

43. $\sqrt{5}\sqrt[3]{7}$

44. $\sqrt[3]{9}\sqrt{2}$

45. $\sqrt[3]{3}\sqrt{5}$

46. $\sqrt[3]{9}\sqrt{5}$

47. $\sqrt[3]{2}\sqrt{2}$

48. $\sqrt{5}\sqrt[3]{5}$

49. $\sqrt[3]{2}\sqrt[5]{8}$

50. $\sqrt[5]{3}\sqrt[3]{2}$

51. $\sqrt{5x}\sqrt[3]{xy}$

52. $\sqrt[3]{4x}\sqrt{xy}$

53. $\sqrt[3]{25x}\sqrt[5]{3y^2}$

54. $\sqrt[3]{3x}\sqrt[5]{2x^2}$

55. $\sqrt[7]{xy^3}\sqrt[5]{x^3y^4}$

56. $\sqrt[9]{x^2y}\sqrt[3]{xy^2}$

57. $\dfrac{\sqrt[3]{3}}{\sqrt{2}}$

58. $\dfrac{\sqrt{2}}{\sqrt[3]{3}}$

59. $\dfrac{\sqrt[5]{3}}{\sqrt[3]{4}}$

60. $\dfrac{\sqrt[5]{4}}{\sqrt[3]{4}}$

61. $\dfrac{\sqrt[5]{3}}{\sqrt{3}}$

62. $\dfrac{\sqrt{3}}{\sqrt[5]{3}}$

63. $\dfrac{\sqrt[7]{4x}}{\sqrt{2x}}$

64. $\dfrac{\sqrt[9]{xy}}{\sqrt{xy}}$

65. $\dfrac{\sqrt[5]{3x}}{\sqrt[3]{3}}$

66. $\dfrac{\sqrt[7]{3x}}{\sqrt[3]{3}}$

6.6   RADICAL EQUATIONS

In this section we will consider equations that contain radicals. To solve such equations we will rely on the following theorem, which is often called the **power rule**.

> **Theorem.**   If a, b, and n are real numbers and $a = b$, then
> $$a^n = b^n$$

If we raise both sides of an equation to the same power, the resulting equation may or may not be equivalent to the original equation. For example, if we square both sides of the equation

1. $x = 3$ With a solution set of $\{3\}$

we obtain the equation

2. $x^2 = 9$ With a solution set of $\{3, -3\}$

Equations 1 and 2 are not equivalent because they have different solution sets, and the solution -3 of Equation 2 does not satisfy Equation 1. Because raising both sides of an equation to the same power can introduce extraneous roots that don't check in the original equation, we must check each suspected solution of the original equation.

Example 1   Solve the equation $\sqrt{x + 3} = 4$.

Solution   To eliminate the radical, apply the power rule and square both sides of the equation. Then proceed as follows:

$$\sqrt{x + 3} = 4$$
$$(\sqrt{x + 3})^2 = 4^2$$
$$x + 3 = 16$$
$$x = 13 \qquad \text{Add } -3 \text{ to both sides.}$$

The apparent solution is 13. However, you must check it to verify that it satisfies the original equation.

Check:

$$\sqrt{x + 3} = 4$$
$$\sqrt{13 + 3} \overset{?}{=} 4$$
$$\sqrt{16} \overset{?}{=} 4$$
$$4 = 4$$

Because 13 satisfies the original equation, it is a solution.   ■

Example 2   Solve the equation $\sqrt{3x + 1} = x - 1$.

Solution   To eliminate the radical, square both sides of the equation. Then proceed as follows:

$$\sqrt{3x + 1} = x - 1$$
$$(\sqrt{3x + 1})^2 = (x - 1)^2$$
$$3x + 1 = x^2 - 2x + 1$$
$$0 = x^2 - 5x \qquad \text{Add } -3x \text{ and } -1 \text{ to both sides.}$$
$$0 = x(x - 5) \qquad \text{Factor } x^2 - 5x.$$
$$x = 0 \quad \text{or} \quad x - 5 = 0 \qquad \text{Set each factor equal to 0.}$$
$$x = 5$$

The apparent solutions are 0 and 5. You must check each one to determine if either is extraneous.

Check:

$$\sqrt{3x + 1} = x - 1 \qquad\qquad \sqrt{3x + 1} = x - 1$$
$$\sqrt{3(0) + 1} \overset{?}{=} 0 - 1 \qquad\qquad \sqrt{3(5) + 1} \overset{?}{=} 5 - 1$$
$$\sqrt{1} \overset{?}{=} -1 \qquad\qquad\qquad \sqrt{16} \overset{?}{=} 4$$
$$1 \neq -1 \qquad\qquad\qquad\qquad 4 = 4$$

The apparent solution 0 does not check; it is *extraneous* and must be discarded. The only solution of the original equation is 5.   ■

Example 3   Solve the equation $\sqrt[3]{x^3 + 7} = x + 1$.

Solution   To eliminate the radical, cube both sides of the equation. Then proceed as follows:

$$\sqrt[3]{x^3 + 7} = x + 1$$
$$(\sqrt[3]{x^3 + 7})^3 = (x + 1)^3$$
$$x^3 + 7 = x^3 + 3x^2 + 3x + 1$$
$$0 = 3x^2 + 3x - 6 \qquad \text{Add } -x^3 \text{ and } -7 \text{ to both sides.}$$
$$0 = x^2 + x - 2 \qquad \text{Divide both sides by 3.}$$
$$0 = (x + 2)(x - 1) \qquad \text{Factor } x^2 + x - 2.$$
$$x + 2 = 0 \quad \text{or} \quad x - 1 = 0 \qquad \text{Set each factor equal to 0.}$$
$$x = -2 \qquad\qquad x = 1$$

The apparent solutions are -2 and 1. Check each one to determine if either is extraneous.

Check:

$$\sqrt[3]{x^3 + 7} = x + 1 \qquad\qquad \sqrt[3]{x^3 + 7} = x + 1$$
$$\sqrt[3]{(-2)^3 + 7} \overset{?}{=} -2 + 1 \qquad\qquad \sqrt[3]{1^3 + 7} \overset{?}{=} 1 + 1$$
$$\sqrt[3]{-8 + 7} \overset{?}{=} -1 \qquad\qquad \sqrt[3]{8} \overset{?}{=} 2$$
$$\sqrt[3]{-1} \overset{?}{=} -1 \qquad\qquad 2 = 2$$
$$-1 = -1$$

Both solutions satisfy the original equation. The solution set is $\{-2, 1\}$.   ■

When more than one radical appears in an equation, it is often necessary to apply the power rule more than once.

Example 4   Solve the equation $\sqrt{x} + \sqrt{x + 2} = 2$.

Solution   To remove the radicals, both sides of the equation must be squared. This is easier to do if one radical is on each side of the equation. So, add $-\sqrt{x}$ to both sides and proceed as follows:

$$\sqrt{x} + \sqrt{x + 2} = 2$$
$$\sqrt{x + 2} = 2 - \sqrt{x}$$
$$(\sqrt{x + 2})^2 = (2 - \sqrt{x})^2 \qquad \text{Square both sides.}$$
$$x + 2 = 4 - 4\sqrt{x} + x$$
$$2 = 4 - 4\sqrt{x} \qquad \text{Add } -x \text{ to both sides.}$$
$$-2 = -4\sqrt{x} \qquad \text{Add } -4 \text{ to both sides.}$$
$$\frac{1}{2} = \sqrt{x} \qquad \text{Divide both sides by } -4.$$
$$\frac{1}{4} = x \qquad \text{Square both sides.}$$

Check:

$$\sqrt{x} + \sqrt{x + 2} = 2$$

$$\sqrt{\frac{1}{4}} + \sqrt{\frac{1}{4} + 2} \stackrel{?}{=} 2$$

$$\frac{1}{2} + \sqrt{\frac{9}{4}} \stackrel{?}{=} 2$$

$$\frac{1}{2} + \frac{3}{2} \stackrel{?}{=} 2$$

$$2 = 2$$

The solution does check. The solution set is $\{\frac{1}{4}\}$.   ■

■ EXERCISE 6.6

In Exercises 1–50, solve and check each equation. If an equation has no solutions, so indicate.

1. $\sqrt{5x - 6} = 2$ **2.** $\sqrt{7x - 10} = 12$ **3.** $\sqrt{6x + 1} + 2 = 7$ **4.** $\sqrt{6x + 13} - 2 = 5$

5. $\sqrt{4(4x + 1)} = \sqrt{x + 4}$ **6.** $\sqrt{3(x + 4)} = \sqrt{5x - 12}$

7. $\sqrt[3]{7n - 1} = 3$ **8.** $\sqrt[3]{12m + 4} = 4$ **9.** $\sqrt[4]{10p + 1} = \sqrt[4]{11p - 7}$ **10.** $\sqrt[4]{10y + 2} = 2\sqrt[4]{2}$

11. $x = \dfrac{\sqrt{12x - 5}}{2}$ **12.** $x = \dfrac{\sqrt{16x - 12}}{2}$

13. $r + 2 = \sqrt{5r + 34}$ **14.** $s + 3 = \sqrt{-4s + 20}$

15. $\sqrt{-5x + 24} = 6 - x$ **16.** $\sqrt{-x + 2} = x - 2$

17. $\sqrt{y + 2} = 4 - y$ **18.** $\sqrt{22y + 86} = y + 9$ **19.** $\sqrt{x}\sqrt{x + 16} = 15$ **20.** $\sqrt{x}\sqrt{x + 6} = 4$

21. $\sqrt[3]{x^3 - 7} = x - 1$ **22.** $\sqrt[3]{x^3 + 56} - 2 = x$

23. $\sqrt[4]{x^4 + 4x^2 - 4} = x$ **24.** $\sqrt[4]{8x - 8} + 2 = 0$

25. $\sqrt[4]{12t + 4} + 2 = 0$ **26.** $u = \sqrt[4]{u^4 - 6u^2 + 24}$ **27.** $\sqrt{2y + 1} = 1 - 2\sqrt{y}$ **28.** $\sqrt{u + 3} = \sqrt{u - 3}$

29. $\sqrt{y + 7} + 3 = \sqrt{y + 4}$ **30.** $1 + \sqrt{z} = \sqrt{z + 3}$

31. $\sqrt{v} + \sqrt{3} = \sqrt{v + 3}$ **32.** $\sqrt{x} + 2 = \sqrt{x + 4}$

33. $2 + \sqrt{u} = \sqrt{2u + 7}$ **34.** $5r + 4 = \sqrt{5r + 20} + 4r$

35. $\sqrt{6t + 1} - \sqrt{9t} = -1$ **36.** $\sqrt{4s + 1} - \sqrt{6s} = -1$

37. $\sqrt{2x + 5} + \sqrt{x + 2} = 5$ **38.** $\sqrt{2x + 5} + \sqrt{2x + 1} + 4 = 0$

39. $\sqrt{z - 1} + \sqrt{z + 2} = 3$ **40.** $\sqrt{16v + 1} + \sqrt{8v + 1} = 12$

41. $\sqrt{x - 5} - \sqrt{x + 3} = 4$ **42.** $\sqrt{x + 8} - \sqrt{x - 4} = -2$

43. $\sqrt[4]{x^2 + 2x + 1} = \sqrt{x + 2}$ **44.** $\sqrt{x + 3} = \sqrt[4]{x^2 + 5x + 6}$

45. $\sqrt{x + 1} + \sqrt{3x} = \sqrt{5x + 1}$ **46.** $\sqrt{3x} - \sqrt{x + 1} = \sqrt{x - 2}$

47. $\sqrt{\sqrt{a} + \sqrt{a+8}} = 2$

48. $\sqrt{\sqrt{2y} - \sqrt{y-1}} = 1$

49. $\dfrac{6}{\sqrt{x+5}} = \sqrt{x}$

50. $\dfrac{\sqrt{2x}}{\sqrt{x+2}} = \sqrt{x-1}$

CHAPTER SUMMARY

Key Words

conjugate binomials (6.4)
cube root (6.1)
index of a radical (6.2)
like radicals (6.3)
order of a radical (6.5)
power rule (6.6)

principal nth root (6.1)
radical expression (6.2)
radicand (6.2)
rationalizing the denominator (6.2)
similar radicals (6.3)
square root (6.1)

Key Ideas

(6.1) If n is a natural number and a is a real number, then

If $a > 0$, then $a^{1/n}$ is the positive number such that $(a^{1/n})^n = a$.

If $a = 0$, then $a^{1/n} = 0$.

If $a < 0$ $\begin{cases} \text{and } n \text{ is odd, then } a^{1/n} \text{ is the real number such that } (a^{1/n})^n = a. \\ \text{and } n \text{ is even, then } a^{1/n} \text{ is not a real number.} \end{cases}$

$a^{m/n} = (a^{1/n})^m = (a^m)^{1/n}$

$a^{-m/n} = \dfrac{1}{a^{m/n}}$ and $\dfrac{1}{a^{-m/n}} = a^{m/n}$ (provided $a \neq 0$)

(6.2) If n is a natural number greater than 1 and a is a real number, then

If $a > 0$, then $\sqrt[n]{a}$ is the positive number such that $(\sqrt[n]{a})^n = a$.

If $a = 0$, then $\sqrt[n]{a} = 0$.

If $a < 0$ $\begin{cases} \text{and } n \text{ is odd, then } \sqrt[n]{a} \text{ is the real number such that } (\sqrt[n]{a})^n = a. \\ \text{and } n \text{ is even, then } \sqrt[n]{a} \text{ is not a real number.} \end{cases}$

If n is an even natural number, then $\sqrt[n]{a^n} = |a|$.

If n is an odd natural number, then $\sqrt[n]{a^n} = a$.

$\sqrt[n]{ab} = \sqrt[n]{a}\,\sqrt[n]{b}$ and, if $b \neq 0$, $\sqrt[n]{\dfrac{a}{b}} = \dfrac{\sqrt[n]{a}}{\sqrt[n]{b}}$

Radicals can be removed from the denominator of a fraction by rationalizing the denominator.

(6.3) Like radicals can be combined by addition and subtraction:

$$3\sqrt{2} + 5\sqrt{2} = 8\sqrt{2}$$

Radicals that are not similar can often be converted to radicals that are similar and then combined:

$$\sqrt{2} + \sqrt{8} = \sqrt{2} + \sqrt{4}\sqrt{2} = \sqrt{2} + 2\sqrt{2} = 3\sqrt{2}$$

(6.4) If two radicals have the same index, they can be multiplied:

$$\sqrt{3x}\,\sqrt{6x} = \sqrt{18x^2} = 3x\sqrt{2} \qquad \text{provided that } x \geq 0$$

To rationalize the binomial denominator of a fraction, multiply both the numerator and the denominator by the conjugate of the binomial in the denominator.

(6.5) Radicals of different orders can be added, subtracted, multiplied, and divided when they are converted into radicals with common order.

(6.6) If $a = b$, then $a^n = b^n$.

Raising both sides of an equation to the same power can lead to extraneous solutions. Be sure to check all suspected solutions.

REVIEW EXERCISES

In Review Exercises 1–16, perform each operation and simplify the result, if possible. Assume that all variables represent positive numbers.

1. $25^{1/2}$

2. $-36^{1/2}$

3. $9^{3/2}$

4. $16^{3/2}$

5. $(-8)^{1/3}$

6. $-8^{2/3}$

7. $8^{-2/3}$

8. $8^{-1/3}$

9. $-49^{5/2}$

10. $\dfrac{1}{25^{7/2}}$

11. $\left(\dfrac{1}{4}\right)^{-3/2}$

12. $\left(\dfrac{4}{9}\right)^{-3/2}$

13. $(27x^3y)^{1/3}$

14. $(81x^4y^2)^{1/4}$

15. $(25x^6y^4)^{3/2}$

16. $(27u^2v^3)^{-2/3}$

*In Review Exercises 17–20, perform the indicated multiplications to remove parentheses. **Write all answers without using negative exponents.***

17. $u^{1/2}(u^{1/2} - u^{-1/2})$

18. $v^{2/3}(v^{1/3} + v^{4/3})$

19. $(x^{1/2} + y^{1/2})^2$

20. $(a^{2/3} + b^{2/3})(a^{2/3} - b^{2/3})$

In Review Exercises 21–28, simplify each radical.

21. $\sqrt{49}$

22. $-\sqrt{121}$

23. $-\sqrt{36}$

24. $\sqrt{225}$

25. $\sqrt[3]{-27}$

26. $-\sqrt[3]{216}$

27. $\sqrt[4]{625}$

28. $\sqrt[5]{-32}$

In Review Exercises 29–36, simplify each radical. Use absolute value symbols where necessary.

29. $\sqrt{240}$

30. $\sqrt[3]{54}$

31. $\sqrt[4]{32}$

32. $\sqrt[5]{96}$

33. $\sqrt{8x^3}$

34. $\sqrt{18x^4y^3}$

35. $\sqrt[3]{16x^5y^4z^3}$

36. $\sqrt[3]{250x^7y^3z}$

In Review Exercises 37–42, simplify each radical expression. Assume that all variables represent positive numbers.

37. $\sqrt{5}\sqrt{5}$ **38.** $\sqrt{6}\sqrt{216}$ **39.** $\sqrt{9x}\sqrt{x}$ **40.** $\sqrt[3]{3}\sqrt[3]{9}$

41. $-\sqrt[3]{2x^2}\sqrt[3]{4x}$ **42.** $-\sqrt[4]{256x^5y^{11}}\sqrt[4]{625x^8y^2}$

In Review Exercises 43–46, rationalize each denominator.

43. $\dfrac{1}{\sqrt{3}}$ **44.** $\dfrac{\sqrt{3}}{\sqrt{5}}$ **45.** $\dfrac{x}{\sqrt{xy}}$ **46.** $\dfrac{\sqrt[3]{uv}}{\sqrt[3]{u^5v^7}}$

In Review Exercises 47–48, simplify each radical expression. Assume that all variables represent positive numbers.

47. $\sqrt{x^2 + 6x + 9}$ **48.** $\sqrt[3]{(x + 1)(x^2 + 2x + 1)}$

In Review Exercises 49–56, simplify and combine like radicals. Assume that all variables represent positive numbers.

49. $\sqrt{2} + \sqrt{8}$ **50.** $\sqrt{20} - \sqrt{5}$ **51.** $2\sqrt[3]{3} - \sqrt[3]{24}$ **52.** $\sqrt[4]{32} + 2\sqrt[4]{162}$

53. $2\sqrt{8} + 2\sqrt{200} + \sqrt{50}$ **54.** $3\sqrt{27} - 2\sqrt{3} + 5\sqrt{75}$

55. $\sqrt[3]{54} - 3\sqrt[3]{16} + 4\sqrt[3]{128}$ **56.** $2\sqrt[4]{32} + 4\sqrt[4]{162} - 5\sqrt[4]{512}$

In Review Exercises 57–64, simplify each radical expression. Assume that all variables represent positive numbers.

57. $\sqrt{2}\sqrt{8}$ **58.** $\sqrt{2}(\sqrt{2} + 3)$ **59.** $\sqrt{5}(\sqrt{2} - 1)$ **60.** $\sqrt{7}(\sqrt{3} + \sqrt{2})$

61. $(\sqrt{2} + 1)(\sqrt{2} - 1)$ **62.** $(\sqrt{3} + \sqrt{2})(\sqrt{3} + \sqrt{2})$

63. $(\sqrt{x} + \sqrt{y})(\sqrt{x} - \sqrt{y})$ **64.** $(2\sqrt{u} + 3)(3\sqrt{u} - 4)$

In Review Exercises 65–68, rationalize each denominator and simplify, if possible.

65. $\dfrac{2}{\sqrt{2} - 1}$ **66.** $\dfrac{\sqrt{2}}{\sqrt{3} - 1}$ **67.** $\dfrac{2x - 32}{\sqrt{x} + 4}$ **68.** $\dfrac{\sqrt{a} + 1}{\sqrt{a} - 1}$

In Review Exercises 69–76, write each radical as an expression without radicals or as another radical with a smaller index. Assume that all variables represent positive numbers.

69. $\sqrt[4]{25}$ **70.** $\sqrt[4]{81}$ **71.** $\sqrt[6]{8}$ **72.** $\sqrt[6]{27}$

73. $\sqrt[5]{x^{10}}$ **74.** $\sqrt[6]{64x^{12}}$ **75.** $\sqrt[4]{x^{10}y^8}$ **76.** $\sqrt[12]{u^6v^{12}}$

In Review Exercises 77–84, perform each indicated operation. Express each answer as an expression without radicals or as a single radical in simplest form.

77. $\sqrt{5}\sqrt[3]{2}$ **78.** $\sqrt{2}\sqrt[3]{5}$ **79.** $\sqrt[3]{3}\sqrt[4]{4}$ **80.** $\sqrt[3]{3}\sqrt[4]{2}$

81. $\dfrac{\sqrt{5}}{\sqrt[3]{2}}$ **82.** $\dfrac{\sqrt{2}}{\sqrt[3]{3}}$ **83.** $\dfrac{\sqrt[5]{5}}{\sqrt{3}}$ **84.** $\dfrac{\sqrt[5]{3}}{\sqrt[3]{4}}$

In Review Exercises 85–90, solve and check each radical equation.

85. $\sqrt{y + 5} = \sqrt{2y - 17}$ **86.** $u = \sqrt{25u - 144}$

87. $r = \sqrt{12r - 27}$ **88.** $\sqrt{z + 1} + \sqrt{z} = 2$

89. $\sqrt{2x + 5} - \sqrt{2x} = 1$ **90.** $\sqrt[3]{x^3 + 8} = x + 2$

CHAPTER SIX TEST

In Problems 1–6, simplify each expression. **Write all answers without using negative exponents.** Assume that all variables represent positive numbers.

1. $16^{1/4}$

2. $27^{2/3}$

3. $36^{-3/2}$

4. $\left(-\dfrac{8}{27}\right)^{-2/3}$ ÷

5. $\dfrac{2^{5/3}2^{1/6}}{2^{1/2}}$

6. $\dfrac{(8x^3y)^{1/2}(8xy^5)^{1/2}}{(x^3y^6)^{1/3}}$

In Problems 7–10, simplify each expression. Assume that all variables represent positive numbers.

7. $\sqrt{48}$

8. $\sqrt{250x^3y^5}$

9. $\dfrac{\sqrt[3]{24x^{15}y^4}}{\sqrt[3]{y}}$

10. $\sqrt{\dfrac{3a^5}{48a^7}}$

In Problems 11–14, rationalize each denominator.

11. $\dfrac{1}{\sqrt{5}}$

12. $\dfrac{\sqrt{3}}{\sqrt{8}}$

13. $\dfrac{6}{\sqrt[3]{9}}$

14. $\dfrac{\sqrt{18ab}}{\sqrt{6a^2b}}$

In Problems 15–18, simplify and combine like radicals. Assume that all variables represent positive numbers.

15. $3\sqrt{3} + \sqrt{12} - \sqrt{27}$

16. $2\sqrt[3]{40} - \sqrt[3]{5000} + 4\sqrt[3]{625}$

17. $2\sqrt{48y^5} - 3y\sqrt{12y^3}$

18. $\sqrt[4]{768z^5} + z\sqrt[4]{48z}$

In Problems 19–20, perform each indicated operation and simplify, if possible. Assume that all variables represent positive numbers.

19. $-2\sqrt{xy}(3\sqrt{x} + \sqrt{xy^3})$

20. $(3\sqrt{2} + \sqrt{3})(2\sqrt{2} - 3\sqrt{3})$

In Problems 21–22, rationalize each denominator and simplify, if possible. Assume that all variables represent positive numbers.

21. $\dfrac{-\sqrt{2}}{\sqrt{5} + 3}$

22. $\dfrac{3r - 1}{\sqrt{3r} - 1}$

In Problems 23–24, write each radical as a radical with a smaller index.

23. $\sqrt[4]{64}$

24. $\sqrt[8]{625y^4}$

In Problems 25–28, write each expression as a single radical.

25. $\sqrt[4]{36} + \sqrt{54}$

26. $\sqrt[3]{xy^3} - \sqrt[9]{x^3y^9}$

27. $\sqrt[3]{5}\sqrt{7}$

28. $\dfrac{\sqrt[4]{3}}{\sqrt{3}}$

In Problems 29–30, solve and check each equation.

29. $\sqrt[3]{6n + 4} - 4 = 0$

30. $1 - \sqrt{u} = \sqrt{u - 3}$

CUMULATIVE REVIEW EXERCISES (CHAPTERS 4–6)

In Exercises 1–4, solve each equation and check the result.

1. $2x - 5 = 11$

2. $\dfrac{2}{3}x - 2 = x + 7$

3. $4(y - 3) + 4 = -3(y + 5)$

4. $2x - \dfrac{3(x - 2)}{2} = 7 - \dfrac{x - 3}{3}$

5. The sum of three consecutive even integers is 90. What are the integers?

6. The length of a rectangle is three times its width. The perimeter of the rectangle is 112 centimeters. What are its dimensions?

7. Solve for a in the formula $S = \dfrac{n(a + l)}{2}$.

In Exercises 8–9, solve each equation by factoring.

8. $x^3 - 4x = 0$

9. $6x^2 + 7 = -23x$

In Exercises 10–11, solve and check each equation.

10. $|4x - 3| = 9$

11. $|2x - 1| = |3x + 4|$

In Exercises 12–16, solve each inequality.

12. $-3(x - 4) \geq x - 32$

13. $-8 < -3x + 1 < 10$

14. $x - 2 \leq 3x + 1 \leq 5x - 4$

15. $|3x - 2| \leq 4$

16. $|2x + 3| > 5$

17. Simplify: $\dfrac{2x^2y + xy - 6y}{3x^2y + 5xy - 2y}$.

18. Perform the indicated multiplication and division, and simplify:

$$\frac{x^2 - 4}{x^2 + 9x + 20} \div \frac{x^2 + 5x + 6}{x^2 + 4x - 5} \cdot \frac{x^2 + 3x - 4}{(x - 1)^2}$$

19. Perform the indicated addition and subtraction, and simplify:

$$\frac{2}{x + y} + \frac{3}{x - y} - \frac{x - 3y}{x^2 - y^2}$$

20. Simplify the complex fraction $\dfrac{\dfrac{a}{b} + b}{a - \dfrac{b}{a}}$.

In Exercises 21–22, solve and check each equation.

21. $\dfrac{5x - 3}{x + 2} = \dfrac{5x + 3}{x - 2}$

22. $\dfrac{3}{x - 2} + \dfrac{x^2}{(x + 3)(x - 2)} = \dfrac{x + 4}{x + 3}$

In Exercises 23–36, simplify each expression. Write all answers without using negative exponents. Assume all variables represent positive numbers.

23. $64^{2/3}$

24. $8^{-1/3}$

25. $\dfrac{x^{5/3}x^{1/2}}{x^{3/4}}$

26. $(x^{2/3} - x^{1/3})(x^{2/3} + x^{1/3})$

27. $\sqrt[3]{-27x^3}$

28. $\sqrt{48t^3}$

29. $\sqrt[3]{\dfrac{128x^4}{2x}}$

30. $\sqrt{x^2 + 8x + 16}$

31. $\sqrt{50} - \sqrt{8} + \sqrt{32}$

32. $-3\sqrt[4]{32} - 2\sqrt[4]{162} + 5\sqrt[4]{48}$

33. $3\sqrt{2}(2\sqrt{3} - 4\sqrt{12})$

34. $\dfrac{5}{\sqrt[3]{x}}$

35. $\dfrac{\sqrt{x} + 2}{\sqrt{x} - 1}$

36. $\sqrt[6]{x^3 y^3}$

In Exercises 37–38, solve and check each equation.

37. $5\sqrt{x + 2} = x + 8$

38. $\sqrt{x} + \sqrt{x + 2} = 2$

7 Graphs, Equations of Lines, and Functions

Mathematical expressions are often used to indicate relationships between several quantities. The formula $d = rt$, for example, indicates how distance traveled is related to the rate of speed and time. Because distance depends on rate and time, we say that distance is a function of rate and time. This concept of *function* is one of the fundamental ideas that runs throughout all of mathematics. To introduce this topic, we begin by discussing the rectangular coordinate system.

7.1 THE RECTANGULAR COORDINATE SYSTEM

René Descartes (1596–1650) is credited with the idea of associating ordered pairs of real numbers with points in a geometric plane. His idea is based on two perpendicular number lines, one horizontal and one vertical, that divide the plane into four quadrants numbered as in Figure 7-1. The horizontal number line is called the **x-axis** and the vertical number line is called the **y-axis**. The point where the axes intersect, called the **origin**, is the zero point on each number line. The positive direction on the x-axis is to the right, the positive direction on the y-axis is upward, and the unit distance on each axis is the same. This geometric configuration is called a **rectangular coordinate system**, or a **Cartesian coordinate system**, in honor of its inventor.

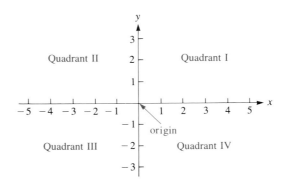

Figure 7-1

To **plot** the point associated with the pair of real numbers (2, 3), we start at the origin and count 2 units to the right, and then 3 units up. See Figure 7-2. The point *P*, which lies in the first quadrant, is called the **graph** of the pair (2, 3). The pair (2, 3) gives the **coordinates** of point *P*. To plot point *Q* with coordinates (−4, 6), we start at the origin and count 4 units to the left, and then 6 units up. Point *Q* lies in the second quadrant. Point *R* with coordinates (6, −4) lies in the fourth quadrant.

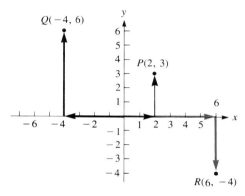

Figure 7-2

Note that the pairs (−4, 6) and (6, −4) represent different points. Because order is important when graphing pairs of real numbers, such pairs are called **ordered pairs**. The first coordinate, *a*, in the ordered pair (*a*, *b*) is called the **x-coordinate** or the **abscissa**. The second coordinate, *b*, is called the **y-coordinate** or the **ordinate**.

Example 1   Graph the set {(−1, −1), (0, 0), (1, 1), (2, 2)}.

Solution   Draw an *x*-axis and a *y*-axis that are perpendicular, and plot each ordered pair. See Figure 7-3. The four points that are determined form the graph of the given set.

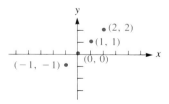

Figure 7-3

■

It is possible to draw a "picture" or a graph of an equation in two variables. The **graph of an equation** in the two variables *x* and *y* is the set of all points on a rectangular coordinate system with coordinates (x, y) that satisfy the equation.

Example 2 Graph the equation $3x + 2y = 12$.

Solution Pick some arbitrary values for either x or y, substitute those values in the equation, and solve for the other variable. For example, if $x = 2$, you can find y as follows:

$$\begin{aligned} 3x + 2y &= 12 && \\ 3(2) + 2y &= 12 && \text{Substitute 2 for } x. \\ 6 + 2y &= 12 && \text{Simplify.} \\ 2y &= 6 && \text{Add } -6 \text{ to both sides.} \\ y &= 3 && \text{Divide both sides by 2.} \end{aligned}$$

Thus, one ordered pair that satisfies the equation is (2, 3).

If $y = 6$, you have

$$\begin{aligned} 3x + 2y &= 12 && \\ 3x + 2(6) &= 12 && \text{Substitute 6 for } y. \\ 3x + 12 &= 12 && \text{Simplify.} \\ 3x &= 0 && \text{Add } -12 \text{ to both sides.} \\ x &= 0 && \text{Divide both sides by 3.} \end{aligned}$$

Thus, another ordered pair that satisfies the equation is (0, 6).

The ordered pairs (2, 3), and (0, 6), and others that satisfy the equation $3x + 2y = 12$ are shown in the table of values in Figure 7-4. Plot each of these ordered pairs on a rectangular coordinate system, as in the figure. Note that the resulting points appear to lie on a straight line. It can be shown that all points representing ordered pairs that satisfy the equation $3x + 2y = 12$ do, in fact, lie on a straight line. Draw the line that joins the five points. This line is the graph of the equation.

$3x + 2y = 12$

x	y
2	3
0	6
4	0
6	−3
−2	9

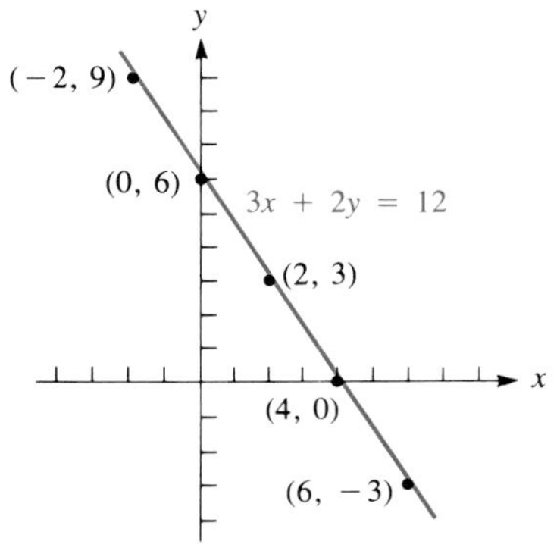

Figure 7-4

■

Because the line in Example 2 intersects the y-axis at the point $(0, 6)$, the number 6 is called the **y-intercept** of the line. Likewise, 4 is called the **x-intercept**.

Example 3 Use the x- and y-intercepts to graph the equation $2x + 5y = 10$.

Solution Begin by finding the x- and y-intercepts. To find the y-intercept, substitute **0** for x and solve for y:

$$2x + 5y = 10$$
$$2(0) + 5y = 10 \qquad \text{Substitute 0 for } x.$$
$$5y = 10 \qquad \text{Simplify.}$$
$$y = 2 \qquad \text{Divide both sides by 5.}$$

Because the y-intercept is 2, the line intersects the y-axis at the point $(0, 2)$. To find the x-intercept, substitute **0** for y and solve for x:

$$2x + 5y = 10$$
$$2x + 5(0) = 10 \qquad \text{Substitute 0 for } y.$$
$$2x = 10 \qquad \text{Simplify.}$$
$$x = 5 \qquad \text{Divide both sides by 2.}$$

Because the x-intercept is 5, the line intersects the x-axis at the point $(5, 0)$.

Although these two points, if calculated correctly, are sufficient to draw the line, it is a good idea to find and plot a third ordered pair to act as a check. To find the coordinates of a third point, substitute any convenient number, such as **1**, for y and solve for x:

$$2x + 5y = 10$$
$$2x + 5(1) = 10 \qquad \text{Substitute 1 for } y.$$
$$2x + 5 = 10 \qquad \text{Simplify.}$$
$$2x = 5 \qquad \text{Add } -5 \text{ to both sides.}$$
$$x = \frac{5}{2} \qquad \text{Divide both sides by 2.}$$

Thus, the line passes through the point $\left(\frac{5}{2}, 1\right)$.

A table of values and the graph of the equation $2x + 5y = 10$ are shown in Figure 7-5.

$2x + 5y = 10$

x	y
0	2
5	0
$\dfrac{5}{2}$	1

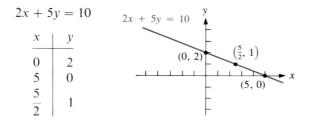

Figure 7-5

Example 4   Graph the equation $y = 3x + 4$.

Solution   Find the x- and y-intercepts: If $x = 0$, then

$$y = 3x + 4$$
$$y = 3(0) + 4$$
$$y = 4 \qquad \text{The } y\text{-intercept is 4.}$$

If $y = 0$, then

$$y = 3x + 4$$
$$0 = 3x + 4$$
$$-4 = 3x$$
$$-\frac{4}{3} = x \qquad \text{The } x\text{-intercept is } -\tfrac{4}{3}.$$

To find the coordinates of a third point, substitute **1** for x, and simplify.

$$y = 3x + 4$$
$$y = 3(\mathbf{1}) + 4$$
$$y = 7$$

A table of values and the graph of the equation $y = 3x + 4$ are shown in Figure 7-6.

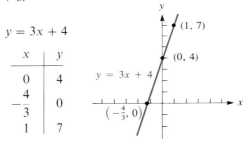

$y = 3x + 4$

x	y
0	4
$-\dfrac{4}{3}$	0
1	7

Figure 7-6

There is a formula, called the **distance formula**, that enables us to find the distance between two points that are graphed on a rectangular coordinate system. Before deriving this formula, we need to review the **Pythagorean theorem** from geometry. This theorem states that, in any right triangle, the square of the hypotenuse (the side opposite the 90° angle) is equal to the sum of the squares of the other two sides. For example, suppose the right triangle shown in Figure 7-7 has sides of 3, 4, and x units. Because of the Pythagorean theorem and the fact that lengths must be positive, we can determine the value of x:

Figure 7-7

$$3^2 + 4^2 = x^2$$
$$9 + 16 = x^2$$
$$25 = x^2$$
$$5 = x$$

Thus, $x = 5$ units.

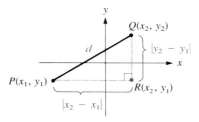

Figure 7-8

We can now derive the distance formula. To find the distance d between points $P(x_1, y_1)$ and $Q(x_2, y_2)$ shown in Figure 7-8, we construct the right triangle PRQ. The distance between P and R is $|x_2 - x_1|$ and the distance between R and Q is $|y_2 - y_1|$. We apply the Pythagorean theorem to the right triangle PRQ to get

$$[d(PQ)]^2 = |x_2 - x_1|^2 + |y_2 - y_1|^2$$
$$= (x_2 - x_1)^2 + (y_2 - y_1)^2 \qquad \text{Because } |x_2 - x_1|^2 = (x_2 - x_1)^2 \text{ and}$$
$$|y_2 - y_1|^2 = (y_2 - y_1)^2.$$

or

$$d(PQ) = \sqrt{(x_2 - x_1)^2 + (y_2 - y_1)^2}$$

Thus, we have the distance formula. Because it is one of the most important formulas in mathematics, take the time to memorize it.

The Distance Formula.   The distance between two points $P(x_1, y_1)$ and $Q(x_2, y_2)$ is given by the formula

$$d(PQ) = \sqrt{(x_2 - x_1)^2 + (y_2 - y_1)^2}$$

Example 5   Find the distance between points $P(-2, 3)$ and $Q(4, -5)$.

Solution   Use the distance formula. Substitute -2 for x_1, 3 for y_1, 4 for x_2, and -5 for y_2, and simplify:

$$d(PQ) = \sqrt{(x_2 - x_1)^2 + (y_2 - y_1)^2}$$
$$= \sqrt{[4 - (-2)]^2 + (-5 - 3)^2}$$
$$= \sqrt{(4 + 2)^2 + (-5 - 3)^2}$$
$$= \sqrt{6^2 + (-8)^2}$$
$$= \sqrt{36 + 64}$$
$$= \sqrt{100}$$
$$= 10$$

The distance between points P and Q is 10 units.   ∎

Once we have the distance formula, it is easy to prove the **midpoint formula**.

The Midpoint Formula.   The midpoint of the line segment joining points $P(x_1, y_1)$ and $Q(x_2, y_2)$ is the point M with coordinates of

$$\left(\frac{x_1 + x_2}{2}, \frac{y_1 + y_2}{2} \right)$$

The midpoint formula indicates that, to find the midpoint of the line segment PQ, we simply average the x-coordinates of P and Q, and average the y-coordinates of P and Q.

To verify this formula, we assume that point M has coordinates of

$$\left(\frac{x_1 + x_2}{2}, \frac{y_1 + y_2}{2} \right)$$

and show that points P, Q, and M lie on the same line, and that $d(PM) = d(MQ)$ (the distance from P to M is equal to the distance from M to Q). See Figure 7-9.

$$d(PM) = \sqrt{ \left(\frac{x_1 + x_2}{2} - x_1 \right)^2 + \left(\frac{y_1 + y_2}{2} - y_1 \right)^2 }$$

$$= \sqrt{ \left(\frac{x_2 - x_1}{2} \right)^2 + \left(\frac{y_2 - y_1}{2} \right)^2 }$$ Find common denominators and perform the subtractions.

$$= \sqrt{ \frac{(x_2 - x_1)^2}{4} + \frac{(y_2 - y_1)^2}{4} }$$

$$= \frac{1}{2} \sqrt{ (x_2 - x_1)^2 + (y_2 - y_1)^2 }$$ Because $\sqrt{\frac{1}{4}} = \frac{1}{2}$.

$$d(MQ) = \sqrt{ \left(x_2 - \frac{x_1 + x_2}{2} \right)^2 + \left(y_2 - \frac{y_1 + y_2}{2} \right)^2 }$$

$$= \sqrt{ \left(\frac{x_2 - x_1}{2} \right)^2 + \left(\frac{y_2 - y_1}{2} \right)^2 }$$

$$= \sqrt{ \frac{(x_2 - x_1)^2}{4} + \frac{(y_2 - y_1)^2}{4} }$$

$$= \frac{1}{2} \sqrt{ (x_2 - x_1)^2 + (y_2 - y_1)^2 }$$

$$d(PQ) = \sqrt{ (x_2 - x_1)^2 + (y_2 - y_1)^2 }$$

Because $d(PM) + d(MQ) = d(PQ)$, points P, Q, and M must lie on the same straight line. Because $d(PM) = d(MQ)$, M is the midpoint of line segment PQ.

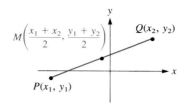

Figure 7-9

Example 6   Find the midpoint of the line segment PQ if P is $(-2, 3)$ and Q is $(3, -5)$.

Solution   The x-coordinate of M is

$$\frac{x_1 + x_2}{2} = \frac{-2 + 3}{2} = \frac{1}{2}$$

The y-coordinate of M is

$$\frac{y_1 + y_2}{2} = \frac{3 + (-5)}{2} = -1$$

Hence, the midpoint of segment PQ is point $M(\frac{1}{2}, -1)$.

EXERCISE 7.1

In Exercises 1–12, graph each equation.

1. $x + y = 4$ **2.** $x - y = 2$ **3.** $2x - y = 3$ **4.** $x + 2y = 5$
5. $3x + 4y = 12$ **6.** $4x - 3y = 12$ **7.** $y = -3x + 2$ **8.** $y = 2x - 3$
9. $3y = 6x - 9$ **10.** $2x = 4y - 10$
11. $3x + 4y - 8 = 0$ **12.** $-2y - 3x + 9 = 0$

In Exercises 13–22, find the distance between P and Q.

13. $Q(0, 0)$; $P(3, -4)$ **14.** $Q(0, 0)$; $P(-6, 8)$
15. $P(2, 4)$; $Q(5, 8)$ **16.** $P(5, 9)$; $Q(8, 13)$
17. $P(-2, -8)$; $Q(3, 4)$ **18.** $P(-5, -2)$; $Q(7, 3)$
19. $P(6, 8)$; $Q(12, 16)$ **20.** $P(10, 4)$; $Q(2, -2)$
21. $Q(-3, 5)$; $P(-5, -5)$ **22.** $Q(2, -3)$; $P(4, -8)$

In Exercises 23–36, find the midpoint of the line segment PQ.

23. $P(2, 4)$; $Q(5, 8)$ **24.** $P(5, 9)$; $Q(8, 13)$
25. $P(-2, -8)$; $Q(3, 4)$ **26.** $P(-5, -2)$; $Q(7, 3)$
27. $P(6, 8)$; $Q(12, 16)$ **28.** $P(10, 4)$; $Q(2, -2)$
29. $Q(-3, 5)$; $P(-5, -5)$ **30.** $Q(2, -3)$; $P(4, -8)$

31. $Q(0, 0)$; $P(3, -4)$ **32.** $Q(0, 0)$; $P(6, -8)$

33. $Q(a, b)$; $P(c, d)$ **34.** $Q(a + b, b)$; $P(c, c + d)$

35. $P(\sqrt{2}, \sqrt{3})$; $Q(\sqrt{3}, \sqrt{2})$ **36.** $P(\sqrt{5}, -\sqrt{3})$; $Q(-\sqrt{3}, 2\sqrt{5})$

37. Show that a triangle with vertices at $(-2, 4)$, $(2, 8)$, and $(6, 4)$ is isosceles (has two sides of equal length).

38. Show that a triangle with vertices at $(-2, 13)$, $(-8, 9)$, and $(-2, 5)$ is isosceles.

39. If $M(-2, 3)$ is the midpoint of segment PQ and the coordinates of P are $(-8, 5)$, find the coordinates of Q.

40. If $M(6, -5)$ is the midpoint of segment PQ and the coordinates of Q are $(-5, -8)$, find the coordinates of P.

41. Every point on the line CD in Illustration 1 is equidistant from points A and B. Use the distance formula to find the equation of line CD.

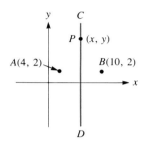

Illustration 1

42. Show that a triangle with vertices at $(2, 3)$, $(-3, 4)$, and $(1, -2)$ is a right triangle.

43. Find the coordinates of the two points on the x-axis that are $\sqrt{5}$ units away from the point $(5, 1)$.

44. The square shown in Illustration 2 has an area of 18 square units and its diagonals lie on the x- and y-axes. Find the coordinates of each corner of the square.

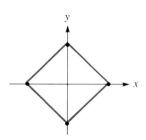

Illustration 2

7.2 SLOPE OF A NONVERTICAL LINE

The **slope of a nonvertical line** drawn in a rectangular coordinate system is a measure of its tilt or inclination. To develop a formula for computing the slope of a nonvertical line, we consider the line in Figure 7-10 that passes through the points $P(2, 3)$ and $Q(6, 9)$. If line RQ is parallel to the y-axis and line PR is parallel to the x-axis, then triangle PRQ is a right triangle and point R has coordinates $(6, 3)$. The distance from point R to point Q is the change in the y-coordinates of points R and Q, often denoted as Δy and read as "delta y." As we move from point R to point Q, $\Delta y = 9 - 3$ or 6 units. The distance from point P to point R is the change in the x-coordinates of points P and R, denoted as Δx and read as "delta x." As we move from point P to point R, $\Delta x = 6 - 2$ or 4 units.

The slope of line PQ is defined to be the distance from R to Q divided by the distance from P to R:

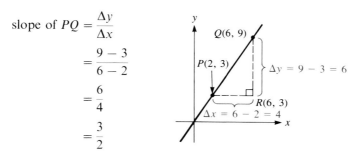

$$\text{slope of } PQ = \frac{\Delta y}{\Delta x}$$

$$= \frac{9 - 3}{6 - 2}$$

$$= \frac{6}{4}$$

$$= \frac{3}{2}$$

Figure 7-10

In general, the slope of a nonvertical line passing through the points $P(x_1, y_1)$ and $Q(x_2, y_2)$ is given by the following definition:

Definition. The **slope of a nonvertical line** passing through the points $P(x_1, y_1)$ and $Q(x_2, y_2)$ is the change in the y-coordinates divided by the corresponding change in the x-coordinates. See Figure 7-11.

In symbols, if m represents the slope of line PQ, then

$$m = \frac{\Delta y}{\Delta x} = \frac{y_2 - y_1}{x_2 - x_1} \qquad (x_2 \neq x_1)$$

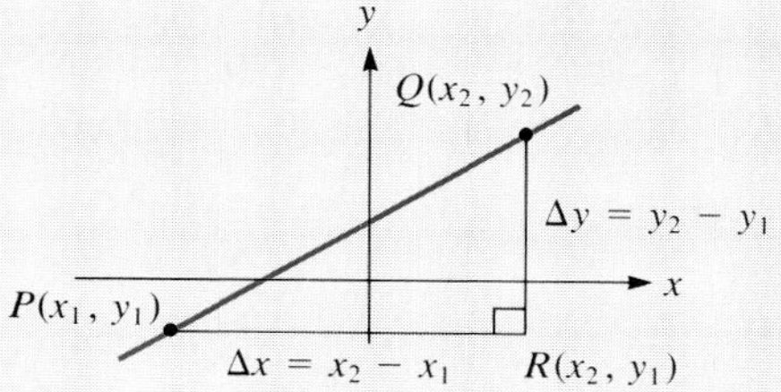

Figure 7-11

Example 1 Point P in Figure 7-12 has coordinates $(-2, 5)$, and point Q has coordinates $(6, -7)$. Find the slope of the line passing through points P and Q.

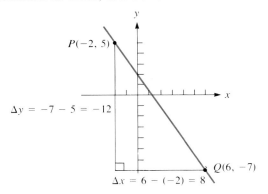

Figure 7-12

Solution   Let $P(x_1, y_1) = P(-2, 5)$ and $Q(x_2, y_2) = Q(6, -7)$. Then

$$m = \frac{\Delta y}{\Delta x} = \frac{y_2 - y_1}{x_2 - x_1}$$

$$= \frac{-7 - 5}{6 - (-2)}$$

$$= \frac{-12}{8}$$

$$= -\frac{3}{2}$$

The slope of the line passing through P and Q is $-\frac{3}{2}$.

Note that you would obtain the same result if you let $P(x_1, y_1) = P(6, -7)$ and $Q(x_2, y_2) = Q(-2, 5)$.   ∎

Example 2   The graph of the equation $3x - 4y = 12$ is a straight line. Find its slope.

Solution   Begin by finding the coordinates of two points on the line. If $x = 0$, for example, then $y = -3$. Thus, the point $(0, -3)$ is on the line. If $y = 0$, then $x = 4$. Thus, the point $(4, 0)$ is on the line.

Let $P(x_1, y_1) = P(0, -3)$ and $Q(x_2, y_2) = Q(4, 0)$, and substitute into the formula for slope to obtain

$$m = \frac{\Delta y}{\Delta x} = \frac{y_2 - y_1}{x_2 - x_1}$$

$$= \frac{0 - (-3)}{4 - 0}$$

$$= \frac{3}{4}$$

The slope of the line is $\frac{3}{4}$.   ∎

If a line has an equation of the form $y = k$, where k is a constant, it is a horizontal line and has a slope of 0. If a line has an equation of the form $x = k$, it is a vertical line. If $P(x_1, y_1)$ and $Q(x_2, y_2)$ are two points on a vertical line, then $x_1 = x_2$ and $x_2 - x_1 = 0$. Because the denominator of the fraction $\dfrac{y_2 - y_1}{x_2 - x_1}$ cannot be 0, a vertical line has no defined slope.

Example 3   Graph the equations   **a.** $y = -2$ and   **b.** $x = 5$.

Solution   **a.**   To graph the equation $y = -2$, note that any ordered pair with a y-coordinate of -2 satisfies the equation. Thus, such points as $(-2, -2)$, $(0, -2)$ and $(1, -2)$ satisfy the equation because each has a y-coordinate of -2. Make a table of values, plot the points, and draw the line. See Figure 7-13a.

b.   To graph the equation $x = 5$, note that points such as $(5, -2)$ and $(5, 1)$ satisfy the equation because each has an x-coordinate of 5. Make a table of values, plot the points, and draw the line. See Figure 7-13b.

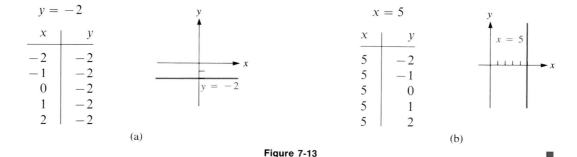

$y = -2$

x	y
-2	-2
-1	-2
0	-2
1	-2
2	-2

(a)

$x = 5$

x	y
5	-2
5	-1
5	0
5	1
5	2

(b)

Figure 7-13

If a line rises as we follow it from left to right, its slope is positive (see Figure 7-14a). If a line drops as we follow it from left to right, its slope is negative (see Figure 7-14b). If a line is horizontal, its slope is 0 (see Figure 7-14c). If a line is vertical, it has no defined slope (see Figure 7-14d).

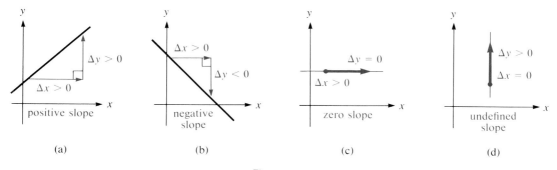

(a) positive slope   (b) negative slope   (c) zero slope   (d) undefined slope

Figure 7-14

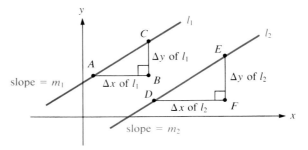

Figure 7-15

A theorem relates parallel lines to their slopes. To see this relationship, we consider the parallel lines l_1 and l_2 in Figure 7-15, with slopes of m_1 and m_2, respectively. Because the right triangles ABC and DFE are similar, it follows that

$$m_1 = \frac{\Delta y \text{ of } l_1}{\Delta x \text{ of } l_1}$$

$$= \frac{\Delta y \text{ of } l_2}{\Delta x \text{ of } l_2}$$

$$= m_2$$

Thus, if two nonvertical lines are parallel, they have the same slope. It is also true that if two lines have the same slope, they are parallel.

Theorem.   Nonvertical parallel lines have the same slope, and lines with the same slope are parallel.

Because vertical lines are parallel, two lines with undefined slope are parallel.

Example 4   Find y if the line passing through $P(3, -2)$ and $Q(-3, 4)$ is parallel to the line passing through $R(-2, 5)$ and $S(3, y)$.

Solution   Because the lines PQ and RS are parallel, they must have equal slopes. Find the slope of each line, set the slopes equal, and solve the resulting equation for y:

Slope of PQ Slope of RS

$$\frac{4 - (-2)}{-3 - 3} = \frac{y - 5}{3 - (-2)}$$

$$\frac{6}{-6} = \frac{y - 5}{5}$$

$$-1 = \frac{y - 5}{5}$$

$$-5 = y - 5$$

$$0 = y$$

Thus $y = 0$. The line passing through $P(3, -2)$ and $Q(-3, 4)$ is parallel to the line passing through $R(-2, 5)$ and $S(3, 0)$.   ∎

Example 5   If graphed on a coordinate system, lines PQ and OR are distinct lines. Is the line passing through $P(-2, 5)$ and $Q(3, 9)$ parallel to the line passing through the origin O and the point $R(5, 4)$?

Solution   Find the slope of each line:

$$\text{Slope of } PQ = \frac{\Delta y}{\Delta x} = \frac{y_2 - y_1}{x_2 - x_1} = \frac{9 - 5}{3 - (-2)} = \frac{4}{5}$$

$$\text{Slope of } OR = \frac{\Delta y}{\Delta x} = \frac{y_2 - y_1}{x_2 - x_1} = \frac{4 - 0}{5 - 0} = \frac{4}{5}$$

Because the slopes are equal, the lines are parallel.   ∎

If a and b are two numbers such that $ab = -1$, they are called **negative reciprocals**. For example,

$$-\frac{4}{3} \quad \text{and} \quad \frac{3}{4}$$

are negative reciprocals because $-\frac{4}{3}(\frac{3}{4}) = -1$.

The following theorem, accepted without proof, relates perpendicular lines to their slopes:

Theorem.   If two nonvertical lines are perpendicular, their slopes are negative reciprocals.

   If the slopes of two lines are negative reciprocals, the lines are perpendicular.

Because a horizontal line is perpendicular to a vertical line, a line with a slope of 0 is perpendicular to a line with undefined slope.

Example 6   Two lines intersect at point $P(3, -4)$. One passes through the origin O and the other passes through point $Q(9, 4)$. Are the lines perpendicular?

Solution   See Figure 7-16. Find the slope of lines OP and PQ.

$$\text{Slope of } OP = \frac{\Delta y}{\Delta x} = \frac{y_2 - y_1}{x_2 - x_1} = \frac{-4 - 0}{3 - 0} = -\frac{4}{3}$$

$$\text{Slope of } PQ = \frac{\Delta y}{\Delta x} = \frac{y_2 - y_1}{x_2 - x_1} = \frac{4 - (-4)}{9 - 3} = \frac{8}{6} = \frac{4}{3}$$

Because the slopes are not negative reciprocals, the lines are not perpendicular.

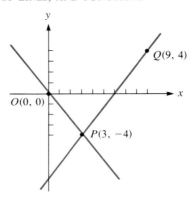

Figure 7-16

EXERCISE 7.2

In Exercises 1–10, find the slope of the line that passes through the given points. If the slope is undefined, so indicate.

1. (0, 0) and (3, 9)

2. (9, 6) and (0, 0)

3. (−1, 8) and (6, 1)

4. (−5, −8) and (3, 8)

5. (3, −1) and (−6, 2)

6. (0, −8) and (−5, 0)

7. (7, 5) and (−9, 5)

8. (2, −8) and (3, −8)

9. (−7, −5) and (−7, −2)

10. (3, −5) and (3, 14)

In Exercises 11–20, find the slope of the line determined by each equation.

11. $3x + 2y = 12$

12. $2x - y = 6$

13. $3x = 4y - 2$

14. $x = y$

15. $y = \dfrac{x - 4}{2}$

16. $x = \dfrac{3 - y}{4}$

17. $4y = 3(y + 2)$

18. $x + y = \dfrac{2 - 3y}{3}$

19. $x(y + 2) = y(x - 3) + 4$

20. $-y(x - 3) + 2 = x(4 - y)$

In Exercises 21–26, tell whether the slope of the line in each graph is positive, negative, 0, or undefined.

21.

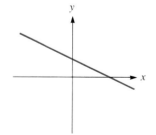

22.

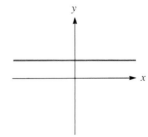

23.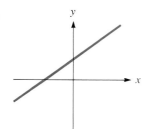

24.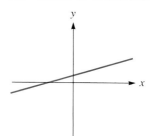

25.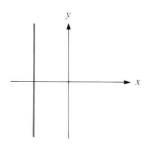

26.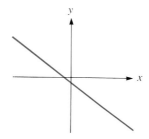

In Exercises 27–34, determine whether the lines with the given slopes are parallel, perpendicular, or neither.

27. $m_1 = 3; \quad m_2 = -\dfrac{1}{3}$

28. $m_1 = \dfrac{1}{4}; \quad m_2 = 4$

29. $m_1 = \sqrt{12}; \quad m_2 = 2\sqrt{3}$

30. $m_1 = \dfrac{\sqrt{3}}{3}; \quad m_2 = \dfrac{1}{\sqrt{3}}$

31. $m_1 = -\sqrt{7}; \quad m_2 = \dfrac{\sqrt{7}}{7}$

32. $m_1 = \sqrt{12}; \quad m_2 = -\dfrac{\sqrt{3}}{6}$

33. $m_1 = \dfrac{2\sqrt{7}}{7}; \quad m_2 = -\dfrac{2}{\sqrt{7}}$

34. $m_1 = 3 - \sqrt{2}; \quad m_2 = -\dfrac{3 + \sqrt{2}}{7}$

In Exercises 35–40, determine if the line passing through points P and Q is parallel or perpendicular to the line passing through R(2, −4) and S(−4, 8). If it is neither, so indicate.

35. $P(3, 4); \quad Q(4, 2)$

36. $P(6, 4); \quad Q(8, 5)$

37. $P(-2, 1); \quad Q(6, 5)$

38. $P(3, 4); \quad Q(-3, -5)$

39. $P(5, 4); \quad Q(6, 6)$

40. $P(-2, 3); \quad Q(4, -9)$

In Exercises 41–46, find the slope of lines PQ and PR and determine whether the points P, Q, and R lie on the same line. (Hint: Two lines with the same slope and a point in common must be the same line.)

41. $P(-2, 4); \quad Q(4, 8); \quad R(10, 12)$

42. $P(6, 10); \quad Q(0, 6); \quad R(3, 8)$

43. $P(-4, 10); \quad Q(-6, 0); \quad R(-1, 5)$

44. $P(-10, -13); \quad Q(-8, -10); \quad R(-12, -16)$

45. $P(-2, 4); \quad Q(0, 8); \quad R(2, 12)$

46. $P(8, -4); \quad Q(0, -12); \quad R(8, -20)$

47. What is the equation of the *x*-axis? What is its slope?

48. What is the equation of the *y*-axis? What is its slope, if any?

49. Show that points with coordinates of $(-3, 4)$, $(4, 1)$, and $(-1, -1)$ are vertices of a right triangle.

50. Show that a triangle with vertices at $(0, 0)$, $(12, 0)$, and $(12, 13)$ is a right triangle.

51. A square has vertices at points $A(a, 0)$, $B(0, a)$, $C(-a, 0)$, and $D(0, -a)$. Show that its adjacent sides are perpendicular.

52. Show that the points $A(2b, a)$, $B(b, b)$, and $C(a, 0)$ are vertices of a right triangle.

53. Show that the points $A(0, 0)$, $B(0, a)$, $C(b, c)$, and $D(b, a + c)$ are the vertices of a parallelogram. (*Hint:* Opposite sides of a **parallelogram** are parallel.)

54. Show that the points $A(0, 0)$, $B(0, b)$, $C(8, b + 2)$, and $D(12, 3)$ are the vertices of a trapezoid. (*Hint:* A **trapezoid** is a four-sided figure with exactly two sides parallel.)

55. The points $A(3, a)$, $B(5, 7)$, and $C(7, 10)$ lie on a line. Find a.

56. The line passing through points $A(1, 3)$ and $B(-2, 7)$ is perpendicular to the line passing through points $C(4, b)$ and $D(8, -1)$. Find b.

7.3 EQUATIONS OF LINES

Any two points on a nonvertical line can be used to determine the slope of the line. Suppose the nonvertical line l shown in Figure 7-17 has a slope of m and passes through the fixed point $P(x_1, y_1)$. Then, if $Q(x, y)$ is another point on line l, by the definition of slope we have

$$m = \frac{y - y_1}{x - x_1}$$

or

$$y - y_1 = m(x - x_1)$$

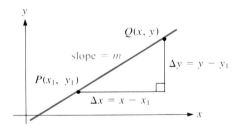

Figure 7-17

Because the equation $y - y_1 = m(x - x_1)$ displays both the coordinates of the fixed point (x_1, y_1) on the line and the line's slope m, it is called the **point–slope form** of the equation of a line.

The point–slope form of the equation of a line.   The equation of the line passing through $P(x_1, y_1)$ with slope m is

$$y - y_1 = m(x - x_1)$$

Example 1   Use the point–slope form to write the equation of a line with a slope of $-\frac{2}{3}$ passing through the point $P(-4, 5)$.

Solution   Substitute $-\frac{2}{3}$ for m, -4 for x_1, and 5 for y_1 in the point–slope form and simplify:

$$y - y_1 = m(x - x_1)$$

$$y - 5 = -\frac{2}{3}[x - (-4)]$$

$$y - 5 = -\frac{2}{3}(x + 4)$$

$$y = 5 - \frac{2}{3}x - \frac{8}{3} \qquad \text{Remove parentheses and add 5 to both sides.}$$

$$y = -\frac{2}{3}x + \frac{7}{3}$$

The desired equation is $y = -\frac{2}{3}x + \frac{7}{3}$.   ■

Example 2   Use the point–slope form of the equation of a line to write the equation of the line passing through points $P(-5, 4)$ and $Q(8, -5)$.

Solution   First find the slope of the line:

$$m = \frac{y_2 - y_1}{x_2 - x_1} = \frac{-5 - 4}{8 - (-5)} = -\frac{9}{13}$$

Because the line passes through both P and Q, choose either point and substitute its coordinates into the equation for the point–slope form. For the purpose of illustration, choose $P(-5, 4)$. Then substitute -5 for x_1, 4 for y_1, and $-\frac{9}{13}$ for m and simplify.

$$y - y_1 = m(x - x_1)$$

$$y - 4 = -\frac{9}{13}[x - (-5)]$$

$$y - 4 = -\frac{9}{13}(x + 5)$$

$$y - 4 = -\frac{9}{13}x - \frac{45}{13}$$

$$y = -\frac{9}{13}x + \frac{7}{13} \qquad \text{Add 4 to both sides.}$$

The desired equation is $y = -\frac{9}{13}x + \frac{7}{13}$.   ■

Slope–Intercept Form of the Equation of a Line

If the y-intercept of the line l with slope m shown in Figure 7-18 is b, the line intersects the y-axis at $P(0, b)$. We can write the equation of this line by sub-

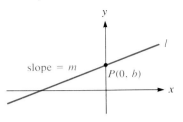

Figure 7-18

stituting 0 for x_1 and b for y_1 in the point–slope form and simplifying:

$$y - y_1 = m(x - x_1)$$
$$y - b = m(x - 0)$$
$$y - b = mx$$
$$y = mx + b$$

Because the equation $y = mx + b$ displays both the slope m and the y-intercept b of the line, it is called the **slope–intercept form** of the equation of a line.

The slope–intercept form of the equation of a line.   The equation of the line with slope m and y-intercept b is

$$y = mx + b$$

Example 3   Use the slope–intercept form to write the equation of the line with slope 4 that passes through the point $P(5, 9)$.

Solution   You are given that $m = 4$ and that the ordered pair $(5, 9)$ satisfies the equation. Substitute **5** for x, **9** for y, and **4** for m in the equation $y = mx + b$. Then solve for b, the y-intercept:

$$y = mx + b$$
$$9 = 4(5) + b$$
$$9 = 20 + b$$
$$-11 = b \qquad \text{Add } -20 \text{ to both sides.}$$

Because $m = 4$ and $b = -11$, the desired equation is $y = 4x - 11$.   ■

It is easy to graph an equation if it is written in slope–intercept form. For example, to graph the equation $y = \frac{4}{3}x - 2$, we first determine that the y-intercept is -2. Thus, the line passes through the point $P(0, -2)$. See Figure 7-19. Because the slope of the line is $\frac{4}{3}$, we can locate another point Q on the line by starting at point P and counting 3 units to the right and 4 units up. Note that the change in x (Δx) from point P to point Q is 3, and that the corre-

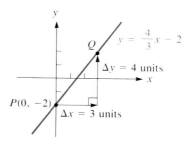

Figure 7-19

sponding change in y (Δy) is 4. The line joining points P and Q is the graph of the equation.

Example 4   Find the slope and the y-intercept of the line with equation $2(x - 3) = -3(y + 5)$.

Solution   Write the equation in the form $y = mx + b$ to determine the slope m and the y-intercept b:

$$2(x - 3) = -3(y + 5)$$
$$2x - 6 = -3y - 15$$
$$3y - 6 = -2x - 15 \qquad \text{Add } 3y - 2x \text{ to both sides.}$$
$$3y = -2x - 9 \qquad \text{Add 6 to both sides.}$$
$$y = -\frac{2}{3}x - 3 \qquad \text{Divide both sides by 3.}$$

The slope of the line is $-\frac{2}{3}$ and the y-intercept is -3.   ■

Example 5   Show that the lines represented by $4x + 8y = 10$ and $2x = 12 - 4y$ are parallel.

Solution   Solve each equation for y and observe that the lines are distinct and that their slopes are equal.

$$4x + 8y = 10 \qquad\qquad\qquad 2x = 12 - 4y$$
$$8y = -4x + 10 \qquad\qquad 4y = -2x + 12$$
$$y = -\frac{1}{2}x + \frac{5}{4} \qquad\qquad y = -\frac{1}{2}x + 3$$

Because the y-intercepts of the lines represented by these equations are different, the lines are distinct. Because the slope of each line is $-\frac{1}{2}$, they are parallel.   ■

Example 6   Show that the lines represented by $4x + 8y = 10$ and $4x - 2y = 21$ are perpendicular.

Solution   Solve each equation for y and observe that their slopes are negative reciprocals:

$$4x + 8y = 10 \qquad\qquad 4x - 2y = 21$$
$$8y = -4x + 10 \qquad\qquad -2y = -4x + 21$$
$$y = -\frac{1}{2}x + \frac{5}{4} \qquad\qquad y = 2x - \frac{21}{2}$$

Because the slopes of these lines are $-\frac{1}{2}$ and 2 (which are negative reciprocals), the lines are perpendicular.   ■

Example 7   Use the slope–intercept form to write the equation of the line passing through the point $P(-2, 5)$ and parallel to the line $y = 8x - 2$.

Solution   The line represented by the desired equation must have a slope of 8 because it is parallel to a line with slope of 8. Substitute -2 for x, 5 for y, and 8 for m in the slope–intercept form and solve for b:

$$y = mx + b$$
$$5 = 8(-2) + b$$
$$5 = -16 + b$$
$$21 = b \qquad\qquad \text{Add 16 to both sides.}$$

Because $m = 8$ and $b = 21$, the desired equation is $y = 8x + 21$.   ■

Example 8   Use the point–slope form to write the equation of the line passing through $P(-2, 5)$ and perpendicular to the line $y = 8x - 2$.

Solution   The slope of the given line is 8. Thus, the slope of the desired line must be $-\frac{1}{8}$, which is the negative reciprocal of 8. Substitute -2 for x_1, 5 for y_1, and $-\frac{1}{8}$ for m into the point–slope form. Then simplify.

$$y - y_1 = m(x - x_1)$$
$$y - 5 = -\frac{1}{8}[x - (-2)]$$
$$y - 5 = -\frac{1}{8}(x + 2)$$
$$8y - 40 = -(x + 2) \qquad\qquad \text{Multiply both sides by 8.}$$
$$8y - 40 = -x - 2$$
$$x + 8y = 38 \qquad\qquad \text{Add } x + 40 \text{ to both sides.}$$

The equation of the line is $x + 8y = 38$.   ■

General Form of the Equation of a Line

The final equation given in Example 8 was written in the form

$$x + 8y = 38$$

This is an example of a form called the **general form** of the equation of a line. Any equation that is written in the form $Ax + By = C$ is said to be written in general form.

> **Theorem.**   If A, B, and C are real numbers and $B \neq 0$, then the graph of the equation
>
> $$Ax + By = C$$
>
> is a nonvertical line with a slope of $-\dfrac{A}{B}$ and a y-intercept of $\dfrac{C}{B}$.

You will be asked to prove the previous theorem in the Exercises.

If $B = 0$ and $A \neq 0$, the equation $Ax + By = C$ represents a vertical line with x-intercept of C/A. Because the graph of any equation that can be written in the form $Ax + By = C$ is a straight line, the equation $Ax + By = C$ is called a **linear equation in x and y**.

Example 9   Show that the lines represented by $4x + 3y = 7$ and $3x - 4y = 12$ are perpendicular.

Solution   To show that the lines are perpendicular, show that their slopes are negative reciprocals. The first equation, $4x + 3y = 7$, is written in general form, with $A = 4$, $B = 3$, and $C = 7$. By the previous theorem, the slope of the line is

$$m_1 = -\frac{A}{B} = -\frac{4}{3}$$

Similarly, the second equation, $3x - 4y = 12$, is written in general form, with $A = 3$, $B = -4$, and $C = 12$. The slope of this line is

$$m_2 = -\frac{A}{B} = -\frac{3}{-4} = \frac{3}{4}$$

Because the slopes of the two lines are negative reciprocals, the lines are perpendicular.   ∎

The following box summarizes the various forms for the equation of a line:

General form of a linear equation	$Ax + By = C$ A and B cannot both be zero
Slope–intercept form of a linear equation	$y = mx + b$ slope is m and the y-intercept is b
Point–slope form of a linear equation	$y - y_1 = m(x - x_1)$ slope is m and the line passes through (x_1, y_1)
A horizontal line	$y = k$ slope of 0 and the y-intercept is k
A vertical line	$x = k$ no defined slope and the x-intercept is k

▪ EXERCISE 7.3 ▬▬▬▬▬

In Exercises 1–6, use the point–slope form to write the equation of the line with the given properties. **Write each equation in general form.**

1. $m = 5$ and passing through $P(0, 7)$
2. $m = -8$ and passing through $P(0, -2)$
3. $m = -3$ and passing through $P(2, 0)$
4. $m = 4$ and passing through $P(-5, 0)$
5. $m = \dfrac{3}{2}$ and passing through $P(2, 5)$
6. $m = -\dfrac{2}{3}$ and passing through $P(-3, 2)$

In Exercises 7–12, use the point–slope form to write the equation of the line passing through the two given points. Write each equation in the form $y = mx + b$.

7. $P(0, 0)$; $Q(4, 4)$
8. $P(-5, -5)$; $Q(0, 0)$
9. $P(3, 4)$; $Q(0, -3)$
10. $P(4, 0)$; $Q(6, -8)$
11. $P(-2, 4)$; $Q(3, -5)$
12. $P(3, -5)$; $Q(-1, 12)$

In Exercises 13–20, use the slope–intercept form to write the equation of the line with the given properties. **Write each equation in slope–intercept form.**

13. $m = 3$ and $b = 17$
14. $m = -2$ and $b = 11$
15. $m = -7$ and passing through $P(7, 5)$
16. $m = 3$ and passing through $P(-2, -5)$
17. $m = 0$ and passing through $P(2, -4)$
18. $m = -7$ and passing through the origin
19. passing through $P(6, 8)$ and $Q(2, 10)$
20. passing through $P(-4, 5)$ and $Q(2, -6)$

In Exercises 21–26, write each equation in slope–intercept form to determine the slope and the y-intercept. Then use the method of Figure 7-19 to graph the equation.

21. $y + 1 = x$
22. $x + y = 2$
23. $x = \dfrac{3}{2}y - 3$
24. $x = -\dfrac{4}{5}y + 2$
25. $3(y - 4) = -2(x - 3)$
26. $-4(2x + 3) = 3(3y + 8)$

In Exercises 27–32, find the slope and the y-intercept of the line determined by the given equation.

27. $3x - 2y = 8$
28. $-2x + 4y = 12$
29. $-2(x + 3y) = 5$
30. $5(2x - 3y) = 4$
31. $x = \dfrac{2y - 4}{7}$
32. $3x + 4 = -\dfrac{2(y - 3)}{5}$

In Exercises 33–44, indicate whether the lines given by each pair of equations are parallel or perpendicular. If they are neither, so indicate.

33. $y = 3x + 4$; $y = 3x - 7$
34. $y = 4x - 13$; $y = \dfrac{1}{4}x + 13$
35. $x + y = 2$; $y = x + 5$
36. $x = y + 2$; $y = x + 3$
37. $y = 3x + 7$; $2y = 6x - 9$
38. $2x + 3y = 9$; $3x - 2y = 5$
39. $x = 3y + 8$; $y = -3x + 7$
40. $3x + 6y = 1$; $y = \dfrac{1}{2}x$
41. $y = 3$; $x = 4$
42. $y = -3$; $y = -7$
43. $x = \dfrac{y - 2}{3}$; $3(y - 3) + x = 0$
44. $2y = 8$; $3(2 + y) = 3(x + 2)$

In Exercises 45–50, write the equation of the line that passes through the given point and is parallel to the given line.

45. $P(0, 0)$; $y = 4x - 7$

46. $P(0, 0)$; $x = -3y - 12$

47. $P(2, 5)$; $4x - y = 7$

48. $P(-6, 3)$; $y + 3x = -12$

49. $P(4, -2)$; $x = \dfrac{5}{4}y - 2$

50. $P(1, -5)$; $x = -\dfrac{3}{4}y + 5$

In Exercises 51–56, write the equation of the line that passes through the given point and is perpendicular to the given line.

51. $P(0, 0)$; $y = 4x - 7$

52. $P(0, 0)$; $x = -3y - 12$

53. $P(2, 5)$; $4x - y = 7$

54. $P(-6, 3)$; $y + 3x = -12$

55. $P(4, -2)$; $x = \dfrac{5}{4}y - 2$

56. $P(1, -5)$; $x = -\dfrac{3}{4}y + 5$

In Exercises 57–60, use the method of Example 9 to determine whether the graphs determined by each pair of equations are parallel, perpendicular, or neither.

57. $4x + 5y = 20$; $5x - 4y = 20$

58. $9x - 12y = 17$; $3x - 4y = 17$

59. $2x + 3y = 12$; $6x + 9y = 32$

60. $5x + 6y = 30$; $6x + 5y = 24$

61. Find the equation of the line perpendicular to the line $y = 3$ and passing through the midpoint of the segment joining $(2, 4)$ and $(-6, 10)$.

62. Find the equation of the line parallel to the line $y = -8$ and passing through the midpoint of the segment joining $(-4, 2)$ and $(-2, 8)$.

63. Find the equation of the line parallel to the line $x = 3$ and passing through the midpoint of the segment joining $(2, -4)$ and $(8, 12)$.

64. Find the equation of the line perpendicular to the line $x = 3$ and passing through the midpoint of the segment joining $(-2, 2)$ and $(4, -8)$.

65. Solve the equation $Ax + By = C$ for y and thereby show that the slope of its graph is $-A/B$ and its y-intercept is C/B.

66. Show that the x-intercept of the graph of $Ax + By = C$ is C/A.

7.4   FUNCTIONS AND FUNCTION NOTATION

The equations we have discussed so far have described a correspondence between two variables. The equation $y = -2x + 3$, for example, describes a correspondence in which each number x determines *exactly one* value of y. Such correspondences are called **functions**.

> **Definition.**   A **function** is a correspondence that assigns to each element x of some set X a single value y of a set Y.
>   The set X is called the **domain** of the function. The value y that corresponds to a particular x in the domain is called the **image** of x under the function. The set Y of all images of x is called the **range** of the function.

Because each value of y depends on some number x, we call y the **dependent variable**. The variable x is called the **independent variable**. Unless indicated otherwise, the domain of a function is its **implied domain**—the set of all real numbers for which the function is defined.

By definition, a function f is a correspondence from the elements of one set, X, to the elements of another set, Y. We can visualize this correspondence with the diagram in Figure 7-20. We represent the function f by drawing arrows from each element of X to the corresponding element of Y. If a function f assigns the element y_1 to the element x_1, we draw an arrow leaving x_1 and pointing to y_1. The set X, consisting of all elements from which arrows originate, is the domain of the function. The set Y, consisting of all elements to which arrows point, is the range.

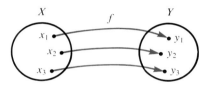

Figure 7-20

A correspondence is still a function if arrows point from several different elements of X to the same element y in the range. See Figure 7-21.

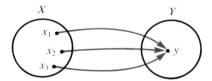

Figure 7-21

However, if arrows leave some element x in the domain and point to several elements in the range, the correspondence is *not* a function because more than one y value corresponds to the number x. See Figure 7-22.

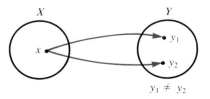

Figure 7-22

Such a correspondence is called a **relation**.

Definition. A **relation** is a correspondence that assigns to each number x in a set X one or more values of y in a set Y.

The set X is called the **domain** of the relation. The **range** of the relation is the set Y of all values of y that correspond to some number x in the domain.

Because of the previous definitions, *a function is always a relation but a relation is not necessarily a function.*

Example 1 Does the equation $y = 4x - 5$ define y to be a function of x? If so, find its domain and range.

Solution By the definition of function, each real number x must determine *exactly one* value of y. To determine y in this equation, 5 must be subtracted from the product of 4 and x. Because this arithmetic gives a single result, only one value of y is produced. Thus, the equation does determine a function.

Because x can be any real number, the implied domain of the function is the set of all real numbers.

Because y can be any real number, the range of the function also is the set of real numbers. ■

Example 2 Does the equation $y^2 = 9x$ determine y to be a function of x? If not, give the domain and the range of the relation.

Solution Let x be the number 4, for example. Then

$$y^2 = 9(4) = 36$$

and y could be either 6 or -6. Because more than one value of y corresponds to $x = 4$, this equation does not determine a function. However, it does determine a relation.

Because y^2 is always a nonnegative number, x must be a nonnegative number also. Thus, the domain of the relation is the set of nonnegative real numbers. Because y can be any real number, the range is the set of all real numbers. ■

Example 3 Does the equation $y = \dfrac{12}{x - 3}$ determine y to be a function of x? If so, find its domain and range.

Solution Since division by 0 is undefined, the denominator of the fraction cannot be 0. Thus, x cannot be 3. Because each real number x other than 3 does determine *exactly one* value of y, the equation does determine a function.

Since x cannot be 3, it follows that the domain of this function is the set of all real numbers except 3.

A fraction with a nonzero numerator cannot be 0. Thus, the range of this function is the set of all real numbers except 0.   ■

Function Notation

There is a notation that reinforces the idea that y is a function of x. If the variable y in a function is equal to some expression that involves the variable x, then y is often denoted as $f(x)$ and read as "f of x." The symbol $f(x)$ indicates the number to substitute for x when evaluating y. For example, if $y = f(x) = 4x + 2$, then $f(3)$ is the value of $4x + 2$ when $x = 3$:

$$f(3) = 4(3) + 2 = 14$$

Likewise,

$$f(-2) = 4(-2) + 2 = -6$$

Example 4 Suppose that y is the function of x determined by $y = f(x) = \dfrac{x}{2} + 1$. Find **a.** $f(4)$, **b.** $f(8)$, and **c.** $f(-12)$.

Solution **a.** $f(4)$ is the value of y when $x = 4$:

$$f(4) = \frac{4}{2} + 1 = 2 + 1 = 3$$

b. $f(8)$ is the value of y when $x = 8$:

$$f(8) = \frac{8}{2} + 1 = 4 + 1 = 5$$

c. $f(-12)$ is the value of y when $x = -12$:

$$f(-12) = \frac{-12}{2} + 1 = -6 + 1 = -5$$ ■

Example 5 If $f(x) = x^2 + 3x + 1$, find **a.** $f(z)$, **b.** $f(-2)$, and **c.** $f(z - 2)$.

Solution **a.** $f(z) = z^2 + 3z + 1$

b. $f(-2) = (-2)^2 + 3(-2) + 1$
$$= 4 - 6 + 1$$
$$= -1$$

c. $f(z - 2) = (z - 2)^2 + 3(z - 2) + 1$
$$= z^2 - 4z + 4 + 3z - 6 + 1$$
$$= z^2 - z - 1$$

Because $f(z) + f(-2) = z^2 + 3z$ and $f(z - 2) = z^2 - z - 1$,

$$f(z) + f(-2) \neq f(z - 2)$$ ■

Composition of Functions

If $f(x)$ and $g(x)$ are both functions of x, then $f(g(x))$ and $g(f(x))$ are also functions of x. Such functions are called **composite functions**. The expression $f(g(x))$ is often denoted as $(f \circ g)(x)$ and read as "f composition g." The expression $g(f(x))$ is often denoted as $(g \circ f)(x)$. For example, if $f(x) = 4x$ and $g(x) = 3x + 2$, then

$$(f \circ g)(x) = f(g(x)) = f(3x + 2) = 4(3x + 2) = 12x + 8$$
$$(g \circ f)(x) = g(f(x)) = g(4x) = 3(4x) + 2 = 12x + 2$$

Note that $(f \circ g)(x) \neq (g \circ f)(x)$. Thus, the composition of functions is not commutative.

Example 6   Suppose that $f(x) = 2x + 1$ and $g(x) = x - 4$. Find   **a.** $(f \circ g)(8)$, **b.** $(g \circ f)(-2)$, and   **c.** $(f \circ g)(x)$.

Solution   **a.** $(f \circ g)(8)$ means $f(g(8))$. Because $g(8) = 8 - 4 = 4$, you have

$$(f \circ g)(8) = f(g(8)) = f(4) = 2(4) + 1 = 9$$

b. $(g \circ f)(-2)$ means $g(f(-2))$. Because $f(-2) = 2(-2) + 1 = -3$, you have

$$(g \circ f)(-2) = g(f(-2)) = g(-3) = -3 - 4 = -7$$

c. $(f \circ g)(x)$ means $f(g(x))$. Because $g(x) = x - 4$, you have

$$(f \circ g)(x) = f(g(x)) = f(x - 4) = 2(x - 4) + 1 = 2x - 7$$ ∎

Algebra of Functions

It is possible to add, subtract, multiply, and divide functions.

Definition.   If the ranges of functions f and g are subsets of the real numbers, then

The **sum** of f and g, denoted as $f + g$, is defined by

$$(f + g)(x) = f(x) + g(x)$$

The **difference** of f and g, denoted as $f - g$, is defined by

$$(f - g)(x) = f(x) - g(x)$$

The **product** of f and g, denoted as $f \cdot g$, is defined by

$$(f \cdot g)(x) = f(x)g(x)$$

The **quotient** of f and g, denoted as f/g, is defined by

$$(f/g)(x) = \frac{f(x)}{g(x)} \qquad [g(x) \neq 0]$$

The domain of each of these functions is the set of all real numbers x that are in the domain of *both* f and g. In the case of the quotient, there is the further restriction that $g(x) \neq 0$.

Example 7   Let $f(x) = x^2$ and $g(x) = 2x + 4$, then

a. $(f + g)(x) = f(x) + g(x) = x^2 + 2x + 4$
The domain of $f + g$ is the set of real numbers that are in the domain of both f and g. Since the domain of both f and g is the set of real numbers, the domain of $f + g$ is also the set of real numbers.

b. $(f - g)(x) = f(x) - g(x) = x^2 - (2x + 4) = x^2 - 2x - 4$
The domain of $f - g$ is the set of real numbers.

c. $(f \cdot g)(x) = f(x)g(x) = x^2(2x + 4) = 2x^3 + 4x^2$
The domain of $f \cdot g$ is the set of real numbers.

d. $(f/g)(x) = \dfrac{f(x)}{g(x)} = \dfrac{x^2}{2x + 4}$

Because the denominator of $\dfrac{x^2}{2x + 4}$ cannot be 0, x cannot be -2. Thus, the domain of $(f/g)(x)$ is the set of real numbers except -2.   ■

■ EXERCISE 7.4

In Exercises 1–10, tell whether the given relation defines y to be a function of x. Assume that x and y represent real numbers in each ordered pair (x, y).

1. $y = 3x - 4$ **2.** $y = -\dfrac{1}{2}x + 7$ **3.** $3x + 2y = 4$ **4.** $x = 3y - 4$

5. $y^2 = 25x$ **6.** $y^2 = x$ **7.** $x = \dfrac{1}{y^2}$ **8.** $y = \dfrac{2}{x + 2}$

9. $x = \dfrac{y + 4}{3}$ **10.** $y^2 = \dfrac{x + 3}{5}$

In Exercises 11–20, give the domain and the range of each function. Assume that x and y represent real numbers in each ordered pair (x, y).

11. $y = 2x + 3$ **12.** $y = \dfrac{1}{2}x - 4$ **13.** $y = \dfrac{4}{2 - x}$ **14.** $y = \dfrac{x - 6}{5}$

15. $y = x^4$ **16.** $y = \dfrac{5}{x - 3}$ **17.** $y = 3$ **18.** $y = \dfrac{1}{2}x^2$

19. $y = \sqrt{x - 2}$ **20.** $y = \sqrt{x^2 - 4}$

In Exercises 21–28, assume that $y = f(x) = 5x + 2$. Evaluate each expression.

21. $f(1)$ **22.** $f(0)$ **23.** $f(-2)$ **24.** $f(-1)$

25. $f\left(-\dfrac{2}{5}\right)$ **26.** $f\left(\dfrac{2}{3}\right)$ **27.** $f(x + 2)$ **28.** $f(x - 1)$

In Exercises 29–36, assume that $y = g(x) = x^2 + 4$. Evaluate each expression.

29. $g(0)$ **30.** $g(1)$ **31.** $g(-1)$ **32.** $g(-2)$

33. $g\left(\dfrac{2}{3}\right)$ **34.** $g\left(-\dfrac{1}{2}\right)$ **35.** $g(x^2)$ **36.** $g\left(\dfrac{1}{x^2}\right)$

In Exercises 37–42, assume that $y = f(x) = 2x + 1$ *and* $g(x) = x^2 - 1$. *Evaluate each expression.*

37. $(f \circ g)(2)$ **38.** $(g \circ f)(2)$ **39.** $(g \circ f)(-3)$ **40.** $(f \circ g)(-3)$
41. $(f \circ g)(x)$ **42.** $(g \circ f)(x)$

In Exercises 43–48, assume that $f(x) = 3x - 2$ *and* $g(x) = x^2 + x$. *Evaluate each expression.*

43. $(f \circ g)(4)$ **44.** $(g \circ f)(4)$ **45.** $(g \circ f)(-3)$ **46.** $(f \circ g)(-3)$
47. $(g \circ f)(x)$ **48.** $(f \circ g)(x)$

49. If $f(x) = x + 1$ and $g(x) = 2x - 5$, show that $(f \circ g)(x) \neq (g \circ f)(x)$.
50. If $f(x) = x^2 + 1$ and $g(x) = 3x^2 - 2$, show that $(f \circ g)(x) \neq (g \circ f)(x)$.
51. If $f(x) = x^2 + 2x - 3$, find $f(a)$, $f(h)$, and $f(a + h)$. Then show that $f(a + h) \neq f(a) + f(h)$.
52. If $g(x) = 2x^2 + 10$, find $g(a)$, $g(h)$, and $g(a + h)$. Then show that $g(a + h) \neq g(a) + g(h)$.
53. If $f(x) = x^2 + 2$, find $\dfrac{f(x + h) - f(x)}{h}$. **54.** If $f(x) = x^3 - 1$, find $\dfrac{f(x + h) - f(x)}{h}$.

In Exercises 55–58, let $f(x) = 2x + 1$ *and* $g(x) = x - 3$. *Find each function and determine its domain.*

55. $f + g$ **56.** $f - g$ **57.** $f \cdot g$ **58.** f/g

In Exercises 59–62, let $f(x) = 3x - 2$ *and* $g(x) = 2x^2 + 1$. *Find each function and determine its domain.*

59. $f - g$ **60.** $f + g$ **61.** f/g **62.** $f \cdot g$

In Exercises 63–66, let $f(x) = x^2 - 1$ *and* $g(x) = x^2 - 4$. *Find each function and determine its domain.*

63. $f - g$ **64.** $f + g$ **65.** g/f **66.** $f \cdot g$

7.5   LINEAR FUNCTIONS AND THEIR INVERSES

A relation defines a set of ordered pairs (x, y), where x is an element in the domain of the relation and y is the value that corresponds to x. The graph of a relation is the graph of all these ordered pairs on a rectangular coordinate system. If the relation is a function defined by the equation $y = f(x)$, the graph of the function consists of those points and only those points in the xy-plane with coordinates $(x, y) = (x, f(x))$.

A linear function is a function whose graph is a straight line. More formally, we define a linear function as follows:

Definition.   A **linear function** is a function defined by an equation that can be written in the form

$$y = mx + b$$

where m is the slope of its straight-line graph and b is its y-intercept.

A linear function is often written in the form $f(x) = mx + b$, where $f(x)$ is just another symbol for y. Thus, $y = f(x)$.

Example 1 Solve the equation $3x + 2y = 10$ for y to show that it defines a linear function. Then graph the line.

Solution Solve the equation for y as follows:

$$3x + 2y = 10$$
$$2y = -3x + 10 \qquad \text{Add } -3x \text{ to both sides.}$$
$$y = -\frac{3}{2}x + 5 \qquad \text{Divide both sides by 2.}$$

Because the equation can be written in the form $y = mx + b$, it defines a linear function. Because the form $y = mx + b$ is the slope–intercept form of the equation of a line, the slope of its graph is $-\frac{3}{2}$ and its y-intercept is 5. The graph appears in Figure 7-23.

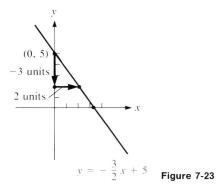

Figure 7-23

A nonempty set of ordered pairs (x, y) defines a relation because it determines a correspondence between values of x and y. For example, a relation R is defined by the set.

$$R = \{(1, 10), (2, 20), (3, 30)\}$$

The domain of R is the set of first components of the ordered pairs, and its range is the set of second components. Thus, the domain of R is $\{1, 2, 3\}$ and the range is $\{10, 20, 30\}$. Because only one second component y corresponds to each first component x of an ordered pair, the relation R is a function. However, the relation Q, where

$$Q = \{(5, 15), (5, 20), (6, 30), (7, 40)\}$$

with domain of $\{5, 6, 7\}$ and range $\{15, 20, 30, 40\}$ is not a function because two values of y (15 and 20) correspond to the first component 5.

Example 2 Let R be a relation defined by ordered pairs (x, y) such that $R = \{(2, 3), (5, 7), (6, 8), (9, 8)\}$. Give the domain and range of R and tell whether R is a function.

Solution   The domain of R is the set of first components of the ordered pairs. Thus, the domain is $\{2, 5, 6, 9\}$.

The range of R is the set of second components of the ordered pairs. Thus, the range is $\{3, 7, 8\}$.

Because only one value of y corresponds to each number x, the relation R is a function.

■

Inverse Functions

If the components of each ordered pair in any given relation are interchanged, a new relation is formed called the **inverse relation**. For example, if R is the relation

$$R = \{(1, 10), (2, 20), (3, 30)\}$$

then the inverse relation of R, denoted as R^{-1}, is

$$R^{-1} = \{(10, 1), (20, 2), (30, 3)\}$$

The -1 in the notation R^{-1} is not an exponent. It refers to the inverse of the relation. The symbol R^{-1} is read as "the inverse relation of R" or just "R inverse."

The domain of R and the range of R^{-1} is $\{1, 2, 3\}$. The range of R and the domain of R^{-1} is $\{10, 20, 30\}$. In general, we have the following definition:

> **Definition.**   If R is any relation and R^{-1} is the relation obtained from R by interchanging the components of each ordered pair of R, then R^{-1} is called the **inverse relation** of R.
>
> The domain of R^{-1} is the range of R, and the range of R^{-1} is the domain of R.

An equation in x and y determines a set of ordered pairs. For example, if $x = 1, 2, 3, 4,$ and 5, the equation $y = 6x$ determines the following set of ordered pairs:

$$T = \{(x, y) : (1, 6), (2, 12), (3, 18), (4, 24), (5, 30)\}$$

To form T^{-1}, we simply interchange the x and y coordinates to obtain

$$T^{-1} = \{(x, y) : (6, 1), (12, 2), (18, 3), (24, 4) (30, 5)\}$$

Example 3   The set of all pairs (x, y) determined by the equation $y = 4x + 2$ determines a function of f. Find the inverse relation of $y = 4x + 2$ and tell whether the inverse is a function.

Solution   To find the inverse relation of $y = 4x + 2$, interchange the variables x and y to obtain

1. $x = 4y + 2$

To decide whether this inverse relation is a function, solve Equation 1 for y:

$$x = 4y + 2$$
$$x - 2 = 4y \qquad \text{Add } -2 \text{ to both sides.}$$
$$y = \frac{x - 2}{4} \qquad \text{Divide both sides by 4 and apply the symmetric}$$
$$\text{property of equality.}$$

Because each number x that is substituted into this equation gives a single value y, the inverse relation is a function. ∎

In Example 3 the inverse relation of the function $y = 4x + 2$ was found to be the function $y = \frac{x - 2}{4}$. In function notation, this inverse function can be denoted as

$$f^{-1}(x) = \frac{x - 2}{4} \qquad \text{Read as "}f\text{ inverse of }x\text{ is }\frac{x - 2}{4}\text{."}$$

Example 4   The set of all pairs (x, y) determined by the equation $3x + 2y = 6$ is a function. Find the inverse function and graph both functions on a single coordinate system.

Solution   To find the inverse function of $3x + 2y = 6$, interchange the x and y to obtain

$$3y + 2x = 6$$

Then solve the equation for y:

$$3y + 2x = 6$$
$$3y = -2x + 6$$
$$y = -\frac{2}{3}x + 2$$

The graphs of the equations $3x + 2y = 6$ and $y = -\frac{2}{3}x + 2$ appear in Figure 7-24.

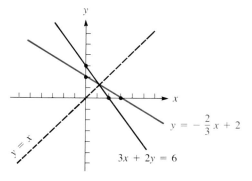

Figure 7-24

In Example 4, the graphs of the equations $3x + 2y = 6$ and $y = -\frac{2}{3}x + 2$ are symmetric about the line $y = x$. This is always the case because, if the coordinates (a, b) satisfy an equation, the coordinates (b, a) will satisfy its inverse.

■ EXERCISE 7.5

In Exercises 1–10, indicate whether the given equation determines a linear function.

1. $3x + 2y = 5$ **2.** $x - 3y = 8$ **3.** $3(x + 2) = 5y$ **4.** $-2(y - 3) = x$

5. $y = \dfrac{3}{x + 2}$ **6.** $y = \dfrac{x + 2}{3}$ **7.** $y = 9$ **8.** $x = 8$

9. $y^2 = x$ **10.** $x(x - y) = y$

In Exercises 11—16, give the domain and range of each relation. If the relation is a function, so indicate.

11. $\{(1, 2), (3, 4), (5, 9), (5, 12)\}$ **12.** $\{(3, 4), (-5, 3), (8, 9), (3, 6)\}$

13. $\{(1, 2), (-1, 3), (4, 4), (-4, 5)\}$ **14.** $\{(4, 0), (3, 0), (2, 0), (1, 0)\}$

15. $\{(5, 8), (6, 9), (5, 10)\}$ **16.** $\{(-2, 0), (-1, 1), (0, 2), (1, 3)\}$

In Exercises 17–22, find the inverse relation of each set of ordered pairs (x, y) and tell whether the inverse relation is a function.

17. $\{(3, 2), (2, 1), (1, 0)\}$ **18.** $\{(4, 1), (5, 1), (6, 1), (7, 1)\}$

19. $\{(1, 2), (2, 3), (1, 3), (1, 5)\}$ **20.** $\{(-1, -1), (0, 0), (1, 1), (2, 2)\}$

21. $\{(1, 1), (2, 4), (3, 9), (4, 16)\}$ **22.** $\{(1, 1), (2, 2), (3, 3), (4, 3)\}$

In Exercises 23–30, find the inverse relation of each set of ordered pairs (x, y) determined by the given equation and tell whether that inverse relation is a function. If the inverse relation is a linear function, express it in the form $f^{-1}(x) = mx + b$.

23. $y = 3x + 1$ **24.** $y + 1 = 5x$ **25.** $x + 4 = 5y$ **26.** $x = 3y + 1$

27. $y = \dfrac{x - 4}{5}$ **28.** $y^2 = \dfrac{2x + 6}{3}$ **29.** $4x - 5y^2 = 20$ **30.** $3x + 5y = 15$

In Exercises 31–40, find the inverse of each linear function. Then graph both the function and its inverse on a single coordinate system. What is the equation of the line of symmetry?

31. $y = 2x - 3$ **32.** $x = 3y - 1$ **33.** $x = \dfrac{y - 2}{3}$ **34.** $y = \dfrac{x + 3}{4}$

35. $3x - y = 5$ **36.** $2x + 3y = 18$

37. $3(x + y) = 2x + 4$ **38.** $-4(y - 1) + x = 2$

39. $\dfrac{3}{2}x = \dfrac{18 - 3y}{3}$ **40.** $2y - \dfrac{6y}{5} = \dfrac{2(3 - x)}{5}$

41. A high-contrast photographic developer uses 5.0 grams of potassium bromide for each liter of developer solution. Find an equation that describes the linear relation between g, the number of grams of potassium bromide, and l, the number of liters of solution.

42. A dentist charges $30, plus $15 for each tooth he fills. Find an equation that describes the relation between n, the number of teeth filled, and c, the amount the dentist charges.

43. To wash windows, Bill charges $10, plus $1 for each window. Find an equation that describes the linear relation between n, the number of windows washed, and c, the amount Bill charges.

44. A 20-minute long-distance telephone call costs $3.15. If that call had lasted 30 minutes, it would have cost $4.35. Find an equation that describes the linear relation between t, the time of the telephone call, and c, its cost.

45. The boiling point of water is 212°F or 100°C. The freezing point of water is 32°F or 0°C. Find an equation that describes the linear relation between temperature as measured on the Fahrenheit and Celsius scales.

46. The population of a town has been growing at the rate of 850 people per year since a census ten years ago. The current population of the town is 38,500 people. Find an equation that describes the linear relation between p (the population) and n (the number of years elapsed since the census year). Use this equation to compute the expected population ten years from now.

7.6 PROPORTION AND VARIATION

An indicated quotient of two numbers is often called a **ratio**. For example, the fraction $\frac{2}{3}$ can be read as "the ratio of 2 to 3." An equation indicating that two ratios are equal is called a **proportion**. Two examples of proportions are

$$\frac{1}{4} = \frac{2}{8} \quad \text{and} \quad \frac{4}{7} = \frac{12}{21}$$

In the proportion $\frac{a}{b} = \frac{c}{d}$, the terms a and d are called the **extremes** of the proportion and the terms b and c are called the **means**.

To develop a fundamental property of proportions, we suppose that

$$\frac{a}{b} = \frac{c}{d}$$

is a proportion and multiply both sides by bd to obtain

$$(bd)\frac{a}{b} = (bd)\frac{c}{d}$$

$$\frac{\not b da}{\not b} = \frac{b \not d c}{\not d}$$

$$ad = bc$$

Thus, in a proportion, *the product of the extremes equals the product of the means.*

Example 1   Solve the proportion $\dfrac{x+1}{x} = \dfrac{x}{x+2}$ for x.

Solution

$$\frac{x + 1}{x} = \frac{x}{x + 2}$$

$$(x + 1)(x + 2) = x \cdot x \qquad \text{The product of the extremes equals the product of the means.}$$

$$x^2 + 3x + 2 = x^2$$

$$3x + 2 = 0 \qquad \text{Add } -x^2 \text{ to both sides.}$$

$$x = -\frac{2}{3} \qquad \text{Add } -2 \text{ to both sides and divide by 3.} \qquad \blacksquare$$

Variation

Consider the formula

$$C = \pi D$$

for the circumference of a circle, where C is the circumference, D is the diameter, and $\pi \approx 3.14159$. If we double the diameter of a circle, we determine another circle with a larger circumference C_1 such that

$$C_1 = \pi(2D) = 2\pi D = 2C$$

Thus, doubling the diameter results in doubling the circumference. Likewise, if we triple the diameter, we triple the circumference. In this formula, we say that the variables C and D **vary directly**, or that they are **directly proportional**. That is, as one variable gets larger, so does the other, and in a predictable way. The constant π is called the **constant of variation**, or the **constant of proportionality**.

Direct variation.   The words "**y varies directly as x**," or "**y is directly proportional to x**" mean that $y = kx$ for some constant k.
k is called the **constant of variation** or the **constant of proportionality**.

An example of direct variation is Hooke's law from physics. Hooke's law states that the distance a spring will stretch varies directly with the force that is applied to it. If d represents a distance and f represents a force, Hooke's law can be expressed mathematically as

$$d = kf$$

where k is the constant of variation. If the spring stretches 10 inches when a force of 6 pounds is attached, k can be computed for this spring as follows:

$$d = kf$$

$$10 = k(6)$$

$$\frac{5}{3} = k$$

To find the force required to stretch the spring by a distance of 35 inches, we can solve the equation $d = kf$ for f, with $d = 35$ and $k = \frac{5}{3}$:

$$d = kf$$

$$35 = \frac{5}{3}f$$

$$105 = 5f \qquad \text{Multiply both sides by 3.}$$

$$21 = f \qquad \text{Divide both sides by 5.}$$

Thus, the force required to stretch the spring by a distance of 35 inches is 21 pounds.

Example 2   The frequency of a vibrating string varies directly as the square root of its tension. If a spring is vibrating at a frequency of 144 hertz due to a tension of 3 pounds, what would the frequency be if the tension were 12 pounds?

Solution   The words "frequency varies directly as the square root of its tension" can be expressed mathematically as

$$f = k\sqrt{t}$$

where k is the constant of variation. To find k, substitute **144** for f and **3** for t and solve for k:

$$144 = k\sqrt{3}$$

$$k = \frac{144}{\sqrt{3}}$$

$$= \frac{144\sqrt{3}}{3}$$

$$= 48\sqrt{3}$$

To find the frequency when the tension is 12 pounds, substitute $48\sqrt{3}$ for k and **12** for t into the formula $f = k\sqrt{t}$. Then simplify.

$$f = k\sqrt{t}$$
$$f = 48\sqrt{3} \cdot \sqrt{12}$$
$$= 48\sqrt{36}$$
$$= 288$$

The frequency is 288 hertz.   ■

In the formula $w = \dfrac{12}{l}$, w gets smaller as l gets larger, and w gets larger as l gets smaller. Since these variables vary in opposite directions in a predictable way, we say that they **vary inversely**, or that they are **inversely proportional**. The constant 12 is the **constant of variation**.

> **Inverse variation.** The words "**y varies inversely with x,**" or "**y is inversely proportional to x**" mean that $y = \dfrac{k}{x}$ for some constant k.
>
> k is called the **constant of variation** or the **constant of proportionality**.

Because of gravity, an object in space is attracted to the earth. The force of this attraction varies inversely with the square of the object's distance from the center of the earth. If f represents the force and d represents the distance, this information can be expressed mathematically with the equation

$$f = \frac{k}{d^2}$$

If we know that an object 4000 miles from the center of the earth is attracted to the earth with a force of 90 pounds, we can compute the constant of variation k:

$$f = \frac{k}{d^2}$$

$$90 = \frac{k}{4000^2}$$

$$k = 90(4000^2)$$

$$= 1.44 \times 10^9$$

To find the force of attraction when the object is 5000 miles from the center of the earth, we substitute **5000** for d and **1.44 × 10⁹** for k and simplify:

$$f = \frac{k}{d^2}$$

$$f = \frac{\mathbf{1.44 \times 10^9}}{\mathbf{5000}^2}$$

$$= 57.6$$

The object will be attracted to the earth with a force of 57.6 pounds when it is 5000 miles from the earth's center.

Example 3 The intensity I of light received by an object from a light source varies inversely with the square of the object's distance from the light source. If the intensity from a light source 4 feet from an object is 8 candelas, what is the intensity at a distance of 2 feet?

Solution The words "intensity varies inversely with the square of the distance d" can be expressed mathematically as

$$I = \frac{k}{d^2}$$

To find k, substitute 8 for I and 4 for d and solve for k:

$$I = \frac{k}{d^2}$$

$$8 = \frac{k}{4^2}$$

$$128 = k$$

To find the intensity when the object is 2 feet from the light source, substitute 2 for d and 128 for k and simplify.

$$I = \frac{k}{d^2}$$

$$I = \frac{128}{2^2}$$

$$= 32$$

The intensity at 2 feet is 32 candelas.   ■

There are many occasions when one variable varies with the product of several variables. For example, the area of a triangle varies directly with the product of its base and height:

$$A = \frac{1}{2}bh$$

Such variation is called **joint variation**.

Joint variation.   If one variable varies directly with the product of two or more variables, the relationship is called **joint variation**; if y varies jointly with x and z, then $y = kxz$. The constant k is called the **constant of variation**.

Example 4   The volume V of a cone varies jointly with its height h and the area of its base B. Express this relationship as an equation and as a proportion.

Solution   "V varies jointly with h and B" means that "V varies directly as the product of h and B." Hence,

$$V = khB$$

To write this equation as a proportion, divide both sides of the equation by hB and express k as $k/1$.

$$\frac{V}{hB} = \frac{k}{1}$$

Note that this relationship is often read as "V is directly proportional to the product of h and B."   ∎

Many applied problems involve a combination of direct and inverse variation. Such variation is called **combined variation**.

Example 5   The time that it takes to build a highway varies directly with the length of the road, but inversely with the number of workers. If it takes 100 workers 4 weeks to build 2 miles of roadway, how long will it take 80 workers to build 10 miles of roadway?

Solution   Let T represent time in weeks, L represent length in miles, and W represent the number of workers. The relationship between these variables is expressed by the equation

$$T = \frac{kL}{W}$$

Substitute $T = 4$, $W = 100$, and $L = 2$ to find the constant of variation:

$$4 = \frac{k(2)}{100}$$

$400 = 2k$ Multiply both sides by 100.

$200 = k$ Divide both sides by 2.

Now, substitute **80** for W, **10** for L, and **200** for k in the equation $T = \dfrac{kL}{W}$, and simplify:

$$T = \frac{kL}{W}$$

$$T = \frac{200(10)}{80}$$

$= 25$ Simplify.

It will take 25 weeks for 80 workers to build 10 miles of roadway.   ∎

■ EXERCISE 7.6

In Exercises 1–12, solve each proportion for the variable, if possible.

1. $\dfrac{x}{5} = \dfrac{15}{25}$

2. $\dfrac{4}{y} = \dfrac{6}{27}$

3. $\dfrac{r-2}{3} = \dfrac{r}{5}$

4. $\dfrac{2}{c} = \dfrac{c-3}{2}$

5. $\dfrac{y}{4} = \dfrac{4}{y}$

6. $\dfrac{2}{3x} = \dfrac{12x}{36}$

7. $\dfrac{3}{n} = \dfrac{2}{n+1}$

8. $\dfrac{4}{x+3} = \dfrac{3}{5}$

9. $\dfrac{x+1}{x-1} = \dfrac{6}{4}$

10. $\dfrac{5}{5z+3} = \dfrac{2z}{2z^2+6}$

11. $\dfrac{9t+6}{t(t+3)} = \dfrac{7}{t+3}$

12. $\dfrac{(x-7)(x+2)}{2} = \dfrac{(x+3)(x+2)}{4}$

In Exercises 13–22, express each sentence as a formula.

13. A varies directly with the square of p.

14. z varies inversely with the cube root of t.

15. v varies inversely with the fourth root of r.

16. r varies directly with the square root of s.

17. B varies jointly with m and n.

18. C varies jointly with x, y, and z.

19. P varies directly with the square of a, and inversely with the cube of j.

20. M varies inversely with the cube of n, and jointly with x and the square of z.

21. The force of attraction F between two masses m_1 and m_2 varies directly with the product of m_1 and m_2, and inversely with the square of the distance between them.

22. The force of wind on a vertical surface varies jointly with the area of the surface and the square of the velocity of the wind.

In Exercises 23–30, express each formula in words. In each formula, k is the constant of variation.

23. $L = kmn$

24. $P = \dfrac{km}{n}$

25. $E = kab^2$

26. $U = krs^2t$

27. $X = \dfrac{kx^2}{y^2}$

28. $Z = \dfrac{kw}{xy}$

29. $R = \dfrac{kL}{d^2}$

30. $e = \dfrac{kPL}{A}$

31. The area of a circle varies directly with the square of its radius with the constant of variation equal to π. Find the area of a circle with a radius of 6 inches.

32. An object in free fall travels a distance s that is directly proportional to the square of the time t. If an object falls 1024 feet in 8 seconds, how far will it fall in 10 seconds?

33. The distance that a car can travel is directly proportional to the number of gallons of gasoline that it consumes. If a car can go 288 miles on 12 gallons of gasoline, how far can it go on a full tank of 18 gallons?

34. A farmer's harvest in bushels varies directly as the number of acres planted. If 144 bushels can be reaped from 8 acres, how many acres are required to produce 1152 bushels?

35. The length of time that a given number of bushels of corn will last when feeding cattle varies inversely with the number of animals. If x bushels will feed 25 cows for 10 days, how long will the feed last for 10 cows?

36. For a fixed area, the length of a rectangle is inversely proportional to its width. A rectangle has a width of 18 feet and a length of 12 feet. If the length is increased to 16 feet, how wide is the rectangle?

37. Under constant temperature, the volume occupied by a gas is inversely proportional to the pressure applied. If the gas occupies a volume of 20 cubic inches under 6 pounds per square inch of pressure, what is the volume of the gas when it is subjected to 10 pounds per square inch of pressure?

38. Assume that the value of a car varies inversely with its age. If a car is worth $7000 when it is 3 years old, how much will it be worth when it is 7 years old?

39. The frequency of vibration of air in an organ pipe is inversely proportional to the length of the pipe. If a pipe 2 feet long vibrates 256 times per second, how many times per second will a 6-foot pipe vibrate?

40. The area of a rectangle varies jointly with its length and width. If both the length and width are tripled, by what factor is the area multiplied?

41. The volume of a rectangular solid varies jointly with its length, width, and height. If the length is doubled, the width is tripled, and the height is doubled, by what factor is the volume multiplied?

42. When you go shopping, the cost of like items varies jointly with the number of units purchased and the price per unit. If 15 items cost $105, what is the cost of 35 items?

43. The number of gallons of oil that can be stored in a cylindrical tank varies jointly with the height of the tank and the square of the radius of its base. The constant of proportionality is π. Find the number of gallons of oil that can be stored in a cylindrical tank with a height of 20 feet and a circular base with a diameter of 15 feet.

44. The quantity L varies jointly with x and y and inversely with z. The value of L is 30 when $x = 15$, $y = 5$, and $z = 10$. Evaluate the constant of variation and express this relationship with an equation.

45. The voltage measured across an electrical component called a resistor is directly proportional to the current flowing through the resistor. The voltage is measured in volts, the current in amperes, and the constant of proportionality is called the **resistance**, measured in ohms. If 6 volts is measured across a resistor through which a current of 2 amperes flows, what is the resistance?

46. The power lost (usually in the form of heat) in a resistor is directly proportional to the square of the current passing through it. The constant of proportionality is the resistance, measured in ohms. What power is lost in a 5-ohm resistor carrying a 3-ampere current?

47. The deflection of a beam is inversely proportional to its width and the cube of its depth. If the deflection of a 4-inch by 4-inch beam is 1.1 inches, calculate the deflection of a 2-inch by 8-inch beam in each of its two orientations (on its side; on its edge). See Illustration 1.

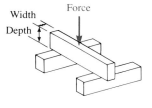

Illustration 1

48. The pressure of a certain amount of gas is directly proportional to the temperature (measured in degrees Kelvin), and inversely proportional to the volume. A sample of gas at a pressure of 1 atmosphere occupies a volume of 1 cubic meter at a temperature of 273 Kelvin (about 0° Celsius). When heated, the gas expands to twice its volume, but the pressure remains constant. To what temperature was it heated?

7.7 GRAPHS OF LINEAR INEQUALITIES IN TWO VARIABLES

The **graph of an inequality** in x and y is the graph of all ordered pairs (x, y) that satisfy the inequality. In this section we consider graphs of **linear inequalities**— inequalities that can be expressed in a form such as $Ax + By < C$, $Ax + By > C$, $Ax + By \leq C$, or $Ax + By \geq C$.

To graph the inequality $y > 3x + 2$, for example, we first note that exactly one of the following statements is true:

$$y < 3x + 2, \qquad y = 3x + 2, \qquad \text{or} \qquad y > 3x + 2$$

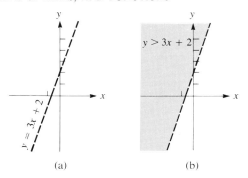

Figure 7-25

Because the equation $y = 3x + 2$ determines a linear function, its graph is a straight line. See Figure 7-25a. The graph of each inequality is a half-plane, one on each side of that line. Thus, we can think of the graph of $y = 3x + 2$ as a boundary separating the two half-planes. The graph of $y = 3x + 2$ is drawn with a broken line to indicate that it is not part of the desired graph for $y > 3x + 2$. To determine which half-plane is the graph of $y > 3x + 2$, we can substitute the coordinates of the origin, $(0, 0)$, into the inequality and simplify:

$$y > 3x + 2$$
$$0 > 3(0) + 2$$
$$0 \not> 2 \qquad \text{Read as "0 is not greater than 2."}$$

Because the coordinates of the origin do not satisfy the inequality, the origin is not in the half-plane that is the graph of $y > 3x + 2$. Thus, the half-plane on the other side of the broken line is the graph. The graph of the inequality $y > 3x + 2$ is shown in Figure 7-25b.

Example 1   Graph the inequality $2x - 3y \leq 6$.

Solution   This inequality is the combination of the inequality $2x - 3y < 6$ and the equation $2x - 3y = 6$. Begin by graphing the linear equation $2x - 3y = 6$ to establish the boundary that separates the two half-planes. However, this time draw a solid line because equality is permitted. See Figure 7-26a. To decide which half-plane represents $2x - 3y < 6$, check to see whether the coordinates of the origin satisfy the inequality:

$$2x - 3y < 6$$
$$2(0) - 3(0) < 6$$
$$0 < 6$$

In this case the origin is in the half-plane that is the graph of $2x - 3y < 6$. The complete graph is shown in Figure 7-26b.

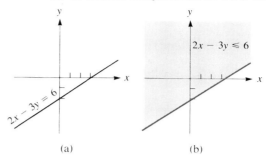

Figure 7-26

Example 2   Graph the inequality $y < 2x$.

Solution   Begin by graphing the equation $y = 2x$. Because it is not part of the graph, use a broken line as in Figure 7-27a. To decide which half-plane represents $y < 2x$, check to see whether the coordinates of some fixed point satisfies the inequality. This time, however, the origin cannot be used as a test point because the boundary line passes through the origin. Choose some other point, say (3, 1), for a test point:

$$y < 2x$$
$$1 < 2(3)$$
$$1 < 6$$

Because $1 < 6$, the point (3, 1) is in the graph. Thus, the graph is as shown in Figure 7-27b.

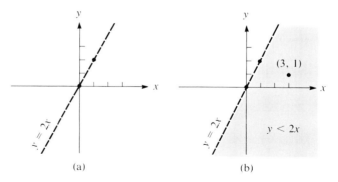

Figure 7-27

Example 3   Graph the inequality $2 < x \le 5$.

Solution   The double inequality $2 < x \le 5$ is equivalent to the inequalities

$$2 < x \quad \text{and} \quad x \le 5$$

Thus, the graph of $2 < x \le 5$ must contain all points in the plane that satisfy the inequalities $2 < x$ and $x \le 5$ simultaneously. These points are in the shaded region of Figure 7-28.

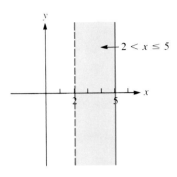

Figure 7-28

■ EXERCISE 7.7

In Exercises 1–18, graph each inequality.

1. $y > x + 1$ **2.** $y < 2x - 1$ **3.** $y \ge x$ **4.** $y \le 2x$

5. $2x + y \le 6$ **6.** $x - 2y \ge 4$ **7.** $3x \ge -y + 3$ **8.** $2x \le -3y - 12$

9. $y \ge 1 - \dfrac{3}{2}x$ **10.** $y < \dfrac{1}{3}x - 1$ **11.** $x < 4$ **12.** $y \ge -2$

13. $-2 \le x < 0$ **14.** $0 < y \le 5$

15. $y < -2 \quad \text{or} \quad y > 3$ **16.** $-x \le 1 \quad \text{or} \quad x \ge 2$

17. $-3 < y \le -1$ **18.** $-5 \ge x > -8$

In Exercises 19–28, find the equation of the boundary line or lines. Then give the inequality whose graph is shown.

19.

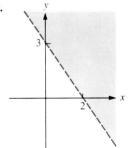

20.

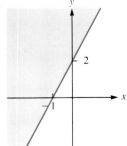

21.

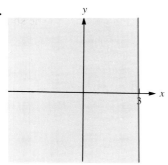

22.

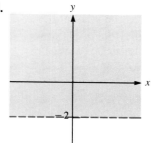

23.

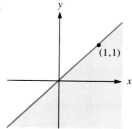

24.

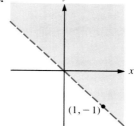

25.

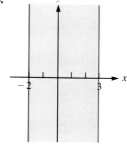

26.

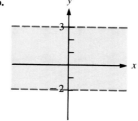

27.

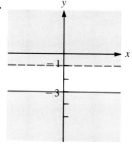

28.

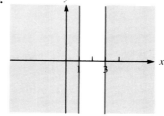

CHAPTER SUMMARY

Key Words

abscissa (7.1)
Cartesian coordinate system (7.1)
composite functions (7.4)
constant of variation (7.6)
dependent variable (7.4)
direct variation (7.6)
domain (7.4)
extremes of a proportion (7.6)
function (7.4)
graph of an equation (7.1)
graph of an inequality (7.7)
image (7.4)
independent variable (7.4)
inverse relation (7.5)
inverse variation (7.6)
joint variation (7.6)
linear equation in x and y (7.2)

linear inequalities (7.7)
means of a proportion (7.6)
ordered pairs (7.1)
ordinate (7.1)
origin (7.1)
proportion (7.6)
ratio (7.6)
rectangular coordinate system (7.1)
relation (7.4)
slope of a nonvertical line (7.2)
x-axis (7.1)
x-coordinate (7.1)
x-intercept (7.1)
y-axis (7.1)
y-coordinate (7.1)
y-intercept (7.1)

Key Ideas

(7.1)   The **distance formula**: $d(PQ) = \sqrt{(x_2 - x_1)^2 + (y_2 - y_1)^2}$

The **midpoint formula**:   If $P(x_1, y_1)$ and $Q(x_2, y_2)$ are two points on a line, then the midpoint of the line segment PQ is point M, where the coordinates of M are

$$\left(\frac{x_1 + x_2}{2}, \frac{y_1 + y_2}{2} \right)$$

(7.2)   The **slope of a nonvertical line**: $m = \dfrac{\Delta y}{\Delta x} = \dfrac{y_2 - y_1}{x_2 - x_1}$

Nonvertical parallel lines have the same slope, and lines with the same slope are parallel.

If two nonvertical lines are perpendicular, their slopes are negative reciprocals.

If the slopes of two lines are negative reciprocals, the lines are perpendicular.

(7.3)   **Point–slope form** of a linear equation: $y - y_1 = m(x - x_1)$

Slope–intercept form of a linear equation: $y = mx + b$

General form of a linear equation: $Ax + By = C$

(7.4)   If $y = f(x)$ is a function, then $f(a)$ represents the value of y when $x = a$.

$$(f \circ g)(x) = f(g(x)) \qquad (f + g)(x) = f(x) + g(x) \qquad (f - g)(x) = f(x) - g(x)$$

$$(f \cdot g)(x) = f(x)g(x) \qquad (f/g)(x) = \frac{f(x)}{g(x)} \qquad [g(x) \neq 0]$$

(7.5)   A **linear function** is defined by an equation that can be written in the form $y = f(x) = mx + b$, where m and b are constants.

If R is a relation, then R^{-1} is the relation formed by interchanging the components of each ordered pair of R.

(7.6)   In a proportion, the product of the extremes is equal to the product of the means.

If $y = kx$ and k is a constant, then x and y **vary directly**.

If $y = k/x$ and k is a constant, then x and y **vary inversely**.

If $y = kxz$ and k is a constant, then y **varies jointly** with x and z.

The expression $y = kx/z$ (k is a constant) indicates **combined variation**, with y and x varying directly and y and z varying inversely.

(7.7)   To graph an inequality such as $y > ax + b$, first graph the linear function defined by $y = ax + b$. The line graph will determine two half-planes, one on each side of the line. Then determine which half-plane represents the graph of $y > ax + b$.

REVIEW EXERCISES

In Review Exercises 1–4, graph each equation.

1. $x + y = 4$ **2.** $2x - y = 8$ **3.** $y = 3x + 4$ **4.** $x = 4 - 2y$

In Review Exercises 5–8, find the distance between each pair of points.

5. $P(2, 6)$; $Q(5, 10)$ **6.** $P(-2, 5)$; $Q(3, 17)$
7. $P(-2, -5)$; $Q(6, 8)$ **8.** $P(4, -5)$; $Q(-6, 12)$

In Review Exercises 9–12, find the midpoint of each line segment PQ.

9. $P(2, 6)$; $Q(2, 12)$ **10.** $P(8, -2)$; $Q(-6, -2)$
11. $P(2, -6)$; $Q(5, 10)$ **12.** $P(-3, -7)$; $Q(10, -6)$

In Review Exercises 13–16, find the slope of the line passing through points P and Q.

13. $P(2, 5)$; $Q(5, 8)$ **14.** $P(-3, -2)$; $Q(6, 12)$
15. $P(-3, 4)$; $Q(-5, -6)$ **16.** $P(5, -4)$; $Q(-6, -9)$

17.   Use the point–slope form to write the equation of the line with slope of $-\frac{3}{2}$ that passes through $P(-2, 5)$.
18.   Use the slope–intercept form to write the equation of the line with slope of $-\frac{3}{2}$ that passes through $P(-2, 5)$.

In Review Exercises 19–22, write the equation of the line with the given properties. **Write each answer in general form.**

19.   Slope of 3 and passing through $P(-8, 5)$ **20.**   Passing through the points $(-2, 4)$ and $(6, -9)$
21.   Passing through the point $(-3, -5)$ and parallel to the graph of $3x - 2y = 7$
22.   Passing through the point $(-3, -5)$ and perpendicular to the graph of $3x - 2y = 7$

In Review Exercises 23–28, find the domain and range of each relation. Assume that all ordered pairs (x, y) consist of real numbers. If a relation is a function, so indicate.

23. $y = 4x - 1$ **24.** $x = 3y - 10$ **25.** $y = 3x^2 + 1$ **26.** $y = \dfrac{4}{2 - x}$

27. $x = \dfrac{y + 3}{2}$ **28.** $y^2 = 4x$

In Review Exercises 29–34, let $f(x) = 3x + 2$ and $g(x) = x^2 - 4$. Find each indicated value.

29. $f(-3)$ **30.** $g(8)$ **31.** $(g \circ f)(-2)$ **32.** $(f \circ g)(3)$

33. $(f \circ g)(x)$ **34.** $(g \circ f)(x)$

In Review Exercises 35–38, let $f(x) = 2x + 1$ and $g(x) = 3x - 2$. Find each function and determine its domain.

35. $f + g$ **36.** $f - g$ **37.** $f \cdot g$ **38.** f/g

In Review Exercises 39–40, find the inverse relation of each function defined by ordered pairs (x, y). If the inverse relation is a function, so indicate.

39. $y = 7x + 2$ **40.** $5 = \dfrac{3y + 4}{x - 2}$

In Review Exercises 41–42, solve each proportion.

41. $\dfrac{x + 1}{8} = \dfrac{4x - 2}{24}$ **42.** $\dfrac{1}{x + 6} = \dfrac{x + 10}{12}$

43. Assume that x varies directly with y. If $x = 12$ when $y = 2$, what is the value of x when $y = 12$?

44. Assume that x varies inversely with y. If $x = 24$ when $y = 3$, what is the value of y when $x = 12$?

45. Assume that x varies jointly with y and z. What is the constant of variation if $x = 24$ when $y = 3$ and $z = 4$?

46. Assume that x varies directly with t and inversely with y. Find the constant of variation if $x = 2$ when $t = 8$ and $y = 64$.

In Review Exercises 47–50, graph each inequality.

47. $2x + 3y > 6$ **48.** $y < 4 - x$

49. $-2 < x < 4$ **50.** $y \le -2$ or $y > 1$

CHAPTER SEVEN TEST

1. Graph the equation $2x - 5y = 10$.

2. Find the x- and y-intercepts of the graph of $y = \dfrac{x - 3}{5}$.

In Problems 3–5, consider points $P(-5, -6)$ and $Q(5, -2)$.

3. Find the distance between P and Q. **4.** Find the midpoint of line segment PQ.

5. Find the slope of the line that passes through points P and Q.

6. Find the slope of the straight line graph of the equation $x = \dfrac{3y - 8}{2}$.

7. Write the equation of the line with slope of $\frac{2}{3}$ that passes through the point $P(4, -5)$. Give the answer in slope–intercept form.

8. Write the equation of the line that passes through $P(-2, 6)$ and $Q(-4, -10)$. Give the answer in general form.

9. Find the slope and the y-intercept of the graph of $-2(x - 3) = 3(2y + 5)$.

10. Determine whether the graphs of $4x - y = 12$ and $y = \frac{1}{4}x + 3$ are parallel, perpendicular, or neither.

11. Determine whether the graphs of $y = -\frac{2}{3}x + 4$ and $2y = 3x - 3$ are parallel, perpendicular, or neither.

12. Write the equation of the line that passes through the origin and is parallel to the graph of $y = \frac{3}{2}x - 7$.

13. Write the equation of the line that passes through the point $P(-3, 6)$ and is perpendicular to the graph of $y = -\frac{2}{3}x - 7$.

14. Does $|y| = x$ determine y to be a function of x? Explain.

15. Find the domain and the range of the function determined by $y = \dfrac{9}{x - 2}$.

In Problems 16–22, let $f(x) = 3x + 1$ and $g(x) = x^2 - 2$. Find each quantity.

16. $f(3)$ **17.** $g(0)$ **18.** $f(g(-2))$ **19.** $g(f(x))$

20. $(f + g)(x)$ **21.** $(f \cdot g)(x)$ **22.** $(f/g)(x)$

23. Does the equation $y(x + 3) + 4 = x(y - 2)$ determine a linear function?

24. Find the inverse of the linear function $y = -\frac{1}{2}x + 5$. Give the answer using $f^{-1}(x)$ notation.

25. Solve the proportion $\dfrac{3}{x - 2} = \dfrac{x + 3}{2x}$.

26. The force of attraction F between two masses m_1 and m_2 varies directly with the product of m_1 and m_2 and inversely with the square of the distance between them. If k is the constant of variation express this relationship with an equation.

27. Assume that x varies directly with y. If $x = 30$ when $y = 4$, find x when $y = 9$.

28. Assume that V varies inversely with t. If $V = 55$ when $t = 20$, find t when $V = 75$.

29. Graph the inequality $3x + 2y \geq 6$.

30. Graph the inequality $-2 \leq y < 5$.

Quadratic Equations and Inequalities

So far we have discussed how to solve linear equations and certain quadratic equations in which the quadratic expression is factorable. In this chapter we will discuss more-general methods for solving quadratic equations and discuss methods for solving quadratic inequalities.

8.1 SOLVING QUADRATIC EQUATIONS BY COMPLETING THE SQUARE

Recall that a quadratic equation is an equation of the form $ax^2 + bx + c = 0$, where a, b, and c are real numbers and $a \neq 0$. In Chapter 4 we discussed how to solve quadratic equations by using factoring. For example, to solve the equation $6x^2 - 7x - 3 = 0$, we first factor the quadratic trinomial and then apply the zero-factor theorem.

$$6x^2 - 7x - 3 = 0$$
$$(2x - 3)(3x + 1) = 0$$
$$2x - 3 = 0 \quad \text{or} \quad 3x + 1 = 0$$
$$x = \frac{3}{2} \qquad \qquad x = -\frac{1}{3}$$

A check will show that both solutions satisfy the original equation.

If the quadratic expression in a quadratic equation factors easily, the factoring method for solving quadratic equations is very convenient. Unfortunately, quadratic expressions do not always factor easily. For example, it would be difficult to factor the left-hand side of the equation $2x^2 + 4x + 1 = 0$ because it cannot be factored by using only integers.

To develop methods for solving all quadratic equations, we first consider the equation $x^2 = c$. If c is positive, the two real solutions of $x^2 = c$ can be found by adding $-c$ to both sides, factoring the binomial $x^2 - c$, setting each factor equal to 0, and solving for x.

$$x^2 = c$$
$$x^2 - c = 0$$
$$x^2 - (\sqrt{c})^2 = 0$$
$$(x + \sqrt{c})(x - \sqrt{c}) = 0$$
$$x + \sqrt{c} = 0 \qquad \text{or} \qquad x - \sqrt{c} = 0$$
$$x = -\sqrt{c} \qquad \qquad \qquad x = \sqrt{c}$$

Thus, the solutions of the equation $x^2 = c$ are $x = \sqrt{c}$ and $x = -\sqrt{c}$. This fact is often called the **square root property**.

The Square Root Property.   If $c > 0$, then the equation $x^2 = c$ has two real solutions. They are

$$x = \sqrt{c} \qquad \text{and} \qquad x = -\sqrt{c}$$

Example 1   Solve the equation $x^2 - 12 = 0$.

Solution   Write the equation as $x^2 = 12$ and use the square root property.

$$x^2 - 12 = 0$$
$$x^2 = 12 \qquad \qquad \text{Add 12 to both sides.}$$
$$x = \sqrt{12} \quad \text{or} \quad x = -\sqrt{12} \qquad \text{Use the square root property.}$$
$$x = 2\sqrt{3} \qquad \qquad x = -2\sqrt{3} \qquad \text{Simplify each radical.}$$

Verify that both solutions check.   ∎

Example 2   Solve the equation $(x - 3)^2 = 16$.

Solution   Use the square root property.

$$(x - 3)^2 = 16$$
$$x - 3 = \sqrt{16} \quad \text{or} \quad x - 3 = -\sqrt{16}$$
$$x - 3 = 4 \qquad \qquad x - 3 = -4$$
$$x = 3 + 4 \qquad \qquad x = 3 - 4$$
$$x = 7 \qquad \qquad \qquad x = -1$$

Verify that both solutions check.   ∎

Completing the Square

All quadratic equations can be solved by a method called **completing the square**. This method is based on the special products

$$x^2 + 2yx + y^2 = (x + y)^2$$

and

$$x^2 - 2yx + y^2 = (x - y)^2$$

The trinomials $x^2 + 2yx + y^2$ and $x^2 - 2yx + y^2$ are both perfect trinomial squares because both factor as the square of a binomial. In each case, the coefficient of the first term is 1, and if we take one-half of the coefficient of x in the middle term and square it, we obtain the third term.

$$\left[\frac{1}{2}(2y)\right]^2 = y^2$$

$$\left[\frac{1}{2}(-2y)\right]^2 = (-y)^2 = y^2$$

Thus, to make an expression such as $x^2 + 10x$ a perfect square, we must take one-half of 10, which gives 5, square 5, which gives 25, and add 25 to $x^2 + 10x$.

$$x^2 + 10x + \left[\frac{1}{2}(10)\right]^2 = x^2 + 10x + (5)^2$$

$$= x^2 + 10x + 25$$

Note that $x^2 + 10x + 25 = (x + 5)^2$.

To make the expression $x^2 - 6x$ a perfect square, we must take one-half of -6, which gives -3, square -3, which gives 9, and add 9 to $x^2 - 6x$.

$$x^2 - 6x + \left[\frac{1}{2}(-6)\right]^2 = x^2 - 6x + (-3)^2$$

$$= x^2 - 6x + 9$$

Note that $x^2 - 6x + 9 = (x - 3)^2$.

Example 3   Use completing the square to solve the equation $x^2 + 8x + 7 = 0$.

Solution   Note that the coefficient of x^2 is 1. This is a necessary condition before the square can be completed. Begin by adding -7 to both sides of the equation to get the constant on the right-hand side of the equal sign.

$$x^2 + 8x + 7 = 0$$
$$x^2 + 8x \quad\;\; = -7$$

To complete the square, you must add a number k to both sides of the equation so that $x^2 + 8x + k$ is a perfect trinomial square. To determine k, take one-half of the coefficient of x (one-half of 8 is 4) and square it (4 squared is 16). Thus, $k = 16$. Add 16 to both sides of the equation to obtain

$$x^2 + 8x + 16 = 16 - 7$$

The left-hand side of the previous equation is a perfect trinomial square because $x^2 + 8x + 16 = (x + 4)^2$. Now factor the left-hand side and combine terms on the right-hand side to obtain

$$(x + 4)^2 = 9$$

Solve this equation using the square root property.

$$(x + 4)^2 = 9$$

$x + 4 = \sqrt{9}$ or $x + 4 = -\sqrt{9}$ Use the square root property.

$x + 4 = 3$ $x + 4 = -3$

$x = -1$ $x = -7$

Verify that both solutions check.   ∎

Example 4   Solve $6x^2 + 5x - 6 = 0$.

Solution   Begin by dividing both sides of the equation by 6 to make the coefficient of x^2 equal to 1. Then add 1 to both sides.

$$6x^2 + 5x - 6 = 0$$

$$x^2 + \frac{5}{6}x - 1 = 0$$

$$x^2 + \frac{5}{6}x = 1$$

To complete the square on x, take one-half of $\frac{5}{6}$, which gives $\frac{5}{12}$, square $\frac{5}{12}$, which gives $\frac{25}{144}$, and add $\frac{25}{144}$ to both sides of the equation.

$$x^2 + \frac{5}{6}x + \frac{25}{144} = \frac{25}{144} + 1$$

$$\left[x + \frac{5}{12}\right]^2 = \frac{169}{144}$$ Factor and add the fractions.

Apply the square root property.

$x + \frac{5}{12} = \sqrt{\frac{169}{144}}$ or $x + \frac{5}{12} = -\sqrt{\frac{169}{144}}$

$x + \frac{5}{12} = \frac{13}{12}$ $x + \frac{5}{12} = -\frac{13}{12}$

$x = -\frac{5}{12} + \frac{13}{12}$ $x = -\frac{5}{12} - \frac{13}{12}$

$x = \frac{8}{12}$ $x = -\frac{18}{12}$

$x = \frac{2}{3}$ $x = -\frac{3}{2}$

Verify that both solutions check.   ∎

The solution used in Example 4 suggests a list of steps to follow when using the method of completing the square to solve quadratic equations of the form $ax^2 + bx + c = 0$.

---

1. Make sure that the coefficient of x^2 is 1. If it is not, make it 1 by dividing both sides of the equation by the coefficient of x^2.
2. If necessary, add a number to both sides of the equation to get the constant term on the right-hand side of the equal sign.
3. Complete the square:
   a. Identify the coefficient of x.
   b. Find one-half of the coefficient of x and square it.
   c. Add that square to both sides of the equation.
4. Factor the trinomial square and combine terms.
5. Solve the resulting equation by applying the square root property.

Example 5   Solve $2x^2 + 4x + 1 = 0$.

Solution   Use the method of completing the square.

$$2x^2 + 4x + 1 = 0$$

$$x^2 + 2x + \frac{1}{2} = 0 \qquad \text{Divide both sides by 2 to make the coefficient of } x^2 \text{ equal to 1.}$$

$$x^2 + 2x = -\frac{1}{2} \qquad \text{Add } -\tfrac{1}{2} \text{ to both sides.}$$

$$x^2 + 2x + 1 = 1 - \frac{1}{2} \qquad \text{Square half the coefficient of } x, \text{ and add it to both sides.}$$

$$(x + 1)^2 = \frac{1}{2} \qquad \text{Factor and combine terms.}$$

$$x + 1 = \sqrt{\frac{1}{2}} \qquad \text{or} \qquad x + 1 = -\sqrt{\frac{1}{2}} \qquad \text{Apply the square root property.}$$

$$x + 1 = \frac{\sqrt{2}}{2} \qquad\qquad\qquad x + 1 = -\frac{\sqrt{2}}{2}$$

$$x = -1 + \frac{\sqrt{2}}{2} \qquad\qquad x = -1 - \frac{\sqrt{2}}{2}$$

$$x = \frac{-2 + \sqrt{2}}{2} \qquad\qquad x = \frac{-2 - \sqrt{2}}{2}$$

Both solutions check.   ■

Example 6   Tickets for a symphony concert cost $9 and the average attendance at a concert has been 760 persons. To obtain a larger audience, the symphony manager recommends a decrease in the ticket price. He projects that for every 25-cent decrease in the ticket price, the audience will increase by 20 people. At what ticket price will the concert receipts be $6825?

Solution   If q represents the number of quarters that the ticket price is to be reduced, the cost of a ticket will be

$$9 - 0.25q$$

Because each 25-cent decrease in the ticket price will raise the attendance by 20 people, the projected attendance at the concert will be

$$760 + 20q$$

The product of $9 - 0.25q$ (the cost of a ticket) and $760 + 20q$ (the number of people who buy a ticket) will equal the total receipts of $6825. Thus,

$$(9 - 0.25q)(760 + 20q) = 6825$$
$$6840 + 180q - 190q - 5q^2 = 6825$$
$$-5q^2 - 10q + 15 = 0$$
$$q^2 + 2q - 3 = 0$$
$$(q + 3)(q - 1) = 0$$
$$q + 3 = 0 \quad \text{or} \quad q - 1 = 0$$
$$q = -3 \quad \quad \quad q = 1$$

Because the price of a ticket cannot be reduced by -3 quarters, the only reasonable result is $q = 1$. Thus, if the ticket price is reduced by 25 cents to $8.75, then 780 people will attend and the concert receipts will be $6825.   ■

Recall that we can find a quadratic equation with known solutions. For example, to find a quadratic equation with solutions of $\sqrt{3}$ and $5\sqrt{3}$, we form the binomials $x - \sqrt{3}$ and $x - 5\sqrt{3}$, set their product equal to 0, and simplify.

$$(x - \sqrt{3})(x - 5\sqrt{3}) = 0$$
$$x^2 - 6\sqrt{3}x + 15 = 0$$

To show that $\sqrt{3}$ and $5\sqrt{3}$ are both solutions of $x^2 - 6\sqrt{3}x + 15 = 0$, we show that each one satisfies the equation.

$$x^2 - 6\sqrt{3}x + 15 = 0 \qquad\qquad x^2 - 6\sqrt{3}x + 15 = 0$$
$$(\sqrt{3})^2 - 6\sqrt{3}(\sqrt{3}) + 15 = 0 \qquad (5\sqrt{3})^2 - 6\sqrt{3}(5\sqrt{3}) + 15 = 0$$
$$3 - 18 + 15 = 0 \qquad\qquad 75 - 90 + 15 = 0$$
$$0 = 0 \qquad\qquad\qquad 0 = 0$$

▰ EXERCISE 8.1

In Exercises 1–24, solve each quadratic equation by factoring.

1. $6x^2 + 12x = 0$ **2.** $5x^2 + 11x = 0$ **3.** $x^2 + x = 0$ **4.** $x^2 - 3x = 0$

5. $2y^2 - 50 = 0$ **6.** $4y^2 - 64 = 0$ **7.** $r^2 + 6r + 8 = 0$ **8.** $x^2 + 9x + 20 = 0$

9. $x^2 - 3x + 2 = 0$ **10.** $x^2 - 7x + 12 = 0$ **11.** $x^2 - 7x + 6 = 0$ **12.** $t^2 - 5t + 6 = 0$

13. $x^2 - 6x - 7 = 0$ **14.** $x^2 + 12x + 20 = 0$ **15.** $2z^2 - 5z + 2 = 0$ **16.** $2x^2 - x - 1 = 0$

17. $6s^2 + 11s - 10 = 0$ **18.** $3x^2 + 10x - 8 = 0$ **19.** $3x^2 - 5x + 2 = 0$ **20.** $3x^2 - 8x + 4 = 0$

21. $5x^2 = 10x$ **22.** $2x^2 = 8$ **23.** $x^2 + 9 = 6x$ **24.** $6x^2 = 4 - 5x$

In Exercises 25–36, solve each equation by using the square root property.

25. $x^2 = 36$ **26.** $x^2 = 144$ **27.** $z^2 = 5$ **28.** $u^2 = 24$

29. $3x^2 - 16 = 0$ **30.** $5x^2 - 49 = 0$ **31.** $(x + 1)^2 = 1$ **32.** $(x - 1)^2 = 4$

33. $(s - 7)^2 - 9 = 0$ **34.** $(t + 4)^2 = 16$ **35.** $(x + 5)^2 - 3 = 0$ **36.** $(x + 3)^2 - 7 = 0$

In Exercises 37–50, solve each equation by completing the square.

37. $x^2 + 2x - 8 = 0$ **38.** $x^2 + 6x + 5 = 0$ **39.** $x^2 - 6x + 8 = 0$ **40.** $x^2 + 8x + 15 = 0$

41. $x^2 + 5x + 4 = 0$ **42.** $x^2 - 11x + 30 = 0$ **43.** $2x^2 - x - 1 = 0$ **44.** $2x^2 - 5x + 2 = 0$

45. $6x^2 + 11x + 3 = 0$ **46.** $6x^2 + x - 2 = 0$ **47.** $8r^2 + 6r = 9$ **48.** $3w^2 - 11w = -10$

49. $\dfrac{7x + 1}{5} = -x^2$ **50.** $\dfrac{3x^2}{8} = \dfrac{1}{8} - x$

In Exercises 51–66, solve each word problem.

51. The product of two consecutive even integers is 288. Find the integers.

52. The product of two consecutive odd integers is 143. Find the integers.

53. The sum of the squares of two consecutive positive integers is 85. Find the integers.

54. The sum of the squares of three consecutive positive integers is 77. Find the integers.

55. A rectangle is 4 feet longer than it is wide. The area of the rectangle is 96 square feet. Find its dimensions.

56. One side of a rectangle is 3 times another. The area of the rectangle is 147 square meters. Find its dimensions.

57. The area of a certain square is numerically equal to its perimeter. What is the perimeter of the square?

58. A rectangle is 2 inches longer than it is wide. Numerically, its area exceeds its perimeter by 11 inches. What is the area of the rectangle?

59. Movie tickets at a certain theater cost $4 and the average nightly attendance is 300 persons. It is projected that for every 10¢ increase in ticket price, the average attendance will decrease by 5. At what ticket price will nightly receipts be $1248?

60. A bus company has 3000 passengers daily, each paying a 25¢ fare. For each nickel increase in fare, the company estimates that it will lose 80 passengers. What increase in fare will produce $994 in daily revenue?

61. The Gazette's profit is $20 per year for each of its 3000 subscribers. The management estimates that the profit per subscriber would increase by 1¢ for each additional subscriber over the current 3000. How many subscribers will bring a total profit of $120,000?

62. A woman deposits $1000 in a savings bank, where interest is compounded annually at a rate r. After 1 year she deposits an additional $2000. After 2 years the balance in the account is

$$1000(1 + r)^2 + 2000(1 + r)$$

dollars. If this amount is $3368.10, what is the interest rate r?

63. The frame surrounding a 10-inch by 12-inch photograph has a constant width. The area of the frame equals the area of the photograph. How wide is the frame? (*Hint:* You will need to complete the square.)

In Exercises 64–67, find a quadratic equation with the given solutions.

64. $\sqrt{5}, 3\sqrt{5}$

65. $\sqrt{7}, -5\sqrt{7}$

66. $1 + \sqrt{2}, 1 - \sqrt{2}$

67. $\sqrt{3}, 1$

8.2   THE QUADRATIC FORMULA

All quadratic equations can be solved by the method of completing the square. However, the method is sometimes tedious. Fortunately, there is a formula, called the **quadratic formula**, that gives the solutions of any quadratic equation with less effort. To develop the quadratic formula, we will use the method of completing the square.

Recall that a quadratic equation is any equation that can be written in the form $ax^2 + bx + c = 0$, with $a \neq 0$. If we solve this general form of a quadratic equation by completing the square, we are solving every possible quadratic equation at one time. The solution of the general quadratic equation results in the quadratic formula.

To solve the equation $ax^2 + bx + c = 0$, with $a \neq 0$, we first divide both sides by a and then proceed as follows:

$$ax^2 + bx + c = 0$$

$$x^2 + \frac{bx}{a} + \frac{c}{a} = \frac{0}{a}$$

$$x^2 + \frac{bx}{a} = -\frac{c}{a} \qquad \text{Simplify } \frac{0}{a} \text{ and add } -\frac{c}{a} \text{ to both sides.}$$

$$x^2 + \frac{b}{a}x + \left(\frac{b}{2a}\right)^2 = \left(\frac{b}{2a}\right)^2 - \frac{c}{a} \qquad \begin{array}{l}\text{Complete the square on } x \text{ and} \\ \text{add } \left(\frac{b}{2a}\right)^2 \text{ to both sides.}\end{array}$$

$$x^2 + \frac{b}{a}x + \frac{b^2}{4a^2} = \frac{b^2}{4a^2} - \frac{4ac}{4aa} \qquad \begin{array}{l}\text{Remove parentheses and get a common} \\ \text{denominator on the right-hand side.}\end{array}$$

1. $\left(x + \frac{b}{2a}\right)^2 = \frac{b^2 - 4ac}{4a^2} \qquad \begin{array}{l}\text{Factor the left-hand side and add} \\ \text{the fractions on the right-hand side.}\end{array}$

We can solve Equation 1 by using the square root property.

$$x + \frac{b}{2a} = \sqrt{\frac{b^2 - 4ac}{4a^2}} \qquad \text{or} \qquad x + \frac{b}{2a} = -\sqrt{\frac{b^2 - 4ac}{4a^2}}$$

$$x + \frac{b}{2a} = \frac{\sqrt{b^2 - 4ac}}{2a} \qquad\qquad x + \frac{b}{2a} = -\frac{\sqrt{b^2 - 4ac}}{2a}$$

$$x = -\frac{b}{2a} + \frac{\sqrt{b^2 - 4ac}}{2a} \qquad\qquad x = -\frac{b}{2a} - \frac{\sqrt{b^2 - 4ac}}{2a}$$

$$x = \frac{-b + \sqrt{b^2 - 4ac}}{2a} \qquad\qquad x = \frac{-b - \sqrt{b^2 - 4ac}}{2a}$$

These two values of x are the solutions to the equation $ax^2 + bx + c = 0$, with $a \neq 0$. They are usually written as a single expression called the **quadratic formula**. Read the symbol $\pm$ as "plus or minus."

The Quadratic Formula.   If $a \neq 0$, then the solutions of $ax^2 + bx + c = 0$ are given by the formula

$$x = \frac{-b \pm \sqrt{b^2 - 4ac}}{2a}$$

This formula should be read twice: once using the $+$ sign and once using the $-$ sign. The quadratic formula is an extremely important formula and should be memorized.

Example 1   Use the quadratic formula to solve $x^2 + 6x + 8 = 0$.

Solution   In this equation $a = 1$, $b = 6$, and $c = 8$. Substitute these values into the quadratic formula, and simplify.

$$x = \frac{-b \pm \sqrt{b^2 - 4ac}}{2a}$$

$$= \frac{-6 \pm \sqrt{6^2 - 4(1)(8)}}{2(1)}$$

$$= \frac{-6 \pm \sqrt{36 - 32}}{2}$$

$$= \frac{-6 \pm \sqrt{4}}{2}$$

$$= \frac{-6 \pm 2}{2}$$

$$x = \frac{-6 + 2}{2} \quad \text{or} \quad x = \frac{-6 - 2}{2}$$

$$x = -2 \quad \quad \quad x = -4$$

Verify that both solutions check. Note that this equation could have been solved by factoring. ∎

Example 2   Solve the equation $2x^2 - 3x - 5 = 0$.

Solution   In this equation $a = 2$, $b = -3$, and $c = -5$. Substitute these values into the quadratic formula, and simplify.

$$x = \frac{-b \pm \sqrt{b^2 - 4ac}}{2a}$$

$$= \frac{-(-3) \pm \sqrt{(-3)^2 - 4(2)(-5)}}{2(2)}$$

$$= \frac{3 \pm \sqrt{9 + 40}}{4}$$

$$= \frac{3 \pm \sqrt{49}}{4}$$

$$= \frac{3 \pm 7}{4}$$

$$x = \frac{3 + 7}{4} \quad \text{or} \quad x = \frac{3 - 7}{4}$$

$$= \frac{10}{4} \qquad\qquad = \frac{-4}{4}$$

$$= \frac{5}{2} \qquad\qquad = -1$$

Verify that both solutions check.

Example 3   Solve the equation $2x^2 + 4x + 1 = 0$.

Solution   In this equation $a = 2$, $b = 4$, and $c = 1$.

$$x = \frac{-b \pm \sqrt{b^2 - 4ac}}{2a}$$

$$= \frac{-4 \pm \sqrt{4^2 - 4(2)(1)}}{2(2)}$$

$$= \frac{-4 \pm \sqrt{16 - 8}}{4}$$

$$= \frac{-4 \pm \sqrt{8}}{4}$$

$$= \frac{-4 \pm 2\sqrt{2}}{4}$$

$$= \frac{-2 \pm \sqrt{2}}{2}$$

$$x = \frac{-2 + \sqrt{2}}{2} \quad \text{or} \quad x = \frac{-2 - \sqrt{2}}{2}$$

The solutions check.

Solutions of a Quadratic Equation

The solutions of a quadratic equation have some interesting properties. For example, if r_1 and r_2 are the solutions of the quadratic equation $ax^2 + bx + c = 0$, with $a \neq 0$, then $r_1 + r_2 = -\dfrac{b}{a}$ and $r_1 r_2 = \dfrac{c}{a}$. To prove this fact, we note that the solutions to the equation are given by the quadratic formula

$$r_1 = \frac{-b + \sqrt{b^2 - 4ac}}{2a} \quad \text{and} \quad r_2 = \frac{-b - \sqrt{b^2 - 4ac}}{2a}$$

Thus,

$$\begin{aligned} r_1 + r_2 &= \frac{-b + \sqrt{b^2 - 4ac}}{2a} + \frac{-b - \sqrt{b^2 - 4ac}}{2a} \\ &= \frac{-b + \sqrt{b^2 - 4ac} - b - \sqrt{b^2 - 4ac}}{2a} \\ &= -\frac{2b}{2a} \\ &= -\frac{b}{a} \end{aligned}$$

and

$$\begin{aligned} r_1 r_2 &= \frac{-b + \sqrt{b^2 - 4ac}}{2a} \cdot \frac{-b - \sqrt{b^2 - 4ac}}{2a} \\ &= \frac{b^2 - (b^2 - 4ac)}{4a^2} \\ &= \frac{b^2 - b^2 + 4ac}{4a^2} \\ &= \frac{4ac}{4a^2} \\ &= \frac{c}{a} \end{aligned}$$

It is also true that if the sum of two numbers r_1 and r_2 is $-\frac{a}{b}$ and if the product of the same two numbers is $\frac{c}{a}$, then r_1 and r_2 are the solutions of the quadratic equation $ax^2 + bx + c = 0$. This fact can be used to check the solutions of quadratic equations.

Example 4 Show that $\frac{3}{2}$ and $-\frac{1}{3}$ are solutions of the quadratic equation $6x^2 - 7x - 3 = 0$.

Solution Note that in the quadratic equation $6x^2 - 7x - 3 = 0$, $a = 6$, $b = -7$, and $c = -3$. If $\frac{3}{2}$ and $-\frac{1}{3}$ are two numbers such that

$$\frac{3}{2} + \left(-\frac{1}{3}\right) = -\frac{b}{a} = -\left(\frac{-7}{6}\right) = \frac{7}{6}$$

and

$$\frac{3}{2}\left(-\frac{1}{3}\right) = \frac{c}{a} = \frac{-3}{6} = -\frac{1}{2}$$

then $\frac{3}{2}$ and $-\frac{1}{3}$ are solutions of the given equation. Do the arithmetic to verify that these results are true.

$$\frac{3}{2} + \left(-\frac{1}{3}\right) = \frac{9}{6} - \frac{2}{6} = \frac{7}{6}$$

$$\frac{3}{2}\left(-\frac{1}{3}\right) = -\frac{1}{2}$$

■

Example 5   The length of a rectangle is 12 centimeters more than its width, and the area of the rectangle is 253 square centimeters. Find the dimensions of the rectangle.

Solution   Let w represent the width of the rectangle shown in Figure 8-1. Then, $w + 12$ represents its length. Because the area of a rectangle is found by multiplying its length and width, and because that area is given to be 253 square centimeters, you can form the equation

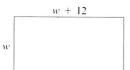

$$w(w + 12) = 253$$

Figure 8-1

Solve this equation for w as follows.

$$w(w + 12) = 253$$
$$w^2 + 12w = 253 \qquad \text{Remove parentheses.}$$
$$w^2 + 12w - 253 = 0 \qquad \text{Add } -253 \text{ to both sides.}$$

Solution by factoring

$$(w - 11)(w + 23) = 0$$
$$w - 11 = 0 \quad \text{or} \quad w + 23 = 0$$
$$w = 11 \qquad\qquad w = -23$$

Solution by formula

$$w = \frac{-12 \pm \sqrt{12^2 - 4(1)(-253)}}{2(1)}$$
$$= \frac{-12 \pm \sqrt{144 + 1012}}{2}$$
$$= \frac{-12 \pm \sqrt{1156}}{2}$$
$$= \frac{-12 \pm 34}{2}$$
$$w = 11 \quad \text{or} \quad w = -23$$

Because a rectangle cannot have a width that is negative, the root -23 must be discarded. Thus, the dimensions of the rectangle are 11 centimeters by $(11 + 12)$ centimeters, or 11 centimeters by 23 centimeters.

Note that 23 is 12 more than 11, and that the area of a rectangle that is 11 centimeters by 23 centimeters is 253 square centimeters.   ■

EXERCISE 8.2

In Exercises 1–24, use the quadratic formula to solve each equation. Verify that the sum of the solutions is $-\dfrac{b}{a}$ and that the product of the solutions is $\dfrac{c}{a}$.

1. $x^2 + 3x + 2 = 0$ **2.** $x^2 - 3x + 2 = 0$ **3.** $x^2 - x - 2 = 0$ **4.** $x^2 + x - 2 = 0$

5. $x^2 + 2x = 0 \; (c = 0)$ **6.** $3x^2 + x = 0 \; (c = 0)$

7. $x^2 - 36 = 0 \; (b = 0)$ **8.** $x^2 - 121 = 0 \; (b = 0)$

9. $2x^2 - 2x - 4 = 0$ **10.** $3x^2 + 9x + 6 = 0$ **11.** $x^2 + 12x = -36$ **12.** $x^2 - 18x = -81$

13. $8x = -4x^2 - 3$ **14.** $4x + 3 = 4x^2$ **15.** $3x^2 - 4x = \dfrac{5}{3}$ **16.** $-2x = x^2 + \dfrac{5}{9}$

17. $16x^2 + 8x - 3 = 0$ **18.** $16x^2 + 16x + 3 = 0$

19. $\dfrac{x^2}{2} + \dfrac{5}{2}x = -1$ **20.** $-3x = \dfrac{x^2}{2} + 2$ **21.** $5x^2 + 5x + 1 = 0$ **22.** $4x^2 + 6x + 1 = 0$

23. $90x^2 - 90x = 30$ **24.** $120x^2 - 100x = -20$

In Exercises 25–36, solve each word problem.

25. The width of a rectangle is 5 feet less than its length and its area is 50 square feet. Find the dimensions of the rectangle.

26. The length of a rectangle is 7 feet longer than it is wide. Find the perimeter of the rectangle if its area is 60 square feet.

27. The height of a triangle is 5 centimeters longer than three times its base. Find the base of the triangle if its area is 6 square centimeters.

28. The height of a triangle is 4 meters longer than twice its base. Find the height of the triangle if its area is 15 square meters.

29. One leg of a right triangle is 3 inches longer than the other. Find the length of the hypotenuse of the triangle if its area is 2 square inches.

30. One leg of a right triangle is twice as long as the other, and the area is 9 square inches. Find the length of its hypotenuse.

31. Find the side of a square whose area in square meters is equal to its perimeter in meters.

32. The area of a square numerically exceeds its perimeter by 5 centimeters. Find the area of the square.

33. June drives 150 miles at r miles per hour. She could have gone the same distance in 2 hours less time if she had increased her speed by 20 miles per hour. Find r.

34. Jeff bicycles 160 miles at r miles per hour. The same trip would have taken 2 hours longer if he had decreased his speed by 4 miles per hour. Find r.

35. The number -3 is a solution of $3x^2 + bx + 9 = 0$. Find b and then find the other root.

36. The number $-\frac{1}{2}$ is a solution of $6x^2 + bx + 9 = 0$. Find b and then find the other root.

8.3 COMPLEX NUMBERS

So far, all the work with quadratic expressions has involved only real numbers. The solutions of some quadratic equations are not real numbers. Consider the following example.

Example 1   Solve the quadratic equation $x^2 + x + 1 = 0$.

Solution   Because the factoring method does not work conveniently, use the quadratic formula, with $a = 1$, $b = 1$, and $c = 1$.

$$x = \frac{-b \pm \sqrt{b^2 - 4ac}}{2a}$$

$$= \frac{-1 \pm \sqrt{1^2 - 4(1)(1)}}{2(1)}$$

$$= \frac{-1 \pm \sqrt{1 - 4}}{2}$$

$$= \frac{-1 \pm \sqrt{-3}}{2}$$

$$x = \frac{-1 + \sqrt{-3}}{2} \quad \text{or} \quad x = \frac{-1 - \sqrt{-3}}{2} \qquad \blacksquare$$

Each solution in Example 1 involves the number $\sqrt{-3}$. This number is not a real number, because there is no real number whose square equals -3; the square of any real number is never negative. For years, mathematicians believed that numbers like $\sqrt{-3}$, $\sqrt{-1}$, and $\sqrt{-9}$ were nonsense, as illegal as division by zero. Even the great English mathematician Sir Isaac Newton (1642–1727) called them impossible. In the 17th century, these numbers were named **imaginary numbers** by René Descartes (1596–1650). That term is still used today.

Mathematicians no longer think of imaginary numbers as being fictitious or ridiculous. In fact, imaginary numbers have important uses such as describing the behavior of alternating current in electronics.

The imaginary number $\sqrt{-1}$ occurs often enough to warrant a special symbol; the letter i is used to denote $\sqrt{-1}$. Because i represents the square root of -1, it follows that

$$i^2 = -1$$

The powers of the imaginary number i produce an interesting pattern.

$$i = \sqrt{-1} = i \qquad\qquad i^5 = i^4 \cdot i = 1 \cdot i = i$$
$$i^2 = \sqrt{-1}\sqrt{-1} = -1 \qquad\qquad i^6 = i^4 \cdot i^2 = 1(-1) = -1$$
$$i^3 = i^2 \cdot i = -1 \cdot i = -i \qquad\qquad i^7 = i^4 \cdot i^3 = 1(-i) = -i$$
$$i^4 = i^2 \cdot i^2 = (-1)(-1) = 1 \qquad\qquad i^8 = i^4 \cdot i^4 = (1)(1) = 1$$

The pattern continues $i, -1, -i, 1, \ldots$.

If we assume that multiplication of imaginary numbers is commutative and associative, then

$$(2i)^2 = 2^2 i^2 = 4(-1) = -4$$

Because $(2i)^2 = -4$, it follows that $2i$ is a square root of -4, and we write

$$\sqrt{-4} = 2i$$

Note that this result could have been obtained by the following process:

$$\sqrt{-4} = \sqrt{4(-1)}$$
$$= \sqrt{4}\sqrt{-1}$$
$$= 2i$$

Similarly, we have

$$\sqrt{-25} = \sqrt{25(-1)} = \sqrt{25}\sqrt{-1} = 5i$$

$$\sqrt{-\frac{1}{9}} = \sqrt{\frac{1}{9}(-1)} = \sqrt{\frac{1}{9}}\sqrt{-1} = \frac{1}{3}i$$

and

$$\sqrt{\frac{-100}{49}} = \sqrt{\frac{100}{49}(-1)} = \frac{\sqrt{100}}{\sqrt{49}}\sqrt{-1} = \frac{10}{7}i$$

The previous examples illustrate the following rule.

If at least one of a and b is a nonnegative real number and if there are no divisions by 0, then

$$\sqrt{ab} = \sqrt{a}\sqrt{b} \qquad \text{and} \qquad \sqrt{\frac{a}{b}} = \frac{\sqrt{a}}{\sqrt{b}}$$

Imaginary numbers such as $\sqrt{-3}$, $\sqrt{-1}$, and $\sqrt{-9}$ form a subset of a broader set of numbers called **complex numbers**.

Definition.   A **complex number** is any number that can be written in the form $a + bi$, where a and b are real numbers, and $i = \sqrt{-1}$. The number a is called the **real part** and the number b is called the **imaginary part** of the complex number $a + bi$.

If $b = 0$, the complex number $a + bi$ is a real number. If $b \neq 0$ and $a = 0$, the complex number $0 + bi$ (or just bi) is an imaginary number. Any imaginary number such as $\sqrt{-3}$, $\sqrt{-1}$, and $\sqrt{-9}$ can be expressed in bi form.

$$\sqrt{-3} = \sqrt{3(-1)} = \sqrt{3}\sqrt{-1} = \sqrt{3}i$$
$$\sqrt{-1} = i$$
$$\sqrt{-9} = \sqrt{9(-1)} = \sqrt{9}\sqrt{-1} = 3i$$

We now discuss some properties of complex numbers.

Definition.   The complex numbers $a + bi$ and $c + di$ are **equal** if and only if $a = c$ and $b = d$.

Example 2 **a.** $2 + 3i = \sqrt{4} + \dfrac{6}{2}i$, because $2 = \sqrt{4}$ and $3 = \dfrac{6}{2}$.

b. $4 - 5i = \dfrac{12}{3} - \sqrt{25}\,i$, because $4 = \dfrac{12}{3}$ and $-5 = -\sqrt{25}$.

c. $x + yi = 4 + 7i$ if and only if $x = 4$ and $y = 7$. ■

Definition. Complex numbers are added as if they were binomials.

$$(a + bi) + (c + di) = (a + c) + (b + d)i$$

Example 3 **a.** $(8 + 4i) + (12 + 8i) = 8 + 4i + 12 + 8i$
$$= 20 + 12i$$

b. $(7 - 4i) + (9 + 2i) = 7 - 4i + 9 + 2i$
$$= 16 - 2i$$

c. $(-6 + i) - (3 - 4i) = -6 + i - 3 + 4i$
$$= -9 + 5i$$

d. $(2 - 4i) - (-4 + 3i) = 2 - 4i + 4 - 3i$
$$= 6 - 7i$$ ■

To multiply a complex number by an imaginary number, we use the distributive property to remove parentheses and then simplify. For example,

$$-5i(4 - 8i) = -5i(4) - (-5i)(8i)$$
$$= -20i + 40i^2$$
$$= -40 - 20i \qquad \text{Remember } i^2 = -1.$$

To multiply two complex numbers, we use the following definition:

Definition. Complex numbers are multiplied as if they were binomials, with $i^2 = -1$.

$$(a + bi)(c + di) = ac + adi + bci + bdi^2$$
$$= (ac - bd) + (ad + bc)i$$

Example 4 **a.** $(2 + 3i)(3 - 2i) = 6 - 4i + 9i - 6i^2$
$$= 6 + 5i + 6$$
$$= 12 + 5i$$

b. $(3 + i)(1 + 2i) = 3 + 6i + i + 2i^2$
$$= 3 + 7i - 2$$
$$= 1 + 7i$$

$$\textbf{c.} \quad (-4 + 2i)(2 + i) = -8 - 4i + 4i + 2i^2$$
$$= -8 - 2$$
$$= -10 \qquad \blacksquare$$

The next example shows how to write several complex numbers in $a + bi$ form. When writing answers, it is common practice to accept the form $a - bi$ as a substitute for the form $a + (-b)i$.

Example 5   **a.** $7 = 7 + 0i$

b. $3i = 0 + 3i$

c. $4 - \sqrt{-16} = 4 - \sqrt{-1(16)} = 4 - \sqrt{16}\sqrt{-1} = 4 - 4i$

d. $5 + \sqrt{-11} = 5 + \sqrt{-1(11)} = 5 + \sqrt{11}\sqrt{-1} = 5 + \sqrt{11}\,i$

e. $2i^2 + 4i^3 = 2(-1) + 4(-i) = -2 - 4i$

f. $\dfrac{3}{2i} = \dfrac{3}{2i} \cdot \dfrac{i}{i} = \dfrac{3i}{2i^2} = \dfrac{3i}{2(-1)} = \dfrac{3i}{-2} = 0 - \dfrac{3}{2}i$

g. $-\dfrac{5}{i} = -\dfrac{5}{i} \cdot \dfrac{i^3}{i^3} = -\dfrac{5(-i)}{1} = 5i = 0 + 5i \qquad \blacksquare$

We must rationalize denominators to write complex numbers such as

$$\frac{1}{3 + i}, \qquad \frac{3 - i}{2 + i}, \qquad \text{and} \qquad \frac{5 + i}{5 - i}$$

in $a + bi$ form. To this end, we make the following definition.

Definition.   The complex numbers $a + bi$ and $a - bi$ are called **complex conjugates** of each other.

For example,

$$3 + 4i \quad \text{and} \quad 3 - 4i \quad \text{are complex conjugates}$$
$$5 - 7i \quad \text{and} \quad 5 + 7i \quad \text{are complex conjugates}$$
$$8 + 17i \quad \text{and} \quad 8 - 17i \quad \text{are complex conjugates}$$

Example 6   Find the product of the complex number $3 + i$ and its complex conjugate.

Solution   The complex conjugate of $3 + i$ is $3 - i$. Find the product of these two binomials as follows.

$$(3 + i)(3 - i) = 9 - 3i + 3i - i^2$$
$$= 9 - i^2$$
$$= 9 - (-1) \qquad \text{Because } i^2 = -1.$$
$$= 10 \qquad \blacksquare$$

In general, the product of the complex number $a + bi$ and its complex conjugate $a - bi$ is the real number $a^2 + b^2$, as the following work shows.

$$\begin{aligned}(a + bi)(a - bi) &= a^2 - abi + abi - b^2i^2 \\ &= a^2 - b^2(-1) \\ &= a^2 + b^2\end{aligned}$$

Thus, we have

$$(a + bi)(a - bi) = a^2 + b^2$$

Example 7   Write $\dfrac{1}{3 + i}$ in $a + bi$ form.

Solution   Because the product of $3 + i$ and its conjugate is a real number, rationalize the denominator by multiplying both the numerator and the denominator of the fraction by the complex conjugate of the denominator, and simplify.

$$\begin{aligned}\frac{1}{3 + i} &= \frac{1}{3 + i} \cdot \frac{3 - i}{3 - i} \\ &= \frac{3 - i}{9 - 3i + 3i - i^2} \\ &= \frac{3 - i}{9 - (-1)} \\ &= \frac{3 - i}{10} \\ &= \frac{3}{10} - \frac{1}{10}i\end{aligned}$$
∎

Example 8   Write $\dfrac{3 - i}{2 + i}$ in $a + bi$ form.

Solution   Rationalize the denominator by multiplying both the numerator and the denominator of the fraction by the complex conjugate of the denominator, and simplify.

$$\begin{aligned}\frac{3 - i}{2 + i} &= \frac{3 - i}{2 + i} \cdot \frac{2 - i}{2 - i} \\ &= \frac{6 - 3i - 2i + i^2}{4 - 2i + 2i - i^2} \\ &= \frac{5 - 5i}{4 - (-1)} \\ &= \frac{5(1 - i)}{5} \qquad \text{Factor out 5 in the numerator.} \\ &= 1 - i \qquad \text{Simplify.}\end{aligned}$$
∎

Example 9   Divide $5 + i$ by $5 - i$ and express the quotient in $a + bi$ form.

Solution   The quotient obtained when dividing $5 + i$ by $5 - i$ can be expressed as the fraction $\dfrac{5 + i}{5 - i}$. To express this quotient in $a + bi$ form, rationalize the denominator by multiplying both the numerator and the denominator by the complex conjugate of the denominator. Then simplify.

$$\frac{5 + i}{5 - i} = \frac{5 + i}{5 - i} \cdot \frac{5 + i}{5 + i}$$

$$= \frac{25 + 5i + 5i + i^2}{25 + 5i - 5i - i^2}$$

$$= \frac{25 + 10i - 1}{25 - (-1)}$$

$$= \frac{24 + 10i}{26}$$

$$= \frac{2(12 + 5i)}{26} \qquad \text{Factor out 2 in the numerator.}$$

$$= \frac{12 + 5i}{13} \qquad \text{Simplify.}$$

$$= \frac{12}{13} + \frac{5}{13} i \qquad\qquad\qquad\qquad\qquad\qquad ■$$

In most cases, the complex numbers that you encounter will not be in $a + bi$ form. To avoid mistakes, always put complex numbers in $a + bi$ form before doing any arithmetic involving the numbers.

Example 10   Write $\dfrac{4 + \sqrt{-16}}{2 + \sqrt{-4}}$ in $a + bi$ form.

Solution $$\frac{4 + \sqrt{-16}}{2 + \sqrt{-4}} = \frac{4 + 4i}{2 + 2i}$$

$$= \frac{2(2 + 2i)}{1(2 + 2i)} \qquad \text{Factor out 2 in the numerator and simplify.}$$

$$= 2 + 0i \qquad\qquad\qquad\qquad\qquad\qquad ■$$

Definition.   The **absolute value** of the complex number $a + bi$ is $\sqrt{a^2 + b^2}$. In symbols,

$$|a + bi| = \sqrt{a^2 + b^2}$$

Example 11   **a.** $|3 + 4i| = \sqrt{3^2 + 4^2} = \sqrt{9 + 16} = \sqrt{25} = 5$

b. $|5 - 12i| = \sqrt{5^2 + (-12)^2} = \sqrt{25 + 144} = \sqrt{169} = 13$

c. $|1 + i| = \sqrt{1^2 + 1^2} = \sqrt{1 + 1} = \sqrt{2}$

d. $|a + 0i| = \sqrt{a^2 + 0^2} = \sqrt{a^2} = |a|$

Note that the absolute value of any complex number is a nonnegative real number. Note also that the result of part d is consistent with the definition of the absolute value of a real number. ∎

Example 12   If a and b are both negative numbers, is the formula $\sqrt{a}\sqrt{b} = \sqrt{ab}$ still true?

Solution   Let $a = -4$ and $b = -1$. Then, compute $\sqrt{a}\sqrt{b}$ and $\sqrt{ab}$ to see if their values are equal.

$$\sqrt{a}\sqrt{b} = \sqrt{-4}\sqrt{-1}$$
$$= 2i \cdot i$$
$$= 2i^2$$
$$= -2$$

On the other hand, you have

$$\sqrt{ab} = \sqrt{(-4)(-1)}$$
$$= \sqrt{4}$$
$$= 2$$

Because the results are different, the formula $\sqrt{ab} = \sqrt{a}\sqrt{b}$ is *not* true if both a and b are negative. ∎

■ EXERCISE 8.3

In Exercises 1–10, solve each quadratic equation. Write all solutions in bi or a + bi form.

1. $x^2 + 9 = 0$

2. $x^2 + 16 = 0$

3. $3x^2 = -16$

4. $2x^2 = -25$

5. $x^2 + 2x + 2 = 0$

6. $x^2 + 3x + 3 = 0$

7. $2x^2 + x + 1 = 0$

8. $3x^2 + 2x + 1 = 0$

9. $3x^2 - 4x + 2 = 0$

10. $2x^2 - 3x + 2 = 0$

In Exercises 11–18, simplify each expression.

11. i^{21}

12. i^{19}

13. i^{27}

14. i^{22}

15. i^{100}

16. i^{42}

17. i^{97}

18. i^{200}

In Exercises 19–60, express each number in a + bi form, if necessary, and perform the indicated operations. Give all answers in a + bi form.

19. $(3 + 4i) + (5 - 6i)$

20. $(5 + 3i) - (6 - 9i)$

21. $(7 - 3i) - (4 + 2i)$

22. $(8 + 3i) + (-7 - 2i)$

23. $(8 + \sqrt{-25}) + (7 + \sqrt{-4})$

24. $(-7 + \sqrt{-81}) - (-2 - \sqrt{-64})$

25. $(-8 - \sqrt{-3}) - (7 - \sqrt{-27})$

26. $(2 + \sqrt{-8}) + (-3 - \sqrt{-2})$

27. $3i(2 - i)$

28. $-4i(3 + 4i)$

29. $(2 + i)(3 - i)$

30. $(4 - i)(2 + i)$

31. $(2 - 4i)(3 + 2i)$

32. $(3 - 2i)(4 - 3i)$

33. $(2 + \sqrt{-2})(3 - \sqrt{-2})$

34. $(5 + \sqrt{-3})(2 - \sqrt{-3})$

35. $(-2 - \sqrt{-16})(1 + \sqrt{-4})$

36. $(-3 - \sqrt{-81})(-2 + \sqrt{-9})$

37. $(2 + \sqrt{-3})(3 - \sqrt{-2})$

38. $(1 + \sqrt{-5})(2 - \sqrt{-3})$

39. $(8 - \sqrt{-5})(-2 - \sqrt{-7})$

40. $(-1 + \sqrt{-6})(2 - \sqrt{-3})$

41. $\dfrac{1}{i}$

42. $\dfrac{1}{i^3}$

43. $\dfrac{4}{5i^3}$

44. $\dfrac{3}{2i}$

45. $\dfrac{3i}{8\sqrt{-9}}$

46. $\dfrac{5i^3}{2\sqrt{-4}}$

47. $\dfrac{-3}{5i^5}$

48. $\dfrac{-4}{6i^7}$

49. $\dfrac{-6}{\sqrt{-32}}$

50. $\dfrac{5}{\sqrt{-125}}$

51. $\dfrac{3}{5 + i}$

52. $\dfrac{-2}{2 - i}$

53. $\dfrac{-12}{7 - \sqrt{-1}}$

54. $\dfrac{4}{3 + \sqrt{-1}}$

55. $\dfrac{5i}{6 + 2i}$

56. $\dfrac{-4i}{2 - 6i}$

57. $\dfrac{3 - 2i}{3 + 2i}$

58. $\dfrac{2 + 3i}{2 - 3i}$

59. $\dfrac{3 + \sqrt{-2}}{2 + \sqrt{-5}}$

60. $\dfrac{2 - \sqrt{-5}}{3 + \sqrt{-7}}$

In Exercises 61–70, find each indicated value.

61. $|6 + 8i|$

62. $|12 + 5i|$

63. $|12 - 5i|$

64. $|3 - 4i|$

65. $|5 + 7i|$

66. $|6 - 5i|$

67. $|4 - \sqrt{-2}|$

68. $|3 + \sqrt{-3}|$

69. $|8 + \sqrt{-5}|$

70. $|7 - \sqrt{-6}|$

71. Show that $1 - 5i$ is a solution of $x^2 - 2x + 26 = 0$.

72. Show that $3 - 2i$ is a solution of $x^2 - 6x + 13 = 0$.

73. Show that i is a solution of $x^4 - 3x^2 - 4 = 0$.

74. Show that $2 + i$ is *not* a solution of $x^2 + x + 1 = 0$.

8.4   THE DISCRIMINANT AND THE SOLUTIONS OF QUADRATIC EQUATIONS

As we have seen, the solutions of a quadratic equation could be real numbers or nonreal complex numbers. It is possible to determine the type of solutions for any quadratic equation with *real* coefficients without actually solving the equation. To show that this is true, we assume that the coefficients of the quadratic equation $ax^2 + bx + c = 0$ are all real numbers and that $a \neq 0$. The solutions to this quadratic equation are given by the quadratic formula.

$$x = \frac{-b \pm \sqrt{b^2 - 4ac}}{2a}$$

These solutions might be real or nonreal complex numbers depending on the value of the expression $b^2 - 4ac$, called the **discriminant**.

If $b^2 - 4ac > 0$, the discriminant is positive and the solutions of the quadratic equation are unequal real numbers.

If $b^2 - 4ac = 0$, then the discriminant is zero and

$$x = \frac{-b \pm 0}{2a}$$

This implies that the solutions are equal real numbers and that each solution is $-b/2a$.

If $b^2 - 4ac < 0$, the discriminant is a negative number, and its square root is an imaginary number. Thus, the solutions of the quadratic equation are nonreal complex numbers occurring in complex conjugate pairs.

If the coefficients a, b, and c are rational numbers, even more information can be obtained. If $b^2 - 4ac$ is equal to a nonzero perfect square, then $\sqrt{b^2 - 4ac}$ is a rational number and the solutions of the equation are unequal rational numbers.

If $b^2 - 4ac = 0$, then the solutions of the equation are equal rational numbers.

If $b^2 - 4ac$ is positive but not a perfect square, then $\sqrt{b^2 - 4ac}$ is an irrational number. This implies that the solutions of the equation are unequal irrational numbers.

The various possibilities are summarized in the following table, where a, b, and c are real numbers.

If a, b, and c are real numbers and	
if $b^2 - 4ac$ is ...	the solutions are ...
positive	real numbers and unequal.
0	real numbers and equal.
negative	nonreal complex numbers and complex conjugates.

If a, b, and c are rational numbers and	
if $b^2 - 4ac$ is ...	the solutions are ...
a nonzero perfect square	rational numbers and unequal.
0	rational numbers and equal.
positive and not a perfect square	irrational numbers and unequal.

Example 1   Determine the type of solutions for the quadratic equation $x^2 + x + 1 = 0$.

Solution   Calculate the discriminant as follows.

$$b^2 - 4ac = 1^2 - 4(1)(1) \qquad a = 1, b = 1, \text{ and } c = 1.$$
$$= -3$$

Because the discriminant is negative, the given equation has solutions that are nonreal complex numbers.   ∎

Example 2   Determine the type of solutions for the quadratic equation $3x^2 + 5x + 2 = 0$.

Solution   Calculate the discriminant as follows.

$$b^2 - 4ac = 5^2 - 4(3)(2) \qquad a = 3, b = 5, \text{ and } c = 2.$$
$$= 25 - 24$$
$$= 1$$

Because a, b, and c are rational numbers and the discriminant is positive and a perfect square, the solutions of the given quadratic equation are rational numbers, and they are unequal.   ∎

Example 3   For what value of k will the solutions of the equation $kx^2 - 12x + 9 = 0$ be equal?

Solution   Calculate the discriminant as follows.

$$b^2 - 4ac = (-12)^2 - 4(k)(9) \qquad a = k, b = -12, \text{ and } c = 9.$$
$$= -36k + 144$$

Because the solutions of the quadratic equation are to be equal, set $-36k + 144$ equal to zero, and solve for k.

$$-36k + 144 = 0$$
$$-36k = -144 \qquad \text{Add } -144 \text{ to both sides.}$$
$$k = 4 \qquad \text{Divide both sides by } -36.$$

If $k = 4$, then the solutions to $kx^2 - 12x + 9 = 0$ will be equal. Verify that this is true by solving the equation $4x^2 - 12x + 9 = 0$.   ∎

Example 4   For what values of k will the solutions of the equation $(k - 2)x^2 + (k + 1)x + 4 = 0$ be equal?

Solution   Calculate the discriminant and demand that it be zero.

$$b^2 - 4ac = (k + 1)^2 - 4(k - 2)(4)$$
$$0 = k^2 + 2k + 1 - 16k + 32 \qquad \text{Remove parentheses.}$$
$$= k^2 - 14k + 33 \qquad \text{Combine terms.}$$
$$= (k - 3)(k - 11) \qquad \text{Factor.}$$

$$k - 3 = 0 \quad \text{or} \quad k - 11 = 0 \qquad \text{Set each factor equal to zero.}$$
$$k = 3 \qquad\qquad k = 11$$

If $k = 3$, the equation $(k - 2)x^2 + (k + 1)x + 4 = 0$ becomes the equation $x^2 + 4x + 4 = 0$. This equation has two equal solutions. Both of them are -2. If $k = 11$, the equation $(k - 2)x^2 + (k + 1)x + 4 = 0$ becomes $9x^2 + 12x + 4 = 0$. This equation has two equal solutions also. Both of them are $-\frac{2}{3}$. ∎

EXERCISE 8.4

In Exercises 1–8, use the discriminant to determine what type of solutions exist for each quadratic equation.

1. $4x^2 - 4x + 1 = 0$ **2.** $6x^2 - 5x - 6 = 0$ **3.** $5x^2 + x + 2 = 0$ **4.** $3x^2 + 10x - 2 = 0$

5. $2x^2 + 1 = 4x$ **6.** $9x^2 + 4 = 12x$ **7.** $2x^2 - 3x = 20$ **8.** $x^2 - 3x = -10$

In Exercises 9–16, find the value(s) of k that will make the solutions of each equation equal.

9. $x^2 + kx + 9 = 0$ **10.** $kx^2 - 12x = -4$ **11.** $9x^2 + 4 = -kx$ **12.** $9x^2 - kx + 25 = 0$

13. $(k - 1)x^2 + (k - 1)x + 1 = 0$ **14.** $(k + 3)x^2 + 2kx + 4 = 0$

15. $(k + 4)x^2 + 2kx + 9 = 0$ **16.** $(k + 15)x^2 + (k - 30)x + 4 = 0$

17. Use the discriminant to determine if the solutions of $1492x^2 + 1776x - 1984 = 0$ are real numbers.

18. Use the discriminant to determine if the solutions of $1776x^2 - 1492x + 1984 = 0$ are real numbers.

19. Determine k so that the solutions of $3x^2 + 4x = k$ are not real numbers.

20. Determine k so that the solutions of $kx^2 - 4x = 7$ are real numbers.

21. Use the quadratic formula to solve the equation $x^2 + \sqrt{5}x + 1 = 0$.

22. Solve the equation $2x^2 + ix - 4 = 0$, where $i^2 = -1$.

8.5   SOLVING OTHER NONLINEAR EQUATIONS

There are many types of equations that, although not quadratic equations, can be put into quadratic form. These equations can then be solved by using techniques for solving quadratic equations. For example, to solve $x^4 - 5x^2 + 4 = 0$, we can proceed as follows:

$$x^4 - 5x^2 + 4 = 0$$
$$(x^2)^2 - 5(x^2) + 4 = 0$$
$$y^2 - 5y + 4 = 0 \qquad \text{Let } y = x^2.$$
$$(y - 4)(y - 1) = 0 \qquad \text{Factor } y^2 - 5y + 4.$$
$$y - 4 = 0 \quad \text{or} \quad y - 1 = 0$$
$$y = 4 \qquad\qquad y = 1$$

Because $x^2 = y$, it follows that $x^2 = 4$ or $x^2 = 1$. Thus,

$$x^2 = 4 \qquad\qquad\qquad \text{or} \qquad\qquad x^2 = 1$$
$$x = 2 \quad \text{or} \quad x = -2 \qquad\qquad x = 1 \quad \text{or} \quad x = -1$$

The equation has four solutions. Verify that each one satisfies the original equation.

Note that this equation could be solved directly by factoring.

Example 1   Solve the equation $x - 7x^{1/2} + 12 = 0$.

Solution   This equation is not a quadratic equation. However, if y^2 is substituted for x and y is substituted for $x^{1/2}$, the equation

$$x - 7x^{1/2} + 12 = 0$$

becomes a quadratic equation that can be solved by factoring:

$$y^2 - 7y + 12 = 0$$
$$(y - 3)(y - 4) = 0 \qquad \text{Factor } y^2 - 7y + 12.$$
$$y - 3 = 0 \quad \text{or} \quad y - 4 = 0$$
$$y = 3 \qquad\qquad y = 4$$

Because $x = y^2$, it follows that

$$x = 3^2 = 9 \quad \text{or} \quad x = 4^2 = 16$$

Verify that both solutions satisfy the original equation.   ■

Example 2   Solve the equation $\dfrac{24}{x} + \dfrac{12}{x + 1} = 11$.

Solution   Because the denominator of a fraction cannot be 0, x cannot be 0 or -1. If either 0 or -1 appears as a suspected solution, it is extraneous and must be discarded. Solve the equation as follows:

$$\frac{24}{x} + \frac{12}{x + 1} = 11$$

$$x(x + 1)\left(\frac{24}{x} + \frac{12}{x + 1}\right) = x(x + 1)11 \qquad \begin{array}{l}\text{Multiply both sides by}\\ x(x + 1).\end{array}$$

$$24(x + 1) + 12x = (x^2 + x)11$$
$$24x + 24 + 12x = 11x^2 + 11x$$
$$36x + 24 = 11x^2 + 11x$$
$$0 = 11x^2 - 25x - 24 \qquad \begin{array}{l}\text{Add } -36x \text{ and } -24\\ \text{to both sides.}\end{array}$$
$$0 = (11x + 8)(x - 3)$$
$$11x + 8 = 0 \qquad \text{or} \qquad x - 3 = 0$$
$$x = -\frac{8}{11} \qquad\qquad x = 3$$

Because both $-\frac{8}{11}$ and 3 are in the domain of x, each is a solution of the original equation. Verify this by checking each solution.   ■

Example 3   Solve the equation $s = 16t^2 - 32$ for t.

Solution   Proceed as follows:

$$s = 16t^2 - 32$$

$$s + 32 = 16t^2 \qquad \text{Add 32 to both sides.}$$

$$\frac{s + 32}{16} = t^2 \qquad \text{Divide both sides by 16.}$$

$$t^2 = \frac{s + 32}{16} \qquad \text{Apply the symmetric property of equality.}$$

$$t = \pm\sqrt{\frac{s + 32}{16}} \qquad \text{Apply the square root property.}$$

$$t = \pm\frac{\sqrt{s + 32}}{\sqrt{16}} \qquad \sqrt{\frac{a}{b}} = \frac{\sqrt{a}}{\sqrt{b}}$$

$$t = \frac{\pm\sqrt{s + 32}}{4}$$

■ EXERCISE 8.5

In Exercises 1–30, solve each equation, if possible.

1. $x^4 - 17x^2 + 16 = 0$ **2.** $x^4 - 10x^2 + 9 = 0$

3. $x^4 - 3x^2 = -2$ **4.** $x^4 - 29x^2 = -100$

5. $x^4 = 6x^2 - 5$ **6.** $x^4 = 8x^2 - 7$ **7.** $2x^4 - 10x^2 = -8$ **8.** $2x^4 + 24 = 26x^2$

9. $2x + x^{1/2} - 3 = 0$ **10.** $2x - x^{1/2} - 1 = 0$

11. $3x + 5x^{1/2} + 2 = 0$ **12.** $3x - 4x^{1/2} + 1 = 0$

13. $x^{2/3} + 5x^{1/3} + 6 = 0$ **14.** $x^{2/3} - 7x^{1/3} + 12 = 0$

15. $x^{2/3} - 2x^{1/3} - 3 = 0$ **16.** $x^{2/3} + 4x^{1/3} - 5 = 0$

17. $x + 5 + \dfrac{4}{x} = 0$ **18.** $x - 4 + \dfrac{3}{x} = 0$ **19.** $x + 1 = \dfrac{20}{x}$ **20.** $x + \dfrac{15}{x} = 8$

21. $\dfrac{1}{x - 1} + \dfrac{3}{x + 1} = 2$ **22.** $\dfrac{6}{x - 2} - \dfrac{12}{x - 1} = -1$

23. $\dfrac{1}{x + 2} + \dfrac{24}{x + 3} = 13$ **24.** $\dfrac{36}{x} + \dfrac{24}{x + 1} = 17$

25. $x^{-4} - 2x^{-2} + 1 = 0$ **26.** $1 - 13x^{-2} + 36x^{-4} = 0$

27. $4x^{-4} + 1 = 5x^{-2}$ **28.** $9y^{-4} - 10y^{-2} + 1 = 0$

29. $5s^{-4} + 1 = 6s^{-2}$ **30.** $12t^{-4} + 1 = 7t^{-2}$

In Exercises 31–38, solve each equation for the indicated variable.

31. $x^2 + y^2 = r^2$ for x **32.** $x^2 + y^2 = r^2$ for y

33. $I = \dfrac{k}{d^2}$ for d

34. $V = \dfrac{1}{3}\pi r^2 h$ for r

35. $xy^2 + 3xy + 7 = 0$ for y

36. $kx = ay - x^2$ for x

37. $\sigma = \sqrt{\dfrac{\sum x^2}{N} - \mu^2}$ for μ^2

38. $\sigma = \sqrt{\dfrac{\sum x^2}{N} - \mu^2}$ for N

In Exercises 39–42, solve each word problem.

39. The sum of a number and its reciprocal is $\frac{29}{10}$. Find the number.

40. The difference between a positive number and its reciprocal is $\frac{5}{6}$. Find the number.

41. An appliance store manager paid $1924 for several tape decks, 5 of which were stolen from the delivery truck. By selling the remaining decks at $20 over cost, the manager made a total profit of $380. How many tape decks were purchased originally?

42. Jim bought several shares of stock for $21,600. When the stock was worth $3 more per share, Jim sold all but 100 shares and regained his original investment. How many shares did he sell?

8.6 QUADRATIC AND OTHER NONLINEAR INEQUALITIES

We now turn our attention to solving quadratic inequalities. Consider the quadratic inequality

$$x^2 + x - 6 < 0$$

To find the values of x that make this inequality true is to *solve the inequality*. We begin by factoring the quadratic trinomial

$$(x + 3)(x - 2) < 0$$

Here we have a product of two quantities that is less than 0. This can happen only if the values of $x + 3$ and $x - 2$ are opposite in sign. The best way to keep track of the positiveness or negativeness of these factors is to construct a "sign chart," as in Figure 8-2. This chart indicates that the binomial $x - 2$ is zero when $x = 2$, is negative when $x < 2$, and is positive when $x > 2$. It also indicates that the binomial $x + 3$ is zero when $x = -3$, is negative when $x < -3$, and is positive when $x > -3$. The only place where the signs are opposite is in the interval between -3 and 2; this interval is described as $-3 < x < 2$. This is the solution to the inequality. The graph of the solution set is shown on the number line in the sign chart.

Figure 8-2

Example 1   Solve the inequality $(x - 1)(x + 3) \geq 0$.

Solution   Construct a sign chart as in Figure 8-3. The binomial $x - 1$ is zero when $x = 1$, is negative when $x < 1$, and is positive when $x > 1$. The binomial $x + 3$ is zero when $x = -3$, is negative when $x < -3$, and is positive when $x > -3$. The product of $x - 1$ and $x + 3$ is greater than zero when the signs of the binomials are the same. This is when $x < -3$ or $x > 1$. The numbers -3 and 1 are included because they make the product equal to zero. The solution set is shown on the number line in the sign chart in Figure 8-3. The solution set can be written as $\{x : x \leq -3 \text{ or } x \geq 1\}$.

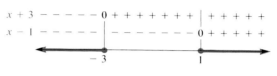

Figure 8-3

Making a sign chart also is useful when solving certain inequalities that are neither linear nor quadratic.

Example 2   Solve the inequality $\dfrac{1}{x} < 6$.

Solution   Add -6 to both sides, find a common denominator, and add the fractions.

$$\frac{1}{x} < 6$$

$$\frac{1}{x} - 6 < 0$$

$$\frac{1}{x} - \frac{6x}{x} < 0$$

$$\frac{1 - 6x}{x} < 0$$

Now, make a sign chart as in Figure 8-4. The denominator, x, is zero when $x = 0$, is positive when $x > 0$, and is negative when $x < 0$. The numerator, $1 - 6x$, is zero when $x = \frac{1}{6}$, is positive when $x < \frac{1}{6}$, and is negative when $x > \frac{1}{6}$.

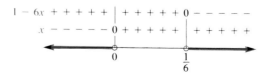

Figure 8-4

The quotient $\dfrac{1 - 6x}{x}$ is less than zero when the binomial $1 - 6x$ and the mono-mial x have different signs. This is true when $x < 0$ or when $x > \frac{1}{6}$. The graph of the solution set $\{x : x < 0 \text{ or } x > \frac{1}{6}\}$ is shown on the number line in the sign chart.   ■

Example 3   Solve the inequality $\dfrac{x^2 - 3x + 2}{x - 3} \geq 0$.

Solution   Rewrite the fraction and factor the numerator.

$$\frac{(x - 2)(x - 1)}{x - 3} \geq 0$$

This time, the signs of three binomials must be considered. To do so, construct the sign chart in Figure 8-5.

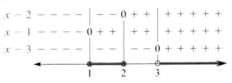

Figure 8-5

The fraction will be positive in the intervals where all factors are positive or where two factors are negative. The numbers 1 and 2 are included because they make the numerator, and thus the fraction, equal to zero. The number 3 is not included because it leads to a zero in the denominator. The graph of the solution set $\{x : x > 3 \text{ or } 1 \leq x \leq 2\}$ appears on the number line in the sign chart.   ■

Example 4   Solve $\dfrac{3}{x - 1} < \dfrac{2}{x}$.

Solution   Add $-\dfrac{2}{x}$ to both sides, find a common denominator, and add the fractions.

$$\frac{3}{x - 1} < \frac{2}{x}$$

$$\frac{3}{x - 1} - \frac{2}{x} < 0$$

$$\frac{3x}{(x - 1)x} - \frac{2(x - 1)}{x(x - 1)} < 0$$

$$\frac{3x - 2x + 2}{x(x - 1)} < 0$$

$$\frac{x + 2}{x(x - 1)} < 0$$

Keep track of the signs of three polynomials with the sign chart in Figure 8-6. The fraction will be negative in those regions where there are either one or three negative factors. The graph of $\{x : x < -2 \text{ or } 0 < x < 1\}$ is shown in the sign chart.

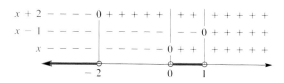

Figure 8-6

■ **EXERCISE 8.6**

Solve each inequality and graph its solution set.

1. $x^2 - 5x + 4 < 0$

2. $x^2 - 3x - 4 > 0$

3. $x^2 - 8x + 15 > 0$

4. $x^2 + 2x - 8 < 0$

5. $x^2 + x - 12 \leq 0$

6. $x^2 + 7x + 12 \geq 0$

7. $x^2 + 2x \geq 15$

8. $x^2 - 8x \leq -15$

9. $x^2 + 8x < -16$

10. $x^2 - 6x > -9$

11. $x^2 \geq 9$

12. $x^2 \geq 16$

13. $2x^2 - 50 < 0$

14. $3x^2 - 240 < 0$

15. $\dfrac{1}{x} < 2$

16. $\dfrac{1}{x} > 3$

17. $\dfrac{4}{x} \geq 2$

18. $-\dfrac{6}{x} < 12$

19. $-\dfrac{5}{x} < 3$

20. $\dfrac{4}{x} \geq 8$

21. $\dfrac{x^2 - x - 12}{x - 1} < 0$

22. $\dfrac{x^2 + x - 6}{x - 4} \geq 0$

23. $\dfrac{x^2 + x - 20}{x + 2} \geq 0$

24. $\dfrac{x^2 - 10x + 25}{x + 5} < 0$

25. $\dfrac{2x^2 + x - 6}{x - 3} \leq 0$

26. $\dfrac{2x^2 - 5x + 2}{x + 2} > 0$

27. $\dfrac{6x^2 - 5x + 1}{2x + 1} > 0$

28. $\dfrac{6x^2 + 11x + 3}{3x - 1} < 0$

29. $\dfrac{3}{x - 2} < \dfrac{4}{x}$

30. $\dfrac{-6}{x + 1} \geq \dfrac{1}{x}$

31. $\dfrac{-5}{x + 2} \geq \dfrac{4}{2 - x}$

32. $\dfrac{-6}{x - 3} < \dfrac{5}{3 - x}$

33. $\dfrac{7}{x - 3} \geq \dfrac{2}{x + 4}$

34. $\dfrac{-5}{x - 4} < \dfrac{3}{x + 1}$

35. $\dfrac{x}{x + 4} \leq \dfrac{1}{x + 1}$

36. $\dfrac{x}{x + 9} \geq \dfrac{1}{x + 1}$

37. $\dfrac{x}{x + 16} > \dfrac{1}{x + 1}$

38. $\dfrac{x}{x + 25} < \dfrac{1}{x + 1}$

39. $(x + 2)^2 > 0$

40. $(x - 3)^2 < 0$

CHAPTER SUMMARY

Key Words

absolute value of a complex number (8.3)
completing the square (8.1)
complex conjugates (8.3)
complex numbers (8.3)

discriminant (8.4)
imaginary numbers (8.3)
quadratic formula (8.2)
square root property (8.1)

Key Ideas

(8.1)   An equation of the form $ax^2 + bx + c = 0$, where $a \neq 0$, is called a **quadratic equation**.

The **incomplete quadratic equation** $x^2 = c$ has two roots:

$$x = \sqrt{c} \quad \text{and} \quad x = -\sqrt{c}$$

All quadratic equations can be solved by completing the square.

(8.2)   The **quadratic formula** is $x = \dfrac{-b \pm \sqrt{b^2 - 4ac}}{2a}$.

The sum of the roots of the quadratic equation $ax^2 + bx + c = 0$ $(a \neq 0)$ is $-\frac{b}{a}$. The product of the roots is $\frac{c}{a}$.

(8.3)   The square root of a negative number is an **imaginary number**.

A **complex number** is any number that can be written in the form $a + bi$, where a and b are real numbers and $i = \sqrt{-1}$.

An **imaginary number** is any number of the form bi.

The complex numbers $a + bi$ and $c + di$ are equal if and only if $a = c$ and $b = d$.

Complex numbers are added and multiplied as if they were binomials.

The complex numbers $a + bi$ and $a - bi$ are **complex conjugates** of each other.

To **rationalize the denominator** of a fraction whose denominator is a nonreal complex number, multiply both the numerator and the denominator of that fraction by the complex conjugate of its denominator.

$$|a + bi| = \sqrt{a^2 + b^2}$$

(8.4)   The **discriminant** of the quadratic equation $ax^2 + bx + c = 0$, with $a \neq 0$, is $b^2 - 4ac$.

The discriminant can be used to determine the type of solutions that exist for any quadratic equation with real number coefficients.

(8.5)   Many equations that are not quadratic can be put in quadratic form and then solved.

(8.6)   Make a sign chart to solve nonlinear inequalities.

REVIEW EXERCISES

In Review Exercises 1–4, solve each quadratic equation by factoring. Check each answer.

1. $12x^2 + x - 6 = 0$

2. $6x^2 + 17x + 5 = 0$

3. $15x^2 + 2x - 8 = 0$

4. $20x^2 - 21x - 5 = 0$

In *Review Exercises 5–8, solve each quadratic equation by completing the square. Check each answer.*

5. $x^2 - 2x - 15 = 0$ **6.** $x^2 + x - 42 = 0$
7. $2x^2 - 9x + 7 = 0$ **8.** $3x^2 + 11x + 8 = 0$

In *Review Exercises 9–12, solve each quadratic equation using the quadratic formula. Check each answer.*

9. $x^2 - 8x - 9 = 0$

10. $x^2 - 10x + 9 = 0$

11. $2x^2 + 13x - 7 = 0$

12. $3x^2 - 20x - 7 = 0$

13. Find the sum of the solutions of the equation $3x^2 - 14x + 3 = 0$.

14. Find the product of the solutions of the equation $3x^2 - 14x + 3 = 0$.

15. The length of a rectangle is 2 inches longer than its width. If both the length and width are doubled, its area increases by 72 square inches. What are the dimensions of the original rectangle?

16. The length of a rectangle is 1 foot longer than its width. If the length is tripled and the width is doubled, the area is increased by 30 square feet. What are the dimensions of the original rectangle?

17. Solve the equation $2x^2 + x + 4 = 0$.   **18.** Solve the equation $3x^2 + x + 1 = 0$.

In *Review Exercises 19–38, perform the indicated operations. Give all answers in $a + bi$ form.*

19. $(5 + 4i) + (7 - 12i)$

20. $(-6 - 40i) - (-8 + 28i)$

21. $(-32 + \sqrt{-144}) - (64 + \sqrt{-81})$

22. $(-8 + \sqrt{-8}) + (6 - \sqrt{-32})$

23. $(2 - 7i)(-3 + 4i)$

24. $(-5 + 6i)(2 + i)$

25. $(5 - \sqrt{-27})(-6 + \sqrt{-12})$

26. $(2 + \sqrt{-128})(3 - \sqrt{-98})$

27. $\dfrac{3}{4i}$

28. $\dfrac{-2}{5i^3}$

29. $\dfrac{6}{2 + i}$

30. $\dfrac{7}{3 - i}$

31. $\dfrac{4 + i}{4 - i}$

32. $\dfrac{3 - i}{3 + i}$

33. $\dfrac{3}{5 + \sqrt{-4}}$

34. $\dfrac{2}{3 - \sqrt{-9}}$

35. $\dfrac{3 + i}{2 + \sqrt{-2}}$

36. $\dfrac{2 - i}{3 - \sqrt{-3}}$

37. $|9 + 12i|$

38. $|24 - 10i|$

In *Review Exercises 39–42, use the discriminant to determine what type of solutions exist for each quadratic equation.*

39. $3x^2 + 4x - 3 = 0$

40. $4x^2 - 5x + 7 = 0$

41. Find the values of k that will make the solutions of $(k - 8)x^2 + (k + 16)x = -49$ equal.

42. Find the values of k so that the solutions of $3x^2 + 4x = k + 1$ are real numbers.

In *Review Exercises 43–48, solve each equation. Check all answers.*

43. $x^4 - 13x^2 + 36 = 0$

44. $x^4 - 26x^2 = -25$

45. $x = \sqrt{15x - 44}$ **46.** $x = \sqrt{12x - 27}$

47. $\sqrt{x + 1} + \sqrt{x} = 2$ **48.** $\sqrt{2x + 5} - \sqrt{2x} = 1$

In *Review Exercises 49–56, solve each inequality and graph the solution set on a number line.*

49. $x^2 + 2x - 35 > 0$

50. $x^2 + 7x - 18 < 0$

51. $\dfrac{3}{x} \le 5$

52. $\dfrac{2}{x} \ge 3$

53. $\dfrac{2x^2 - x - 28}{x - 1} \le 0$

54. $\dfrac{3x^2 - x - 24}{x + 2} > 0$

55. $\dfrac{4}{x - 4} > \dfrac{5}{x - 9}$

56. $\dfrac{3}{x + 1} < \dfrac{-2}{x + 2}$

CHAPTER EIGHT TEST

In Problems 1–2, solve each equation.

1. $x^2 + 3x - 18 = 0$

2. $x(6x + 19) = -15$

In Problems 3–4, determine what number must be added to each binomial to make it a perfect square.

3. $x^2 + 24x$

4. $x^2 - 50x$

In Problems 5–6, solve each equation.

5. $x^2 + 4x + 1 = 0$

6. $x^2 - 5x - 3 = 0$

7. One leg of a right triangle is 14 inches longer than the other, and the length of the hypotenuse is 26 inches. How long is the shortest side of the triangle?

8. The sum of a number and its reciprocal is $-\dfrac{34}{15}$. Find the number.

In Problems 9–10, solve each equation. Write all solutions in $a + bi$ form.

9. $2x^2 + 32 = 0$

10. $3x^2 - 6x + 5 = 0$

In Problems 11–16, perform the indicated operations. Give all answers in $a + bi$ form.

11. $(2 + 4i) + (-3 + 7i)$

12. $(3 - \sqrt{-9}) - (-1 + \sqrt{-16})$

13. $2i(3 - 4i)$

14. $(3 + 2i)(-4 - i)$

15. $\dfrac{1}{i\sqrt{2}}$

16. $\dfrac{3 + i}{3 - i}$

17. Determine if the solutions of $3x^2 + 5x + 17 = 0$ are real or nonreal.

18. For what value(s) of k are the solutions of $4x^2 - 4kx + k^2 = 0$ equal?

In Problems 19–20, solve each equation.

19. $2y - 3y^{1/2} + 1 = 0$

20. $2\left(x - \dfrac{1}{3x}\right) = \dfrac{1}{3}$

In Problems 21–22, solve each inequality and graph its solution set.

21. $x^2 - 2x - 8 > 0$

22. $\dfrac{x - 2}{x + 3} \le 0$

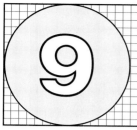

Graphs of Quadratic and Other Nonlinear Functions and Relations

9.1 GRAPHS OF QUADRATIC FUNCTIONS

We have defined a linear function as a correspondence between x and y determined by a first-degree equation that can be written in the form $y = mx + b$. We now discuss another important function called a **quadratic function**.

> **Definition.** A **quadratic function** is a function defined by a second-degree polynomial equation of the form
>
> $$y = ax^2 + bx + c$$
>
> where a, b, and c are real numbers and $a \neq 0$.

To graph the quadratic function determined by $y = x^2 - 3$, for example, we calculate several ordered pairs that satisfy the equation, plot each point, and join them with a smooth curve, as shown in Figure 9-1. This curve is called a **parabola**.

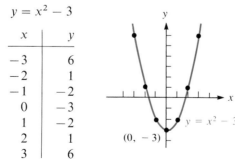

$y = x^2 - 3$

x	y
-3	6
-2	1
-1	-2
0	-3
1	-2
2	1
3	6

Figure 9-1

Example 1 Graph the quadratic function determined by the equation $y = -x^2 + 2x + 1$.

Solution Plot several points whose coordinates satisfy the equation and join them with a smooth curve to obtain the parabola shown in Figure 9-2.

299

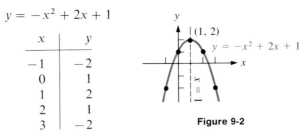

$$y = -x^2 + 2x + 1$$

x	y
-1	-2
0	1
1	2
2	1
3	-2

Figure 9-2

The graph of all functions determined by equations of the form $y = ax^2 + bx + c$, where $a \neq 0$, are parabolas. They open upward when $a > 0$, as in Figure 9-1, and downward when $a < 0$, as in Figure 9-2. The bottom point of a parabola that opens upward or the top point of a parabola that opens downward is called the **vertex** of the parabola. The vertex of the parabola shown in Figure 9-1 is the point $(0, -3)$. The vertex of the parabola in Figure 9-2 is the point $(1, 2)$.

The vertical line that passes through the vertex of a parabola is called an **axis of symmetry** because it divides the parabola into two congruent halves. The axis of symmetry in Figure 9-1 is the y-axis. The axis of symmetry in Figure 9-2 is the line $x = 1$.

If a, h, and k are constants and $a \neq 0$, then the equation

$$y = a(x - h)^2 + k$$

also determines a quadratic function. This is because it takes on the form $y = ax^2 + bx + c$ when the right-hand side is expanded and simplified. The graph of the equation $y = a(x - h)^2 + k$ is a parabola that opens upward when $a > 0$ or downward when $a < 0$. This form of the quadratic equation is useful because it displays the coordinates of the vertex of its parabolic graph, as the following discussion shows.

Suppose that $a > 0$ so that the graph of

$$y = a(x - h)^2 + k$$

is a parabola opening upward, as in Figure 9-3. The vertex of the parabola is the point on the graph that has the smallest possible y value for its coordinate. Because $a > 0$, the smallest possible y value occurs when the nonnegative quantity $a(x - h)^2$ on the right-hand side of the equation is 0. This occurs when

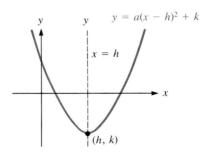

Figure 9-3

$x = h$. When $x = h$, the value of $a(x - h)^2$ is 0 and the value of y is k. Thus, the vertex of the parabola is at the point with coordinates (h, k). A similar argument holds when $a < 0$.

The previous discussion leads to the following theorem:

Theorem.   The graph of the equation

$$y = a(x - h)^2 + k$$

where $a \neq 0$, is a parabola with vertex at (h, k). The parabola opens upward when $a > 0$ and downward when $a < 0$. The axis of symmetry is the line $x = h$.

Example 2   Find the vertex of the parabola determined by the quadratic equation $y = 2x^2 + 6x - 3$ and graph the parabola.

Solution   Complete the square on the right-hand side of the given equation, as follows:

$$\begin{aligned}
y &= 2x^2 + 6x - 3 \\
&= 2(x^2 + 3x) - 3 && \text{Factor 2 out from } 2x^2 + 6x. \\
&= 2\left(x^2 + 3x + \frac{9}{4}\right) - 3 - \frac{9}{2} && \text{Add and subtract } \tfrac{9}{2}. \\
&= 2\left(x + \frac{3}{2}\right)^2 - \frac{15}{2} && \text{Factor } x^2 + 3x + \tfrac{9}{4}. \\
&= 2\left[x - \left(-\frac{3}{2}\right)\right]^2 + \left(-\frac{15}{2}\right)
\end{aligned}$$

Thus, the vertex is the point with coordinates $\left(-\frac{3}{2}, -\frac{15}{2}\right)$. The graph of $y = 2x^2 + 6x - 3$ appears in Figure 9-4. Note that the parabola has the line $x = -\frac{3}{2}$ as an axis of symmetry.

$$y = 2x^2 + 6x - 3$$

x	y
2	17
1	5
0	-3
-1	-7
-2	-7
-3	-3
-4	5

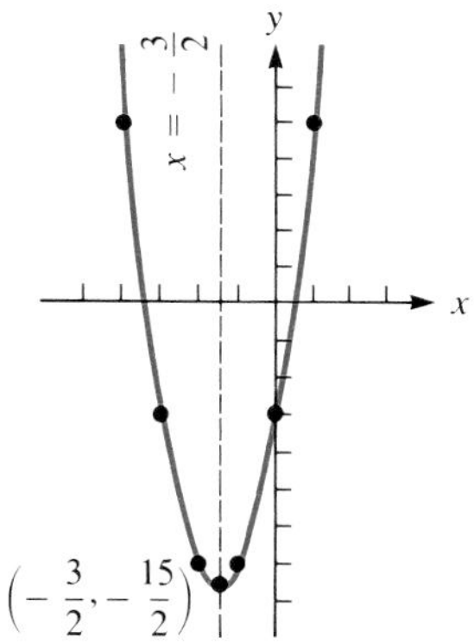

$\left(-\dfrac{3}{2}, -\dfrac{15}{2}\right)$

Figure 9-4

Example 3   Suppose that a ball is thrown straight up into the air with an initial velocity of 128 feet per second. The quadratic function $s = 128t - 16t^2$ gives the relation between s and t, where s represents the number of feet that the ball is above the ground and t represents the time measured in seconds. How high did the ball travel?

Solution   The equation $s = -16t^2 + 128t$ represents a quadratic function, so its graph is a parabola. The maximum height attained by the ball is given by the s-coordinate of the vertex of the parabola. Find the coordinates of the vertex by completing the square.

$$s = -16t^2 + 128t$$
$$= -16(t^2 - 8t) \qquad \text{Factor out } -16.$$
$$= -16(t^2 - 8t + 16) + 256 \qquad \text{Subtract and add 256.}$$
$$= -16(t - 4)^2 + 256 \qquad \text{Factor } t^2 - 8t + 16.$$

Thus, the coordinates of the vertex are (4, 256). Because $t = 4$ and $s = 256$ are the coordinates of the vertex, the ball reaches a maximum height of 256 feet in 4 seconds.

Because a parabola is symmetric, it will take an additional 4 seconds for the ball to return to earth. The total time of the flight is 8 seconds. Note that if $t = 8$, the value of s in the equation $s = -16t^2 + 128t$ is zero, and the ball is back to earth. Although this quadratic function describes the height of the ball in relation to time, it does not describe the path traveled by the ball. The ball went straight up and came back straight down.   ■

Example 4   A man wants to build a rectangular pen to house his dog. To save fencing, he intends to use one side of his garage. Find the maximum area that he can enclose with 80 feet of fencing.

Solution   Let the width of the area be represented by w. Then the length is represented by $80 - 2w$. See Figure 9-5.

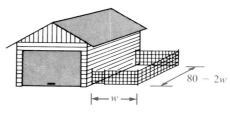

Figure 9-5

The area of the pen is given by the product of the length and the width. Thus, you have

$$A = w(80 - 2w)$$

Find the maximum value of A as follows:

$$A = w(80 - 2w)$$
$$= 80w - 2w^2 \qquad \text{Remove parentheses.}$$
$$= -2(w^2 - 40w) \qquad \text{Factor out } -2 \text{ and rearrange terms.}$$
$$= -2(w^2 - 40w + 400) + 800 \qquad \text{Subtract and add 800.}$$
$$= -2(w - 20)^2 + 800 \qquad \text{Factor } w^2 - 40w + 400.$$

Thus, the coordinates of the vertex of the graph of the quadratic function are (20, 800), and the maximum area is 800 square feet.   ■

It is easy to show that the vertex of the parabola determined by the equation $y = ax^2 + bx + c$ is the point with coordinates

$$\left(-\frac{b}{2a}, c - \frac{b^2}{4a} \right)$$

To do so, we use the method of completing the square to write the equation $y = ax^2 + bx + c$ in the form $y = a(x - h)^2 + k$ to determine the coordinates of the vertex.

$$y = ax^2 + bx + c$$
$$= a\left(x^2 + \frac{b}{a}x \right) + c \qquad \text{Factor out } a.$$
$$= a\left(x^2 + \frac{b}{a}x + \frac{b^2}{4a^2} \right) + c - \frac{b^2}{4a} \qquad \text{Add and subtract } \frac{b^2}{4a}.$$
$$= a\left(x + \frac{b}{2a} \right)^2 + c - \frac{b^2}{4a} \qquad \text{Factor the trinomial.}$$
$$= a\left[x - \left(-\frac{b}{2a} \right) \right]^2 + \left(c - \frac{b^2}{4a} \right)$$

Thus, the vertex is the point with coordinates of $\left(-\frac{b}{2a}, c - \frac{b^2}{4a} \right)$.

EXERCISE 9.1

In Exercises 1–12, graph each function determined by the given quadratic equation.

1. $y = x^2$ **2.** $y = -x^2$ **3.** $y = x^2 + 2$ **4.** $y = x^2 - 3$

5. $y = -(x - 2)^2$ **6.** $y = (x + 2)^2$ **7.** $y = -3x^2 + x$ **8.** $y = 5x + x^2$

9. $y = x^2 + x - 6$ **10.** $y = x^2 - x - 6$

11. $y = 6x^2 + 6x - 12$ **12.** $y = -4x^2 + 8x + 12$

In Exercises 13–24, find the coordinates of the vertex and the axis of symmetry of the graph of each equation. If necessary, complete the square on x to write the equation in the form $y = a(x - h)^2 + k$. **Do not graph the equation.**

13. $y = (x - 1)^2 + 2$ **14.** $y = 2(x - 2)^2 - 1$

15. $y = 2(x + 3)^2 - 4$ **16.** $y = -3(x + 1)^2 + 3$

17. $y = -3x^2$ **18.** $y = 3x^2 - 3$ **19.** $y = 2x^2 - 4x$ **20.** $y = 3x^2 + 6x$

21. $y = -4x^2 + 16x + 5$ **22.** $y = 5x^2 + 20x + 25$

23. $y - 7 = 6x^2 - 5x$ **24.** $y - 2 = 3x^2 + 4x$

25.   The equation $y - k = (x - h)^2$ represents a quadratic function whose graph is a parabola. Find its vertex.

26.   Show that $y = ax^2$, where $a \neq 0$, represents a quadratic function whose vertex is at the origin.

27.   The sum of two numbers is 50 and their product is maximum. Find the numbers.

28.   The sum of two numbers is 10 and the sum of their squares is minimum. Find the numbers.

29.   If a ball is thrown straight up with an initial velocity of 48 feet per second, its height after t seconds is given by the equation $s = 48t - 16t^2$. Find the maximum height attained by the ball and the time it takes for the ball to return to earth.

30.   From the top of a building 48 feet tall, a ball is thrown straight upward with an initial velocity of 32 feet per second. The equation $s = -16t^2 + 32t + 48$ gives the height of the ball t seconds after it was thrown. Find the maximum height reached by the ball and find the time it will take for the ball to hit the ground.

31.   Find the dimensions of the rectangle of maximum area that can be constructed with 200 feet of fencing. What is the maximum area?

32.   A farmer wants to fence in three sides of a rectangular field with 1000 feet of fencing. The other side of the rectangle is to be a river. If the enclosed area is to be maximum, find the dimensions of the field.

33.   When priced at $30 each, the annual sales of a toy are 4000 units. The manufacturer estimates that each dollar increase in cost will decrease sales by 100 units. What unit price will maximize total revenue? (*Hint:*   Total revenue = price • the number of units sold.)

34.   When priced at $57, the annual sales of a radio are 525 units. For each dollar the radio is reduced in price, the sales are expected to increase by 75 units. What unit price will maximize total revenue? (*Hint:*   Total revenue = price • the number of units sold.)

9.2   GRAPHS OF POLYNOMIAL FUNCTIONS

We have defined linear functions as functions defined by equations of the form

$$y = mx + b$$

and quadratic functions as functions defined by equations of the form

$$y = ax^2 + bx + c$$

where $a \neq 0$. These types of functions are examples of a broader set of functions called **polynomial functions**.

> **Definition.** A **polynomial function** in one independent variable, say x, is determined by an equation of the form $y = P(x)$ where $P(x)$ is a polynomial in the variable x.

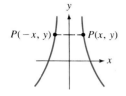

Figure 9-6

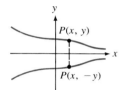

Figure 9-7

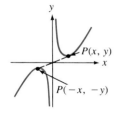

Figure 9-8

We have seen that graphs of quadratic functions are parabolas that exhibit a symmetry about their axes, making half of the parabola a mirror image of the other half. The graphs of many polynomial functions of higher degree also exhibit certain kinds of symmetry. It is much easier to graph such functions if we are aware of these symmetries beforehand.

If the point $(-x, y)$ lies on a graph whenever the point (x, y) does, then the graph is said to be **symmetric about the y-axis**. See Figure 9-6. It is easy to check for y-axis symmetry of the graph of a polynomial function. If $y = f(x)$ is equivalent to $y = f(-x)$; that is, if $y = f(x)$ remains unchanged when x is replaced by $-x$, then the graph of the function is symmetric about the y-axis.

If the point $(x, -y)$ lies on a graph whenever the point (x, y) does, then the graph is said to be **symmetric about the x-axis**. See Figure 9-7. Except for the function $y = f(x) = 0$, a graph symmetric to the x-axis cannot represent a function.

If the point $(-x, -y)$ lies on a graph whenever the point (x, y) does, then the graph is said to be **symmetric about the origin**. See Figure 9-8. To test the graph of $y = f(x)$ for symmetry about the origin, we replace x with $-x$ and y with $-y$. If the resulting equation is equivalent to the original equation, then the graph is symmetric about the origin.

The previous discussion is summarized as follows.

> **Tests for Symmetry.** If the equations $y = f(x)$ and $y = f(-x)$ are equivalent, then the graph of $y = f(x)$ is symmetric about the y-axis.
>
> If $(x, -y)$ lies on a graph whenever (x, y) does, then the graph is symmetric about the x-axis.
>
> If the equations $y = f(x)$ and $-y = f(-x)$ are equivalent, then the graph of $y = f(x)$ is symmetric about the origin.

We illustrate these concepts of symmetry in the following examples.

Example 1 Graph the cubic polynomial function $y = f(x) = x^3 - x$.

Solution Calculate both $f(x)$ and $f(-x)$ as follows.

$$f(x) = x^3 - x$$
$$f(-x) = (-x)^3 - (-x)$$
$$= -x^3 + x$$

Because $y = f(x)$ is not equivalent to $y = f(-x)$, there is no symmetry about the y-axis. Because replacing y with $-y$ does not give an equivalent equation, there is no symmetry about the x-axis either. However, if x and y are replaced with $-x$ and $-y$, respectively, the resulting equation is equivalent to the original equation.

$$y = x^3 - x$$
$$-y = (-x)^3 - (-x) \qquad \text{Replace } x \text{ with } -x \text{ and } y \text{ with } -y.$$
$$-y = -x^3 + x \qquad \text{Simplify.}$$
$$y = x^3 - x \qquad \text{Multiply both sides by } -1.$$

Because the final equation is identical to the original equation, the graph is symmetric about the origin.

It is also useful to know about the graph's x-intercepts. These intercepts are the numbers x for which $f(x) = 0$. To find them, solve the equation $x^3 - x = 0$.

$$x^3 - x = 0$$
$$x(x^2 - 1) = 0 \qquad \text{Factor.}$$
$$x(x + 1)(x - 1) = 0 \qquad \text{Factor.}$$
$$x = 0 \quad \text{or} \quad x + 1 = 0 \quad \text{or} \quad x - 1 = 0 \qquad \begin{array}{l}\text{Set each factor}\\ \text{equal to 0.}\end{array}$$
$$x = -1 \qquad\qquad x = 1$$

Thus, the x-intercepts are at $x = 0$, $x = -1$, and $x = 1$.

Finally, plot a few points for positive x, and use the graph's symmetry to draw the rest of the curve. Although you could determine values for $f(x)$ by direct substitution, it is often easier to use synthetic division and the remainder theorem. For example, to find the value $f(2)$, proceed as follows.

$$\begin{array}{r|rrrr} 2 & 1 & 0 & -1 & 0 \\ & & 2 & 4 & 6 \\ \hline & 1 & 2 & 3 & 6 \end{array}$$

A table of values and the graph appear in Figure 9-9.

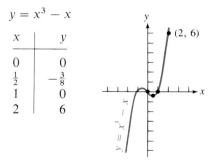

Figure 9-9

Example 2   Graph the function $y = f(x) = x^4 - 5x^2 + 4$.

Solution   Because the variable x appears only with even exponents, $y = f(x)$ is equivalent to $y = f(-x)$; that is, the value of y is the same whether you evaluate $y = f(x)$ or $y = f(-x)$.

$$y = x^4 - 5x^2 + 4$$
$$y = (-x)^4 - 5(-x)^2 + 4 = x^4 - 5x^2 + 4$$

Thus, the graph is symmetric about the y-axis. It is not, however, symmetric about either the x-axis or the origin.

The x-intercepts of the graph are those numbers x for which $y = 0$. To find them, set y equal to zero and solve the equation for x.

$$y = x^4 - 5x^2 + 4$$
$$0 = x^4 - 5x^2 + 4$$
$$0 = (x^2 - 4)(x^2 - 1) \qquad \text{Factor.}$$
$$0 = (x + 2)(x - 2)(x + 1)(x - 1) \qquad \text{Factor.}$$

$x + 2 = 0$ or $x - 2 = 0$ or $x + 1 = 0$ or $x - 1 = 0$ Set each factor equal to 0.
$x = -2$ | $x = 2$ | $x = -1$ | $x = 1$

The x-intercepts are at $x = -2$, $x = 2$, $x = -1$, and $x = 1$. To graph this function, plot the intercepts and several other points whose coordinates satisfy the equation, and make use of the known symmetry of the graph. The graph appears in Figure 9-10.

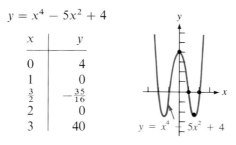

$y = x^4 - 5x^2 + 4$

x	y
0	4
1	0
$\frac{3}{2}$	$-\frac{35}{16}$
2	0
3	40

$y = x^4 - 5x^2 + 4$

Figure 9-10

If the values of a polynomial function increase as x increases, we say the function is *increasing*. See Figure 9-11a. If the values of a polynomial function decrease as x increases, we say the function is *decreasing*. See Figure 9-11b. If the values of a polynomial function are unchanged as x increases, we say the function is a *constant function*. See Figure 9-11c.

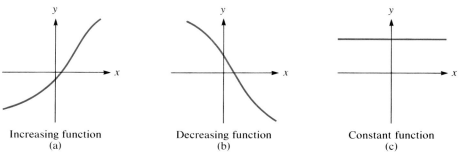

Increasing function
(a)

Decreasing function
(b)

Constant function
(c)

Figure 9-11

The previous discussion is summarized as follows.

Definition.   A function is increasing if $f(x_1) < f(x_2)$ whenever $x_1 < x_2$. A function is decreasing if $f(x_1) > f(x_2)$ whenever $x_1 < x_2$. A function is constant if $f(x_1) = f(x_2)$ for all x_1 and x_2.

Example 3   Graph the function $y = x^3 - 3x$ and determine where it is increasing and where it is decreasing.

Solution   The graph of the function appears in Figure 9-12. The function is increasing when $x \leq -1$, is decreasing when $-1 \leq x \leq 1$, and is again increasing when $x \geq 1$.

$$y = x^3 - 3x$$

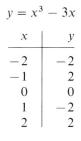

x	y
-2	-2
-1	2
0	0
1	-2
2	2

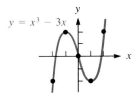

Figure 9-12

EXERCISE 9.2

In Exercises 1–10, tell whether the graph of each function is symmetric about the y-axis.

1. $y = 3x + 4$ 2. $y = 3x^2 - 3$ 3. $y = x^2$ 4. $y = -x^2$

5. $y = x^3 + x$ 6. $y = x^3$ 7. $y = x^4 + 2x^2$ 8. $y = 3x^3 + 2x$

9. $y = -3x^2 + 4$ 10. $y = -2x^4 + x^2$

In Exercises 11–20, tell whether the graph determined by each equation is symmetric about the x-axis.

11. $y^2 = x$ **12.** $y^2 = x^2$ **13.** $-y = x^2$ **14.** $-y = -x^2$

15. $y^2 = x + 2$ **16.** $y = x^3$ **17.** $y = x^4 + 2x^2$ **18.** $y^6 = 3x^3 + 2x$

19. $y^4 = -3x^2 + 4$ **20.** $y = -2x^4 + x^2$

In Exercises 21–30, tell whether the graph of each function is symmetric about the origin.

21. $y = x$ **22.** $y = -x$ **23.** $y = x^2$ **24.** $y = -x^2$

25. $y = x^3 + x$ **26.** $y = x^3$ **27.** $y = x^4 + 2x^2$ **28.** $y = 3x^3 + 2x$

29. $y = -3x^2 + 4$ **30.** $y = -2x^4 + x^2$

In Exercises 31–42, graph each polynomial function.

31. $y = x^3$ **32.** $y = x^4$ **33.** $y = x^3 + x^2$ **34.** $y = x^3 - x^2$

35. $y = x^5 - x^3$ **36.** $y = x^5 + x^3$ **37.** $y = x^4 - 2x^2 + 1$ **38.** $y = x^3 + x^2 - 6x$

39. $y = x^3 + 2x^2 - x - 2$ **40.** $y = x^3 + x^2 - 4x - 4$

41. $y = x^{10}$ **42.** $y = x^{11}$

In Exercises 43–48, tell where each function is increasing and decreasing.

43. $y = 2x^3 - 3x^2$ **44.** $y = 2x^3 + 6x^2$ **45.** $y = x^3 + 3x^2$ **46.** $y = 2x^3 - 9x^2$

47. $y = x^3 - 1$ **48.** $y = -x^3 - 1$

9.3 GRAPHS OF RATIONAL FUNCTIONS

We now discuss functions, called **rational functions**, that are defined by equations of the form

$$y = \frac{P(x)}{Q(x)}$$

where $P(x)$ and $Q(x)$ are polynomials. In this section, we assume that the fraction $P(x)/Q(x)$ is in simplified form. Because $Q(x)$ appears in the denominator, the domain of the rational function must exclude all values of x for which $Q(x) = 0$.

Example 1   Find the domain of the rational function defined by $y = f(x) = \dfrac{x^2 - 4}{x^2 - 1}$, and find the symmetries of its graph.

Solution   Factor both the numerator and the denominator of the fraction to obtain

$$y = \frac{(x + 2)(x - 2)}{(x - 1)(x + 1)}$$

Observe that the numbers 1 and -1 make the denominator equal to 0. Hence the domain of the function $y = f(x)$ is the set of all real numbers except 1 and -1.

The graph of the function is symmetric with respect to the y-axis because the variable x appears with even exponents only. Note that the equations $y = f(x)$ and $y = f(-x)$ are equivalent:

$$y = f(x) = \frac{x^2 - 4}{x^2 - 1} \qquad y = f(-x) = \frac{(-x)^2 - 4}{(-x)^2 - 1}$$

$$= \frac{x^2 - 4}{x^2 - 1}$$

■

Example 2   Graph the rational function defined by $y = \dfrac{x^2 - 4}{x^2 - 1}$.

Solution   Because the denominator of a fraction cannot be 0, x cannot be 1 or -1. To discover what happens when x is near 1, calculate values of y for numbers x that are close to 1.

$x < 1$		$x > 1$	
x	y	x	y
0.5	5	1.5	-1.4
0.9	16.8	1.1	-13.3
0.99	151.8	1.01	-148.3
0.999	1501.8	1.001	-1498.3

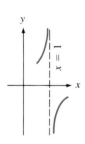

Figure 9-13

Plotting these points suggests a curve that approaches the vertical line $x = 1$ but never touches it. See Figure 9-13. Because there are only even exponents for x in this function, the curve is symmetric to the y-axis. Thus, similar behavior occurs near the line $x = -1$.

The y-intercept of the curve is determined by setting x equal to 0 and computing y; the y-intercept is 4.

The numbers $x = 2$ and $x = -2$ reduce the numerator of the rational expression to 0. The corresponding values of y, therefore, are both 0, and the x-intercepts of the curve are 2 and -2. You can now sketch most of the curve, as shown in Figure 9-14.

To discover the shape of the curve to the right of $x = 2$ and to the left of $x = -2$, examine the behavior of

$$y = \frac{x^2 - 4}{x^2 - 1}$$

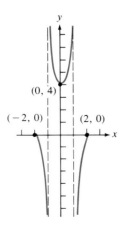

Figure 9-14

as x gets very large. Do this by performing a long division and writing the answer in *quotient* $+ \dfrac{remainder}{divisor}$ form:

$$\begin{array}{r} 1 \\ x^2 - 1 \overline{)\, x^2 - 4} \\ \underline{x^2 - 1} \\ -3 \end{array}$$

Hence,

$$y = \frac{x^2 - 4}{x^2 - 1} = 1 + \frac{-3}{x^2 - 1}$$

If x becomes very large, the denominator of the fraction $-3/(x^2 - 1)$ becomes very large also, and the magnitude of the fraction itself becomes very small. Because the term $-3/(x^2 - 1)$ is negative and approaches 0 as x becomes very large, it becomes negligible, and the value of y (which is less than 1) approaches the value 1. As x increases without bound, the value of the function defined by $y = (x^2 - 4)/(x^2 - 1)$ approaches 1 from below. Hence, as x increases, the curve approaches the line $y = 1$ from below. Because of symmetry, the curve also approaches the line $y = 1$ as x decreases without bound. See Figure 9-15.

The broken lines in Figure 9-15 are called **asymptotes**. The function $y = (x^2 - 4)/(x^2 - 1)$ has two vertical asymptotes, the lines $x = 1$ and $x = -1$, and one horizontal asymptote, the line $y = 1$. Although a curve might intersect a horizontal asymptote when $|x|$ is small, it will approach, but never touch, a horizontal asymptote when $|x|$ grows large. The graph of the rational function $y = (x^2 - 4)/(x^2 - 1)$ is shown in Figure 9-15.

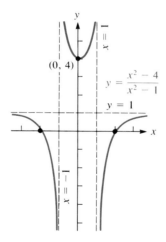

Figure 9-15   ■

Let's summarize the work done in the previous example. First you found the vertical asymptotes $x = 1$ and $x = -1$ by setting the denominator of the rational expression equal to 0 and solving that equation for x. Then you found the y-intercept 4 by letting x equal 0 in the rational expression and evaluating y. Next you found the x-intercepts by finding the numbers x (2 and -2) that make the numerator of the rational expression equal to 0, and you found the horizontal asymptote $y = 1$ by performing a long division and ignoring the remainder. Finally, you made use of symmetry to graph the part of the curve to the left of the y-axis.

Example 3   Graph the rational function defined by $y = \dfrac{3x}{x-2}$.

Solution   First look for symmetry about the y-axis. Because x appears to an odd power, the function is not symmetric about the y-axis. The y-intercept is found by setting $x = 0$ and solving for y; the y-intercept is 0. Because $y = 0$ when $x = 0$, the curve passes through the origin.

The x-intercepts are found by setting the numerator of the rational expression equal to 0 and solving for x:

$$3x = 0$$

$$x = 0$$

Thus, the only x-intercept is at 0.

The vertical asymptotes are found by determining which real numbers lead to zeros in the denominator of the rational expression. If x is replaced by 2 in the denominator $x - 2$, that denominator is 0. Hence, the line $x = 2$ is a vertical asymptote.

The horizontal asymptotes, if any, are found by dividing $3x$ by $x - 2$ and expressing the answer in $quotient + \dfrac{remainder}{divisor}$ form.

$$y = \frac{3x}{x-2} = 3 + \frac{6}{x-2}$$

As $|x|$ increases without bound, the fraction $6/(x-2)$ approaches 0. So, the curve approaches the line $y = 3$ as $|x|$ becomes larger. The line $y = 3$ is a horizontal asymptote. The previous results provide a basis for the graph. See Figure 9-16.

To discover what happens to the graph when x is greater than 2, pick a value of x that is greater than 2 and find the corresponding value of y. If $x = 3$, for example, the value of y is 9. After plotting the point $(3, 9)$, you can use the intercepts and asymptotes to sketch the graph. This curve, shown in Figure 9-17, is called a **hyperbola**.

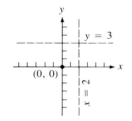

Figure 9-16

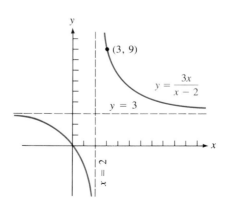

Figure 9-17

Example 4   Graph the rational function defined by $y = \dfrac{x^2 + x - 2}{x - 3}$.

Solution   First factor the numerator of the rational expression:

$$y = \frac{(x - 1)(x + 2)}{x - 3}$$

Most of the information is straightforward:

- The function is not symmetric about the y-axis or origin.
- The y-intercept is $\frac{2}{3}$.
- The x-intercepts are 1 and -2.
- A vertical asymptote is $x = 3$.

Perform the long division and write the rational expression as

$$y = \frac{x^2 + x - 2}{x - 3} = x + 4 + \frac{10}{x - 3}$$

As before, the fraction $10/(x - 3)$ becomes insignificant as x grows large. This time, however, the graph does not approach a constant. Instead, it approaches the line given by $y = x + 4$. Because this line is not horizontal, the graph has no horizontal asymptotes. However, it does have a **slant asymptote** or an **oblique asymptote**: the line $y = x + 4$. Put all of this information together and graph the rational function. See Figure 9-18.

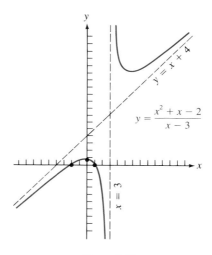

Figure 9-18   ■

Example 5   Discuss the nature of the asymptotes of the following rational functions:

a. $y = \dfrac{x + 2}{x^2 - 1}$ **b.** $y = \dfrac{x^2 + x + 2}{x^2 - 1}$

c. $y = \dfrac{3x^3 + 2x^2 + 2}{x^2 - 1}$ **d.** $y = \dfrac{x^4 + x + 2}{x^2 - 1}$

Solution All four functions have vertical asymptotes at $x = 1$ and $x = -1$ because at these values the denominators are 0. The nature of the remaining asymptotes must be considered.

a. $y = \dfrac{x + 2}{x^2 - 1}$

Because the degree of the numerator is less than the degree of the denominator, long division is not possible. Try a different approach, dividing both numerator and denominator by x^2, which is the largest power of x in the denominator.

$$y = \frac{x + 2}{x^2 - 1} = \frac{\dfrac{x}{x^2} + \dfrac{2}{x^2}}{\dfrac{x^2}{x^2} - \dfrac{1}{x^2}} = \frac{\dfrac{1}{x} + \dfrac{2}{x^2}}{1 - \dfrac{1}{x^2}}$$

The three fractions in the final result, $\dfrac{1}{x}$, $\dfrac{2}{x^2}$, and $\dfrac{1}{x^2}$, all approach 0 as $|x|$ increases without bound. Hence, y approaches

$$\frac{0 + 0}{1 - 0} = 0$$

The graph of this function has a horizontal asymptote of $y = 0$.

In each of the three remaining functions, a long division can be performed.

b. $y = \dfrac{x^2 + x + 2}{x^2 - 1} = 1 + \dfrac{x + 3}{x^2 - 1}$

As $|x|$ increases without bound, the fraction $(x + 3)/(x^2 - 1)$ approaches 0 (for reasons discussed in part **a**) and y approaches 1. This curve has a horizontal asymptote of $y = 1$.

c. $y = \dfrac{3x^3 + 2x^2 + 2}{x^2 - 1} = 3x + 2 + \dfrac{3x + 4}{x^2 - 1}$

Again, the last fraction approaches 0 as $|x|$ increases without bound, and the curve approaches the slant asymptote $y = 3x + 2$.

d. $y = \dfrac{x^4 + x + 2}{x^2 - 1} = x^2 + 1 + \dfrac{x + 3}{x^2 - 1}$

As $|x|$ increases, the fractional part again approaches 0 and the curve approaches $y = x^2 + 1$. However, $y = x^2 + 1$ does not represent a line. This curve has neither horizontal nor slant asymptotes. ∎

We generalize the results of Example 5 and summarize the techniques discussed in this section as follows.

Perform the following steps when you graph the rational function $y = \dfrac{P(x)}{Q(x)}$, where $\dfrac{P(x)}{Q(x)}$ is in simplified form.

Check for symmetry.   If the polynomials $P(x)$ and $Q(x)$ involve only even powers of x, the graph is symmetric about the y-axis. Otherwise, y-axis symmetry does not exist.

Look for y-intercepts.   Set x equal to 0. The resulting value of y is the y-intercept of the graph.

Look for x-intercepts.   Set $P(x)$ equal to 0. The solutions of the equation $P(x) = 0$ (if any) are the x-intercepts of the graph.

Look for vertical asymptotes.   Set $Q(x)$ equal to 0. The solutions of the equation $Q(x) = 0$ (if any) determine the vertical asymptotes of the graph.

Look for horizontal asymptotes.   If the degree of $P(x)$ is less than the degree of $Q(x)$, then the line $y = 0$ is a horizontal asymptote.

   If the degrees of $P(x)$ and $Q(x)$ are equal, then the line $y = p/q$, where p and q are the lead coefficients of $P(x)$ and $Q(x)$, is a horizontal asymptote. (Be sure that $P(x)$ and $Q(x)$ are written in descending powers of x before applying this rule.)

   If the degree of $P(x)$ is greater than the degree of $Q(x)$, then there is no horizontal asymptote.

Look for slant asymptotes.   If the degree of $P(x)$ is exactly one greater than the degree of $Q(x)$, there is a slant asymptote.

To find it, perform the long division $Q(x) \overline{) P(x)}$ and ignore the remainder.

■ EXERCISE 9.3

In Exercises 1–24, find all asymptotes (vertical, horizontal, and slant asymptotes) and then graph each rational function.

1. $y = \dfrac{1}{x - 2}$ **2.** $y = \dfrac{3}{x + 3}$ **3.** $y = \dfrac{x}{x - 1}$ **4.** $y = \dfrac{x}{x + 2}$

5. $y = \dfrac{x + 1}{x + 2}$ **6.** $y = \dfrac{x - 1}{x - 2}$ **7.** $y = \dfrac{2x - 1}{x - 1}$ **8.** $y = \dfrac{3x + 2}{x - 1}$

9. $y = \dfrac{x^2 - 9}{x^2 - 4}$ **10.** $y = \dfrac{x^2 - 4}{x^2 - 9}$ **11.** $y = \dfrac{x^2 - 5x + 6}{x^2 - 2x + 1}$ **12.** $y = \dfrac{x^2 + 7x + 12}{x^2 - 4x + 4}$

13. $y = \dfrac{3x^2}{x^2 + 1}$ **14.** $y = \dfrac{x^2 - 9}{2x^2 + 1}$ **15.** $y = \dfrac{2x^2 - 2}{x^2 - 25}$ **16.** $y = \dfrac{x^2 - 4}{3x^2 - 27}$

17. $y = \dfrac{2x^2 - 3x - 2}{x^2 + x - 2}$ **18.** $y = \dfrac{3x^2 - 4x + 1}{2x^2 + 3x + 1}$ **19.** $y = \dfrac{x^2 - 9}{2x^2 - 8}$ **20.** $y = \dfrac{3x^2 - 12}{x^2}$

21. $y = \dfrac{x^2 - 2x - 8}{x - 1}$ **22.** $y = \dfrac{x^2 + x - 6}{x + 2}$ **23.** $y = \dfrac{x^3 + x^2 + 6x}{x^2 - 1}$ **24.** $y = \dfrac{x^3 - 2x^2 + x}{x^2 - 4}$

25. Can a rational function have more than one horizontal asymptote? Explain.

26. The graph of a rational function cannot cross a vertical asymptote. Can it cross a horizontal asymptote? Explain.

9.4   GRAPHS OF OTHER FUNCTIONS AND RELATIONS

In this section we continue discussing the graphs of functions and relations.

Example 1   Graph the equation $y = |x|$ and tell if it defines a function.

Solution   Make a table of values as in Figure 9-19. Plot each ordered pair and join the points as in the figure to get the graph of the equation $y = |x|$. Note that this equation *does* define a function because for each number x, there corresponds exactly one value of y. This is easy to see from the graph. For example, if $x = -2$, there is one corresponding y value; it is the value 2.

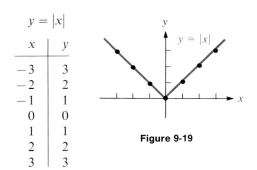

$y = |x|$

x	y
-3	3
-2	2
-1	1
0	0
1	1
2	2
3	3

Figure 9-19

The Vertical-Line Test

There is a test, called the **vertical-line test**, that can be used to decide if the relation represented by a graph is a function. If a vertical line intersects a graph more than once, the relation represented by that graph *cannot* be a function.

This is because to one number x there corresponds more than one value of y. The graph in Figure 9-20a represents a function because every vertical line that intersects the graph does so in a single point. However, the graph in Figure 9-20b does not represent a function because some vertical lines intersect the graph in more than one point.

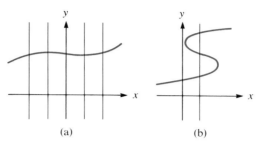

(a)   (b)

Figure 9-20

Note that in Example 1, every vertical line that intersects the graph of $y = |x|$ would do so exactly once. Thus, the vertical-line test indicates that the equation $y = |x|$ *does* define a function.

Example 2   Graph the equation $xy = 6$ and use the vertical line test to decide if the equation defines a function.

Solution   Make a table of values as in Figure 9-21, and plot the points to draw the graph. Because neither x nor y can be 0, the curve cannot cross either the x-axis or the y-axis. The curve in Figure 9-21 is called a **hyperbola**. To see if the equation $xy = 6$ defines a function, draw several vertical lines that intersect the curve. See Figure 9-22. Because each vertical line that intersects the curve does so exactly once, the equation *does* define a function.

$xy = 6$

x	y
1	6
2	3
3	2
6	1
-1	-6
-2	-3
-3	-2
-6	-1

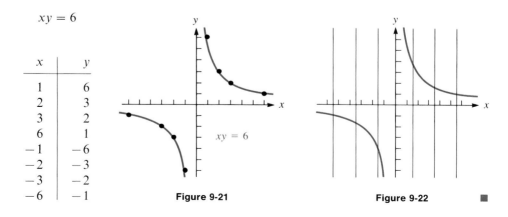

Figure 9-21   **Figure 9-22**

Example 3   Graph the equation $y^2 = -4x$ and tell if it defines a function.

Solution   A table of values is shown in Figure 9-23. Plot each ordered pair and note that the points lie on a curve. Join the points with a smooth curve to determine the graph of $y^2 = -4x$. This parabola opens to the left. Because some vertical lines that intersect the parabola do so twice, the equation $y^2 = -4x$ *does not* define a function. See Figure 9-24.

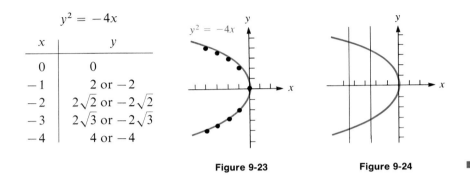

$y^2 = -4x$	
x	y
0	0
-1	2 or -2
-2	$2\sqrt{2}$ or $-2\sqrt{2}$
-3	$2\sqrt{3}$ or $-2\sqrt{3}$
-4	4 or -4

Figure 9-23   Figure 9-24

Example 4   Graph the equation $|x + y| = 4$ and tell if it defines a function.

Solution   Make a table of values as in Figure 9-25 and plot each point. This time, the points lie on two straight lines that are parallel. Because a vertical line would intersect the graph in two points, the equation *does not* define a function.

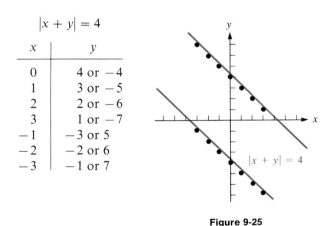

$|x + y| = 4$	
x	y
0	4 or -4
1	3 or -5
2	2 or -6
3	1 or -7
-1	-3 or 5
-2	-2 or 6
-3	-1 or 7

Figure 9-25

A function called the **greatest integer function** is used occasionally in mathematics and often in computer programming. The ordered pairs (x, y) of this function are determined by the equation $y = [x]$. The value of y that corresponds to x is the greatest integer that is less than or equal to the number x. For example, the greatest integer that is less than or equal to π ($\pi = 3.14159\ldots$) is the number 3. Thus, $[\pi] = 3$. Study each of the following equalities to understand the behavior of the greatest integer function.

$$[3.7] = 3$$
$$[-3.7] = -4$$
$$[5] = 5$$
$$[-5] = -5$$
$$[0] = 0$$
$$[0.999999999] = 0$$
$$[-0.999999999] = -1$$

Example 5 Graph the function determined by $y = [x]$.

Solution For values of x that are strictly between two consecutive integers, the corresponding value of y is the smaller of the two integers. For *integer* values of x, the corresponding value of y is just the integer x. A table of values and the graph of the function appear in Figure 9-26. Note the positions of the solid circles and the hollow circles on the graph.

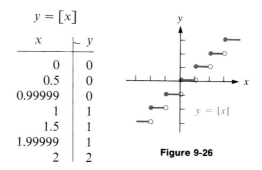

$y = [x]$	
x	y
0	0
0.5	0
0.99999	0
1	1
1.5	1
1.99999	1
2	2

Figure 9-26

EXERCISE 9.4

In Exercises 1–30, graph each equation and use the vertical-line test to decide if each one defines a function.

1. $x = |y|$

2. $y = |x - 2|$

3. $y = \frac{1}{2}|x + 4|$

4. $y = |x| - 2$

5. $|x| - y = 4$

6. $x + |y| = 1$

7. $x = y^2 + 4$

8. $x = 2y^2 - 2$

9. $x = -y^2 - 2$

10. $x = -2y^2 + 4$

11. $xy = 12$

12. $xy = 24$

13. $xy = -24$

14. $-xy = 12$

15. $y = x^3$

16. $x = y^3$

17. $x = -y^3$ **18.** $y = -x^3$ **19.** $x = y^3 - 10$ **20.** $y = \dfrac{1}{8}x^3 - 4$

21. $|x + y| = 2$ **22.** $2|x + y| = 6$ **23.** $4|x + y| = 4$ **24.** $|x + y| = 0$

25. $y = [2x]$ **26.** $y = [3x]$ **27.** $y = [-x]$ **28.** $y = \left[\dfrac{x}{2}\right]$

29. $y = [3 - x]$ **30.** $y = [|x|]$

31. Computer programmers use a function, called the **signum function**, that is defined in the following way:

if $x < 0$, then $y = -1$

if $x = 0$, then $y = 0$

if $x > 0$, then $y = 1$

The signum function is denoted by the equation $y = \text{sgn } x$. Graph this function.

9.5   MORE ON INVERSE FUNCTIONS AND THEIR GRAPHS

We have seen that any linear function has an inverse function. For example, to find the inverse function of $y = -5x + 2$, we simply interchange the positions of x and y and solve the resulting equation for y.

$$y = -5x + 2$$
$$x = -5y + 2 \qquad \text{Interchange } x \text{ and } y.$$
$$x - 2 = -5y$$
$$\frac{x - 2}{-5} = y$$
$$y = \frac{2 - x}{5}$$

Thus, the inverse of $y = -5x + 2$ is $y = f^{-1}(x) = \dfrac{2 - x}{5}$.

If we graph both $y = -5x + 2$ and $y = \dfrac{2 - x}{5}$ on the same set of coordinate axes, as in Figure 9-27, we obtain two straight lines that are symmetric about the line $y = x$.

Other functions also have inverses, although those inverses may or may not be functions. To find the inverse of the quadratic function $y = x^2$, for example, we interchange the positions of x and y and solve the resulting equation for y.

$$y = x^2$$
$$x = y^2 \qquad \text{Interchange } x \text{ and } y.$$
$$y = \pm\sqrt{x} \qquad \text{Use the square root property.}$$

Thus, the inverse of $y = x^2$ is $y = f^{-1}(x) = \pm\sqrt{x}$. Because two values of y correspond to each number x in the equation $y = \pm\sqrt{x}$, the inverse relation of $y = x^2$ is not a function. However, it is a relation.

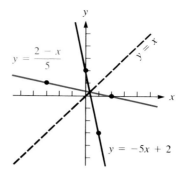

Figure 9-27

If we graph both $y = x^2$ and $y = \pm\sqrt{x}$ on the same set of coordinate axes, we obtain the two parabolas shown in Figure 9-28. The line of symmetry $y = x$ is included for reference.

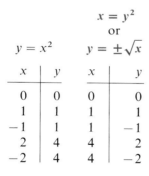

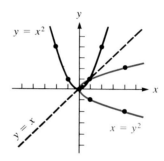

Figure 9-28

Example 1 Find the inverse of $y = f(x) = x^3 + 3$ and graph both the function and its inverse on a single set of coordinate axes.

Solution Find the inverse of the function $y = x^3 + 3$ by interchanging the positions of x and y and solving the resulting equation for y.

$$y = x^3 + 3$$
$$x = y^3 + 3 \qquad \text{Interchange } x \text{ and } y.$$
$$x - 3 = y^3$$
$$y = \sqrt[3]{x - 3}$$

Thus, $f^{-1}(x) = \sqrt[3]{x - 3}$. Because to each number x in the equation $y = \sqrt[3]{x - 3}$ there corresponds exactly one value of y, the inverse relation of $y = x^3 + 3$ is a function. The graphs $y = x^3 + 3$ and $y = \sqrt[3]{x - 3}$ appear in Figure 9-29, along with the axis of symmetry $y = x$.

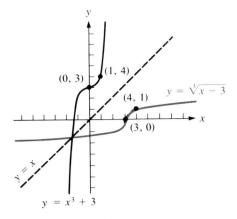

Figure 9-29

One-to-One Functions

If the inverse of a function f is also a function, then f is called a **one-to-one function**. Stated another way, we have the following definition.

> **Definition.**   A function is called **one-to-one** if and only if each element in the range of the function corresponds to only one element in the domain of the function.

There is a test, called the **horizontal-line test**, that can be used to determine whether a graph represents a one-to-one function. If any horizontal line intersects the graph of a function more than once, the function represented by the graph is not one-to-one. See Figure 9-30. However, if every horizontal line that intersects the graph does so exactly once, the function represented by the graph is one-to-one. See Figure 9-31.

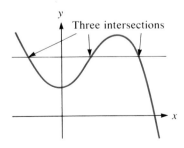

Not a one-to-one function

Figure 9-30

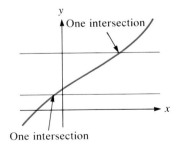

A one-to-one function

Figure 9-31

Example 2   Use the horizontal-line test to decide if the function defined by $y = x^3$ is one-to-one.

Solution   Graph the equation, as in Figure 9-32. Because each horizontal line that intersects the graph does so exactly once, each value of y corresponds to only one number x. Thus, the function defined by $y = x^3$ is one-to-one.

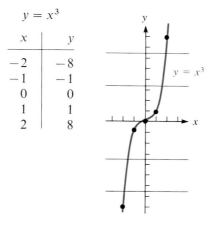

$y = x^3$

x	y
-2	-8
-1	-1
0	0
1	1
2	8

Figure 9-32

Example 3   Use the horizontal-line test to decide whether the function defined by $y = x^2 - 4$ is one-to-one.

Solution   Graph the equation as in Figure 9-33. Because many horizontal lines that intersect the graph do so twice, some values of y correspond to two numbers x. Thus, this function is not one-to-one.

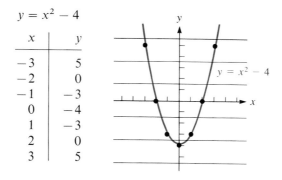

$y = x^2 - 4$

x	y
-3	5
-2	0
-1	-3
0	-4
1	-3
2	0
3	5

Figure 9-33

Because a one-to-one function and its inverse determine reverse correspondences, the inverse of a one-to-one function undoes whatever the function does. For example, we have seen that $y = x^3 + 3$ and $y = \sqrt[3]{x} - 3$ define inverse functions. The function $y = x^3 + 3$ takes a number such as $x = 4$ and turns it into a y value of $4^3 + 3$, or 67. However, the inverse function $y = \sqrt[3]{x} - 3$ turns the number $x = 67$ back into $\sqrt[3]{67 - 3}$, or 4. Likewise, the function $y = x^3 + 3$ takes the number -5 and turns it into a y value of $(-5)^3 + 3$, or -122. The inverse function $y = \sqrt[3]{x} - 3$ turns the number $x = -122$ back into $\sqrt[3]{-122 - 3}$, or -5.

Figure 9-34 illustrates a function f from set X to a set Y. Because several arrows point to a single value of y, the function is not one-to-one. If the arrows of Figure 9-34 were reversed, the diagram would not represent a function because several numbers x in set X would correspond to some value y of set Y. However, if the arrows in Figure 9-35 were reversed, the diagram would still represent a function. This backward function is the inverse function of the original function f.

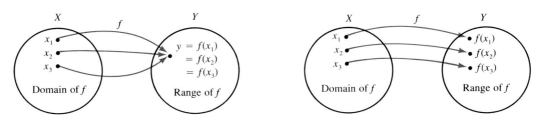

Figure 9-34   Figure 9-35

In Figure 9-36, to the element x in the domain of f there corresponds its image $f(x)$ in the range of f. This element $f(x)$, however, is also in the domain of f^{-1}. The image of $f(x)$ under the function f^{-1} is $f^{-1}(f(x))$, which is the original number x. Thus, $(f^{-1} \circ f)(x) = f^{-1}(f(x)) = x$. Likewise, if y is an element of the domain of f^{-1}, then $(f \circ f^{-1})(y) = f(f^{-1}(y)) = y$.

Theorem.   If f is a one-to-one function with domain X and range Y, then there is a one-to-one function f^{-1} with domain Y and range X such that

$$(f^{-1} \circ f)(x) = x$$

and

$$(f \circ f^{-1})(y) = y$$

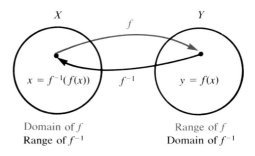

Domain of f Range of f
Range of f^{-1} Domain of f^{-1}

Figure 9-36

To show that one function is the inverse of another, we must show that their composition is the **identity function**—the function that assigns x itself as the image of each real number x.

Example 4   Show that the function $y = f(x) = x^3$ is the inverse of the function $g(x) = \sqrt[3]{x}$.

Solution   Show that the composition of f and g (in both directions) is the identity function.

$$(f \circ g)(x) = f(g(x)) = f(\sqrt[3]{x}) = (\sqrt[3]{x})^3 = x$$
$$(g \circ f)(x) = g(f(x)) = g(x^3) = \sqrt[3]{x^3} = x$$

∎

Example 5   The function f defined by the equation $y = f(x) = x^2 + 3$ is not one-to-one. However, it becomes one-to-one if you restrict its domain to a carefully chosen subset of the real numbers, such as the set $\{x : x \le 0\}$. Find   **a.**   the range of f,   **b.**   the inverse of f along with the domain and range of the inverse, and finally   **c.**   graph each function.

Solution   **a.**   The function f is defined by $y = f(x) = x^2 + 3$ with given domain of $\{x : x \le 0\}$. If x is replaced with numbers from this domain, y ranges over the values 3 and above. Thus, the range of f is the set $\{y : y \ge 3\}$.

b.   To find the inverse of f, interchange x and y in the equation that defines f and solve for y:

$$y = x^2 + 3 \qquad \text{where } x \le 0$$
$$x = y^2 + 3 \qquad \text{where } y \le 0 \qquad \text{Interchange } x \text{ and } y.$$
$$x - 3 = y^2 \qquad \text{where } y \le 0 \qquad \text{Add } -3 \text{ to both sides.}$$

To solve this equation for y, take the square root of both sides. Because $y \le 0$, you have

$$y = -\sqrt{x - 3} \qquad \text{where } y \le 0$$

Thus, the inverse of f is defined by the equation $y = f^{-1}(x) = -\sqrt{x - 3}$. It has domain of $\{x : x \ge 3\}$ and range $\{y : y \le 0\}$.

c.   The graphs of these two functions appear in Figure 9-37. Note that the line of symmetry is $y = x$.

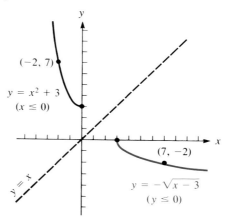

Figure 9-37

∎

If a function f is defined by the equation $y = f(x)$, we can often find the domain of f by inspection. Finding the range can be more difficult. One way to find the range of f is to find the domain of f^{-1}.

Example 6   Find the domain and the range of the function defined by $y = f(x) = \dfrac{2}{x} + 3$.

Solution   Because x cannot be 0, the domain of f is $\{x : x$ is a real number and $x \neq 0\}$. To find the range of f, find the domain of f^{-1}. To find f^{-1}, proceed as follows:

$$y = \frac{2}{x} + 3$$

$$x = \frac{2}{y} + 3 \qquad \text{Interchange } x \text{ and } y.$$

$$xy = 2 + 3y \qquad \text{Multiply both sides by } y.$$

$$xy - 3y = 2 \qquad \text{Add } -3y \text{ to both sides.}$$

$$y(x - 3) = 2 \qquad \text{Factor out } y.$$

$$y = \frac{2}{x - 3} \qquad \text{Divide both sides by } x - 3.$$

This final equation defines f^{-1} whose domain is $\{x : x$ is a real number and $x \neq 3\}$. Because the range of f is equal to the domain of f^{-1}, the range of f is

$$\{y : y \text{ is a real number and } y \neq 3\} \qquad \blacksquare$$

▬ EXERCISE 9.5

In Exercises 1–12, find the inverse relation of each set of ordered pairs (x, y) determined by the given equation. Tell whether the inverse relation is a function.

1. $y = 3x + 1$ **2.** $y + 1 = 5x$ **3.** $x + 4 = 5y$ **4.** $x = 3y + 1$

5. $y = x^2 + 4$ **6.** $y + 2 = x^2$ **7.** $y = x^3 - 1$ **8.** $8y = x^3$

9. $x^2 + y^2 = 1$ **10.** $xy = 4$ **11.** $y = \sqrt{x}$ **12.** $y = \sqrt[3]{x}$

In Exercises 13–16, use the horizontal-line test to determine if each graph represents a one-to-one function.

13.

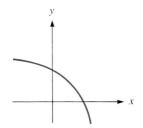

14.

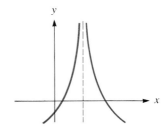

15.

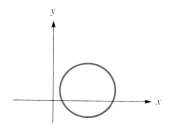

16.

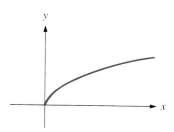

In Exercises 17–28, each equation represents a function. Graph each equation and use the horizontal-line test to decide if each function is one-to-one.

17. $y = 4x - 3$ **18.** $y = 5 - 3x$ **19.** $y = \dfrac{x + 7}{8}$ **20.** $y = \dfrac{5 - x}{2}$

21. $y = 3x^2 + 2$ **22.** $y = 5 - x^2$ **23.** $y = \sqrt[3]{x}$ **24.** $y = \sqrt{x}$

25. $y = x^3 - x$ **26.** $y = -x^4 + x^2$ **27.** $x = y^3 + 1$ **28.** $x = y^5 - 2$

In Exercises 29–36, each equation defines a one-to-one function f. Determine f^{-1} and verify that $f \circ f^{-1}$ and $f^{-1} \circ f$ are the identity function.

29. $y = 3x$ **30.** $y = \dfrac{1}{3}x$ **31.** $y = 2x - 4$ **32.** $y = 3x - 1$

33. $y = \dfrac{1}{x + 3}$ **34.** $y = \dfrac{1}{x - 2}$ **35.** $y = \dfrac{1}{2x}$ **36.** $y = \dfrac{1}{x^3}$

In Exercises 37–42, the function f defined by the given equation is one-to-one on the given domain. Find $f^{-1}(x)$.

37. $f(x) = x^2 - 3$ $\{x : x \le 0\}$

38. $f(x) = \dfrac{1}{x^2}$ $\{x : x > 0\}$

39. $f(x) = x^4 - 8$ $\{x : x \ge 0\}$

40. $f(x) = -\dfrac{1}{x^4}$ $\{x : x < 0\}$

41. $f(x) = \sqrt{4 - x^2}$ $\{x : 0 \le x \le 2\}$

42. $f(x) = \sqrt{x^2 - 1}$ $\{x : x \le -1\}$

In Exercises 43–46, find the domain and the range of f. Find the range by finding the domain of f^{-1}.

43. $f(x) = \dfrac{x}{x - 1}$ **44.** $f(x) = \dfrac{x - 2}{x + 3}$ **45.** $f(x) = \dfrac{1}{x} - 2$ **46.** $f(x) = \dfrac{3}{x} - \dfrac{1}{2}$

9.6   GRAPHS OF NONLINEAR INEQUALITIES IN TWO VARIABLES

In Section 7.7 we saw how to graph linear inequalities in two variables. We now discuss how to graph nonlinear inequalities in two variables.

Example 1   Graph $y < -x^2 + 4$.

Solution   In this example, the graph of the equation $y = -x^2 + 4$ can be thought of as a "fence" separating the region represented by $y < -x^2 + 4$ and the region represented by $y > -x^2 + 4$. Graph the quadratic function $y = -x^2 + 4$ using a broken curve because equality is not permitted. Note that the coordinates of the origin, $(0, 0)$, satisfy the inequality $y < -x^2 + 4$. Hence, the origin is in the graph of $y < -x^2 + 4$. The graph is shown in Figure 9-38.

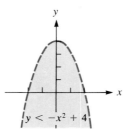

Figure 9-38

Example 2   Graph $x \le |y|$.

Solution   As in the previous example, graph the equality $x = |y|$. Use a solid line because equality is permitted. See Figure 9-39. This time, the coordinates of the origin cannot be used to establish the proper region because the origin is on the graph of $x = |y|$. However, any other convenient point, such as $(1, 0)$, will do. Substitute 1 for x and 0 for y into the inequality $x \le |y|$, and note that the result is a false statement. Because $(1, 0)$ does not satisfy $x \le |y|$, it is *not* in the graph. Hence, the graph is to the left of the graph of $x = |y|$. The complete graph of $x \le |y|$ is shown in Figure 9-40.

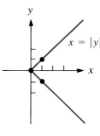

Figure 9-39

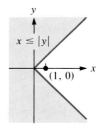

Figure 9-40

■ EXERCISE 9.6

Graph the following inequalities.

1. $y < x^2 + 1$ **2.** $y > x^2 - 3$ **3.** $x \ge y^2 - 3$ **4.** $x \le y^2 + 1$

5. $y < x^2 + 5x + 6$ **6.** $y > x^2 + 5x + 4$ **7.** $x^2 - y - 6 < x$ **8.** $x^2 - y - 6 > -x$

9. $y \ge (x + 3)(x - 2)$ **10.** $y \le (x + 1)(x - 1)$ **11.** $y \le (x + 2)^2$ **12.** $y \le (x - 2)^2$

13. $y < |x + 4|$ **14.** $y \ge |x - 3|$ **15.** $xy > 6$ **16.** $xy < 6$

17. $y \le -|x| + 2$ **18.** $y \ge |x| - 2$

CHAPTER SUMMARY

Key Words

asymptote   (9.3)

axis of symmetry   (9.1)

greatest integer function   (9.4)

horizontal-line test   (9.5)

hyperbola   (9.3)

identity function   (9.5)

one-to-one function   (9.5)

parabola   (9.1)

polynomial function   (9.2)

quadratic function   (9.1)

rational function   (9.3)

vertex of a parabola   (9.1)

vertical-line test   (9.4)

Key Ideas

(9.1)   A **quadratic function** is a function that is determined by an equation of the form $y = ax^2 + bx + c$, where a, b, and c are constants and $a \neq 0$.

The graph of $y = a(x - h)^2 + k$, with $a \neq 0$, is a parabola with vertex at (h, k). The parabola opens upward if $a > 0$, or downward if $a < 0$. The axis of symmetry is $x = h$.

(9.2)   A **polynomial function in x** is defined by the equation $y = P(x)$, where $P(x)$ is a polynomial in x.

If the equations $y = f(x)$ and $y = f(-x)$ are equivalent, then the graph of $y = f(x)$ is symmetric about the y-axis.

If $(x, -y)$ lies on a graph whenever (x, y) does, then the graph is symmetric about the x-axis.

If the equations $y = f(x)$ and $-y = f(-x)$ are equivalent, then the graph of $y = f(x)$ is symmetric about the origin.

A function is increasing if $f(x_1) < f(x_2)$ whenever $x_1 < x_2$.
A function is decreasing if $f(x_1) > f(x_2)$ whenever $x_1 < x_2$.
A function is constant if $f(x_1) = f(x_2)$ for all x_1 and x_2.

(9.3)   Perform these steps when graphing rational functions of the form $y = \dfrac{P(x)}{Q(x)}$.

1. Check for symmetry.
2. Look for y-intercepts.
3. Look for x-intercepts.
4. Look for vertical asymptotes.
5. Look for horizontal asymptotes.
6. Look for slant asymptotes.
7. If necessary, plot some points.
8. Draw the graph.

(9.4)   The **vertical-line test** can be used to decide if the relation represented by a graph is a function.

(9.5)   A function is one-to-one if and only if each element in the range of the function corresponds to exactly one element in the domain of the function.

A **horizontal-line test** can be used to decide if a function is one-to-one.

To show that one function is the inverse of another, we must show that their composition is the **identity function**.

To find the range of a given one-to-one function, find the domain of its **inverse**.

(9.6)   To graph an inequality with two variables such as $y < f(x)$, first graph the equation $y = f(x)$. This will separate the plane into two regions. Then determine which region is the graph of $y < f(x)$.

REVIEW EXERCISES

In Review Exercises 1–4, graph each equation and give the coordinates of the vertex of the resulting parabola.

1. $y = \dfrac{x^2}{4}$ **2.** $y = 9x^2$ **3.** $y = 4x^2 + 5$ **4.** $y = -2x^2 - 1$

In Review Exercises 5–8, tell whether the graph of each equation is symmetric to either the y-axis, the x-axis, or the origin.

5. $y = x^2 + 2$ **6.** $-y = x^3 - 3x$ **7.** $-y^2 = x + 2$ **8.** $y = 3x$

In Review Exercises 9–10, graph each function.

9. $y = x^3 + 2x^2 - 3x$ **10.** $y = x^4 + 2x^2 + 1$

In Review Exercises 11–12, tell when each function is increasing or decreasing.

11. $y = x^3 - 12x$ **12.** $y = 2x^3 + 3x^2$

In Review Exercises 13–14, graph each rational function.

13. $y = \dfrac{2}{x - 4}$ **14.** $y = \dfrac{x - 2}{x^2 - 3x - 4}$

In Review Exercises 15–18, graph each equation and use the vertical-line test to decide whether it defines a function.

15. $y = 2x^2 - 1$ **16.** $y = |2x + 4|$ **17.** $x = y^2 - 5$ **18.** $|x + y| = 1$

In Review Exercises 19–22, find the inverse of each relation consisting of ordered pairs (x, y). Indicate if each inverse is a function.

19. $y = -2x + 7$ **20.** $x = 4y + 3$ **21.** $xy = -8$ **22.** $x^3 = y + 3$

In Review Exercises 23–24, each equation represents a function consisting of ordered pairs (x, y). Graph the equation and use the horizontal-line test to decide whether the equation defines a one-to-one function.

23. $y = 2(x - 3)$ **24.** $y = x(2x - 3)$

In Review Exercises 25–26, each equation represents a one-to-one function f consisting of ordered pairs (x, y). Find f^{-1} and verify that it is the inverse of f by showing that the composition of f and f^{-1} is the identity function.

25. $y = \dfrac{1}{x + 2}$

26. $y = x^3 - 27$

In Review Exercises 27–28, find the domain and range of each function. Find the range by finding the domain of the function's inverse.

27. $y = f(x) = \dfrac{2x + 1}{2x - 1}$

28. $y = f(x) = \dfrac{2}{x} + \dfrac{1}{2}$

In Review Exercises 29–30, graph each inequality.

29. $y \le 4 - x^2$

30. $y \ge |2x + 4|$

CHAPTER NINE TEST

1. Graph the equation $y = x^2 - 2x$.

2. Find the coordinates of the vertex of the parabola whose equation is $y = x^2 - 4x + 3$.

3. Give the equation of the axis of symmetry of the parabola given in Problem 2.

In Problems 4–6, consider the polynomial function defined by the equation $y = x^3 - x$.

4. State if the graph is symmetric to the x-axis, the y-axis, or the origin.

5. Graph the equation $y = x^3 - x$.

6. State if the function is increasing or decreasing as x increases from 1 to 5.

In Problems 7–12, consider the rational function defined by the equation $y = \dfrac{x - 2}{x - 3}$.

7. Give the equation of all vertical asymptotes, if any.

8. Give the equation of any horizontal asymptotes.

9. Give the x-intercept.

10. Give the y-intercept.

11. Is the graph symmetric about the y-axis?

12. Graph the function $y = \dfrac{x - 2}{x - 3}$.

13. Graph $y = -|x + 1|$ and use the vertical-line test to determine whether it defines a function.

14. Find the inverse of $y = \dfrac{2}{x + 2}$ and solve it for y.

15. Graph the equation $y = \dfrac{1}{x}$ and use the horizontal-line test to decide if the equation determines a one-to-one function.

In Problems 16–17, find the range of each function by finding the domain of the function's inverse.

16. $y = \dfrac{2x - 3}{x + 1}$

17. $y = \dfrac{3x}{4} - \dfrac{3}{5}$

18. Graph $y \le 3 - 2x$.

CUMULATIVE REVIEW EXERCISES (CHAPTERS 7–9)

1. Graph the equation $2x - 3y = 6$ and tell whether it represents a function.

2. Find the distance between $P(-2, 5)$ and $Q(8, -9)$.

In Problems 3–5, consider the points $P(-2, 5)$ and $Q(8, -9)$.

3. Find the midpoint of PQ.

4. Find the slope of PQ.

5. Write the equation of line PQ.

6. Are the lines represented by $3x + 2y = 12$ and $2x - 3y = 5$ parallel or perpendicular?

In Exercises 7–10, assume that $f(x) = 3x^2 + 2$ and $g(x) = 2x - 1$. Evaluate each expression.

7. $f(-1)$

8. $(g \circ f)(2)$

9. $(f \circ g)(x)$

10. $(g \circ f)(x)$

11. Find the inverse relation of the function $y = \dfrac{x + 3}{3}$ and tell whether it is a function.

12. Solve the proportion $\dfrac{x + 3}{2x} = \dfrac{3x}{6x + 5}$.

13. Express the following statement as a formula: "y varies directly with the product of x and z but inversely with the product of r and s."

14. The volume of a cylindrical tank varies jointly with the height of the tank and the square of the radius of its circular base. The volume is 4π cubic feet when $h = 4$ feet and $r = 1$ foot. Find the height when $V = 8\pi$ cubic feet and $r = 2$ feet.

15. Graph the inequality $2x - 3y \leq 12$.

16. Use the method of completing the square to solve the equation $2x^2 + x - 3 = 0$.

17. Use the quadratic formula to solve the equation $3x^2 + 4x - 1 = 0$.

18. Solve $x^4 - 13x^2 + 12 = 0$.

19. Solve $x - x^{1/2} - 12 = 0$.

20. Solve $x^2 - x - 6 > 0$ and graph the solution set.

21. Solve $\dfrac{x^2 - 3x - 4}{x - 1} \leq 0$ and graph the solution set.

22. Write in $a + bi$ form: $(3 - 2i) - (4 + i)^2$.

23. Write in $a + bi$ form: $\dfrac{1}{3 - i} + |3 + \sqrt{-4}|$.

24. Simplify $|3 + 4i|$.

25. For what values of k will the solutions of $2x^2 + 4x = k$ be equal?

26. Graph the equation $y = \frac{1}{2}x^2 - x + 1$ and find the coordinates of its vertex.

27. Graph the polynomial function $y = x^3 + 2x$ and tell whether the graph is symmetric to either axis or the origin.

28. Graph the rational function $y = \dfrac{-3x}{x^2 - 1}$.

29. Graph the equation $2y = |x|$ and tell whether the graph represents a function.

30. Is the function determined by $y = x^3 + 2$ one-to-one?

31. Find the range of the function $y = \dfrac{2x}{x - 5}$.

32. Graph the inequality $x \geq y^2$.

Systems of Equations and Inequalities

In the previous chapter, we considered many equations that contained two variables (usually x and y). We found that there was an unlimited number of ordered pairs (x, y) that satisfied each given equation. We now consider **systems of equations**: either two equations, each with two variables; or three equations, each with three variables. We will find pairs (x, y) or triples (x, y, z) that satisfy all equations of the system.

10.1 SOLUTION BY GRAPHING

Consider the pair of equations

$$\begin{cases} x + 2y = 4 \\ 2x - y = 3 \end{cases}$$

There are infinitely many ordered pairs (x, y) that satisfy the first equation, and there are infinitely many ordered pairs (x, y) that satisfy the second equation. However, there is only *one* ordered pair (x, y) that satisfies *both* equations simultaneously. The process of finding the ordered pair (x, y) that satisfies both of these equations simultaneously is called **solving the system of simultaneous equations**. The first example shows how to use a graphing method to solve this system.

Example 1 Solve the system $\begin{cases} x + 2y = 4 \\ 2x - y = 3 \end{cases}$ by graphing.

Solution Graph both equations on a single set of coordinate axes, as shown in Figure 10-1. Although an infinite number of pairs (x, y) satisfy the equation $x + 2y = 4$, and an infinite number of pairs (x, y) satisfy the equation $2x - y = 3$, only the coordinates of the point where the graphs intersect satisfy both equations simultaneously. The solution to this system is $x = 2$ and $y = 1$, or just $(2, 1)$. To check the answers, substitute **2** for x and **1** for y in each equation, and verify that $(2, 1)$ satisfies each equation.

$$x + 2y \stackrel{?}{=} 4 \qquad\qquad 2x - y \stackrel{?}{=} 3$$
$$2 + 2(1) \stackrel{?}{=} 4 \qquad\qquad 2(2) - 1 \stackrel{?}{=} 3$$
$$4 = 4 \qquad\qquad 3 = 3$$

333

$$x + 2y = 4 \qquad 2x - y = 3$$

x	y
4	0
0	2
-2	3

x	y
1	-1
0	-3
-1	-5

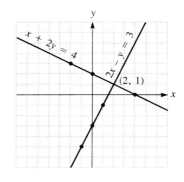

Figure 10-1

In Example 1, the graphs of the two equations were two distinct lines and the system had a solution. If two equations have distinct graphs, the equations are called **independent**. Otherwise, they are called **dependent**. If a system of equations has a solution, the system is called a **consistent system of equations**. If a system of equations does not have a solution, the system is called an **inconsistent system of equations**.

Example 2   Use the graphing method to solve the system $\begin{cases} 2x + 3y = 6 \\ 4x + 6y = 24 \end{cases}$.

Solution   Graph both equations on the same set of coordinate axes, as in Figure 10-2. The lines in the figure must be parallel because the slopes of the two lines are equal. Verify that the slope of each line is $-\frac{2}{3}$ by writing each equation in slope–intercept form. Because the graphs of these two equations are distinct lines, the two equations are independent equations. However, because they are parallel lines and parallel lines do not intersect, the system does not have a solution. Thus, this system is inconsistent.

$$2x + 3y = 6 \qquad 4x + 6y = 24$$

x	y
3	0
0	2
-3	4

x	y
6	0
0	4
-3	6

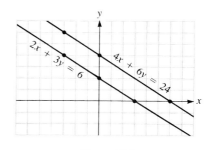

Figure 10-2

Example 3   Use the graphing method to solve the system $\begin{cases} 2y - x = 4 \\ 2x + 8 = 4y \end{cases}$.

Solution   Graph each equation on the same set of coordinate axes, as in Figure 10-3. In this example, the graphs of the equations coincide. This system is consistent because there is an infinite number of simultaneous solutions. Because the equations are essentially the same, any pair that satisfies one of the equations satisfies the other also. For this reason, these equations are dependent equations.

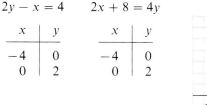

$$2y - x = 4 \qquad 2x + 8 = 4y$$

x	y		x	y
-4	0		-4	0
0	2		0	2

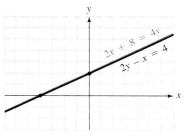

Figure 10-3   ■

The following box summarizes the possibilities that can occur when two equations, each with two variables, are graphed.

If the	**Then**
lines are distinct and intersect,	the equations are independent and the system is consistent. One simultaneous solution exists.
lines are distinct and parallel,	the equations are independent and the system is inconsistent. No simultaneous solution exists.
lines coincide,	the equations are dependent and the system is consistent. An infinite number of simultaneous solutions exist.

Example 4   Use the graphing method to solve the system $\begin{cases} \dfrac{3}{2}x - y = \dfrac{5}{2} \\ x + \dfrac{1}{2}y = 4 \end{cases}$.

Solution   Multiply both sides of the equation $\frac{3}{2}x - y = \frac{5}{2}$ by 2 to clear it of fractions and, thereby, obtain the equation $3x - 2y = 5$. Multiply both sides of the equation $x + \frac{1}{2}y = 4$ by 2 to clear it of fractions and, thereby, obtain the equation $2x + y = 8$. The new system

$$\begin{cases} 3x - 2y = 5 \\ 2x + y = 8 \end{cases}$$

has the same simultaneous solution as the given system of equations, but with no fractions it is easier to solve. Graph each equation in this new system as in Figure 10-4. The coordinates of the point of intersection of the two lines are (3, 2), and this pair is the solution to both the new and the original system. Verify that (3, 2) satisfies each of the equations in the original system. In this example, the equations are independent and the system is consistent.

$$3x - 2y = 5 \qquad 2x + y = 8$$

x	y
0	$-\frac{5}{2}$
$\frac{5}{3}$	0

x	y
4	0
1	6

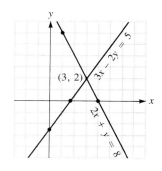

Figure 10-4

Example 5   Is the system $\begin{cases} y = 3x + 7 \\ 3x - y = 12 \end{cases}$ consistent?

Solution   Note that the slope of the graph of $y = 3x + 7$ is 3 and the slope of the graph of $3x - y = 12$ (or $y = 3x - 12$) is 3 also. Because both lines have the same slope, either the lines are parallel or they coincide. Because the y-intercept of the graph of $y = 3x + 7$ is 7 and the y-intercept of the graph of $3x - y = 12$ is -12, the graphs cannot coincide. Because the lines are distinct and parallel, the system is inconsistent.

▪ EXERCISE 10.1

In Exercises 1–20, solve each system of equations by the graphing method. If a system is inconsistent or if the equations of a system are dependent, so indicate.

1. $\begin{cases} x + y = 6 \\ x - y = 2 \end{cases}$

2. $\begin{cases} x - y = 4 \\ 2x + y = 5 \end{cases}$

3. $\begin{cases} 2x + y = 1 \\ x - 2y = -7 \end{cases}$

4. $\begin{cases} 3x - y = -3 \\ 2x + y = -7 \end{cases}$

5. $\begin{cases} x = 13 - 4y \\ 3x = 4 + 2y \end{cases}$

6. $\begin{cases} 3x = 7 - 2y \\ 2x = 2 + 4y \end{cases}$

7. $\begin{cases} x = 3 - 2y \\ 2x + 4y - 6 = 0 \end{cases}$

8. $\begin{cases} 3x = 5 - 2y \\ 3x + 2y - 7 = 0 \end{cases}$

9. $\begin{cases} x = 5 \\ y = \dfrac{9 - x}{2} \end{cases}$

10. $\begin{cases} y = -2 \\ x = \dfrac{4 + 3y}{2} \end{cases}$

11. $\begin{cases} y = 5 \\ x = 2 \end{cases}$

12. $\begin{cases} 2x + 3y = -15 \\ 2x + y = -9 \end{cases}$

13. $\begin{cases} x = \dfrac{11 - 2y}{3} \\ y = \dfrac{11 - 6x}{4} \end{cases}$

14. $\begin{cases} x = \dfrac{1 - 3y}{4} \\ y = \dfrac{12 + 3x}{2} \end{cases}$

15. $\begin{cases} \dfrac{5}{2}x + y = \dfrac{1}{2} \\ 2x - \dfrac{3}{2}y = 5 \end{cases}$

16. $\begin{cases} \dfrac{5}{2}x + 3y = 6 \\ y = \dfrac{24 - 10x}{12} \end{cases}$

17. $\begin{cases} x = \dfrac{5y-4}{2} \\ x - \dfrac{5}{3}y + \dfrac{1}{3} = 0 \end{cases}$ **18.** $\begin{cases} 2x = 5y - 11 \\ 3x = 2y \end{cases}$ **19.** $\begin{cases} x = -\dfrac{3}{2}y \\ x = \dfrac{3}{2}y - 2 \end{cases}$ **20.** $\begin{cases} x = \dfrac{3y-1}{4} \\ y = \dfrac{4-8x}{3} \end{cases}$

21.   Form an independent system of equations with the simultaneous solution $(-5, 2)$.

22.   Form a dependent system of equations with one possible solution of $(-5, 2)$.

10.2   SOLUTION BY SUBSTITUTION AND ADDITION

The graphing method provides a nice way to visualize the process of solving systems of equations. However, it has two major deficiencies: The method gives exact answers only if the lines in a graph happen to intersect exactly at a point whose coordinates can be read accurately from the graph, and the method cannot be used to solve systems of higher order, such as three equations, each with three variables.

In this section, we will discuss two algebraic methods of solving systems of two equations in two variables. We begin with the **substitution method**.

Example 1   Use the substitution method to solve the system $\begin{cases} 4x + y = 13 \\ -2x + 3y = -17 \end{cases}$.

Solution   There is a two-part strategy to the substitution method. First, solve one of the equations for one of its variables. Second, substitute that quantity for the same variable in the other equation. In this example, it is most convenient to solve the first equation for y, because y has a coefficient of 1 and no fractions are introduced. Then substitute that value of y for y in the second equation and thereby get one equation with one variable:

$$\begin{cases} 4x + y = 13 \Rightarrow y = \boxed{-4x + 13} \\ -2x + 3y = -17 \end{cases}$$

$$-2x + 3(-4x + 13) = -17$$

Solve this new equation for x as follows:

$$-2x + 3(-4x + 13) = -17$$
$$-2x - 12x + 39 = -17 \qquad \text{Remove parentheses.}$$
$$-14x = -56 \qquad \text{Combine terms and add } -39 \text{ to both sides.}$$
$$x = 4 \qquad \text{Divide both sides by } -14.$$

To find y, substitute 4 for x in the equation $y = -4x + 13$ and simplify:

$$y = -4x + 13$$
$$= -4(4) + 13$$
$$= -3$$

The solution to this system is $x = 4$ and $y = -3$, or just $(4, -3)$. Verify that this solution satisfies each equation in the given system.   ■

Example 2   Use the substitution method to solve the system $\begin{cases} \dfrac{4}{3}x + \dfrac{1}{2}y = -\dfrac{2}{3} \\ \dfrac{1}{2}x + \dfrac{2}{3}y = \dfrac{5}{3} \end{cases}$.

Solution   First, find an equivalent system (one with the same solution) that has no fractions. Do this by multiplying each side of each equation by 6 to obtain the system

$$\begin{cases} 8x + 3y = -4 \\ 3x + 4y = 10 \end{cases}$$

Because no variable has a coefficient of 1, it is impossible to avoid fractions when solving either equation for a variable. For sake of argument, solve the second equation for x, and substitute for x in the first equation:

$$\begin{cases} 8x + 3y = -4 \\ 3x + 4y = 10 \end{cases} \Rightarrow x = \boxed{\dfrac{10 - 4y}{3}}$$

$$8\left(\frac{10 - 4y}{3}\right) + 3y = -4$$

$$\frac{8}{3}(10 - 4y) + 3y = -4$$

Clear this equation of fractions by multiplying each side by 3, and then solve for y:

$$8(10 - 4y) + 9y = -12$$
$$80 - 32y + 9y = -12 \qquad \text{Remove parentheses.}$$
$$-23y = -92 \qquad \text{Combine terms and add } -80 \text{ to both sides.}$$
$$y = 4 \qquad \text{Divide both sides by } -23.$$

Find x by substituting 4 for y in the equation $x = \dfrac{10 - 4y}{3}$ and simplifying:

$$x = \frac{10 - 4y}{3}$$
$$= \frac{10 - 4(4)}{3}$$
$$= \frac{-6}{3}$$
$$= -2$$

The solution to this system is the pair $(-2, 4)$. Verify that this solution satisfies each equation in the original system. ∎

We now consider a second algebraic method of solving systems of equations, called **solution by addition**.

Example 3   Use the addition method to solve the system $\begin{cases} 4x + y = 13 \\ -2x + 3y = -17 \end{cases}$.

Solution   Note that this system is repeated from Example 1. The strategy of the addition method is to adjust the equations so that, if you add their left-hand sides and add their right-hand sides, one of the variables drops out. It is then possible to solve for the remaining variable. In this example, it is convenient to multiply the second equation by 2 to obtain the system

$$\begin{cases} 4x + y = 13 \\ -4x + 6y = -34 \end{cases}$$

When these equations are added, the terms involving x drop out, and you get

$$7y = -21$$
$$y = -3 \qquad \text{Divide both sides by 7.}$$

To solve for x, get the terms involving y to drop out by multiplying the first equation of the original system by -3. This gives the system

$$\begin{cases} -12x - 3y = -39 \\ -2x + 3y = -17 \end{cases}$$

When these equations are added, the terms involving y drop out, and you get

$$-14x = -56$$
$$x = 4 \qquad \text{Divide both sides by } -14.$$

The solution to this system is $x = 4$ and $y = -3$, or just $(4, -3)$. You have already verified, in Example 1, that this solution satisfies each of the original equations. ∎

Example 4   Use the addition method to solve the system $\begin{cases} \dfrac{4}{3}x + \dfrac{1}{2}y = -\dfrac{2}{3} \\ \dfrac{1}{2}x + \dfrac{2}{3}y = \dfrac{5}{3} \end{cases}$.

Solution   Note that this system is repeated from Example 2. As in that example, begin by finding an equivalent system that has no fractions. Again, multiply each side of each equation by 6 to obtain the system

$$\begin{array}{ll} \textbf{1.} & \begin{cases} 8x + 3y = -4 \\ 3x + 4y = 10 \end{cases} \\ \textbf{2.} & \end{array}$$

To solve for x, get the terms involving y to drop out by multiplying each side of Equation 1 by 4, and each side of Equation 2 by -3. This produces the system

$$\begin{cases} 32x + 12y = -16 \\ -9x - 12y = -30 \end{cases}$$

When these equations are added, the terms involving y drop out, and you get

$$23x = -46$$
$$x = -2 \qquad \text{Divide both sides by 23.}$$

To solve for y, you could get the terms involving x to drop out by multiplying each side of Equation 1 by 3, and each side of Equation 2 by -8 and adding the equations. However, it is easier to substitute -2 for x in either Equation 1 or Equation 2 and solve for y. For sake of argument, substitute -2 for x in Equation 2 and solve for y:

$$3x + 4y = 10$$
$$3(-2) + 4y = 10$$
$$-6 + 4y = 10 \qquad \text{Simplify.}$$
$$4y = 16 \qquad \text{Add 6 to both sides.}$$
$$y = 4 \qquad \text{Divide both sides by 4.}$$

The solution to this system is $(-2, 4)$. You verified that this pair of values satisfied each of the equations in the given system in Example 2.   ■

Example 5   Solve the system $\begin{cases} y = 2x + 4 \\ 8x - 4y = 7 \end{cases}$.

Solution   Because the first equation in this system is already solved for y, use the substitution method and substitute $2x + 4$ for y in the second equation:

$$\begin{cases} y = \boxed{2x + 4} \\ 8x - 4y = 7 \end{cases}$$

$$8x - 4(2x + 4) = 7$$

Solve this equation as follows:

$$8x - 8x - 16 = 7 \qquad \text{Remove parentheses.}$$
$$-16 \neq 7 \qquad \text{Combine terms.}$$

Of course, -16 is not equal to 7. This impossible result indicates that the equations in the given system are independent and that the system is inconsistent. If each equation in this system were graphed, the lines would be parallel. There is no solution to this system.   ■

Example 6   Solve the system $\begin{cases} 4x + 6y = 12 \\ -2x - 3y = -6 \end{cases}$.

Solution   Use the addition method. Multiply each side of the second equation by 2 to get the system

$$\begin{cases} 4x + 6y = 12 \\ -4x - 6y = -12 \end{cases}$$

Add the left-hand sides and the right-hand sides of these equations to obtain the equation

$$0x + 0y = 0$$

In this case, both the x and y terms drop out. However, the statement $0 = 0$ is true. This indicates that the equations in this system are dependent and that the system is consistent. Note that the equations are equivalent because, when the second equation is multiplied by -2, it becomes the first equation. If both equations in this system were graphed, the two lines would coincide. Any ordered pair that satisfies one of the equations in the system satisfies the other also.   ∎

Example 7   Hi-Fi Electronics sells two models of CB radios. One model sells for $67 and the other for $100. In one week, 36 radios were sold. If the receipts from the sale of the radios totaled $2940, how many of each model were sold?

Solution   Let x represent the number of radios sold for $67, and let y represent the number of radios sold for $100. Then the receipts for the sale of the less expensive model were $67x$, and the receipts for the sale of the more expensive model were $100y$. The information in the problem gives the following two equations:

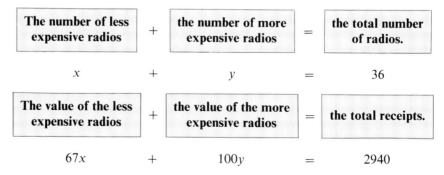

Now solve the following system of equations for x and y to find out how many of each model were sold:

$$\begin{cases} x + y = 36 \\ 67x + 100y = 2940 \end{cases}$$

Multiply both sides of the first equation by -100, add the resulting equation to the second equation, and solve for x:

$$-100x - 100y = -3600$$
$$\underline{67x + 100y = 2940}$$
$$-33x = -660$$
$$x = 20 \qquad \text{Divide both sides by } -33.$$

To find y, substitute **20** for x in the equation $x + y = 36$, and solve for y:

$$x + y = 36$$
$$\mathbf{20} + y = 36$$
$$y = 16 \qquad \text{Add } -20 \text{ to both sides.}$$

Twenty of the less expensive and 16 of the more expensive radios were sold.

Check: Note that if 20 of one model were sold and 16 of the other model were sold, then a total of 36 radios were sold. Also note that, because the value of the less expensive radios is $20(\$67) = \$1340$ and the value of the more expensive radios is $16(\$100) = \$1600$, the total value is $2940. ▪

Example 8 How many ounces of a 10% saline solution and how many ounces of a 20% saline solution must be mixed together to obtain 50 ounces of a 15% saline solution?

Solution Let x represent the number of ounces of the 10% solution, and let y represent the number of ounces of the 20% solution that are to be mixed. The information given in the problem gives the following two equations:

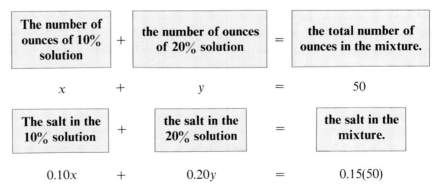

Thus, solve the following system of equations for x and y to find how many ounces of each are needed:

$$\begin{cases} x + y = 50 \\ 0.10x + 0.20y = 0.15(50) \end{cases}$$

Multiply the second equation by 100 to eliminate the decimal fractions, and solve the resulting system as follows:

$$\begin{cases} x + y = 50 \\ 10x + 20y = 15(50) \end{cases} \Rightarrow \quad y = \boxed{50 - x}$$

$$10x + 20(50 - x) = 750$$
$$10x + 1000 - 20x = 750 \qquad \text{Remove parentheses.}$$
$$-10x + 1000 = 750 \qquad \text{Combine terms.}$$
$$-10x = -250 \qquad \text{Add } -1000 \text{ to both sides.}$$
$$x = 25 \qquad \text{Divide both sides by } -10.$$

Because $y = 50 - x$ and $x = 25$, it follows that

$$y = 50 - x$$
$$= 50 - 25$$
$$= 25$$

To obtain 50 ounces of a 15% solution, you must mix 25 ounces each of the 10% and 20% solutions. ∎

■ EXERCISE 10.2

In Exercises 1–10, solve each system of equations by the substitution method, if possible. If a system is inconsistent, or if the equations are dependent, so indicate.

1. $\begin{cases} y = x \\ x + y = 4 \end{cases}$ **2.** $\begin{cases} y = x + 2 \\ x + 2y = 16 \end{cases}$ **3.** $\begin{cases} x - y = 2 \\ 2x + y = 13 \end{cases}$ **4.** $\begin{cases} x - y = -4 \\ 3x - 2y = -5 \end{cases}$

5. $\begin{cases} x + 2y = 6 \\ 3x - y = -10 \end{cases}$ **6.** $\begin{cases} 2x - y = -21 \\ 4x + 5y = 7 \end{cases}$ **7.** $\begin{cases} 3x = 2y - 4 \\ 6x - 4y = -4 \end{cases}$ **8.** $\begin{cases} 8x = 4y + 10 \\ 4x - 2y - 5 = 0 \end{cases}$

9. $\begin{cases} 3x - 4y = 9 \\ x + 2y = 8 \end{cases}$ **10.** $\begin{cases} 3x - 2y = -10 \\ 6x + 5y = 25 \end{cases}$

In Exercises 11–20, solve each system of equations by the addition method. If a system is inconsistent, or if the equations are dependent, so indicate.

11. $\begin{cases} x - y = 3 \\ x + y = 7 \end{cases}$ **12.** $\begin{cases} x + y = 1 \\ x - y = 7 \end{cases}$ **13.** $\begin{cases} 2x + y = -10 \\ 2x - y = -6 \end{cases}$ **14.** $\begin{cases} x + 2y = -9 \\ x - 2y = -1 \end{cases}$

15. $\begin{cases} 2x + 3y = 8 \\ 3x - 2y = -1 \end{cases}$ **16.** $\begin{cases} 5x - 2y = 19 \\ 3x + 4y = 1 \end{cases}$ **17.** $\begin{cases} 4x + 9y = 8 \\ 2x - 6y = -3 \end{cases}$ **18.** $\begin{cases} 4x + 6y = 5 \\ 8x - 9y = 3 \end{cases}$

19. $\begin{cases} 8x - 4y = 16 \\ 2(x - 2) = y \end{cases}$ **20.** $\begin{cases} x = \dfrac{3}{2}y + 4 \\ 2x - 3y = 8 \end{cases}$

In Exercises 21–28, solve each system of equations by any method.

21. $\begin{cases} \dfrac{x}{2} + \dfrac{y}{2} = 6 \\ \dfrac{x}{2} - \dfrac{y}{2} = -2 \end{cases}$

22. $\begin{cases} \dfrac{x}{2} - \dfrac{y}{3} = -4 \\ \dfrac{x}{2} + \dfrac{y}{9} = 0 \end{cases}$

23. $\begin{cases} \dfrac{3}{4}x + \dfrac{2}{3}y = 7 \\ \dfrac{3}{5}x - \dfrac{1}{2}y = 18 \end{cases}$

24. $\begin{cases} \dfrac{2}{3}x - \dfrac{1}{4}y = -8 \\ \dfrac{1}{2}x - \dfrac{3}{8}y = -9 \end{cases}$

25. $\begin{cases} \dfrac{3x}{2} - \dfrac{2y}{3} = 0 \\ \dfrac{3x}{4} + \dfrac{4y}{3} = \dfrac{5}{2} \end{cases}$

26. $\begin{cases} \dfrac{3x}{5} + \dfrac{5y}{3} = 2 \\ \dfrac{6x}{5} - \dfrac{5y}{3} = 1 \end{cases}$

27. $\begin{cases} \dfrac{2}{5}x - \dfrac{1}{6}y = \dfrac{7}{10} \\ \dfrac{3}{4}x - \dfrac{2}{3}y = \dfrac{19}{8} \end{cases}$

28. $\begin{cases} \dfrac{5}{6}x + \dfrac{2}{3}y = \dfrac{7}{6} \\ \dfrac{10}{7}x - \dfrac{4}{9}y = \dfrac{17}{21} \end{cases}$

In Exercises 29–32, solve each system of equations for x and y. Consider solving for $\dfrac{1}{x}$ and $\dfrac{1}{y}$ first.

29. $\begin{cases} \dfrac{1}{x} + \dfrac{1}{y} = \dfrac{5}{6} \\ \dfrac{1}{x} - \dfrac{1}{y} = \dfrac{1}{6} \end{cases}$

30. $\begin{cases} \dfrac{1}{x} + \dfrac{1}{y} = \dfrac{9}{20} \\ \dfrac{1}{x} - \dfrac{1}{y} = \dfrac{1}{20} \end{cases}$

31. $\begin{cases} \dfrac{1}{x} + \dfrac{2}{y} = -1 \\ \dfrac{2}{x} - \dfrac{1}{y} = -7 \end{cases}$

32. $\begin{cases} \dfrac{3}{x} - \dfrac{2}{y} = -30 \\ \dfrac{2}{x} - \dfrac{3}{y} = -30 \end{cases}$

In Exercises 33–43, use two variables to solve each word problem.

33. The sum of two numbers is 49 and their difference is 7. Find the numbers.

34. The sum of the ages of two persons is 98 and the difference of their ages is 16. How old is each person?

35. The perimeter of a rectangle is 72 inches. Find the dimensions of the rectangle if twice the length added to three times the width is 88 inches.

36. A sporting goods salesperson sells 2 fishing reels and 5 rods for $270. The next day, the salesperson sells 4 reels and 2 rods for $220. How much does each cost?

37. In a certain right triangle, one acute angle is 15° greater than two times the other acute angle. Find the difference between the two acute angles.

38. Sam invested part of $8000 at 10% and the rest at 12% interest. His annual income from these investments was $900. How much did he invest at each rate?

39. How many ounces each of an 8% alcohol solution and a 15% alcohol solution must be mixed to obtain 100 ounces of a 12.2% solution?

40. How many pounds each of nuts that cost $2 per pound and $4 per pound must be mixed to obtain 60 pounds of nuts that are worth $3 per pound?

41. A car travels 50 miles in the same time that a plane travels 180 miles. The speed of the plane is 143 miles per hour faster than the speed of the car. Find the speed of the car.

42. In a certain two-digit number, the sum of the digits is 11. If the digits are reversed, the number is decreased by 45. What is the number? (*Hint:* Let t represent the tens digit and u the units digit. Then, $10t + u$ represents the number and $10u + t$ represents the number with its digits reversed.)

43. The manager of an apartment complex is also a tenant. He pays only three-quarters of the rent that each of the remaining 5 tenants pays. Each month, the landlord collects a total of $2070 from the 6 occupants. How much rent does the manager pay?

44. If $r_1 + r_2 = -b/a$, and if $r_1 r_2 = c/a$ $(a \neq 0)$, show that r_1 and r_2 are solutions of the quadratic equation $ax^2 + bx + c = 0$.

10.3   SOLUTION BY DETERMINANTS

We now discuss a fourth method of solving certain systems of two equations in two variables. This method, named after the 18th-century mathematician Gabriel Cramer, involves a special number called a **determinant**, which is associated with a square array of numbers.

Definition.   A **matrix** is any rectangular array of numbers.

The following rectangular arrays of numbers are examples of matrices:

$$A = \begin{bmatrix} 1 & 2 & 3 \\ 4 & 5 & 6 \end{bmatrix} \qquad B = \begin{bmatrix} 1 & 2 \\ 3 & 4 \\ 5 & 6 \end{bmatrix} \qquad C = \begin{bmatrix} 2 & 4 & 6 \\ 8 & 10 & 12 \\ 14 & 16 & 18 \end{bmatrix}$$

Because matrix A has two rows and three columns, it is called a 2 by 3 (read as "two by three" and denoted as 2×3) matrix. Matrix B is a 3×2 matrix, because the matrix has three rows and two columns. Matrix C is a 3×3 matrix (three rows and three columns). Any matrix that has the same number of rows as columns is called a **square matrix**. Thus, matrix C is an example of a square matrix.

There is a function, called the **determinant function**, that associates a numerical value with every square matrix. For any square matrix A, the symbol $\det(A)$ or the symbol $|A|$ represents the determinant of A.

Definition.   If a, b, c, and d are numbers, then the **determinant** of the square matrix $A = \begin{bmatrix} a & b \\ c & d \end{bmatrix}$ is

$$\det(A) = \begin{vmatrix} a & b \\ c & d \end{vmatrix} = ad - bc$$

Note that the determinant of a 2×2 matrix A is the *number* that is equal to the product of the entries on the major diagonal

$$\begin{vmatrix} a & b \\ c & d \end{vmatrix}$$

minus the product of the entries on the other diagonal

$$\begin{vmatrix} a & b \\ c & d \end{vmatrix}$$

Example 1   Find the values of the determinants associated with the matrices

a. $\begin{bmatrix} 3 & 2 \\ 6 & 9 \end{bmatrix}$,   **b.** $\begin{bmatrix} -2 & 7 \\ 8 & -5 \end{bmatrix}$, and   **c.** $\begin{bmatrix} -5 & \frac{1}{2} \\ -1 & 0 \end{bmatrix}$

Solution   **a.** $\det\left(\begin{bmatrix} 3 & 2 \\ 6 & 9 \end{bmatrix}\right) = \begin{vmatrix} 3 & 2 \\ 6 & 9 \end{vmatrix} = 3(9) - 2(6) = 27 - 12 = 15$

   b. $\det\left(\begin{bmatrix} -2 & 7 \\ 8 & -5 \end{bmatrix}\right) = \begin{vmatrix} -2 & 7 \\ 8 & -5 \end{vmatrix} = (-2)(-5) - 7(8)$

   $= 10 - 56 = -46$

   c. $\det\left(\begin{bmatrix} -5 & \frac{1}{2} \\ -1 & 0 \end{bmatrix}\right) = \begin{vmatrix} -5 & \frac{1}{2} \\ -1 & 0 \end{vmatrix} = -5(0) - \frac{1}{2}(-1) = 0 + \frac{1}{2} = \frac{1}{2}$ ∎

We now turn our attention to solving the general system of two equations in two variables. Consider the system

$$\begin{cases} ax + by = e \\ cx + dy = f \end{cases}$$

with variables x and y, and arbitrary constants a, b, c, d, e, and f. We will use the addition method to solve this system for x and y. We multiply each side of the first equation by d, each side of the second equation by $-b$, and add the equations to eliminate the variable y:

$$\begin{aligned} adx + bdy &= ed \\ -bcx - bdy &= -bf \\ \hline adx - bcx &= ed - bf \end{aligned}$$

We factor out the x on the left-hand side and divide each side by $ad - bc$ to solve for x:

$$(ad - bc)x = ed - bf$$

$$x = \frac{ed - bf}{ad - bc} \qquad \text{Provided that } ad - bc \neq 0$$

The value of y can be found in a similar manner. After eliminating the x variable, we get

$$y = \frac{af - ec}{ad - bc} \qquad \text{Provided that } ad - bc \neq 0$$

These formulas for x and y are not easy to remember because they involve so many quantities. However, determinants provide an easy way of remembering these formulas. Note that the denominator for the values of both x and y is

$$\begin{vmatrix} a & b \\ c & d \end{vmatrix} = ad - bc$$

The numerators can be expressed as determinants also:

$$x = \frac{ed - bf}{ad - bc} = \frac{\begin{vmatrix} e & b \\ f & d \end{vmatrix}}{\begin{vmatrix} a & b \\ c & d \end{vmatrix}} \qquad \text{and} \qquad y = \frac{af - ec}{ad - bc} = \frac{\begin{vmatrix} a & e \\ c & f \end{vmatrix}}{\begin{vmatrix} a & b \\ c & d \end{vmatrix}}$$

Compare these formulas with the original system of equations:

$$\begin{cases} ax + by = e \\ cx + dy = f \end{cases}$$

Note that, in the previous formulas for x and y, the denominator determinant is formed by using the coefficients a, b, c, and d of the variables in the equations. The numerator determinants are similar to the denominator determinant. However, the column of coefficients of the variable for which we are solving is replaced with the column of constants e and f. Thus, to form the numerator determinant used in solving for x, the coefficients of x (a and c) in the matrix $\begin{bmatrix} a & b \\ c & d \end{bmatrix}$ are replaced by the constants e and f. Similarly, when solving for y, the coefficients of y (b and d) are replaced by the constants e and f:

$$x = \frac{\begin{vmatrix} e & b \\ f & d \end{vmatrix}}{\begin{vmatrix} a & b \\ c & d \end{vmatrix}} \qquad y = \frac{\begin{vmatrix} a & e \\ c & f \end{vmatrix}}{\begin{vmatrix} a & b \\ c & d \end{vmatrix}}$$

Example 2   Solve the system $\begin{cases} 4x - 3y = 6 \\ -2x + 5y = 4 \end{cases}$ by using determinants.

Solution   The solution for x is the quotient of two determinants. The denominator determinant involves the matrix of the four coefficients of x and y. To solve for x, form a numerator determinant from that denominator determinant by replacing its first column (the coefficients of x) with the column of constants. The second column remains unchanged.

$$x = \frac{\begin{vmatrix} 6 & -3 \\ 4 & 5 \end{vmatrix}}{\begin{vmatrix} 4 & -3 \\ -2 & 5 \end{vmatrix}}$$

To solve for y, replace the second column (the coefficients of y) of the denominator determinant with the column of constants to form the numerator determinant. The first column remains unchanged.

$$y = \frac{\begin{vmatrix} 4 & 6 \\ -2 & 4 \end{vmatrix}}{\begin{vmatrix} 4 & -3 \\ -2 & 5 \end{vmatrix}}$$

There are three determinants to evaluate: $\begin{vmatrix} 4 & -3 \\ -2 & 5 \end{vmatrix}$, $\begin{vmatrix} 6 & -3 \\ 4 & 5 \end{vmatrix}$, and $\begin{vmatrix} 4 & 6 \\ -2 & 4 \end{vmatrix}$. Always begin by evaluating the denominator determinant because, if it is 0, the system is a special case and the other determinants might not have to be evaluated. If the determinant in the denominator equals 0, then either the equations are dependent (there are an infinite number of solutions) or the system is inconsistent (there are no solutions). Evaluate the denominator determinant as follows:

$$\begin{vmatrix} 4 & -3 \\ -2 & 5 \end{vmatrix} = 4(5) - (-3)(-2) = 20 - 6 = 14$$

Because the denominator determinant is not 0, the equations in this system are independent and the system is consistent. Evaluate the other two determinants to complete the solutions for x and y:

$$\begin{vmatrix} 6 & -3 \\ 4 & 5 \end{vmatrix} = 6(5) - (-3)(4) = 30 + 12 = 42$$

$$\begin{vmatrix} 4 & 6 \\ -2 & 4 \end{vmatrix} = 4(4) - 6(-2) = 16 + 12 = 28$$

Hence, you have

$$x = \frac{\begin{vmatrix} 6 & -3 \\ 4 & 5 \end{vmatrix}}{\begin{vmatrix} 4 & -3 \\ -2 & 5 \end{vmatrix}} = \frac{42}{14} = 3 \quad \text{and} \quad y = \frac{\begin{vmatrix} 4 & 6 \\ -2 & 4 \end{vmatrix}}{\begin{vmatrix} 4 & -3 \\ -2 & 5 \end{vmatrix}} = \frac{28}{14} = 2$$

The solution to this system is $(3, 2)$. Verify that $x = 3$ and $y = 2$ satisfy each equation in the given system.   ■

The method used in Example 2 is called **Cramer's Rule**.

Example 3   Use Cramer's Rule to solve the system $\begin{cases} 7x = 8 - 4y \\ 2y = 3 - \dfrac{7}{2}x \end{cases}$.

Solution   Multiply each side of the second equation by 2 to clear the fractions and rewrite the system in the form

$$\begin{cases} 7x + 4y = 8 \\ 7x + 4y = 6 \end{cases}$$

Because the two equations are different (independent) and because the determinant in the denominator is 0,

$$\begin{vmatrix} 7 & 4 \\ 7 & 4 \end{vmatrix} = 7(4) - 4(7) = 0$$

this system is inconsistent. It has no solutions.   ■

Cramer's Rule for Two Equations in Two Variables.
If the system

$$\begin{cases} ax + by = e \\ cx + dy = f \end{cases}$$

has a unique solution, it is given by

$$x = \frac{D_x}{D} \quad \text{and} \quad y = \frac{D_y}{D}$$

where

$$D = \begin{vmatrix} a & b \\ c & d \end{vmatrix}, \quad D_x = \begin{vmatrix} e & b \\ f & d \end{vmatrix}, \quad \text{and } D_y = \begin{vmatrix} a & e \\ c & f \end{vmatrix}.$$

If the denominators and the numerators of these fractions are *all* 0, the system is consistent, but the equations are dependent.

If the denominators are 0 and one of the numerators is *not* 0, the system is inconsistent.

■ EXERCISE 10.3

In Exercises 1–10, evaluate each determinant.

1. $\begin{vmatrix} 2 & 3 \\ -2 & 1 \end{vmatrix}$
2. $\begin{vmatrix} 3 & -2 \\ -2 & 4 \end{vmatrix}$
3. $\begin{vmatrix} -1 & 2 \\ 3 & -4 \end{vmatrix}$
4. $\begin{vmatrix} -1 & -2 \\ -3 & -4 \end{vmatrix}$

5. $\begin{vmatrix} x & y \\ y & x \end{vmatrix}$
6. $\begin{vmatrix} -x & 2 \\ x & 2 \end{vmatrix}$
7. $\begin{vmatrix} x & 2x \\ 3x & 4x \end{vmatrix}$
8. $\begin{vmatrix} x & y \\ x & y \end{vmatrix}$

9. $\begin{vmatrix} x+1 & x+1 \\ x+1 & x-1 \end{vmatrix}$
10. $\begin{vmatrix} x+y & x-y \\ x-y & x+y \end{vmatrix}$

In Exercises 11–24, use determinants to solve each system of equations for x and y, if possible. If a system is inconsistent or if the equations are dependent, so indicate.

11. $\begin{cases} x + y = 6 \\ x - y = 2 \end{cases}$
12. $\begin{cases} x - y = 4 \\ 2x + y = 5 \end{cases}$
13. $\begin{cases} 2x + y = 1 \\ x - 2y = -7 \end{cases}$
14. $\begin{cases} 3x - y = -3 \\ 2x + y = -7 \end{cases}$

15. $\begin{cases} 2x + 3y = 0 \\ 4x - 6y = -4 \end{cases}$
16. $\begin{cases} 4x - 3y = -1 \\ 8x + 3y = 4 \end{cases}$
17. $\begin{cases} y = \dfrac{-2x + 1}{3} \\ 3x - 2y = 8 \end{cases}$
18. $\begin{cases} 2x + 3y = -1 \\ x = \dfrac{y - 9}{4} \end{cases}$

19. $\begin{cases} y = \dfrac{11 - 3x}{2} \\ x = \dfrac{11 - 4y}{6} \end{cases}$
20. $\begin{cases} x = \dfrac{12 - 6y}{5} \\ y = \dfrac{24 - 10x}{12} \end{cases}$
21. $\begin{cases} x = \dfrac{5y - 4}{2} \\ y = \dfrac{3x - 1}{5} \end{cases}$
22. $\begin{cases} y = \dfrac{1 - 5x}{2} \\ x = \dfrac{3y + 10}{4} \end{cases}$

23. $\begin{cases} ax + y = k \\ x + dy = q \end{cases}$
24. $\begin{cases} rx + sy = t \\ x + ry = s \end{cases}$

In Exercises 25–28, evaluate each determinant and solve the resulting equation.

25. $\begin{vmatrix} x & 1 \\ 3 & 2 \end{vmatrix} = 1$

26. $\begin{vmatrix} x & -x \\ 2 & -3 \end{vmatrix} = -5$

27. $\begin{vmatrix} x & -2 \\ 3 & 1 \end{vmatrix} = \begin{vmatrix} 4 & 2 \\ x & 3 \end{vmatrix}$

28. $\begin{vmatrix} x & 3 \\ x & 2 \end{vmatrix} = \begin{vmatrix} 3 & 2 \\ 1 & 1 \end{vmatrix}$

10.4   SOLUTIONS OF THREE EQUATIONS IN THREE VARIABLES

We have previously shown that a solution to the system of equations

$$\begin{cases} ax + by = e \\ cx + dy = f \end{cases}$$

is an ordered pair of real numbers (x, y) that satisfies both of the given equations simultaneously. Likewise, a solution to the system

$$\begin{cases} ax + by + cz = j \\ dx + ey + fz = k \\ gx + hy + iz = l \end{cases}$$

is an ordered triple of numbers (x, y, z) that satisfies each of the three given equations simultaneously.

A linear equation in two variables has a graph that is a straight line. A system of two linear equations in two variables is consistent or inconsistent depending on whether a pair of lines intersect or are parallel.

The graph of an equation in three variables of the form $ax + by + cz = j$ is a flat surface called a **plane**. A system of three equations in three variables is consistent or inconsistent depending on how the three planes corresponding to the three equations intersect. The drawings in Figure 10-5 illustrate some of the possibilities.

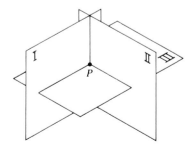

The three planes intersect at a
single point P:
One solution
(a)

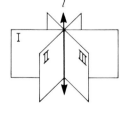

The three planes have a line l
in common:
An infinite number of solutions
(b)

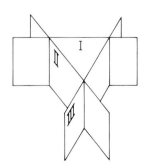

The three planes have no point in
common:
No solutions
(c)

Figure 10-5

Example 1 discusses a consistent system of three equations in three variables. Example 2 discusses a system that is inconsistent.

Example 1 Solve the system $\begin{cases} 2x + y + 4z = 12 \\ x + 2y + 2z = 9 \\ 3x - 3y - 2z = 1 \end{cases}$.

Solution You are given the following system of equations in three variables:

1. $\begin{cases} 2x + y + 4z = 12 \\ x + 2y + 2z = 9 \\ 3x - 3y - 2z = 1 \end{cases}$
2.
3.

Use the addition method to eliminate the variable z and, thereby, obtain a system of two equations in two variables. If Equations 2 and 3 are added, the variable z is eliminated:

2. $x + 2y + 2z = 9$
3. $3x - 3y - 2z = 1$
4. $\overline{4x - y \quad\quad = 10}$

Now pick a different pair of equations and eliminate the variable z again. If each side of Equation 3 is multiplied by 2 and the resulting equation is added to Equation 1, the variable z is eliminated again:

1. $2x + y + 4z = 12$
$\ 6x - 6y - 4z = 2$
5. $\overline{8x - 5y \quad\quad = 14}$

Equations 4 and 5 form a system of two equations in two variables:

4. $\begin{cases} 4x - y = 10 \\ 8x - 5y = 14 \end{cases}$
5.

To solve this system, multiply Equation 4 by -5, add the resulting equation to Equation 5 to eliminate the variable y, and solve for x:

$\ -20x + 5y = -50$
5. $\ 8x - 5y = 14$
$\overline{-12x \ = -36}$
$x = 3$ \quad\quad Divide both sides by -12.

To find the variable y, substitute 3 for x in an equation containing the variables x and y, such as Equation 5, and solve for y:

5. $8x - 5y = 14$
$8(3) - 5y = 14$
$24 - 5y = 14$ \quad\quad Simplify.
$-5y = -10$ \quad\quad Add -24 to both sides.
$y = 2$ \quad\quad Divide both sides by -5.

To find the variable z, substitute 3 for x and 2 for y in an equation containing the variables x, y, and z, such as Equation 1, and solve for z:

1. $2x + y + 4z = 12$

$2(3) + 2 + 4z = 12$

$8 + 4z = 12$ Simplify.

$4z = 4$ Add -8 to both sides.

$z = 1$ Divide both sides by 4.

The solution of this system is $(x, y, z) = (3, 2, 1)$. Verify that these values satisfy each of the equations in the system.   ■

Example 2   Solve the system $\begin{cases} 2x + y - 3z = -3 \\ 3x - 2y + 4z = 2 \\ 4x + 2y - 6z = -7 \end{cases}$.

Solution   You are given the following system of equations:

1. $\begin{cases} 2x + y - 3z = -3 \\ 3x - 2y + 4z = 2 \\ 4x + 2y - 6z = -7 \end{cases}$
2.
3.

Begin by multiplying Equation 1 by 2 and adding the resulting equation to Equation 2 to eliminate the variable y:

$\qquad 4x + 2y - 6z = -6$
2. $\underline{3x - 2y + 4z = \quad 2}$
4. $7x \qquad - 2z = -4$

Now add Equations 2 and 3 to eliminate the variable y again:

2. $3x - 2y + 4z = \quad 2$
3. $\underline{4x + 2y - 6z = -7}$
5. $7x \qquad - 2z = -5$

Equations 4 and 5 form the system

4. $\begin{cases} 7x - 2z = -4 \\ 7x - 2z = -5 \end{cases}$
5.

Because $7x - 2z$ cannot equal both -4 and -5, this system must be inconsistent. Thus, the original system has no solutions, either; it is inconsistent.   ■

Example 3   The sum of three integers is 2. The third integer is 2 greater than the second and 17 greater than the first. Find the three integers.

Solution   Let a, b, and c represent the three integers. Because their sum is 2, you know that

$a + b + c = 2$

Because the third integer is 2 greater than the second and 17 greater than the first, you know that

$$c - b = 2$$
$$c - a = 17$$

Put these three equations together to form a system of three equations in three variables:

1. $a + b + c = 2$
2. $ -b + c = 2$
3. $-a + c = 17$

Add Equations 1 and 2 to get Equation 4:

4. $a + 2c = 4$

Equations 3 and 4 form a system of two equations in two variables:

3. $-a + c = 17$
4. $a + 2c = 4$

Add Equations 3 and 4 to get the equation

$$3c = 21$$
$$c = 7$$

Substitute 7 for c in Equation 4 to find a:

4. $a + 2c = 4$
   $a + 2(7) = 4$
   $a + 14 = 4$ \quad Simplify.
   $a = -10$ \quad Add -14 to both sides.

Substitute 7 for c in Equation 2 to find b:

2. $-b + c = 2$
   $-b + 7 = 2$
   $-b = -5$ \quad Add -7 to both sides.
   $b = 5$ \quad Divide both sides by -1.

Thus, the three integers are -10, 5, and 7. Note that these three integers have a sum of 2, that 7 is 2 greater than 5, and that 7 is 17 greater than -10. ■

▪ EXERCISE 10.4

In Exercises 1–12, solve each system of equations. If a system of equations is inconsistent, or if the equations are dependent, so indicate.

1. $\begin{cases} x + y + z = 4 \\ 2x + y - z = 1 \\ 2x - 3y + z = 1 \end{cases}$

2. $\begin{cases} x + y + z = 4 \\ x - y + z = 2 \\ x - y - z = 0 \end{cases}$

3. $\begin{cases} 2x + 2y + 3z = 10 \\ 3x + y - z = 0 \\ x + 2z = 6 \end{cases}$

4. $\begin{cases} x - y + z = 4 \\ x + 2y - z = -1 \\ x + y - 3z = -2 \end{cases}$

5. $\begin{cases} x + y + 2z = 7 \\ x + 2y + z = 8 \\ 2x + y + z = 9 \end{cases}$

6. $\begin{cases} x + 2y + 2z = 10 \\ 2x + y + 2z = 9 \\ 2x + 2y + z = 11 \end{cases}$

7. $\begin{cases} 2x + y - z = 1 \\ x + 2y + 2z = 2 \\ 4x + 5y + 3z = 3 \end{cases}$

8. $\begin{cases} 4x + 3z = 4 \\ 2y - 6z = -1 \\ 8x + 4y + 3z = 9 \end{cases}$

9. $\begin{cases} 2x + 3y + 4z - 6 = 0 \\ 2x - 3y - 4z + 4 = 0 \\ 4x + 6y + 8z - 12 = 0 \end{cases}$

10. $\begin{cases} x - 3y + 4z - 2 = 0 \\ 2x + y + 2z - 3 = 0 \\ 4x - 5y + 10z - 7 = 0 \end{cases}$

11. $\begin{cases} x + \dfrac{1}{3}y + z = 13 \\ \dfrac{1}{2}x - y + \dfrac{1}{3}z = -2 \\ x + \dfrac{1}{2}y - \dfrac{1}{3}z = 2 \end{cases}$

12. $\begin{cases} x - \dfrac{1}{5}y - z = 9 \\ \dfrac{1}{4}x + \dfrac{1}{5}y - \dfrac{1}{2}z = 5 \\ 2x + y + \dfrac{1}{6}z = 12 \end{cases}$

In Exercises 13–22, solve each word problem.

13. The sum of three numbers is 18. The third number is four times the second, and the second number is 6 more than the first. Find the numbers.

14. The sum of three numbers is 48. If the first number is doubled, the sum is 60. If the second number is doubled, the sum is 63. Find the numbers.

15. Three numbers have a sum of 30. The third number is 8 less than the sum of the first and second, and the second number is half the sum of the first and third. Find the numbers.

16. The sum of the three angles in any triangle is $180°$. In triangle ABC, angle A is $100°$ less than the sum of angles B and C, and angle C is $40°$ less than twice angle B. Find each angle.

17. A collection of 17 nickels, dimes, and quarters has a value of $1.50. There are twice as many nickels as dimes. How many of each kind are there?

18. A unit of food contains 1 gram of fat, 1 gram of carbohydrate, and 2 grams of protein. A second contains 2 grams of fat, 1 gram of carbohydrate, and 1 gram of protein. A third contains 2 grams of fat, 1 gram of carbohydrate, and 2 grams of protein. How many units of each must be used to provide exactly 11 grams of fat, 6 grams of carbohydrate, and 10 grams of protein?

19. A factory manufactures three types of footballs at a monthly cost of $2425 for 1125 footballs. The manufacturing costs for the three types of footballs are $4, $3, and $2. These footballs sell for $16, $12, and $10, respectively. How many of each type are manufactured if the monthly profit is $9275? (*Hint:* Profit = income − cost)

20. A retailer purchased 105 radios from sources A, B, and C. Five fewer units were purchased from C than from A and B combined. If twice as many had been purchased from A, the total would have been 130. Find the number purchased from each source.

21. Tickets for a concert cost $5, $3, and $2. Twice as many $5 tickets were sold as $2 tickets. The receipts for 750 tickets were $2625. How many of each price ticket were sold?

22. The owner of a candy store wants to mix some peanuts worth $3 per pound, some cashews worth $9 per pound, and some brazil nuts worth $9 per pound to get 50 pounds of a mixture that will sell for $6 per pound. She used 15 fewer pounds of cashews than peanuts. How many pounds of each did she use?

10.5 SOLUTIONS OF THREE EQUATIONS IN THREE VARIABLES BY DETERMINANTS

The determinant of a 3×3 matrix may be defined so that Cramer's Rule can be used to solve many systems of three equations in three variables. Finding the value of the determinant of a 3×3 matrix requires a process known as **expanding a determinant by minors**.

> **Definition.** If a is the element in the ith row and the jth column of a 3×3 matrix, the **minor** of a is the determinant of the 2×2 matrix formed by those elements in the 3×3 matrix that do not lie in the ith row or the jth column.

Example 1 Find the minor of the element 3 in the matrix $\begin{bmatrix} 1 & 2 & 7 \\ 3 & 5 & 9 \\ -2 & -1 & 4 \end{bmatrix}$.

Solution The number 3 is in the 2nd row and the 1st column. The minor of 3 is the determinant of the 2×2 matrix formed by those elements that are not in the 2nd row and are not in the 1st column:

$$\begin{bmatrix} 1 & 2 & 7 \\ 3 & 5 & 9 \\ -2 & -1 & 4 \end{bmatrix}$$

The minor of 3 is $\det\left(\begin{bmatrix} 2 & 7 \\ -1 & 4 \end{bmatrix}\right)$ or $\begin{vmatrix} 2 & 7 \\ -1 & 4 \end{vmatrix}$. ■

Example 2 Find the minor of the element -7 in the matrix $\begin{bmatrix} 3 & -2 & 5 \\ 0 & -5 & 4 \\ 1 & -7 & 6 \end{bmatrix}$.

Solution Because -7 is in the 3rd row and the 2nd column, cross out the 3rd row and the 2nd column to find the minor of -7:

$$\begin{bmatrix} 3 & -2 & 5 \\ 0 & -5 & 4 \\ 1 & -7 & 6 \end{bmatrix}$$

The minor of -7 is the determinant of the remaining 2×2 matrix:

$$\begin{vmatrix} 3 & 5 \\ 0 & 4 \end{vmatrix}$$

■

Definition.   If a is an element in the ith row and jth column of a 3×3 matrix, then the **cofactor** of a is the minor of a if $i + j$ is even and the negative of the minor of a if $i + j$ is odd.

Example 3   Find the cofactor of   **a.** 3 and   **b.** 7   in the 3×3 matrix

$$\begin{bmatrix} 2 & 3 & 5 \\ 1 & 7 & 4 \\ 9 & -3 & 8 \end{bmatrix}$$

Solution   **a.**   The minor of the element 3 is the 2×2 determinant

$$\begin{vmatrix} 1 & 4 \\ 9 & 8 \end{vmatrix}$$

Because 3 is in the 1st row and 2nd column, and $1 + 2$ equals 3, which is odd, the cofactor of 3 is the negative of this minor. The cofactor of 3 is

$$-\begin{vmatrix} 1 & 4 \\ 9 & 8 \end{vmatrix}$$

b.   The minor of 7 is the 2×2 determinant

$$\begin{vmatrix} 2 & 5 \\ 9 & 8 \end{vmatrix}$$

Because 7 is in the 2nd row and the 2nd column, and $2 + 2$ equals 4, which is even, the cofactor of 7 is equal to its minor. The cofactor of 7 is

$$\begin{vmatrix} 2 & 5 \\ 9 & 8 \end{vmatrix}$$

■

We accept the following theorem without proof.

Theorem.   The value of the determinant of a 3×3 matrix is the sum of the products of each of the elements of any chosen row or column and the cofactors of those elements.

Example 4   Use the method of expanding by minors to evaluate the determinant

$$\begin{vmatrix} 1 & 3 & -2 \\ 2 & 1 & 3 \\ 1 & 2 & 3 \end{vmatrix}$$

Solution The method of expansion by minors works for expansion along any row or column. For sake of argument, expand along the second row with its elements of 2, 1, and 3. The cofactor of 2 is

$$-\begin{vmatrix} 3 & -2 \\ 2 & 3 \end{vmatrix}$$

The cofactor of 1 is

$$\begin{vmatrix} 1 & -2 \\ 1 & 3 \end{vmatrix}$$

The cofactor of 3 is

$$-\begin{vmatrix} 1 & 3 \\ 1 & 2 \end{vmatrix}$$

The value of the determinant is the sum of the products of these elements with their cofactors. Hence, you have

$$\begin{vmatrix} 1 & 3 & -2 \\ 2 & 1 & 3 \\ 1 & 2 & 3 \end{vmatrix} = 2\left(-\begin{vmatrix} 3 & -2 \\ 2 & 3 \end{vmatrix}\right) + 1\left(\begin{vmatrix} 1 & -2 \\ 1 & 3 \end{vmatrix}\right) + 3\left(-\begin{vmatrix} 1 & 3 \\ 1 & 2 \end{vmatrix}\right)$$

$$= -2\begin{vmatrix} 3 & -2 \\ 2 & 3 \end{vmatrix} + \begin{vmatrix} 1 & -2 \\ 1 & 3 \end{vmatrix} - 3\begin{vmatrix} 1 & 3 \\ 1 & 2 \end{vmatrix}$$

$$= -2(9 + 4) + (3 + 2) - 3(2 - 3)$$

$$= -26 + 5 + 3$$

$$= -18 \qquad \blacksquare$$

Example 5 Evaluate $\begin{vmatrix} 1 & 3 & -2 \\ 2 & 1 & 3 \\ 1 & 2 & 3 \end{vmatrix}$ by expanding the determinant by minors along the second column.

Solution The second column contains the elements 3, 1, and 2. The cofactor of 3 is

$$-\begin{vmatrix} 2 & 3 \\ 1 & 3 \end{vmatrix}$$

The cofactor of 1 is

$$\begin{vmatrix} 1 & -2 \\ 1 & 3 \end{vmatrix}$$

The cofactor of 2 is

$$-\begin{vmatrix} 1 & -2 \\ 2 & 3 \end{vmatrix}$$

The value of the determinant is the sum of the products of these elements with their cofactors. Hence, you have

$$\begin{vmatrix} 1 & 3 & -2 \\ 2 & 1 & 3 \\ 1 & 2 & 3 \end{vmatrix} = 3\left(-\begin{vmatrix} 2 & 3 \\ 1 & 3 \end{vmatrix}\right) + 1\left(\begin{vmatrix} 1 & -2 \\ 1 & 3 \end{vmatrix}\right) + 2\left(-\begin{vmatrix} 1 & -2 \\ 2 & 3 \end{vmatrix}\right)$$

$$= -3\begin{vmatrix} 2 & 3 \\ 1 & 3 \end{vmatrix} + \begin{vmatrix} 1 & -2 \\ 1 & 3 \end{vmatrix} - 2\begin{vmatrix} 1 & -2 \\ 2 & 3 \end{vmatrix}$$

$$= -3(6-3) + (3+2) - 2(3+4)$$

$$= -9 + 5 - 14$$

$$= -18$$

Note that the values obtained in Examples 4 and 5 are equal. This illustrates that either rows or columns can be used to expand determinants.

If a row or column of a determinant contains one or more 0s, it is a good idea to expand the determinant along that row or column. This will reduce the amount of arithmetic required because 0 times its cofactor is 0.

We can now solve a system of three equations in three variables by using determinants.

Example 6   Use Cramer's Rule to solve the system $\begin{cases} 2x + y + 4z = 12 \\ x + 2y + 2z = 9 \\ 3x - 3y - 2z = 1 \end{cases}$.

Solution   Follow the same procedure as for the 2×2 case: The denominator determinant is the determinant of the matrix formed by the coefficients of the variables, and the numerator determinants are formed by replacing the coefficients of the variable being solved for by the column of constants. Form the quotients for x, y, and z, and evaluate the determinants:

$$x = \frac{\begin{vmatrix} 12 & 1 & 4 \\ 9 & 2 & 2 \\ 1 & -3 & -2 \end{vmatrix}}{\begin{vmatrix} 2 & 1 & 4 \\ 1 & 2 & 2 \\ 3 & -3 & -2 \end{vmatrix}} = \frac{-72}{-24} = 3$$

$$y = \frac{\begin{vmatrix} 2 & 12 & 4 \\ 1 & 9 & 2 \\ 3 & 1 & -2 \end{vmatrix}}{\begin{vmatrix} 2 & 1 & 4 \\ 1 & 2 & 2 \\ 3 & -3 & -2 \end{vmatrix}} = \frac{-48}{-24} = 2$$

$$z = \frac{\begin{vmatrix} 2 & 1 & 12 \\ 1 & 2 & 9 \\ 3 & -3 & 1 \end{vmatrix}}{\begin{vmatrix} 2 & 1 & 4 \\ 1 & 2 & 2 \\ 3 & -3 & -2 \end{vmatrix}} = \frac{-24}{-24} = 1$$

The solution to this system is (3, 2, 1). ∎

Cramer's Rule for Three Equations in Three Variables.   If the system

$$\begin{cases} ax + by + cz = j \\ dx + ey + fz = k \\ gx + hy + iz = l \end{cases}$$

has a unique solution, it is given by

$$x = \frac{D_x}{D}, \quad y = \frac{D_y}{D}, \quad \text{and} \quad z = \frac{D_z}{D}$$

where

$$D = \begin{vmatrix} a & b & c \\ d & e & f \\ g & h & i \end{vmatrix}$$

and

$$D_x = \begin{vmatrix} j & b & c \\ k & e & f \\ l & h & i \end{vmatrix}, \quad D_y = \begin{vmatrix} a & j & c \\ d & k & f \\ g & l & i \end{vmatrix}, \quad D_z = \begin{vmatrix} a & b & j \\ d & e & k \\ g & h & l \end{vmatrix}$$

If the denominators and the numerators of these fractions are *all* 0, the system is consistent, but the equations are dependent.

If the denominators are 0 and at least one of the numerators is *not* 0, the system is inconsistent.

■ **EXERCISE 10.5**

In Exercises 1–10, evaluate each determinant by expanding the determinant by minors.

1. $\begin{vmatrix} 1 & 0 & 1 \\ 0 & 1 & 0 \\ 1 & 1 & 1 \end{vmatrix}$ **2.** $\begin{vmatrix} 1 & 2 & 0 \\ 0 & 1 & 2 \\ 0 & 0 & 1 \end{vmatrix}$ **3.** $\begin{vmatrix} -1 & 2 & 1 \\ 2 & 1 & -3 \\ 1 & 1 & 1 \end{vmatrix}$ **4.** $\begin{vmatrix} 1 & 2 & 3 \\ 1 & 2 & 3 \\ 1 & 2 & 3 \end{vmatrix}$

5. $\begin{vmatrix} 1 & -2 & 3 \\ -2 & 1 & 1 \\ -3 & -2 & 1 \end{vmatrix}$ **6.** $\begin{vmatrix} 1 & 1 & 2 \\ 2 & 1 & -2 \\ 3 & 1 & 3 \end{vmatrix}$ **7.** $\begin{vmatrix} 1 & 2 & 3 \\ 4 & 5 & 6 \\ 7 & 8 & 9 \end{vmatrix}$ **8.** $\begin{vmatrix} 1 & 4 & 7 \\ 2 & 5 & 8 \\ 3 & 6 & 9 \end{vmatrix}$

9. $\begin{vmatrix} a & 2a & -a \\ 2 & -1 & 3 \\ 1 & 2 & -3 \end{vmatrix}$ **10.** $\begin{vmatrix} 1 & 2b & -3 \\ 2 & -b & 2 \\ 1 & 3b & 1 \end{vmatrix}$

In Exercises 11–24, use Cramer's Rule to solve each system of equations. If Cramer's Rule fails, so indicate.

11. $\begin{cases} x + y + z = 4 \\ x + y - z = 0 \\ x - y + z = 2 \end{cases}$ **12.** $\begin{cases} x + y + z = 4 \\ x - y + z = 2 \\ x - y - z = 0 \end{cases}$

13. $\begin{cases} x + y + 2z = 7 \\ x + 2y + z = 8 \\ 2x + y + z = 9 \end{cases}$ **14.** $\begin{cases} x + 2y + 2z = 10 \\ 2x + y + 2z = 9 \\ 2x + 2y + z = 1 \end{cases}$

15. $\begin{cases} 2x + y - z = 1 \\ x + 2y + 2z = 2 \\ 4x + 5y + 3z = 3 \end{cases}$ **16.** $\begin{cases} 4x + 3z = 4 \\ 2y - 6z = -1 \\ 8x + 4y + 3z = 9 \end{cases}$

17. $\begin{cases} 2x + y + z = 5 \\ x - 2y + 3z = 10 \\ x + y - 4z = -3 \end{cases}$ **18.** $\begin{cases} 3x + 2y - z = -8 \\ 2x - y + 7z = 10 \\ 2x + 2y - 3z = -10 \end{cases}$

19. $\begin{cases} 2x + 3y + 4z - 6 = 0 \\ 2x - 3y - 4z + 4 = 0 \\ 4x + 6y + 8z - 12 = 0 \end{cases}$ **20.** $\begin{cases} x - 3y + 4z - 2 = 0 \\ 2x + y + 2z - 3 = 0 \\ 4x - 5y + 10z - 7 = 0 \end{cases}$

21. $\begin{cases} x + y = 1 \\ \dfrac{y}{2} + z = \dfrac{5}{2} \\ x - z = -3 \end{cases}$ **22.** $\begin{cases} 3x + 4y + 14z = 7 \\ -\dfrac{x}{2} - y + 2z = \dfrac{3}{2} \\ x + \dfrac{3}{2}y + \dfrac{5}{2}z = 1 \end{cases}$

23. $\begin{cases} 4z - y + 2x + 2 = 0 \\ 5x + 7z + 8y = -8 \\ 3y + x + z + 3 = 0 \end{cases}$ **24.** $\begin{cases} \dfrac{1}{2}x + y + z + \dfrac{3}{2} = 0 \\ x + \dfrac{1}{2}y + z - \dfrac{1}{2} = 0 \\ x + y + \dfrac{1}{2}z + \dfrac{1}{2} = 0 \end{cases}$

25. Show that $\begin{vmatrix} x & y & 1 \\ 2 & 3 & 1 \\ 4 & 5 & 1 \end{vmatrix} = 0$ represents the equation of a line passing through (2, 3) and (4, 5).

26. Show that $\begin{vmatrix} a & a & d \\ b & b & e \\ c & c & f \end{vmatrix} = 0.$

10.6 SOLUTION BY MATRICES

We can use matrices to solve systems of linear equations. We begin the discussion by considering the system of equations

$$\begin{cases} x - 2y - z = 6 \\ 2x + 2y - z = 1 \\ -x - y + 2z = 1 \end{cases}$$

This system of equations can be represented by the following matrix, called an **augmented matrix**:

$$\begin{bmatrix} 1 & -2 & -1 & \vdots & 6 \\ 2 & 2 & -1 & \vdots & 1 \\ -1 & -1 & 2 & \vdots & 1 \end{bmatrix}$$

The 3×3 matrix to the left of the dashed line, called the **coefficient matrix**, is determined by the coefficients of x, y, and z in the equations of the system. The 3×1 matrix to the right of the dashed line is determined by the constants in the equations of the system. Note that each row of the augmented matrix represents exactly one equation of the system:

$$\begin{bmatrix} 1 & -2 & -1 & \vdots & 6 \\ 2 & 2 & -1 & \vdots & 1 \\ -1 & -1 & 2 & \vdots & 1 \end{bmatrix} \begin{matrix} \leftrightarrow \\ \leftrightarrow \\ \leftrightarrow \end{matrix} \begin{cases} x - 2y - z = 6 \\ 2x + 2y - z = 1 \\ -x - y + 2z = 1 \end{cases}$$

To solve the given system we shall use a method called **Gaussian elimination**. The strategy is to transform the augmented matrix into the following form, called **triangular form**,

$$\begin{bmatrix} a & b & c & \vdots & d \\ 0 & e & f & \vdots & g \\ 0 & 0 & h & \vdots & i \end{bmatrix} \qquad a, b, c, \ldots, i \text{ are real numbers.}$$

by using three operations called **elementary row operations**.

Elementary Row Operations.
1. Any two rows of a matrix can be interchanged.
2. Any row of a matrix can be multiplied by a nonzero constant.
3. Any row of a matrix can be changed by adding to it a constant multiple of another row.

After we have written the matrix in triangular form, we can solve the corresponding system of equations by a substitution process. Note that a type 1 row operation corresponds to interchanging two equations of the system, a type 2 row operation corresponds to multiplying both sides of an equation by a nonzero constant, and a type 3 row operation corresponds to adding a multiple of one equation to another. None of these operations will change the solution of the given system of equations.

The first example shows how to solve the previous system of equations by matrix methods.

Example 1   Solve the system $\begin{cases} x - 2y - z = 6 \\ 2x + 2y - z = 1 \\ -x - y + 2z = 1 \end{cases}$.

Solution   First represent the system by an augmented matrix:

$$\left[\begin{array}{ccc|c} 1 & -2 & -1 & 6 \\ 2 & 2 & -1 & 1 \\ -1 & -1 & 2 & 1 \end{array}\right]$$

To get 0s under the **1** in the 1st column, use a type 3 row operation twice:

Multiply row 1 by -2 and add to row 2.   Multiply row 1 by 1 and add to row 3.

$$\left[\begin{array}{ccc|c} 1 & -2 & -1 & 6 \\ 2 & 2 & -1 & 1 \\ -1 & -1 & 2 & 1 \end{array}\right] \approx \left[\begin{array}{ccc|c} 1 & -2 & -1 & 6 \\ 0 & 6 & 1 & -11 \\ -1 & -1 & 2 & 1 \end{array}\right] \approx \left[\begin{array}{ccc|c} 1 & -2 & -1 & 6 \\ 0 & 6 & 1 & -11 \\ 0 & -3 & 1 & 7 \end{array}\right]$$

The symbol "$\approx$" is read as "is row equivalent to." Each of the above matrices represents a system of equations, and they are all equivalent.

To get a 0 under the -2 and **6** in the second column of the last matrix, use another type 3 row operation:

Multiply row 2 by $\frac{1}{2}$ and add to row 3.

$$\left[\begin{array}{ccc|c} 1 & -2 & -1 & 6 \\ 0 & 6 & 1 & -11 \\ 0 & -3 & 1 & 7 \end{array}\right] \approx \left[\begin{array}{ccc|c} 1 & -2 & -1 & 6 \\ 0 & 6 & 1 & -11 \\ 0 & 0 & \frac{3}{2} & \frac{3}{2} \end{array}\right]$$

Finally, use a type 2 row operation:

Multiply row 3 by $\frac{2}{3}$.

$$\left[\begin{array}{ccc|c} 1 & -2 & -1 & 6 \\ 0 & 6 & 1 & -11 \\ 0 & 0 & \frac{3}{2} & \frac{3}{2} \end{array}\right] \approx \left[\begin{array}{ccc|c} 1 & -2 & -1 & 6 \\ 0 & 6 & 1 & -11 \\ 0 & 0 & 1 & 1 \end{array}\right]$$

The final matrix represents the system of equations

1. $\begin{cases} x - 2y - z = 6 \\ 0x + 6y + z = -11 \\ 0x + 0y + z = 1 \end{cases}$
2.
3.

From Equation 3, you can read that $z = 1$. To find y, substitute 1 for z in Equation 2 and solve for y:

$$\begin{aligned} \textbf{2.} \quad 6y + z &= -11 \\ 6y + 1 &= -11 \\ 6y &= -12 \\ y &= -2 \end{aligned}$$

Thus, $y = -2$. To find x, substitute 1 for z and -2 for y in Equation 1 and solve for x:

$$\begin{aligned} \textbf{1.} \quad x - 2y - z &= 6 \\ x - 2(-2) - 1 &= 6 \\ x + 4 - 1 &= 6 \\ x + 3 &= 6 \\ x &= 3 \end{aligned}$$

Thus, $x = 3$. The solution to the given system is $(3, -2, 1)$. Verify that this triple satisfies each equation of the original system.   ■

We can use matrices to solve systems of equations that have more equations than variables.

Example 2   Solve the system $\begin{cases} x + y = -1 \\ 2x - y = 7 \\ -x + 2y = -8 \end{cases}$.

Solution   This system can be represented by a 3×3 augmented matrix:

$$\left[\begin{array}{rr|r} 1 & 1 & -1 \\ 2 & -1 & 7 \\ -1 & 2 & -8 \end{array}\right]$$

To get 0s under the 1 in the first column, perform a type 3 row operation twice:

Multiply row 1 by -2 and add to row 2.   Multiply row 1 by 1 and add to row 3.

$$\left[\begin{array}{rr|r} 1 & 1 & -1 \\ 2 & -1 & 7 \\ -1 & 2 & -8 \end{array}\right] \approx \left[\begin{array}{rr|r} 1 & 1 & -1 \\ 0 & -3 & 9 \\ -1 & 2 & -8 \end{array}\right] \approx \left[\begin{array}{rr|r} 1 & 1 & -1 \\ 0 & -3 & 9 \\ 0 & 3 & -9 \end{array}\right]$$

Perform other row operations to get

Multiply row 3 by 1   Interchange   Multiply row 2
and add to row 2.   row 2 and row 3.   by $\frac{1}{3}$.

$$\begin{bmatrix} 1 & 1 & | & -1 \\ 0 & -3 & | & 9 \\ 0 & 3 & | & -9 \end{bmatrix} \approx \begin{bmatrix} 1 & 1 & | & -1 \\ 0 & 0 & | & 0 \\ 0 & 3 & | & -9 \end{bmatrix} \approx \begin{bmatrix} 1 & 1 & | & -1 \\ 0 & 3 & | & -9 \\ 0 & 0 & | & 0 \end{bmatrix} \approx \begin{bmatrix} 1 & 1 & | & -1 \\ 0 & 1 & | & -3 \\ 0 & 0 & | & 0 \end{bmatrix}$$

The final matrix represents the system

$$\begin{cases} x + y = -1 \\ 0x + y = -3 \\ 0x + 0y = 0 \end{cases}$$

The third equation may be discarded because $0x + 0y = 0$ for all x and y. From the second equation, you can read that $y = -3$. To find x, substitute -3 for y in the first equation and solve for x:

$$x + y = -1$$
$$x - 3 = -1$$
$$x = 2$$

The solution to the original system is $(2, -3)$. Verify that this solution satisfies all three equations of the original system. ∎

If the last row of the final matrix of Example 2 had been of the form $0x + 0y = k$, where $k \neq 0$, the system could have no solution. No values of x and y could make the expression $0x + 0y$ equal to a nonzero constant.

Example 3 Solve the system $\begin{cases} x + y - 2z = -1 \\ 2x - y + z = -3 \end{cases}$.

Solution In this example, there are more variables than equations. The system can be represented by the 2×4 augmented matrix

$$\begin{bmatrix} 1 & 1 & -2 & | & -1 \\ 2 & -1 & 1 & | & -3 \end{bmatrix}$$

To get a 0 under the **1** in the first column, perform a type 3 row operation:

Multiply row 1 by -2
and add to row 2.

$$\begin{bmatrix} 1 & 1 & -2 & | & -1 \\ 2 & -1 & 1 & | & -3 \end{bmatrix} \approx \begin{bmatrix} 1 & 1 & -2 & | & -1 \\ 0 & -3 & 5 & | & -1 \end{bmatrix}$$

Then perform a type 2 row operation:

Multiply row 2 by $-\frac{1}{3}$.

$$\begin{bmatrix} 1 & 1 & -2 & | & -1 \\ 0 & -3 & 5 & | & -1 \end{bmatrix} \approx \begin{bmatrix} 1 & 1 & -2 & | & -1 \\ 0 & 1 & -\frac{5}{3} & | & \frac{1}{3} \end{bmatrix}$$

The final matrix represents the system

$$\begin{cases} x + y - 2z = -1 \\ \quad y - \dfrac{5}{3}z = \dfrac{1}{3} \end{cases}$$

Add $\frac{5}{3}z$ to both sides of the second equation to obtain

$$y = \frac{1}{3} + \frac{5}{3}z$$

Substitute $\dfrac{1}{3} + \dfrac{5}{3}z$ for y in the first equation and simplify to get

$$x + y - 2z = -1$$
$$x + \frac{1}{3} + \frac{5}{3}z - 2z = -1$$
$$x + \frac{1}{3} - \frac{1}{3}z = -1$$
$$x - \frac{1}{3}z = -\frac{4}{3}$$
$$x = -\frac{4}{3} + \frac{1}{3}z$$

A solution to this system must have the form

$$\left(-\frac{4}{3} + \frac{1}{3}z, \ \frac{1}{3} + \frac{5}{3}z, \ z \right)$$

for all values of z. Thus, if $z = 0$, then the corresponding solution is $(-\frac{4}{3}, \frac{1}{3}, 0)$. If $z = 1$, the corresponding solution is $(-1, 2, 1)$. Verify that both of these solutions satisfy each equation of the given system.

This system has an infinite number of solutions, a different one for each value of z. The equations of this system are dependent.   ■

We can use matrix methods to solve systems containing any number of equations involving any number of variables. In the next example, we solve a system of four equations in four variables.

Example 4   Solve the system $\begin{cases} w + \ \ x + 2y + \ \ z = \ \ 1 \\ 2w + 3x + 6y + \ \ z = \ \ 2 \\ w \qquad\ + 2y - \ \ z = -1 \\ w + \ \ x + 2y + 2z = \ \ 1 \end{cases}$.

Solution   Write the augmented matrix that represents the given system of equations, and use type 3 row operations to transform it into triangular form, as follows:

Multiply row 1 by -2
and add to row 2.

$$\begin{bmatrix} 1 & 1 & 2 & 1 & | & 1 \\ 2 & 3 & 6 & 1 & | & 2 \\ 1 & 0 & 2 & -1 & | & -1 \\ 1 & 1 & 2 & 2 & | & 1 \end{bmatrix} \approx \begin{bmatrix} 1 & 1 & 2 & 1 & | & 1 \\ 0 & 1 & 2 & -1 & | & 0 \\ 1 & 0 & 2 & -1 & | & -1 \\ 1 & 1 & 2 & 2 & | & 1 \end{bmatrix}$$

Multiply row 1 by -1 and
add to row 3 and to row 4.

$$\approx \begin{bmatrix} 1 & 1 & 2 & 1 & | & 1 \\ 0 & 1 & 2 & -1 & | & 0 \\ 0 & -1 & 0 & -2 & | & -2 \\ 0 & 0 & 0 & 1 & | & 0 \end{bmatrix}$$

Multiply row 2 by 1 and
add to row 3.

$$\approx \begin{bmatrix} 1 & 1 & 2 & 1 & | & 1 \\ 0 & 1 & 2 & -1 & | & 0 \\ 0 & 0 & 2 & -3 & | & -2 \\ 0 & 0 & 0 & 1 & | & 0 \end{bmatrix}$$

The final matrix represents the system of equations

1. $w + x + 2y + z = 1$
2. $x + 2y - z = 0$
3. $2y - 3z = -2$
4. $z = 0$

From equation 4, you can read that $z = 0$. To find y, substitute 0 for z in equation 3 and solve for y:

3. $2y - 3z = -2$
$2y - 3(0) = -2$
$2y = -2$
$y = -1$

Thus, $y = -1$. To find x, substitute 0 for z and -1 for y in equation 2 and solve for x:

2. $x + 2y - z = 0$
$x + 2(-1) - 0 = 0$
$x - 2 = 0$
$x = 2$

Thus, $x = 2$. To find w, substitute 0 for z, -1 for y, and 2 for x in equation 1 and solve for w:

1. $w + x + 2y + z = 1$

$w + 2 + 2(-1) + 0 = 1$

$w = 1$

Thus, $w = 1$. The solution to the given system is $(1, 2, -1, 0)$. Verify that the four values $w = 1$, $x = 2$, $y = -1$, and $z = 0$ satisfy each equation of the original system.   ∎

■ EXERCISE 10.6

In Exercises 1–12, use matrices to solve each system of equations. Each system has one solution.

1. $\begin{cases} x + y = 2 \\ x - y = 0 \end{cases}$

2. $\begin{cases} x + y = 3 \\ x - y = -1 \end{cases}$

3. $\begin{cases} x + 2y = -4 \\ 2x + y = 1 \end{cases}$

4. $\begin{cases} 2x - 3y = 16 \\ -4x + y = -22 \end{cases}$

5. $\begin{cases} 3x + 4z = -12 \\ 9x - 2z = 6 \end{cases}$

6. $\begin{cases} 5x - 4y = 10 \\ x - 7y = 2 \end{cases}$

7. $\begin{cases} x + y + z = 6 \\ x + 2y + z = 8 \\ x + y + 2z = 9 \end{cases}$

8. $\begin{cases} x - y + z = 2 \\ x + 2y - z = 6 \\ 2x - y - z = 3 \end{cases}$

9. $\begin{cases} 2x + y + 3z = 3 \\ -2x - y + z = 5 \\ 4x - 2y + 2z = 2 \end{cases}$

10. $\begin{cases} 3x + 2y + z = 8 \\ 6x - y + 2z = 16 \\ -9x + y - z = -20 \end{cases}$

11. $\begin{cases} 3x - 2y + 4z = 4 \\ x + y + z = 3 \\ 6x - 2y - 3z = 10 \end{cases}$

12. $\begin{cases} 2x + 3y - z = -8 \\ x - y - z = -2 \\ -4x + 3y + z = 6 \end{cases}$

In Exercises 13–18, use matrices to solve each system of equations. If a system has no solution, so indicate.

13. $\begin{cases} x + y = 3 \\ 3x - y = 1 \\ 2x + y = 4 \end{cases}$

14. $\begin{cases} x - y = -5 \\ 2x + 3y = 5 \\ x + y = 1 \end{cases}$

15. $\begin{cases} 2x - y = 4 \\ x + 3y = 2 \\ -x - 4y = -2 \end{cases}$

16. $\begin{cases} 3x - 2y = 5 \\ x + 2y = 7 \\ -3x - y = -11 \end{cases}$

17. $\begin{cases} 2x + y = 7 \\ x - y = 2 \\ -x + 3y = -2 \end{cases}$

18. $\begin{cases} 3x - y = 2 \\ -6x + 3y = 0 \\ -x + 2y = -4 \end{cases}$

In Exercises 19–22, use matrices to solve each system of equations. The equations of each system are dependent.

19. $\begin{cases} x + 2y + 3z = -2 \\ -x - y - 2z = 4 \end{cases}$

20. $\begin{cases} 2x - 4y + 3z = 6 \\ -4x + 6y + 4z = -6 \end{cases}$

21. $\begin{cases} x - y = 1 \\ y + z = 1 \\ x + z = 2 \end{cases}$

22. $\begin{cases} x + z = 1 \\ x + y = 2 \\ 2x + y + z = 3 \end{cases}$

In Exercises 23–28, use matrices to solve each system of equations. Each system has one solution.

23. $\begin{cases} w + x + y + z = 4 \\ \quad x - y + 2z = 3 \\ \quad x + 2y - z = 0 \\ \qquad\quad y + z = 3 \end{cases}$

24. $\begin{cases} w + x + y + z = 5 \\ w \qquad + 2y - z = -3 \\ \quad x + y + 2z = 8 \\ 2x \qquad + z = 7 \end{cases}$

25. $\begin{cases} w + 2x + y - z = 5 \\ w - x + 2y = 6 \\ 2w + x = -1 \\ \quad x - y + 2z = -3 \end{cases}$

26. $\begin{cases} 2w - x + y + z = 5 \\ w + 2x + y - z = 0 \\ w \qquad + z = 2 \\ w - x - y = 3 \end{cases}$

27. $\begin{cases} w + x + y + z = 5 \\ w + 2x - y + z = 2 \\ 2w - x + y - z = 2 \\ w - x + 2y - z = 3 \end{cases}$

28. $\begin{cases} w + x + y + z = 0 \\ w + x - y - z = -2 \\ w - x + y - z = 6 \\ 3w + x - y + 2z = -3 \end{cases}$

10.7   PARTIAL FRACTIONS

In this section we discuss how to express a complicated fraction as the sum of several simpler fractions. This process of decomposing a fraction into **partial fractions** is used in calculus. We begin by reviewing the process of adding fractions.

Example 1   Find the sum: $\dfrac{2}{x} + \dfrac{6}{x+1} + \dfrac{-1}{(x+1)^2}$.

Solution   Write each fraction in a form with the least common denominator, $x(x+1)^2$, and add:

$$\frac{2}{x} + \frac{6}{x+1} + \frac{-1}{(x+1)^2} = \frac{2(x+1)^2}{x(x+1)^2} + \frac{6x(x+1)}{(x+1)x(x+1)} + \frac{-1x}{(x+1)^2 x}$$

$$= \frac{2x^2 + 4x + 2 + 6x^2 + 6x - x}{x(x+1)^2}$$

$$= \frac{8x^2 + 9x + 2}{x(x+1)^2} \qquad\blacksquare$$

Example 2   Express the fraction $\dfrac{3x^2 - x + 1}{x(x-1)^2}$ as the sum of several fractions with denominators of the smallest degree possible.

Solution   Example 1 leads you to suspect that constants A, B, and C can be found such that

$$\frac{3x^2 - x + 1}{x(x-1)^2} = \frac{A}{x} + \frac{B}{x-1} + \frac{C}{(x-1)^2}$$

After you write the terms on the right side as fractions with the common denominator $x(x-1)^2$, combine them:

$$\frac{3x^2 - x + 1}{x(x - 1)^2} = \frac{A(x - 1)^2}{x(x - 1)^2} + \frac{Bx(x - 1)}{x(x - 1)(x - 1)} + \frac{Cx}{(x - 1)^2 x}$$

$$= \frac{Ax^2 - 2Ax + A + Bx^2 - Bx + Cx}{x(x - 1)^2}$$

$$= \frac{(A + B)x^2 + (-2A - B + C)x + A}{x(x - 1)^2}$$

Because the fractions are equal, the numerator $3x^2 - x + 1$ must equal the numerator $(A + B)x^2 + (-2A - B + C)x + A$. These quantities are equal provided their coefficients are equal. Thus,

$$\begin{cases} A + B & = & 3 \qquad \text{The coefficients of } x^2 \\ -2A - B + C & = & -1 \qquad \text{The coefficients of } x \\ A & = & 1 \qquad \text{The constants} \end{cases}$$

This system of three equations in three variables can be solved by substitution. The solutions are $A = 1$, $B = 2$, and $C = 3$. Hence,

$$\frac{3x^2 - x + 1}{x(x - 1)^2} = \frac{A}{x} + \frac{B}{x - 1} + \frac{C}{(x - 1)^2} = \frac{1}{x} + \frac{2}{x - 1} + \frac{3}{(x - 1)^2} \qquad \blacksquare$$

Example 3 Express the fraction $\dfrac{2x^2 + x + 1}{x^3 + x}$ as the sum of fractions with denominators of the smallest possible degree.

Solution Factoring the denominator suggests that this fraction can be expressed as the sum of two fractions, one with a denominator of x and the other with a denominator of $x^2 + 1$.

$$\frac{2x^2 + x + 1}{x(x^2 + 1)} = \frac{}{x} + \frac{}{x^2 + 1}$$

Because the denominator x of the first fraction is of first degree, its numerator must be of degree 0—that is, a constant. Because the denominator $x^2 + 1$ of the second fraction is of second degree, the numerator might be a first-degree polynomial or a constant. You can allow for both possibilities by using a numerator of $Bx + C$. If $B = 0$, then $Bx + C$ is a constant. If $B \neq 0$, then $Bx + C$ is a first-degree polynomial. Thus,

$$\frac{2x^2 + x + 1}{x(x^2 + 1)} = \frac{A}{x} + \frac{Bx + C}{x^2 + 1}$$

$$= \frac{A(x^2 + 1) + (Bx + C)x}{x(x^2 + 1)} \qquad \text{Add the fractions.}$$

$$= \frac{Ax^2 + A + Bx^2 + Cx}{x(x^2 + 1)} \qquad \text{Remove parentheses.}$$

$$= \frac{(A + B)x^2 + Cx + A}{x(x^2 + 1)} \qquad \text{Factor.}$$

Equate the corresponding coefficients of the polynomials $2x^2 + x + 1$ and $(A + B)x^2 + Cx + A$ to produce the following system of equations:

$$\begin{cases} A + B = 2 \\ \quad\;\; C = 1 \\ \quad\;\; A = 1 \end{cases}$$

The solutions are $A = 1$, $B = 1$, $C = 1$. Therefore, the given fraction can be written as a sum:

$$\frac{2x^2 + x + 1}{x^3 + x} = \frac{1}{x} + \frac{x + 1}{x^2 + 1}$$ ∎

The process illustrated in these examples can be summarized: Let $P(x)/Q(x)$ be the quotient of two polynomials with real coefficients, with the degree of $P(x)$ less than the degree of $Q(x)$. Suppose also that the fraction $P(x)/Q(x)$ has been simplified. The polynomial $Q(x)$ can always be factored as a product of first-degree and irreducible second-degree expressions.

If all the identical factors of $Q(x)$ are collected into single factors of the form $(ax + b)^n$ and the form $(ax^2 + bx + c)^n$, then the partial fractions required for the decomposition of $P(x)/Q(x)$ can be found. Each factor of $Q(x)$ of the form $(ax + b)^n$ generates a sum of n partial fractions of the form

$$\frac{A_1}{ax + b} + \frac{A_2}{(ax + b)^2} + \cdots + \frac{A_n}{(ax + b)^n}$$

where each A_i represents a constant. Each factor of the form $(ax^2 + bx + c)^n$ generates the sum of n fractions of the form

$$\frac{B_1 x + C_1}{ax^2 + bx + c} + \frac{B_2 x + C_2}{(ax^2 + bx + c)^2} + \cdots + \frac{B_n x + C_n}{(ax^2 + bx + c)^n}$$

where each B_i and C_i is a constant. After finding a least common denominator and adding the fractions, we obtain a fractional expression that must be equivalent to $P(x)/Q(x)$. Equating the corresponding coefficients of the numerators gives a system of linear equations that can be solved for the constants A_i, B_i, and C_i.

Example 4   What fractions should be used in the decomposition of the rational expression

$$\frac{3x^7 - 5x^5 + 3x + 2}{x^3(x - 3)(x + 2)^2(2x^2 + x + 3)^2(x^2 + 1)^3}$$

Solution   The factor x^3 in the denominator requires three possible fractions in the decomposition:

$$\frac{A}{x} + \frac{B}{x^2} + \frac{C}{x^3}$$

The factor $x - 3$ adds one more to the list:

$$\frac{A}{x} + \frac{B}{x^2} + \frac{C}{x^3} + \frac{D}{x - 3}$$

The factor $(x + 2)^2$ generates two more fractions, each with a constant as numerator:

$$\frac{A}{x} + \frac{B}{x^2} + \frac{C}{x^3} + \frac{D}{x - 3} + \frac{E}{x + 2} + \frac{F}{(x + 2)^2}$$

The factor $(2x^2 + x + 3)^2$ produces two more fractions, each requiring first-degree numerators:

$$\frac{A}{x} + \frac{B}{x^2} + \frac{C}{x^3} + \frac{D}{x - 3} + \frac{E}{x + 2} + \frac{F}{(x + 2)^2} + \frac{Gx + H}{2x^2 + x + 3} + \frac{Jx + K}{(2x^2 + x + 3)^2}$$

Finally, the factor $(x^2 + 1)^3$ requires three more fractions, also with first-degree numerators:

$$\frac{A}{x} + \frac{B}{x^2} + \frac{C}{x^3} + \frac{D}{x - 3} + \frac{E}{x + 2} + \frac{F}{(x + 2)^2} + \frac{Gx + H}{2x^2 + x + 3}$$
$$+ \frac{Jx + K}{(2x^2 + x + 3)^2} + \frac{Lx + M}{x^2 + 1} + \frac{Nx + P}{(x^2 + 1)^2} + \frac{Rx + S}{(x^2 + 1)^3}$$

If you find a common denominator and combine the fractions, equating the corresponding coefficients of the numerators will give 16 equations in 16 variables. These can be solved for the variables A, B, C, ..., S.   ■

Example 5   Express the fraction $\dfrac{x^2 + 4x + 2}{x^2 + x}$ as the sum of several fractions with denominators of the smallest degree possible.

Solution   The method of partial fractions requires that the degree of the numerator be less than the degree of the denominator. Because the degree of both the numerator and denominator are the same in this example, you must perform a long division and express the given fraction in $quotient + \dfrac{remainder}{divisor}$ form:

$$
\begin{array}{r}
1 \\
x^2 + x \overline{)\, x^2 + 4x + 2} \\
x^2 + x \\
\hline
3x + 2
\end{array}
$$

Hence,

$$\frac{x^2 + 4x + 2}{x^2 + x} = 1 + \frac{3x + 2}{x^2 + x}$$

Because the degree of the numerator of the fraction $\dfrac{3x + 2}{x^2 + x}$ is less than the degree of the denominator, you can find the partial fraction decomposition of this fraction:

$$\frac{3x + 2}{x^2 + x} = \frac{3x + 2}{x(x + 1)}$$

$$= \frac{A}{x} + \frac{B}{x + 1}$$

$$= \frac{A(x + 1) + Bx}{x(x + 1)}$$

$$= \frac{(A + B)x + A}{x(x + 1)}$$

Equate the corresponding coefficients in the numerator, and solve the resulting system of equations:

$$\begin{cases} A + B = 3 \\ \quad\ A = 2 \end{cases}$$

The solution is $A = 2$, $B = 1$, and the decomposition of the given fraction is

$$\frac{x^2 + 4x + 2}{x^2 + x} = 1 + \frac{2}{x} + \frac{1}{x + 1}$$

■

■ EXERCISE 10.7

In Exercises 1–24, decompose each expression into partial fractions.

1. $\dfrac{3x + 1}{(x + 1)(x - 1)}$

2. $\dfrac{-2x + 11}{x^2 - x - 6}$

3. $\dfrac{-3x^2 + x - 5}{(x + 1)(x^2 + 2)}$

4. $\dfrac{-x^2 - 3x - 5}{x^3 + x^2 + 2x + 2}$

5. $\dfrac{-2x^2 + x - 2}{x^3 - x^2}$

6. $\dfrac{2x^2 - 7x + 2}{x(x - 1)^2}$

7. $\dfrac{2x^2 + 1}{x^4 + x^2}$

8. $\dfrac{x^2 + x + 1}{x^3}$

9. $\dfrac{5x^2 + 2x + 2}{x^3 + x}$

10. $\dfrac{-2x^3 + 7x^2 + 6}{x^2(x^2 + 2)}$

11. $\dfrac{x^3 + 4x^2 + 2x + 1}{x^4 + x^3 + x^2}$

12. $\dfrac{x^3 + 4x^2 + 3x + 6}{(x^2 + 2)(x^2 + x + 2)}$

13. $\dfrac{x^3 + 3x^2 + 6x + 6}{(x^2 + x + 5)(x^2 + 1)}$

14. $\dfrac{x^2 - 2x - 3}{(x - 1)^3}$

15. $\dfrac{x^4 - x^3 + x^2 - x + 1}{x(x^2 + 1)^2}$

16. $\dfrac{x^2 + 2}{x^3 + 3x^2 + 3x + 1}$

17. $\dfrac{x^3 + 3x^2 + 2x + 4}{(x^2 + 1)(x^2 + x + 2)}$

18. $\dfrac{4x^3 + 5x^2 + 3x + 4}{x^2(x^2 + 1)}$

19. $\dfrac{2x^4 + 6x^3 + 20x^2 + 22x + 25}{x(x^2 + 2x + 5)^2}$

20. $\dfrac{3x^3 + 5x^2 + 3x + 1}{x^2(x^2 + x + 1)}$

21. $\dfrac{2x^3 + 6x^2 + 3x + 2}{x^3 + x^2}$

22. $\dfrac{x^3}{x^2 + 3x + 2}$

23. $\dfrac{x^4 + x^3 + x^2 + x + 1}{x^2}$

24. $\dfrac{x^3 + 2x^2 + 3x + 4}{x^3}$

10.8 SYSTEMS OF INEQUALITIES

In a previous section, we considered graphs of inequalities containing two variables. We now consider the graphs of systems of such inequalities.

Example 1   Graph the solution set of the system $\begin{cases} x + y \le 1 \\ 2x - y > 2 \end{cases}.$

Solution   On the same set of coordinate axes, graph each inequality. See Figure 10-6. The graph of the inequality $x + y \le 1$ includes the line graph of the equation $x + y = 1$ and all points below it. Because the boundary line is included, it is drawn as a solid line. The graph of the inequality $2x - y > 2$ contains only those points below the line graph of the equation $2x - y = 2$. Because the boundary line is not included, it is drawn as a broken line. The area that is shaded twice represents the simultaneous solutions of the given system of inequalities. Any point in the doubly shaded region has coordinates that satisfy both inequalities in the system.

$x + y = 1$			$2x - y = 2$	
x	y		x	y
0	1		0	-2
1	0		1	0

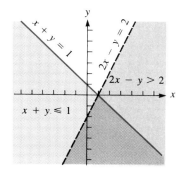

Figure 10-6

Example 2   Graph the solution set of the system $\begin{cases} y < x^2 \\ y > \dfrac{x^2}{4} - 2 \end{cases}.$

Solution   The graph of the equation $y = x^2$ is a parabola opening upward with vertex at the origin. See Figure 10-7. The points with coordinates that satisfy the inequality $y < x^2$ are those points below the parabola.

The graph of $y = x^2/4 - 2$ is a parabola opening upward with vertex at $(0, -2)$. However, this time the points with coordinates that satisfy the inequality are those points above the parabola. Thus, the graph of the solution set of this system is the shaded area between the two parabolas.

$$y = x^2 \qquad y = \frac{x^2}{4} - 2$$

x	y
0	0
1	1
-1	1
2	4
-2	4

x	y
0	-2
2	-1
-2	-1
4	2
-4	2

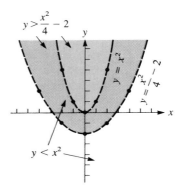

Figure 10-7

Example 3   Graph the solution set of the system $\begin{cases} x \geq 1 \\ y \geq x \\ 4x + 5y < 20 \end{cases}$

Solution   The graph of the solution set of the inequality $x \geq 1$ includes those points on the graph of the equation $x = 1$ and to the right. See Figure 10-8a. The graph of the solution set of the inequality $y \geq x$ includes those points on the graph of the equation $y = x$ and above it. See Figure 10-8b. The graph of the solution set of the inequality $4x + 5y < 20$ includes those points below the line graph of the equation $4x + 5y = 20$. See Figure 10-8c.

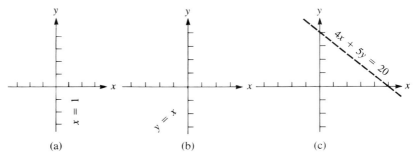

(a)   (b)   (c)

Figure 10-8

If these three graphs are merged onto a single set of coordinate axes, the graph of the original system of inequalities includes those points within the shaded triangle. together with the points on the sides of the triangle drawn as solid lines. See Figure 10-9.

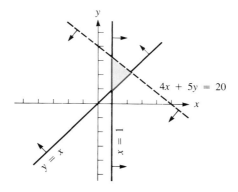

$4x + 5y = 20$

Figure 10-9

■

■ **EXERCISE 10.8**

Graph the solution set of each system of inequalities.

1. $\begin{cases} y < \ \ 3x + 2 \\ y < -2x + 3 \end{cases}$

2. $\begin{cases} y \le \ x - 2 \\ y \ge 2x + 1 \end{cases}$

3. $\begin{cases} 3x + 2y > 6 \\ \ x + 3y \le 2 \end{cases}$

4. $\begin{cases} x + y < 2 \\ x + y \le 1 \end{cases}$

5. $\begin{cases} 3x + \ y \le 1 \\ -x + 2y \ge 9 \end{cases}$

6. $\begin{cases} \ x + 2y < 3 \\ 2x + 4y < 8 \end{cases}$

7. $\begin{cases} 2x - y > 4 \\ y < -x^2 + 2 \end{cases}$

8. $\begin{cases} x \le y^2 \\ y \ge x \end{cases}$

9. $\begin{cases} y > \ \ x^2 - 4 \\ y < -x^2 + 4 \end{cases}$

10. $\begin{cases} x \ge y^2 \\ y \ge x^2 \end{cases}$

11. $\begin{cases} 2x + 3y \le 5 \\ 3x + \ y \le 1 \\ \ \ \ \ \ \ x \le 0 \end{cases}$

12. $\begin{cases} 2x + y \le 2 \\ \ \ \ \ \ y \ge x \\ \ \ \ \ \ x \ge 0 \end{cases}$

13. $\begin{cases} x - y < 4 \\ \ \ \ \ \ y \ge 0 \\ \ \ \ \ xy = 12 \end{cases}$

14. $\begin{cases} xy \le 1 \\ \ x \ge 0 \\ \ y \ge 0 \end{cases}$

15. $\begin{cases} \ \ \ \ \ \ \ x \ge 0 \\ \ \ \ \ \ \ \ y \ge 0 \\ 9x + 3y \le 18 \\ 3x + 6y \le 18 \end{cases}$

16. $\begin{cases} x + y \ge 1 \\ x - y \le 1 \\ x - y \ge 0 \\ \ \ \ \ \ x \le 2 \end{cases}$

10.9   LINEAR PROGRAMMING

Systems of inequalities provide the basis for an area of applied mathematics known as **linear programming**. Linear programming is used to help answer such questions as "How can a business make as much money as possible?" or "How can I plan a nutritious menu at the least cost?" In such problems, the solution depends on certain **constraints**: The business has limited resources, and the nutritious meal must contain sufficient vitamins, minerals, and so on. Any solution that satisfies the constraints is called a **feasible solution**. In linear programming, the constraints are expressed as a system of linear inequalities, and the quantity that is to be maximized (or minimized) is expressed as a linear function of several variables.

Example 1   Many ordered pairs (x, y) satisfy each inequality in the system

$$\begin{cases} x + y \geq 1 \\ x - y \leq 1 \\ x - y \geq 0 \\ \quad\quad x \leq 2 \end{cases}$$

If $Z = y - 2x$, which of these pairs will produce the greatest value of Z?

Solution   Find the solution of the given system of inequalities, and find the coordinates of each corner of region R, as shown in Figure 10-10. Then rewrite the equation

$$Z = y - 2x$$

in the equivalent form

$$y = 2x + Z$$

This is the equation of a straight line with slope of 2 and y-intercept of Z. Many such lines pass through the region R. To decide which of these provides the greatest value of Z, refer to Figure 10-11 and find the line with the greatest y-intercept. It is line l passing through point P, the left-most corner of R. The coordinates of P are $(\frac{1}{2}, \frac{1}{2})$. Thus, the greatest value of Z possible (subject to the given constraints) is

$$Z = \frac{1}{2} - 2\left(\frac{1}{2}\right) = -\frac{1}{2}$$

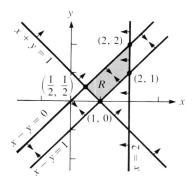

Figure 10-10

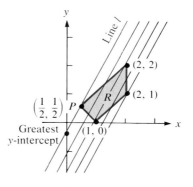

Figure 10-11   ■

Example 1 illustrates this fact:

*The maximum (or minimum) value of a linear function that is subject to the con-
straints of a system of linear inequalities in two variables is always attained at
a corner or along an entire edge of the region R that represents the solution of
the system.*

Example 2   Fred and Donna are in a part-time business manufacturing clock cases. Fred
must work 4 hours and Donna 2 hours to complete one case for a grandfather
clock. To build one case for a wall clock, Fred must work 3 hours and Donna
4 hours. Neither partner wishes to work more than 20 hours per week. If they
receive $80 for each grandfather clock and $64 for each wall clock, how many
of each should they build each week to maximize their profit?

Solution   If the partners manufacture cases for x grandfather clocks and y wall clocks
each week, their profit P (in dollars) is

$P =$	**The profit on one grandfather clock**	·	**the number of grandfather clocks**	+	**the profit on one wall clock**	·	**the number of wall clocks.**

$$P = 80x + 64y$$

The time requirements are summarized in the following chart:

Partner	Time for one grandfather clock	Time for one wall clock
Fred	4 hours	3 hours
Donna	2 hours	4 hours

The profit function is subject to the following constraints:

$$\begin{cases} x \geq 0 \\ y \geq 0 \\ 4x + 3y \leq 20 \\ 2x + 4y \leq 20 \end{cases}$$

The inequalities $x \geq 0$ and $y \geq 0$ state that the number of clock cases to be built cannot be negative. The inequality $4x + 3y \leq 20$ is a constraint on Fred's time because he spends 4 hours on each of the x grandfather clocks and 3 hours on each of the y wall clocks, and his total time cannot exceed 20 hours. Similarly, the inequality $2x + 4y \leq 20$ is a constraint on Donna's time.

Graph each of the constraints to find the **feasibility region R**, as in Figure 10-12. The four corners of region R have coordinates of $(0, 0)$, $(0, 5)$, $(2, 4)$, and $(5, 0)$. Substitute each of these number pairs into the equation $P = 80x + 64y$ to find the maximum profit, P.

Corner	Profit
$(0, 0)$	$P = \$80(0) + \$64(0) = \$0$
$(0, 5)$	$P = \$80(0) + \$64(5) = \$320$
$(2, 4)$	$P = \$80(2) + \$64(4) = \$416$
$(5, 0)$	$P = \$80(5) + \$64(0) = \$400$

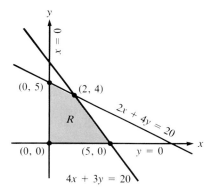

Figure 10-12

Donna and Fred will maximize their profits if they build cases for 2 grandfather clocks and 4 wall clocks each week. If they do so, they will earn $416. ■

■ EXERCISE 10.9

In Exercises 1–6, maximize P subject to the given constraints.

1. $P = 2x + 3y$

$$\begin{cases} x \geq 0 \\ y \geq 0 \\ x + y \leq 4 \end{cases}$$

2. $P = 3x + 2y$

$$\begin{cases} x \geq 0 \\ y \geq 0 \\ x + y \leq 4 \end{cases}$$

3. $P = y + \dfrac{1}{2}x$

$$\begin{cases} 2y - x \leq 1 \\ y - 2x \geq -2 \\ x \geq 0 \\ y \geq 0 \end{cases}$$

4. $P = 4y - x$

$$\begin{cases} 2y - x \leq 1 \\ x \leq 2 \\ x + y \geq 1 \\ y \geq 0 \end{cases}$$

5. $P = 2x + y$

$$\begin{cases} y - x \le 2 \\ 2x + 3y \le 6 \\ 3x + y \le 3 \\ y \ge 0 \end{cases}$$

6. $P = 3x - 2y$

$$\begin{cases} y - x \le 1 \\ x - y \le 1 \\ x \ge -1 \\ x \le 1 \end{cases}$$

7.   Sally and Sandra each have 12 hours a week to make furniture. They obtain a $50 profit from each table and a $10 profit from each chair. Sally must work 3 hours and Sandra 2 to make a chair. Sally must work 2 hours and Sandra 6 to make a table. How many tables and how many chairs should they make each week to maximize profits?

8.   Two machines, A and B, work 24 hours a day to manufacture chewing gum and bubble gum. There is a profit of $150 per case of chewing gum and $100 per case of bubble gum. To make a case of chewing gum, machine A must run 2 hours and machine B must run 8 hours. To make a case of bubble gum, machine A must run 4 hours and machine B must run 2 hours. How many cases of each should be produced each week to maximize profits?

9.   Sarah and her sister Heidi have decided to plant a garden. Sarah wants to plant strawberries; Heidi wants to plant pumpkins. Neither crop may use more than $\frac{3}{4}$ of the 40 square meters of available space. Each square meter of strawberries will earn the children $4, and each square meter of pumpkins will earn the children $3. The children plan to eat half of the strawberries themselves. How should the planting be divided to maximize the total income?

10.   A distributor of hybrid corn has two storehouses, A and B. At A is stored 110 tons of corn; 190 tons are stored at B. Farmer X ordered 60 tons, and farmer Y ordered 80 tons. The shipping costs appear in the following table:

Storehouse	Farmer	Costs per ton
A	X	$5
A	Y	$7
B	X	$8
B	Y	$14

How should the orders be filled to minimize the shipping costs? (*Hint:*   Let x represent the number of tons shipped from A to X, and let y represent the number of tons shipped from A to Y.)

11.   Bill packs two foods for his camping trip. One ounce of food X costs 35¢ and provides 150 calories and 21 units of vitamins. One ounce of food Y costs 27¢ and provides 60 calories and 42 units of vitamins. Every day, Bill needs at least 3000 calories and at least 1260 units of vitamins, but he does not want to carry more than 60 ounces of food for each day of his trip. How much of each food should Bill pack to minimize the cost?

12.   To manufacture two products X and Y, three workers are scheduled as follows:

Worker	Hours required for product X	Hours required for product Y	Time available per week
A	1	4	18
B	2	3	12
C	2	1	6

(*continued on next page*)

The profit on product X is \$40, and on product Y, \$60. How many of each product should be produced to maximize the profit?

CHAPTER SUMMARY

Key Words

augmented matrix   (10.6)
coefficient matrix   (10.6)
cofactor   (10.5)
consistent system of equations
    (10.1)
Cramer's Rule   (10.3, 10.5)
dependent equations   (10.1)
determinant   (10.3)
determinant function   (10.3)
elementary row operations   (10.6)
Gaussian elimination   (10.6)

inconsistent system of equations
    (10.1)
independent equations   (10.1)
linear programming   (10.9)
matrix   (10.3, 10.6)
minor   (10.5)
partial fractions   (10.7)
square matrix   (10.3)
system of equations   (10.1)
triangular form of a matrix   (10.6)

Key Ideas

(10.1)   Systems of two linear equations in two variables can be solved by graphing.

If a system of equations has at least one solution, the system is a **consistent system**. Otherwise, it is an **inconsistent system**.

If the graphs of the equations of a system are distinct, the equations of the system are **independent equations**. Otherwise, they are **dependent equations**.

(10.2)   Systems of two linear equations in two variables can be solved by the **substitution method** or the **addition method**.

(10.3)   A **matrix** is any rectangular array of numbers.

A **determinant** of a square matrix is a real number:

$$\det\left(\begin{bmatrix} a & b \\ c & d \end{bmatrix}\right) = \begin{vmatrix} a & b \\ c & d \end{vmatrix} = ad - bc$$

Many systems of two linear equations in two variables can be solved by using Cramer's Rule.

(10.4)   A system of three equations in three variables can be solved by using the addition method.

(10.5)   The value of the determinants of a 3×3 matrix is the sum of the products of the elements of any chosen row or column and the cofactors of those elements.

Many systems of three linear equations in three variables can be solved by using Cramer's Rule.

(10.6)   Systems of linear equations can be solved by using matrices and the method of Gaussian elimination.

(10.7)   The fraction $\dfrac{P(x)}{Q(x)}$ can be written as the sum of several simpler fractions with denominators determined by the irreducible factors of $Q(x)$.

(10.8)   Systems of inequalities can be solved by graphing.

(10.9)   The maximum or minimum value of a linear function that is subject to the constraints of a system of linear inequalities in two variables is always attained at a corner or along an entire edge of the region R that represents the solution of the system.

REVIEW EXERCISES

In Review Exercises 1–4, solve each system of equations by the graphing method. If a system is inconsistent or if the equations of a system are dependent, so indicate.

1. $\begin{cases} 2x + y = 11 \\ -x + 2y = 7 \end{cases}$ **2.** $\begin{cases} 3x + 2y = 0 \\ 2x - 3y = -13 \end{cases}$ **3.** $\begin{cases} \dfrac{1}{2}x + \dfrac{1}{3}y = 2 \\ y = 6 - \dfrac{3}{2}x \end{cases}$ **4.** $\begin{cases} \dfrac{1}{3}x - \dfrac{1}{2}y = 1 \\ 6x - 9y = 2 \end{cases}$

In Review Exercises 5–8, solve each system of equations by substitution.

5. $\begin{cases} y = x + 4 \\ 2x + 3y = 7 \end{cases}$ **6.** $\begin{cases} y = 2x + 5 \\ 3x - 5y = -4 \end{cases}$ **7.** $\begin{cases} x + 2y = 11 \\ 2x - y = 2 \end{cases}$ **8.** $\begin{cases} 2x + 3y = -2 \\ 3x + 5y = -2 \end{cases}$

In Review Exercises 9–14, solve each system of equations by addition.

9. $\begin{cases} x + y = -2 \\ 2x + 3y = -3 \end{cases}$ **10.** $\begin{cases} 3x + 2y = 1 \\ 2x - 3y = 5 \end{cases}$ **11.** $\begin{cases} x + \dfrac{1}{2}y = 7 \\ -2x = 3y - 6 \end{cases}$ **12.** $\begin{cases} y = \dfrac{x - 3}{2} \\ x = \dfrac{2y + 7}{2} \end{cases}$

13. $\begin{cases} x + y + z = 6 \\ x - y - z = -4 \\ -x + y - z = -2 \end{cases}$ **14.** $\begin{cases} 2x + 3y + z = -5 \\ -x + 2y - z = -6 \\ 3x + y + 2z = 4 \end{cases}$

In Review Exercises 15–18, evaluate each determinant.

15. $\begin{vmatrix} 2 & 3 \\ -4 & 3 \end{vmatrix}$ **16.** $\begin{vmatrix} -3 & -4 \\ 5 & -6 \end{vmatrix}$

17. $\begin{vmatrix} -1 & 2 & -1 \\ 2 & -1 & 3 \\ 1 & -2 & 2 \end{vmatrix}$ **18.** $\begin{vmatrix} 3 & -2 & 2 \\ 1 & -2 & -2 \\ 2 & 1 & -1 \end{vmatrix}$

In Review Exercises 19–22, use Cramer's Rule to solve each system of equations.

19. $\begin{cases} 3x + 4y = 10 \\ 2x - 3y = 1 \end{cases}$ **20.** $\begin{cases} 2x - 5y = -17 \\ 3x + 2y = 3 \end{cases}$

21. $\begin{cases} x + 2y + z = 0 \\ 2x + y + z = 3 \\ x + y + 2z = 5 \end{cases}$ **22.** $\begin{cases} 2x + 3y + z = 2 \\ x + 3y + 2z = 7 \\ x - y - z = -7 \end{cases}$

In Review Exercises 23–24, solve each system of equations by using matrices.

23. $\begin{cases} x + 2y = 4 \\ 2x - y = 3 \end{cases}$ **24.** $\begin{cases} x + y + z = 6 \\ 2x - y + z = 1 \\ 4x + y - z = 5 \end{cases}$

In Review Exercises 25–26, decompose each fraction into partial fractions.

25. $\dfrac{4x^2 + 4x + 1}{x^3 + x}$ **26.** $\dfrac{x^2 + 5}{x^3 + x^2 + 5x}$

In Review Exercises 27–28, graph the solution set of each system of inequalities.

27. $\begin{cases} y \geq x + 1 \\ 3x + 2y < 6 \end{cases}$ **28.** $\begin{cases} y \geq x^2 - 4 \\ y < x + 3 \end{cases}$

In Review Exercises 29–30, maximize P subject to the given conditions.

29. $P = 2x + y$
$\begin{cases} x \geq 0 \\ y \geq 0 \\ x + y \leq 3 \end{cases}$ **30.** $P = 2x - 3y$
$\begin{cases} x \geq 0 \\ y \leq 3 \\ x - y \leq 4 \end{cases}$

31. A company manufactures two fertilizers, X and Y. Each 50-pound bag of fertilizer requires three ingredients, which are available in the limited quantities shown:

Ingredient	Number of pounds in fertilizer X	Number of pounds in fertilizer Y	Total number of pounds available
Nitrogen	6	10	20000
Phosphorus	8	6	16400
Potash	6	4	12000

The profit on each bag of fertilizer X is $6, and on each bag of Y, $5. How many bags of each product should be produced to maximize the profit?

CHAPTER TEN TEST

1. Solve the system $\begin{cases} 2x + y = 5 \\ y = 2x - 3 \end{cases}$ by graphing.

In Problems 2–3, consider the following system of equations:

$$\begin{cases} 3(x + y) = x - 3 \\ -y = \dfrac{2x + 3}{3} \end{cases}$$

2. Are the equations of the given system dependent or independent?

3. Is the system consistent or inconsistent?

4. Use any method to solve the following system for x.

$$\begin{cases} 2x - 4y = 14 \\ x = -2y + 7 \end{cases}$$

5. Use any method to solve the following system for y.

$$\begin{cases} \dfrac{x}{2} - \dfrac{y}{4} = -4 \\ x + y = -2 \end{cases}$$

6. Evaluate $\begin{vmatrix} 2 & -3 \\ 4 & 5 \end{vmatrix}$.

7. Evaluate $\begin{vmatrix} -3 & -4 \\ -2 & 3 \end{vmatrix}$.

In Problems 8–10, consider the system $\begin{cases} x - y = -6 \\ 3x + y = -6 \end{cases}$, which is to be solved with Cramer's Rule.

8. When solving for x, what is the numerator determinant? (Do not evaluate it.)

9. When solving for y, what is the denominator determinant? (Do not evaluate it.)

10. Solve the system for y.

In Problems 11–13, consider the system $\begin{cases} x + y + z = 4 \\ x + y - z = 6 \\ 2x - 3y + z = -1 \end{cases}$.

11. Solve for x.   **12.** Solve for y.   **13.** Solve for z.

14. Evaluate $\begin{vmatrix} 3 & 0 & -2 \\ 3 & 2 & 0 \\ 1 & -2 & -1 \end{vmatrix}$.

15. Write the augmented matrix that represents the system of equations given in Problems 11–13.

In Problems 16–17, decompose each fraction into partial fractions.

16. $\dfrac{4x^3 + 3x + x^2 + 2}{x^4 + x^2}$

17. $\dfrac{x^2 + 1}{(x + 1)^3}$

18.   Use the method of graphing to solve the following system of inequalities.

$$\begin{cases} y \geq x^2 \\ y < x + 3 \end{cases}$$

In Problems 19–20, maximize P subject to the given conditions.

19. $P = 3x - y$

$$\begin{cases} y \geq 1 \\ y \leq 2 \\ y \leq 3x + 1 \\ x \leq 1 \end{cases}$$

20. $P = y - 2x$

$$\begin{cases} x + y \geq 1 \\ x \leq 1 \\ y \leq \dfrac{x}{2} + 2 \\ x + y \leq 2 \end{cases}$$

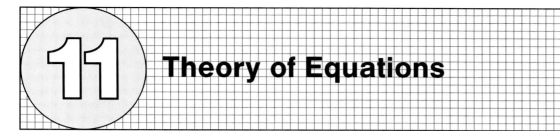

11 Theory of Equations

There are some equations of degree greater than 2 that can be solved by factoring. For example, the equation

$$x^3 - 3x^2 + 2x = 0$$

can be solved as follows:

$$
\begin{aligned}
x^3 - 3x^2 + 2x &= 0 & & \text{Factor out } x. \\
x(x^2 - 3x + 2) &= 0 & & \text{Factor } x^2 - 3x + 2. \\
x(x - 1)(x - 2) &= 0 & & \\
x = 0 \quad \text{or} \quad x - 1 &= 0 \quad \text{or} \quad x - 2 = 0 & & \text{Set each factor equal to 0.} \\
x &= 1 \qquad\qquad\quad x = 2 & &
\end{aligned}
$$

The solution set of the given equation is $\{0, 1, 2\}$.

In this chapter we will discuss how to solve more complicated polynomial equations.

11.1 THE FACTOR AND REMAINDER THEOREMS

A **polynomial equation** is an equation that can be written in the form $P(x) = 0$, where

$$P(x) = a_n x^n + a_{n-1} x^{n-1} + \cdots + a_1 x + a_0$$

is a polynomial of degree n (n is a natural number). A **zero of the polynomial** $P(x)$ is any number r for which $P(r) = 0$. It follows that a zero of the polynomial $P(x)$ is a solution or root of the equation $P(x) = 0$. For example, **2** is a zero of the polynomial

$$P(x) = x^2 - 3x + 2$$

because

$$
\begin{aligned}
P(2) &= 2^2 - 3(2) + 2 \\
&= 4 - 6 + 2 \\
&= 0
\end{aligned}
$$

385

or, by using synthetic division,

$$
\begin{array}{r|rrr}
2 & 1 & -3 & 2 \\
  &   & 2 & -2 \\
\hline
  & 1 & -1 & 0
\end{array}
$$

Note that 2 is a root of the polynomial equation

$$x^2 - 3x + 2 = 0$$

Before attempting to find zeros of more-complicated polynomials, we need to know whether a given polynomial even has a zero. This question was answered by Carl Friedrich Gauss (1777–1855), when he proved the **fundamental theorem of algebra**.

The Fundamental Theorem of Algebra.   If $P(x)$ is a polynomial with positive degree, then $P(x)$ has at least one zero.

The fundamental theorem points out that polynomials such as

$$2x + 3 \quad \text{or} \quad 32.75x^{1984} + ix^3 - (2 + i)x - 5$$

all have zeros. It may be difficult to find the zeros, and we may have to settle for approximations of the zeros, but the zeros do exist.

In Section 2.6 we saw that there is a relationship between a zero r of a polynomial $P(x)$ and the result of a long division of $P(x)$ by the binomial $x - r$. Recall that this relationship is expressed by the **remainder theorem**.

The Remainder Theorem.   If $P(x)$ is a polynomial, r is a real or complex number, and $P(x)$ is divided by $x - r$, then the remainder is $P(r)$.

Proof   To divide $P(x)$ by $x - r$, we must find a quotient $Q(x)$ and a remainder $R(x)$ such that

Dividend = divisor · quotient + remainder

$$P(x) = (x - r) \cdot Q(x) + R(x)$$

Furthermore, the degree of the remainder, $R(x)$, must be less than the degree of the divisor, $x - r$. Because the divisor is of degree 1, the remainder must be a constant R. The expression $P(x) = (x - r)Q(x) + R$ indicates that the polynomial on the left side of the equation is the same as the polynomial on the right. In particular, the values that these polynomials assume for any replacement of the variable x must be equal. Replacing x with the number r, we have $P(r) = (r - r)Q(r) + R$. Because $(r - r) = 0$, it follows that $P(r) = R$; that is, the value of the polynomial $P(x)$ attained at $x = r$ is the remainder produced by dividing $P(x)$ by $x - r$. The proof is complete.   □

The **factor theorem**, a corollary to the remainder theorem, applies when the remainder R is 0.

> **The Factor Theorem.**   Let $P(x)$ be any polynomial and let r be a real or complex number. Then, $P(r) = 0$ if and only if $x - r$ is a factor of $P(x)$.

Proof   First, assume that $P(r) = 0$ and prove that $x - r$ is a factor of $P(x)$. Divide $P(x)$ by $x - r$. The remainder theorem asserts that the remainder must be $P(r)$. But $P(r)$, by assumption, is 0. Hence, $x - r$ is a factor of $P(x)$.

Conversely, assume that $x - r$ is a factor of $P(x)$ and prove that $P(r) = 0$. Because $x - r$ is a factor of $P(x)$, dividing $P(x)$ by $x - r$ gives a remainder of 0. The remainder theorem asserts that this remainder is $P(r)$. Hence, $P(r) = 0$.   □

Example 1   Let $P(x) = 3x^3 - 5x^2 + 3x - 10$. Show that $P(2) = 0$, and use the factor theorem to factor $P(x)$.

Solution   Use synthetic division to find $P(2)$.

$$
\begin{array}{r|rrrr}
2 & 3 & -5 & 3 & -10 \\
  &   & 6 & 2 & 10 \\
\hline
  & 3 & 1 & 5 & 0
\end{array}
$$

Thus, $P(2) = 0$. Because $P(2) = 0$, $x - 2$ must be a factor of $3x^3 - 5x^2 + 3x - 10$ (by the factor theorem). The coefficients of the other factor are given in the bottom row of the synthetic division. Thus,

$$P(x) = 3x^3 - 5x^2 + 3x - 10 = (x - 2)(3x^2 + x + 5)$$ ■

Example 2   Solve the equation $3x^3 - 5x^2 + 3x - 10 = 0$.

Solution   This equation is related to the polynomial of Example 1, so you can use the work already done there:

$$3x^3 - 5x^2 + 3x - 10 = 0$$
$$(x - 2)(3x^2 + x + 5) = 0$$

To solve for x, set each factor equal to 0 and apply the quadratic formula to the equation $3x^2 + x + 5 = 0$. The complete solution set is

$$\left\{ 2, -\frac{1}{6} + \frac{\sqrt{59}}{6}i, -\frac{1}{6} - \frac{\sqrt{59}}{6}i \right\}$$ ■

Example 3   Find a polynomial $P(x)$ that has zeros of 2, 3, and -5.

Solution   By the factor theorem, if 2, 3, and -5 are zeros of $P(x)$, then $x - 2$, $x - 3$, and $x - (-5)$ are all factors of $P(x)$. Hence,

$$P(x) = (x - 2)(x - 3)(x + 5)$$
$$= (x^2 - 5x + 6)(x + 5)$$
$$= x^3 - 19x + 30$$

The polynomial $P(x) = x^3 - 19x + 30$ has zeros of 2, 3, and -5.   ■

Example 4   Is $x + 2$ a factor of the polynomial $P(x) = x^4 - 7x^2 - 6x$?

Solution   By the factor theorem, $x + 2$ will be a factor of $P(x)$ if -2 is a zero of $P(x)$. So, evaluate $P(-2)$ and see if it is a zero of $x^4 - 7x^2 - 6x$:

$$P(x) = x^4 - 7x^2 - 6x$$
$$P(-2) = (-2)^4 - 7(-2)^2 - 6(-2) \quad \text{or}$$
$$= 16 - 28 + 12$$
$$= 0$$

$$\begin{array}{r|rrrrr} -2 & 1 & 0 & -7 & -6 & 0 \\ & & -2 & 4 & 6 & 0 \\ \hline & 1 & -2 & -3 & 0 & 0 \end{array}$$

Thus, $P(-2) = 0$. Because -2 is a zero of the polynomial $P(x)$, then $x - (-2)$, or $x + 2$, is a factor of $P(x) = x^4 - 7x^2 - 6x$.   ■

Example 5   Find the three cube roots of -1.

Solution   The three cube roots of -1 are solutions of the equation $x^3 = -1$, or $x^3 + 1 = 0$. One of the cube roots of -1 is the number -1. Because of the factor theorem, $x - (-1)$ must be a factor of $x^3 + 1$. Hence, $x + 1$ divides $x^3 + 1$. Obtain the other factor of $x^3 + 1$ by synthetic division.

$$\begin{array}{r|rrrr} -1 & 1 & 0 & 0 & 1 \\ & & -1 & 1 & -1 \\ \hline & 1 & -1 & 1 & 0 \end{array}$$

Thus, the equation $x^3 + 1 = 0$ factors as

$$(x + 1)(x^2 - x + 1) = 0$$

Setting each factor equal to 0 and solving for x gives the three cube roots of -1:

$$x = -1, \qquad x = \frac{1}{2} + \frac{\sqrt{3}}{2} i, \qquad x = \frac{1}{2} - \frac{\sqrt{3}}{2} i \qquad \blacksquare$$

■ EXERCISE 11.1

In Exercises 1–6, let $P(x) = 2x^4 - 2x^3 + 5x^2 - 1$. Evaluate the polynomial by substituting the given value of x into the polynomial and simplifying. Then evaluate the polynomial by using the remainder theorem.

1. $P(2)$ **2.** $P(-1)$ **3.** $P(0)$ **4.** $P(1)$ **5.** $P(-4)$ **6.** $P(4)$

7. Let $P(x) = x^5 - 1$. Find $P(2)$ using the remainder theorem.
8. Let $P(x) = x^5 + 4x^2 - 1$. Find $P(-3)$ using the remainder theorem.

In Exercises 9–16, use the factor theorem to decide whether each statement is true. If not, so indicate.

9. $x - 1$ is a factor of $x^7 - 1$.
10. $x - 2$ is a factor of $x^3 - x^2 + 2x - 8$.
11. $x - 1$ is a factor of $3x^5 + 4x^2 - 7$.
12. $x + 1$ is a factor of $3x^5 + 4x^2 - 7$.
13. $x + 3$ is a factor of $2x^3 - 2x^2 + 1$.
14. $x - 3$ is a factor of $3x^5 - 3x^4 + 5x^2 - 13x - 6$.
15. $x - 1$ is a factor of $x^{1984} - x^{1776} + x^{1492} - x^{1066}$.
16. $x + 1$ is a factor of $x^{1984} + x^{1776} - x^{1492} - x^{1066}$.

17. Completely solve $x^3 + 3x^2 - 13x - 15 = 0$, given that $x = -1$ is a root.
18. Completely solve $x^4 + 4x^3 - 10x^2 - 28x - 15 = 0$, given that $x = -1$ is a double root.

In Exercises 19–28, find a polynomial of lowest degree that has the indicated zeros.

19. $1, 1, 1$
20. $1, 0, -1$
21. $2, 4, 5$
22. $7, 6, 3$
23. $-1, 1, -\sqrt{2}, \sqrt{2}$
24. $0, 0, 0, \sqrt{3}, -\sqrt{3}$
25. $\sqrt{2}, i, -i$
26. $i, i, -i, -i$
27. $1 + i, 1 - i, 0$
28. $2 + i, 2 - i, i, -i$

In Exercises 29–32, find the three cube roots of each number.

29. 1
30. 64
31. -125
32. -216

33. Completely solve $x^4 - 5x^3 + 7x^2 - 5x + 6 = 0$, given that $x = 3$ and $x = 2$ are roots.
34. Completely solve $x^4 + 2x^3 - 3x^2 - 4x + 4 = 0$, given that $x = 1$ and $x = -2$ are roots.
35. Completely solve $x^4 - 2x^3 - 9x^2 + 2x + 8 = 0$, given that $x = 4$ and $x = -1$ are roots.
36. If 0 is a zero of $P(x) = a_n x^n + a_{n-1}x^{n-1} + \cdots + a_1 x + a_0$, what is a_0?
37. If 0 occurs as a zero twice in the polynomial $P(x) = a_n x^n + a_{n-1}x^{n-1} + \cdots + a_1 x + a_0$, what is a_1?
38. Explain why the fundamental theorem of algebra guarantees that every polynomial equation has at least one root.
39. Explain why the fundamental theorem of algebra and the factor theorem guarantee that an nth-degree polynomial equation has n roots.
40. The fundamental theorem of algebra demands that a polynomial be of positive degree. Would the theorem still be true if the polynomial were of degree 0? Explain.

11.2   DESCARTES' RULE OF SIGNS AND BOUNDS ON ROOTS

The remainder theorem and synthetic division provide a way of verifying that a particular number is a root of a polynomial equation, but they do not provide the solutions. Selecting numbers at random, checking to see if they work, and hoping for the best is not an efficient technique! Some guidelines are needed to indicate how many solutions to expect, the kind of solutions to expect, and where they can be found. This section presents several theorems that provide such guidelines. The first theorem tells how many solutions to expect when solving a polynomial equation.

> **Theorem.** If multiple roots are counted individually, the polynomial equation $P(x) = 0$ with complex coefficients (which include real coefficients) and degree $n > 0$ has exactly n roots among the complex numbers.

Proof Let $P(x)$ be a polynomial of degree n. The fundamental theorem of algebra asserts that $P(x)$ has a zero, r_1. Therefore, the equation $P(x) = 0$ has r_1 as a root. The factor theorem guarantees that $x - r_1$ is a factor of $P(x)$. Thus,

$$P(x) = (x - r_1)Q_1(x)$$

If the lead coefficient of the nth-degree polynomial $P(x)$ is a_n, then $Q_1(x)$ is a polynomial of degree $n - 1$ whose lead coefficient is also a_n. The fundamental theorem of algebra asserts that $Q_1(x)$ also has a zero, which we call r_2. According to the factor theorem, $x - r_2$ is a factor of $Q_1(x)$, and

$$P(x) = (x - r_1)(x - r_2)Q_2(x)$$

where $Q_2(x)$ is a polynomial of degree $n - 2$ with lead coefficient a_n. This process can continue only to n factors of the form $x - r_i$; the final quotient $Q_n(x)$ is a polynomial of degree $n - n$, or degree 0. A polynomial of degree 0 with lead coefficient a_n is simply the constant a_n. The original polynomial $P(x)$ factors completely as

$$P(x) = a_n(x - r_1)(x - r_2)(x - r_3) \cdots (x - r_n)$$

Each of the n values r_i is a zero of $P(x)$ and a root of the equation $P(x) = 0$. There are no other roots, because no single factor in this product becomes 0 for any value of x not included in the list $r_1, r_2, r_3, \ldots, r_n$.

The theorem is proved.   □

The r_i in the above proof need not be different. Any root that occurs k times is called a **root of multiplicity k.**

The next theorem points out a pattern in the complex roots of real polynomial equations.

> **Theorem.** If a polynomial equation $P(x) = 0$ with real coefficients has a complex root $a + bi$, with $b \neq 0$, then the conjugate $a - bi$ is a root also. (This theorem is often stated as "complex roots of real polynomial equations occur in conjugate pairs.")

The proof of this theorem is omitted.

Example 1   Form a fourth-degree equation with real coefficients and a double root of i.

Solution   Because i is a root of multiplicity two and a fourth-degree equation must have four roots, two more roots are needed. According to the previous theorem, the missing roots must be the conjugates of the given roots. Thus, the complete solution set is

$$\{+i, \ +i, \ -i, \ -i\}$$

The equation is
$$(x - i)(x + i)(x - i)(x + i) = 0$$
$$(x^2 + 1)(x^2 + 1) = 0$$
$$x^4 + 2x^2 + 1 = 0 \qquad \blacksquare$$

Example 2   Can a quadratic equation have a double root of i? If so, find such an equation.

Solution   Complex roots of a quadratic equation with *real* coefficients will be conjugates. A quadratic equation can have two nonreal, nonconjugate roots if the equation has coefficients that are not real. If i is a solution of multiplicity two, the equation is

$$(x - i)(x - i) = 0$$
$$x^2 - 2ix - 1 = 0 \qquad \blacksquare$$

Descartes' Rule of Signs

René Descartes is credited with a theorem known as **Descartes' rule of signs** that enables us to look at a polynomial equation and estimate the number of positive, negative, and nonreal roots.

If a polynomial is written in descending powers of x and we scan it from left to right, a "variation in sign" occurs whenever successive terms have opposite signs. For example,

$$P(x) = 3x^5 - 2x^4 - 5x^3 + x^2 - x - 9$$

has three variations in sign, and

$$P(-x) = 3(-x)^5 - 2(-x)^4 - 5(-x)^3 + (-x)^2 - (-x) - 9$$
$$= -3x^5 - 2x^4 + 5x^3 + x^2 + x - 9$$

has two variations in sign.

Descartes' Rule of Signs.   If $P(x)$ is a polynomial with real coefficients, the number of positive roots of the polynomial equation $P(x) = 0$ is either equal to the number of variations in sign of $P(x)$ or less than that by an even number.

The number of negative roots of $P(x) = 0$ is either equal to the number of variations in sign of $P(-x)$ or less than that by an even number.

The proof of this theorem is omitted.

Example 3   What possible roots can be expected for the polynomial equation

$$P(x) = x^8 + x^6 + x^4 + x^2 + 1 = 0$$

Solution   Because the equation is an eighth-degree polynomial equation, it must have eight roots. Because there are no variations in sign for $P(x)$, none of the roots can be positive. Because there are no variations in sign for $P(-x)$, none of the roots can be negative. Because $P(0) = 1$, zero is not a root. Thus, all eight roots are complex numbers with nonzero imaginary parts, and they occur in four conjugate pairs.   ∎

Example 4   Discuss the possibilities for the roots of $3x^3 - 2x^2 + x - 5 = 0$.

Solution   Let $P(x) = 3x^3 - 2x^2 + x - 5$. Because $P(x)$ has three variations in sign, there could be three positive solutions or only one (because 1 is less than 3 by an even number). Because $P(-x) = -3x^3 - 2x^2 - x - 5$ has no variations in sign, there are no negative roots. Furthermore, 0 is not a root.

If there are three positive roots, all the roots are accounted for; there would be no other possibilities. If there is only one positive root, the remaining two roots must be nonreal. The following list indicates these two possibilities.

Number of positive roots	Number of negative roots	Number of nonreal roots
3	0	0
1	0	2

The number of nonreal roots is the number needed to bring the total number of roots up to three.   ∎

Example 5   Discuss the possibilities for the roots of $5x^5 - 3x^3 - 2x^2 + x - 1 = 0$.

Solution $P(x)$ has three variations in sign; there are either three positive solutions or only one. Because $P(-x) = -5x^5 + 3x^3 - 2x^2 - x - 1$ has two variations in sign, there are either two negative roots or none. Each line of the following list indicates a possible combination of positive, negative, and nonreal roots.

Number of positive roots	Number of negative roots	Number of nonreal roots
1	0	4
3	0	2
1	2	2
3	2	0

Note that in each case the number of nonreal roots is even. This is expected, because this polynomial has real coefficients and its complex roots must occur in conjugate pairs.

∎

Bounds for Roots

A final theorem provides a way of finding **bounds** for the roots, enabling us to concentrate our efforts on those intervals where roots can be found. This theorem is also presented without proof.

Theorem.   Let the lead coefficient of the polynomial $P(x)$ with real coefficients be positive, and do a synthetic division of the coefficients of $P(x)$ by the positive number c. If each term in the last row is nonnegative, then no number greater than c can be a root of $P(x) = 0$. (c is an *upper bound* of the real roots.)

If $P(x)$ is divided synthetically by a negative number d, and the signs in the last row alternate,* then no value less than d can be a root of $P(x) = 0$. (d is a *lower bound* of the real roots.)

Example 6   Establish best integer bounds for the roots of $18x^3 - 3x^2 - 37x + 12 = 0$.

Solution   Try several synthetic divisions, looking for a nonnegative last row (if you synthetically divide by a positive number) or the alternating-sign last row (if you synthetically divide by a negative number). Trying 1 first gives

$$
\begin{array}{r|rrrr}
1 & 18 & -3 & -37 & 12 \\
  &   & 18 & 15 & -22 \\
\hline
  & +18 & +15 & -22 & -10
\end{array}
$$

Because some of the signs in the last row are negative, 1 is not an upper bound of the roots of the equation. Now try 2.

$$
\begin{array}{r|rrrr}
2 & 18 & -3 & -37 & 12 \\
  &   & 36 & 66 & 58 \\
\hline
  & +18 & +33 & +29 & +70
\end{array}
$$

Because the last row is entirely positive, no number greater than 2 can be a root. Because 1 is not an upper bound, the smallest or best integer upper bound of the roots is 2.

---

* If a 0 appears in the third row, that 0 can be assigned either a plus or a minus sign to help the signs alternate.

Now try a negative divisor such as -2.

$$
\begin{array}{r|rrrr}
-2 & 18 & -3 & -37 & 12 \\
   &   & -36 & 78 & -82 \\
\hline
   & +18 & -39 & +41 & -70 \\
\end{array}
$$

The alternating signs in the last row indicate that no number less than -2 can be a root. Try -1 next.

$$
\begin{array}{r|rrrr}
-1 & 18 & -3 & -37 & 12 \\
   &   & -18 & 21 & 16 \\
\hline
   & +18 & -21 & -16 & +28 \\
\end{array}
$$

Because the signs in the last row do not alternate, -1 is not a lower bound. Thus, the largest or best integer lower bound is -2.

All the real roots of this equation lie between -2 and 2.   ■

Example 7   Find bounds for the roots of the equation $x^5 - x^4 - 3x^3 + 3x^2 - 10x + 10 = 0$.

Solution   Perform several divisions and watch for the desired nonnegative last row (if synthetically dividing by a positive number) or the alternating-sign last row (if synthetically dividing by a negative number):

$$
\begin{array}{r|rrrrrr}
-3 & 1 & -1 & -3 & 3 & -10 & 10 \\
   &   & -3 & 12 & -27 & 72 & -186 \\
\hline
   & +1 & -4 & +9 & -24 & +62 & -176 \\
\end{array}
$$

$$
\begin{array}{r|rrrrrr}
-2 & 1 & -1 & -3 & 3 & -10 & 10 \\
   &   & -2 & 6 & -6 & 6 & 8 \\
\hline
   & +1 & -3 & +3 & -3 & -4 & +18 \\
\end{array}
$$

Note the alternation of signs in the synthetic division by -3. You can conclude that -3 is a lower bound; that is, the equation has no roots less than -3. That claim cannot be made for -2, however, because the signs do not alternate.

Now look for an upper bound by dividing synthetically by various positive values:

$$
\begin{array}{r|rrrrrr}
3 & 1 & -1 & -3 & 3 & -10 & 10 \\
  &   & 3 & 6 & 9 & 36 & 78 \\
\hline
  & +1 & +2 & +3 & +12 & +26 & +88 \\
\end{array}
$$

$$
\begin{array}{r|rrrrrr}
2 & 1 & -1 & -3 & 3 & -10 & 10 \\
  &   & 2 & 2 & -2 & 2 & -16 \\
\hline
  & +1 & +1 & -1 & +1 & -8 & -6 \\
\end{array}
$$

When you divide synthetically by 3, you obtain a completely positive last row, which indicates that 3 is an upper bound. You cannot say the same thing for 2 because its last row contains negative numbers.

The best integer bounds are -3 and 3.   ■

- **EXERCISE 11.2**

1. How many roots does $x^{10} = 1$ have?
2. How many roots does $x^{40} = 1$ have?
3. One root of $x(3x^4 - 2) = 12x$ is 0. How many other roots are there?
4. One root of $3x^2(x^7 - 14x + 3) = 0$ is 0. How many other roots are there?

In Exercises 5–18, use Descartes' rule of signs to find the number of possible positive, negative, and nonreal roots of each equation. **Do not attempt to find the roots.**

5. $3x^3 + 5x^2 - 4x + 3 = 0$
6. $3x^3 - 5x^2 - 4x - 3 = 0$
7. $2x^3 + 7x^2 + 5x + 4 = 0$
8. $-2x^3 - 7x^2 - 5x - 4 = 0$
9. $8x^4 = -5$
10. $-3x^3 = -5$
11. $x^4 + 8x^2 - 5x = 10$
12. $5x^7 + 3x^6 - 2x^5 + 3x^4 + 9x^3 + x^2 + x + 1 = 0$
13. $-x^{10} - x^8 - x^6 - x^4 - x^2 - 1 = 0$
14. $x^{10} + x^8 + x^6 + x^4 + x^2 + 1 = 0$
15. $x^9 + x^7 + x^5 + x^3 + x = 0$ (Is 0 a root?)
16. $-x^9 - x^7 - x^5 - x^3 = 0$ (Is 0 a root?)
17. $-2x^4 - 3x^2 + 2x + 3 = 0$
18. $-7x^5 - 6x^4 + 3x^3 - 2x^2 + 7x - 4 = 0$

In Exercises 19–26, find the best integer bounds for the roots of each equation.

19. $x^2 - 5x - 6 = 0$
20. $6x^2 + x - 1 = 0$
21. $6x^2 - 13x - 110 = 0$
22. $3x^2 + 12x + 24 = 0$
23. $x^5 + x^4 - 8x^3 - 8x^2 + 15x + 15 = 0$
24. $12x^3 + 20x^2 - x - 6 = 0$
25. $2x^3 + 9x^2 - 5x = 41$
26. $x^4 - 34x^2 = -225$

27. Prove that any odd-degree polynomial equation with real coefficients must have at least one real root.
28. If a, b, c, and d are positive numbers, prove that $ax^4 + bx^2 + cx - d = 0$ has exactly two nonreal roots.

11.3   RATIONAL ROOTS OF POLYNOMIAL EQUATIONS

This section considers a method for actually finding the rational roots of polynomial equations with integral coefficients.

> **Theorem.**   If the polynomial equation
> $$P(x) = a_n x^n + a_{n-1} x^{n-1} + a_{n-2} x^{n-2} + \cdots + a_1 x + a_0 = 0$$
> has integral coefficients and the rational number p/q (in lowest terms) is a root of the equation, then p is a factor of the constant term a_0, and q is a factor of the lead coefficient a_n.

Proof   Let p/q be a rational root in lowest terms of the equation $P(x) = 0$. The equation is satisfied by p/q:

$$a_n \left(\frac{p}{q}\right)^n + a_{n-1} \left(\frac{p}{q}\right)^{n-1} + a_{n-2} \left(\frac{p}{q}\right)^{n-2} + \cdots + a_1 \left(\frac{p}{q}\right) + a_0 = 0$$

By multiplying both sides of the equation by the lowest common denominator q^n, we clear the equation of fractions. (Remember that p, q, and each of the a_i are integers.)

1. $a_n p^n + a_{n-1} p^{n-1} q + a_{n-2} p^{n-2} q^2 + \cdots + a_1 p q^{n-1} + a_0 q^n = 0$

Note that all the terms but the last share a common factor of p. We rewrite the equation in the form

$$p(a_n p^{n-1} + a_{n-1} p^{n-2} q + a_{n-2} p^{n-3} q^2 + \cdots + a_1 q^{n-1}) = -a_0 q^n$$

Because p is a factor of the left side, it must also be a factor of the right side. It cannot be a factor of q^n, because the fraction p/q is in lowest terms, and p and q share no common factor. Therefore, p and q^n share no common factors either. It follows that p must be a factor of a_0.

We return to Equation 1. Note that all terms but the first share a common factor of q, and rewrite Equation 1 as

$$q(a_{n-1} p^{n-1} + a_{n-2} p^{n-2} q + a_{n-3} p^{n-3} q^2 + \cdots + a_0 q^{n-1}) = -a_n p^n$$

Now q is a factor of the left side and must therefore be a factor of the right side as well. Because q cannot be a factor of p^n, it must be a factor of a_n.

The theorem is proved.   □

Example 1   What are the only possible rational roots of the equation

$$\frac{1}{2} x^4 + \frac{2}{3} x^3 + 3x^2 - \frac{3}{2} x + 3 = 0$$

Solution   The previous theorem applies to polynomial equations with *integral* coefficients. To clear this equation of its fractional coefficients, multiply both sides by 6 to get

$$3x^4 + 4x^3 + 18x^2 - 9x + 18 = 0$$

The only possible numerators available for a rational root are the factors of the constant term 18: ± 1, ± 2, ± 3, ± 6, ± 9, and ± 18. The only possible denominators are the factors of the lead coefficient 3: ± 1 and ± 3. You can form the list of possible rational solutions by listing all the combinations of values from these two sets.

$$\pm\frac{1}{1},\ \pm\frac{2}{1},\ \pm\frac{3}{1},\ \pm\frac{6}{1},\ \pm\frac{9}{1},\ \pm\frac{18}{1},\ \pm\frac{1}{3},\ \pm\frac{2}{3},\ \pm\frac{3}{3},\ \pm\frac{6}{3},\ \pm\frac{9}{3},\ \pm\frac{18}{3}$$

Several of these are duplicates, so you can condense the list to obtain

Possible Rational Roots

$$\pm 1,\ \pm 2,\ \pm 3,\ \pm 6,\ \pm 9,\ \pm 18,\ \pm\frac{1}{3},\ \pm\frac{2}{3}$$ ■

Example 2   Prove that $\sqrt{2}$ is irrational.

Solution $\sqrt{2}$ is a real root of the polynomial equation $x^2 - 2 = 0$. Any rational solution of the equation must have a numerator of either ± 1 or ± 2 and a denominator of ± 1. The only possible rational solutions, therefore, are ± 1 and ± 2, but none of these satisfies the equation. Therefore, the solution $\sqrt{2}$ must be irrational.

■

Example 3   Solve the equation $P(x) = x^3 + x^2 - 10x + 8 = 0$.

Solution   Because the equation is of third degree, it must have three roots. According to Descartes' rule of signs, there are two possible combinations of positive, negative, and nonreal roots.

Number of positive roots	Number of negative roots	Number of nonreal roots
2	1	0
0	1	2

The only possible rational roots are

$$\pm \frac{8}{1}, \ \pm \frac{4}{1}, \ \pm \frac{2}{1}, \ \pm \frac{1}{1}$$

or

$$-8, \ -4, \ -2, \ -1, \ 1, \ 2, \ 4, \ 8$$

Check each one, crossing out those that do not satisfy the equation. Start, for example, with $x = 4$:

$$
\begin{array}{r|rrrr}
4 & 1 & 1 & -10 & 8 \\
  &   & 4 & 20 & 40 \\
\hline
  & 1 & 5 & 10 & \bigm| 48 \\
\end{array}
$$

Because the remainder is not 0, the number 4 is not a root and can be crossed off the list. Because the last row in the synthetic division is entirely positive, 4 is an upper bound of the equation's roots. Thus, 8 cannot be a root either and can also be crossed off the list.

$$-8, \ -4, \ -2, \ -1, \ 1, \ 2, \ \cancel{4}, \ \cancel{8}$$

Now try $x = 2$:

$$
\begin{array}{r|rrrr}
2 & 1 & 1 & -10 & 8 \\
  &   & 2 & 6   & -8 \\
\hline
  & 1 & 3 & -4 & \bigm| 0 \\
\end{array}
$$

Because the remainder is 0, the number 2 is a root, and the binomial $x - 2$ is a factor of $P(x)$. Any remaining roots must be supplied by the remaining factor, which is the quotient $1x^2 + 3x - 4$. The other roots can be found by solving the equation

$$x^2 + 3x - 4 = 0$$

This equation, called the **depressed equation**, is a quadratic equation that can be solved by factoring:

$$x^2 + 3x - 4 = 0$$
$$(x - 1)(x + 4) = 0$$
$$x - 1 = 0 \quad \text{or} \quad x + 4 = 0$$
$$x = 1 \qquad\qquad x = -4$$

The solution set is $\{2, 1, -4\}$. Note that two solutions are positive, one is negative, and none are nonreal. This is one of the possibilities predicted by Descartes' rule of signs. ■

Example 4   Solve the equation $x^7 - 2x^6 - 5x^5 + 6x^4 - x^3 + 2x^2 + 5x - 6 = 0$.

Solution   Being of seventh degree, the equation must have seven roots. According to Descartes' rule of signs, there are six possible combinations of positive, negative, and nonreal roots for this equation.

Number of positive roots	Number of negative roots	Number of nonreal roots
5	2	0
3	2	2
1	2	4
5	0	2
3	0	4
1	0	6

The only possible rational roots are

$$-6, \ -3, \ -2, \ -1, \ 1, \ 2, \ 3, \ 6$$

Check each one, crossing off those that do not satisfy the equation. Begin with -3:

$$
\begin{array}{r|rrrrrrrr}
-3 & 1 & -2 & -5 & 6 & -1 & 2 & 5 & -6 \\
   &   & -3 & 15 & -30 & 72 & -213 & 633 & -1914 \\
\hline
   & 1 & -5 & 10 & -24 & 71 & -211 & 638 & -1920
\end{array}
$$

Because the last number in the synthetic division is not 0, -3 is not a root and can be crossed off the list. Because the last row is alternately positive and negative, -3 is a lower bound. Thus, you can cross off -6 as well:

$$-6, -3, -2, -1, 1, 2, 3, 6$$

Now try -2:

$$
\begin{array}{r|rrrrrrrr}
-2 & 1 & -2 & -5 & 6 & -1 & 2 & 5 & -6 \\
   &   & -2 & 8 & -6 & 0 & 2 & -8 & 6 \\
\hline
   & 1 & -4 & 3 & 0 & -1 & 4 & -3 & 0 \\
\end{array}
$$

Because the remainder is 0, -2 is a root.

This root is negative, so you can revise the chart of positive/negative/nonreal possibilities. (Until now, 0 negative roots was a possibility.)

Number of positive roots	Number of negative roots	Number of nonreal roots
5	2	0
3	2	2
1	2	4

Because -2 is a root, the factor theorem asserts that $x - (-2)$, or $x + 2$, is a factor of $P(x)$. Any remaining roots can be found by solving the depressed equation

$$x^6 - 4x^5 + 3x^4 - x^2 + 4x - 3 = 0$$

Because the constant term of this equation is different from the constant term of the original equation, you can cross off some other possible rational roots. The numbers 2 and 6 must go because neither is a factor of the constant, 3. The number -2 cannot be a root a second time because -2 is not a factor of 3. The list of candidates is now

$$-6, -3, -2, -1, 1, 2, 3, 6$$

The only solution found thus far is -2. Try -1 next because you know there must be one more negative root. The coefficients are those of the depressed equation. (Don't forget the missing x^3.)

$$
\begin{array}{r|rrrrrrr}
-1 & 1 & -4 & 3 & 0 & -1 & 4 & -3 \\
   &   & -1 & 5 & -8 & 8 & -7 & 3 \\
\hline
   & 1 & -5 & 8 & -8 & 7 & -3 & 0 \\
\end{array}
$$

Because the remainder is 0, the number -1 is another root. The roots found so far are -1 and -2. The root -1 cannot appear again because there can be only two negative roots, and you have found them both. The current list of candidates is now

$$-6, -3, -2, -1, 1, 2, 3, 6$$

Other roots can be found by solving the depressed equation

$$x^5 - 5x^4 + 8x^3 - 8x^2 + 7x - 3 = 0$$

Try 1 next:

$$\begin{array}{r|rrrrrr}
1 & 1 & -5 & 8 & -8 & 7 & -3 \\
  &   & 1 & -4 & 4 & -4 & 3 \\
\hline
  & 1 & -4 & 4 & -4 & 3 & 0
\end{array}$$

The solution 1 joins the growing list of solutions. To see if 1 is a multiple solution, try it again in the depressed equation.

$$\begin{array}{r|rrrrr}
1 & 1 & -4 & 4 & -4 & 3 \\
  &   & 1 & -3 & 1 & -3 \\
\hline
  & 1 & -3 & 1 & -3 & 0
\end{array}$$

Again, 1 is a root. Will it work a third time?

$$\begin{array}{r|rrrr}
1 & 1 & -3 & 1 & -3 \\
  &   & 1 & -2 & -1 \\
\hline
  & 1 & -2 & -1 & -4
\end{array}$$

No, 1 is only a double root.

Solutions found thus far are -2, -1, 1, and 1. Now try 3:

$$\begin{array}{r|rrrr}
3 & 1 & -3 & 1 & -3 \\
  &   & 3 & 0 & 3 \\
\hline
  & 1 & 0 & 1 & 0
\end{array}$$

The solution 3 is added to the list of roots. So far the roots are -2, -1, 1, 1, and 3.

The depressed equation is now the quadratic equation $x^2 + 1 = 0$, which can be solved as follows:

$$x^2 + 1 = 0$$
$$x^2 = -1$$
$$x = i \qquad \text{or} \qquad x = -i$$

Because i and $-i$ are solutions, the complete solution set of the original seventh-degree equation is

$$\{-2, -1, 1, 1, 3, i, -i\}$$

Note that this list contains three positives, two negatives, and two conjugate complex numbers. This combination was one of the predicted possibilities. ∎

■ EXERCISE 11.3

In Exercises 1–22, find all roots for each equation.

1. $x^3 - 2x^2 - x + 2 = 0$

2. $x^3 + 2x^2 - x - 2 = 0$

3. $x^4 - 10x^3 + 35x^2 - 50x + 24 = 0$

4. $x^4 + 4x^3 + 6x^2 + 4x + 1 = 0$

5. $x^5 - 2x^4 - 2x^3 + 4x^2 + x - 2 = 0$

6. $x^5 - x^3 - 8x^2 + 8 = 0$

7. $x^4 + 3x^3 - 13x^2 - 9x + 30 = 0$

8. $x^4 - 8x^3 + 14x^2 + 8x - 15 = 0$

9. $x^7 - 12x^5 + 48x^3 - 64x = 0$

10. $x^7 + 7x^6 + 21x^5 + 35x^4 + 35x^3 + 21x^2 + 7x + 1 = 0$

11. $6x^5 - 7x^4 - 48x^3 + 81x^2 - 4x - 12 = 0$

12. $x^6 - 3x^5 - x^4 + 9x^3 - 10x^2 + 12x - 8 = 0$

13. $4x^5 - 12x^4 + 15x^3 - 45x^2 - 4x + 12 = 0$

14. $12x^4 + 20x^3 - 41x^2 + 20x - 3 = 0$

15. $3x^4 - 14x^3 + 11x^2 + 16x - 12 = 0$

16. $2x^4 - x^3 - 2x^2 - 4x - 40 = 0$

17. $4x^4 - 8x^3 - x^2 + 8x - 3 = 0$

18. $3x^3 - 2x^2 + 12x - 8 = 0$

19. $30x^3 - 47x^2 - 9x + 18 = 0$

20. $x^{-5} - 8x^{-4} + 25x^{-3} - 38x^{-2} + 28x^{-1} - 8 = 0$

21. $1 - x^{-1} - x^{-2} - 2x^{-3} = 0$

22. $x^3 - \frac{19}{6}x^2 + \frac{1}{6}x + 1 = 0$

23. If n is an even positive integer and c is a positive constant, prove that the equation $x^n + c = 0$ has no real roots.

24. If n is an even positive integer and c is a positive constant, prove that the equation $x^n - c = 0$ has exactly two real roots.

11.4   IRRATIONAL ROOTS OF POLYNOMIAL EQUATIONS

First-degree equations are easy to solve, and quadratic equations can be solved by the quadratic formula. There are also formulas for solving general third- and fourth-degree polynomial equations, although these formulas are complicated.

However, there are no explicit algebraic formulas for solving polynomial equations of degree 5 or greater. This fact was proven for fifth-degree equations by the Norwegian mathematician Niels Henrik Abel (1802–1829) and for equations of degree greater than 5 by the French mathematician Évariste Galois (1811–1832). To solve a polynomial equation of high degree with integer coefficients, we could use the methods of Section 7.3 to find the rational roots. Once they were found, however, the remaining depressed equation would have to be a first- or second-degree equation or we could not finish. The purpose of this section is to provide techniques for approximating the real roots of equations of high degree, even though the exact roots cannot be found. The following theorem provides one method for locating a root.

> **Theorem.**   Let $P(x)$ be a polynomial with real coefficients. If $P(a)$ and $P(b)$ have opposite signs, there is at least one number r between a and b for which $P(r) = 0$.

Justification.   A proof of this theorem requires the use of calculus. The theorem becomes plausible if we consider the graph of the polynomial $y = P(x)$. Graphs of polynomials are *continuous* curves, a technical term that means, roughly, that they can be drawn without lifting the pencil from the paper. If $P(a)$ and $P(b)$ have opposite signs, the points $A(a, P(a))$ and $B(b, P(b))$ on the graph of $y = P(x)$

lie on opposite sides of the x-axis, which separates them like a fence. The continuous curve joining A and B has no gaps; thus, it must cross the x-axis at least once. The point of crossing, $x = r$, is a zero of $P(x)$, and a solution of the equation $P(x) = 0$.   ☐

The previous theorem provides a method for finding roots of $P(x) = 0$ to any degree of accuracy desired. Suppose we find, by trial and error, the numbers x_L and x_R (for left and right) that straddle a root; that is, $x_L < x_R$ and $P(x_L)$ and $P(x_R)$ have opposite signs. For purposes of discussion, $P(x_L)$ will be negative and $P(x_R)$ will be positive. We compute a number c that is halfway between x_L and x_R (c is the average of x_L and x_R), and then evaluate $P(c)$. If $P(c)$ is 0, we've found a root. More likely, however, $P(c)$ will not be 0.

If $P(c)$ is negative, the root, r, lies between c and x_R, as shown in Figure 11-1. In such a case, let c become the *new* x_L, and repeat the procedure.

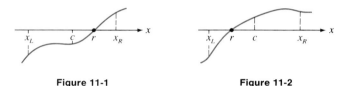

Figure 11-1   **Figure 11-2**

If $P(c)$ is positive, however, the root lies between x_L and c, as shown in Figure 11-2. In this case, let c become the new x_R, and repeat the process.

At any stage in this procedure, the root is contained between the current numbers x_L and x_R. If the original bounds were, say, 1 unit apart, after 10 repetitions of this procedure, the root would be contained between fences that were 2^{-10}, or about 0.001, units apart. After 20 repetitions the bounds are only 0.000001 units apart. The actual zero of $P(x)$ is within 0.000001 of either x_L or x_R. This procedure, called **binary chopping**, is well suited for solving equations by computer.

Example 1   Find $\sqrt{2}$ to two decimal places.

Solution $\sqrt{2}$ is a root of the polynomial equation $P(x) = x^2 - 2 = 0$. Note that the values $P(1) = 1^2 - 2 = -1$ and $P(2) = 2^2 - 2 = 2$ have opposite signs. Set x_L equal to 1 and x_R equal to 2 and compute the midpoint, $c = (1 + 2)/2 = 1.5$.

Because $P(c) = P(1.5) = 0.25$ is a positive number, c becomes the new x_R and we calculate a new c. Tabulating the information in a chart helps keep things straight.

Step	x_L	c	x_R	$P(x_L)$	$P(c)$	$P(x_R)$
0	1	1.5	2	negative	positive	positive
1	1	1.25	1.5	negative	negative	positive

At this point, $P(c)$ and $P(x_R)$ are of opposite signs, so c becomes the new x_L. The process continues, but without a hand calculator it can be difficult.

Step	x_L	c	x_R	$P(x_L)$	$P(c)$	$P(x_R)$
0	1	1.5	2	negative	positive	positive
1	1	1.25	1.5	negative	negative	positive
2	1.25	1.375	1.5	negative	negative	positive
3	1.375	1.4375	1.5	negative	positive	positive
4	1.375	1.40625	1.4375	negative	negative	positive
5	1.40625	1.421875	1.4375	negative	positive	positive
6	1.40625	1.4140625	1.421875	negative	negative	positive
7	1.4140625	1.41796875	1.421875	negative	positive	positive
8	1.4140625	1.416015625	1.41796875	negative	positive	positive

In step 7, the bounds x_R and x_L agree to only one decimal place; our approximation of $\sqrt{2}$ is 1.4. In step 8, x_R and x_L agree to two decimal places. Thus, $\sqrt{2} \approx 1.41$. ■

■ EXERCISE 11.4

In Exercises 1–10, show that each equation has at least one real root between the numbers specified.

1. $2x^2 + x - 3 = 0$; $-2, -1$
2. $2x^3 + 17x^2 + 31x - 20 = 0$; $-1, 2$
3. $3x^3 - 11x^2 - 14x = 0$; 4, 5
4. $2x^3 - 3x^2 + 2x - 3 = 0$; 1, 2
5. $x^4 - 8x^2 + 15 = 0$; 1, 2
6. $x^4 - 8x^2 + 15 = 0$; 2, 3
7. $30x^3 + 10 = 61x^2 + 39x$; 2, 3
8. $30x^3 + 10 = 61x^2 + 39x$; $-1, 0$
9. $30x^3 + 10 = 61x^2 + 39x$; 0, 1
10. $5x^3 - 9x^2 - 4x + 9 = 0$; $-1, 2$
11. Use binary chopping to evaluate $\sqrt{3}$ to two decimal places.
12. Use binary chopping to evaluate $\sqrt[3]{53}$ to two decimal places.
13. Use binary chopping to evaluate $\sqrt{5}$ to three decimal places.
14. Use binary chopping to evaluate $\sqrt[3]{102}$ to three decimal places.
15. Use binary chopping to find a root of $2x^3 - x^2 + 2x - 1 = 0$ to two decimal places.
16. Use binary chopping to find a root of $35x^3 + 12x^2 + 8x + 1 = 0$ to one decimal place.

CHAPTER SUMMARY

Key Words

binary chopping   (11.4)
bounds on roots   (11.2)

depressed equation   (11.3)
Descartes' rule of signs   (11.2)

factor theorem   (11.1)   remainder theorem   (11.1)
fundamental theorem of algebra   roots of multiplicity k   (11.2)
   (11.1)   zeros of a polynomial   (11.1)

Key Ideas

(11.1)   Every polynomial with complex coefficients (which includes real coefficients) and positive degree has a complex zero.

The Remainder Theorem.   If $P(x)$ is any polynomial and r is any number, and $P(x)$ is divided by $x - r$, the remainder is $P(r)$.

The Factor Theorem.   Let $P(x)$ be any polynomial and let r be any number. Then, $P(r) = 0$ if and only if $x - r$ is a factor of $P(x)$.

(11.2)   If multiple roots are counted individually, a polynomial equation $P(x) = 0$ with complex coefficients (which includes real coefficients) and degree $n > 0$ has exactly n roots among the complex numbers.

Complex roots of polynomial equations with real coefficients occur in conjugate pairs.

Descartes' Rule of Signs.   If $P(x)$ is a polynomial with real coefficients, the number of positive roots of the polynomial equation $P(x) = 0$ is either equal to the number of variations in sign of $P(x)$ or less than that by an even number.
   The number of negative roots of $P(x) = 0$ is either equal to the number of variations in sign of $P(-x)$ or less than that by an even number.

Let the lead coefficient of the polynomial $P(x)$ with real coefficients be positive, and do a synthetic division of the coefficients of $P(x)$ by the positive number c. If none of the terms in the last row is negative, then c is an upper bound for the real roots of $P(x) = 0$.
   If $P(x)$ is divided synthetically by a negative number d, and the signs in the last row alternate, then d is a lower bound for the real roots of $P(x) = 0$.

(11.3)   If the polynomial equation $P(x) = a_n x^n + a_{n-1} x^{n-1} + a_{n-2} x^{n-2} + \cdots + a_1 x + a_0 = 0$ has integral coefficients, and the rational number p/q (written in lowest terms) is a root of the equation, then p is a factor of the constant term a_0, and q is a factor of the lead coefficient a_n.

(11.4)   Let $P(x)$ be a polynomial with real coefficients. If $P(a)$ and $P(b)$ have opposite signs, then there is at least one number r between a and b for which $P(r) = 0$.

REVIEW EXERCISES

In Review Exercises 1–4, let $P(x) = 4x^4 + 2x^3 - 3x - 2$. Use synthetic division to evaluate the polynomial for the given value.

1. $P(0)$ **2.** $P(2)$ **3.** $P(-3)$ **4.** $P(\frac{1}{2})$

In Review Exercises 5–8, use the factor theorem to decide whether each statement is true. If not, so indicate.

5. $x - 2$ is a factor of $x^3 + 4x^2 - 2x + 4$.

6. $x + 3$ is a factor of $2x^4 + 10x^3 + 4x^2 + 7x + 21$.

7. $x - 5$ is a factor of $x^5 - 3125$.   **8.** $x - 6$ is a factor of $x^5 - 6x^4 - 4x + 24$.

9.   Find the three cube roots of -64.   **10.**   Find the three cube roots of 343.

11.   Find the polynomial of lowest degree with zeros of -1, 2, and $\frac{3}{2}$.

12.   Find the polynomial equation of lowest degree with roots of 1, -3, and $\frac{1}{2}$.

13.   Use synthetic division to find the quotient when the polynomial $3x^4 + 2x^2 + 3x + 7$ is divided by $x - 3$.

14.   Use synthetic division to find the quotient when the polynomial $5x^5 - 4x^4 + 3x^3 - 2x^2 + x - 1$ is divided by $x + 2$.

15.   How many roots does the polynomial equation $3x^6 - 4x^5 + 3x + 2 = 0$ have?

16.   How many roots does the equation $x^{1984} - 1 = 0$ have?

In Review Exercises 17–20, use Descartes' rule of signs to find the number of possible positive, negative, and nonreal roots.

17. $3x^4 + 2x^3 - 4x + 2 = 0$ **18.** $4x^5 + 3x^4 + 2x^3 + x^2 + x = 7$

19. $x^4 + x^2 + 24{,}567 = 0$ **20.** $-x^7 - 5 = 0$

21.   Find all roots of the equation $2x^3 + 17x^2 + 41x + 30 = 0$.

22.   Find all roots of the equation $3x^3 + 2x^2 + 2x = 1$.

23.   Show that $5x^3 + 37x^2 + 59x + 18 = 0$ has a root between $x = 0$ and $x = -1$.

24.   Show that $6x^3 - x^2 - 10x - 3 = 0$ has a root between $x = 1$ and $x = 2$.

25.   Use binary chopping to find $\sqrt{7}$ to the nearest hundredth.

26.   Use binary chopping to find an approximation of the root of the equation $0 = 3x - 1$. What is the exact root?

CHAPTER ELEVEN TEST

In Problems 1–2, use the remainder theorem to find the remainder in each division.

1. $x - 1 \overline{)\, x^5 - 3x + 3}$ **2.** $x + 2 \overline{)\, x^6 - 3}$

In Problems 3–4, use the factor theorem to decide whether each statement is true.

3. $x - 2$ is a factor of $x^5 - 32$.   **4.** $x + 1$ is a factor of $x^9 - 9$.

In Problems 5–6, find the polynomials of lowest degree with the indicated zeros.

5. $x = 2, x = 3$ **6.** $x = 1, x = -1, x = i, x = -i$

In Problems 7–8, consider the polynomial $P(x) = 2x^3 + x^2 - 3x + 1$.

7.   Use synthetic division to find $P(2)$.   **8.**   Use synthetic division to find $P(-1)$.

In Problems 9–13, consider the polynomial equation $P(x) = x^5 - 9x^4 + 21x^3 + x^2 - 30x = 0$.

9.   How many solutions does $P(x)$ have?

10.   Use Descartes' rule of signs to determine the maximum number of possible positive real solutions.

11.   Use Descartes' rule of signs to determine the maximum number of possible negative real solutions.

12.   Use synthetic division to determine if 4 is an upper bound for the solutions of $P(x) = 0$.

13.   Use synthetic division to determine if -2 is a lower bound for the solutions of $P(x) = 0$.

In Problems 14–15, consider the polynomial equation $P(x) = x^3 + 2x^2 + x + 2 = 0$.

14.   Find all real solutions of $P(x) = 0$, if any.   **15.**   Find all nonreal solutions of $P(x)$, if any.

In Problems 16–17, consider the polynomial equation $P(x) = 2x^3 + x^2 - 5x + 2 = 0$.

16.   Find all real solutions of $P(x) = 0$, if any.   **17.**   Find all nonreal solutions of $P(x)$, if any.

In Problems 18–19, consider the polynomial equation $P(x) = x^3 + 2x^2 - 3x - 6 = 0$.

18.   Is there a solution of $P(x) = 0$ between $x = 1$ and $x = 2$?

19.   Is there a solution of $P(x) = 0$ between $x = -4$ and $x = -1$?

20.   Use binary chopping to find the value of $\sqrt{7}$ to one decimal place.

Exponential and Logarithmic Functions

In this chapter, we discuss two functions that are important in certain applications of mathematics. The *exponential function* can be used, for example, to compute compound interest and to provide a model for population growth and radioactivity. The *logarithmic function* can be used to simplify calculations, measure the acidity of a solution or the intensity of an earthquake, and determine safe noise levels for factory workers.

12.1 EXPONENTIAL FUNCTIONS

In the discussion of exponential functions, we will consider expressions such as 3^x where x is a *real* number. Because we have only defined 3^x where x is a *rational* number, we must now give meaning to 3^x where x is an *irrational* number.

To this end, we consider the expression $3^{\sqrt{2}}$, where $\sqrt{2}$ is the irrational number 1.414213562 . . . . Because $1 < \sqrt{2} < 2$, it can be shown that $3^1 < 3^{\sqrt{2}} < 3^2$. Similarly, $1.4 < \sqrt{2} < 1.5$, so $3^{1.4} < 3^{\sqrt{2}} < 3^{1.5}$.

The value of $3^{\sqrt{2}}$ is bounded by two numbers involving only rational powers of 3, as shown in the following list. As the list continues, $3^{\sqrt{2}}$ gets squeezed into a smaller and smaller interval:

$$3^1 = 3 \qquad < 3^{\sqrt{2}} < 9 \qquad = 3^2$$
$$3^{1.4} \approx 4.656 \qquad < 3^{\sqrt{2}} < 5.196 \qquad \approx 3^{1.5}$$
$$3^{1.41} \approx 4.7070 \qquad < 3^{\sqrt{2}} < 4.7590 \qquad \approx 3^{1.42}$$
$$3^{1.414} \approx 4.727695 < 3^{\sqrt{2}} < 4.732892 \approx 3^{1.415}$$

There is exactly one real number that is larger than any of the increasing numbers on the left of the previous list and less than all the decreasing numbers on the right. By definition, that number is $3^{\sqrt{2}}$.

To find an approximation for $3^{\sqrt{2}}$, we can press the following keys on a calculator:

3 $\boxed{y^x}$ 2 $\boxed{\sqrt{}}$ $\boxed{=}$

The display will show 4.7288044. Thus,

$$3^{\sqrt{2}} \approx 4.7288044$$

In general, if b is a *positive* real number and x is *any* real number, then the exponential expression b^x represents a unique positive real number. If $b > 0$ and $b \neq 1$, the function defined by the equation $y = f(x) = b^x$ is called an **exponential function**.

Definition.   The **exponential function with base b** is defined by the equation

$$y = f(x) = b^x$$

where $b > 0$ and $b \neq 1$.

The domain of the exponential function with base b is the set of real numbers. Its range is the set of positive real numbers.

Example 1   Graph the exponential functions $y = 2^x$ and $y = 7^x$.

Solution   Calculate several pairs (x, y) that satisfy each equation. Plot the points and join them with a smooth curve. The graph of $y = 2^x$ appears in Figure 12-1a, and the graph of $y = 7^x$ appears in Figure 12-1b.

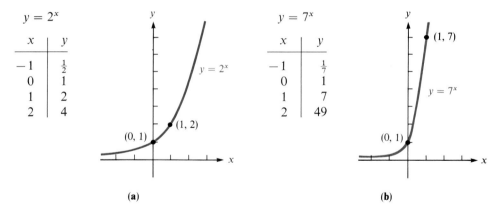

$y = 2^x$	
x	y
-1	$\frac{1}{2}$
0	1
1	2
2	4

$y = 7^x$	
x	y
-1	$\frac{1}{7}$
0	1
1	7
2	49

(a)   (b)

Figure 12-1

Note that $y = 2^x$ and $y = 7^x$ are *increasing* functions, that each graph passes through the point $(0, 1)$, and that the x-axis is an asymptote of each graph. Note also that the graph of $y = 2^x$ passes through the point $(1, 2)$, and that of $y = 7^x$ passes through the point $(1, 7)$.   ■

Example 2   Graph the exponential functions $y = \left(\dfrac{1}{2}\right)^x$ and $y = \left(\dfrac{1}{7}\right)^x$.

Solution   Calculate and plot several pairs (x, y) that satisfy each equation. The graph of $y = (\frac{1}{2})^x$ appears in Figure 12-2a, and the graph of $y = (\frac{1}{7})^x$ in Figure 12-2b.

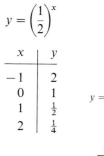

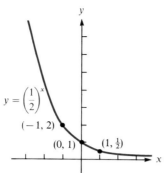

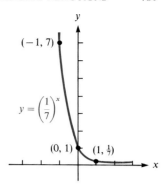

Figure 12-2

Note that $y = (\frac{1}{2})^x$ and $y = (\frac{1}{7})^x$ are *decreasing* functions, that each graph passes through the point $(0, 1)$, and that the x-axis is an asymptote of each graph. Note also that the graph of $y = (\frac{1}{2})^x$ passes through the point $(1, \frac{1}{2})$, and that of $y = (\frac{1}{7})^x$ passes through $(1, \frac{1}{7})$. ∎

Examples 1 and 2 suggest that an exponential function with base b is either increasing (for $b > 1$) or decreasing (for $0 < b < 1$). Thus, distinct real numbers x will determine distinct values b^x. The exponential function, therefore, is one-to-one. This fact is the basis of an important fact involving exponential expressions.

> If $b > 0$, $b \neq 1$ and $b^r = b^s$, then $r = s$.

Example 3   On the same set of coordinate axes, graph $y = \left(\dfrac{3}{2}\right)^x$ and $y = \left(\dfrac{2}{3}\right)^x$.

Solution   Plot several pairs (x, y) that satisfy each equation and draw each graph as in Figure 12-3.

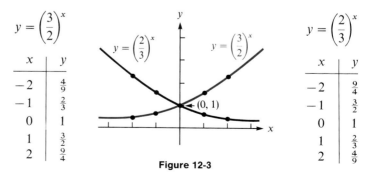

Figure 12-3

Note that $\frac{3}{2}$ and $\frac{2}{3}$ are reciprocals of each other and that the graphs are reflections of each other in the y-axis. This follows from the properties of exponents. If the number x in the first equation $y = (\frac{3}{2})^x$ is replaced with $-x$, the result is the second equation, $y = (\frac{2}{3})^x$.

$$y = \left(\frac{3}{2}\right)^x$$

$$y = \left(\frac{3}{2}\right)^{-x} \qquad \text{Replace } x \text{ with } -x.$$

$$= \left(\frac{2}{3}\right)^x$$

The symmetry discussed in this example is not the same as the y-axis symmetry discussed in Chapter 9. There, you considered curves that are reflections of themselves in the y-axis. Here, *two* curves are reflections of each other.   ■

We summarize the properties of the exponential function with base b as follows:

If $b > 1$, then $y = b^x$ defines an *increasing* function.
If $0 < b < 1$, then $y = b^x$ defines a *decreasing* function.
The graph of $y = b^x$ passes through the points $(0, 1)$ and $(1, b)$.
The x-axis is an asymptote of the graph of $y = b^x$.
The graphs of $y = b^x$ and $y = b^{-x}$ are reflections of each other in the y-axis.
The exponential function defined by $y = b^x$ is one-to-one.

Example 4   Graph the function $y = 2(3^{x/2})$, and determine its domain and range.

Solution   Plot several pairs (x, y) that satisfy the equation $y = 2(3^{x/2})$, and join them with a smooth curve. The graph appears in Figure 12-4. From the graph, you can

$y = 2(3^{x/2})$

x	y
-2	$\frac{2}{3}$
0	2
2	6
4	18

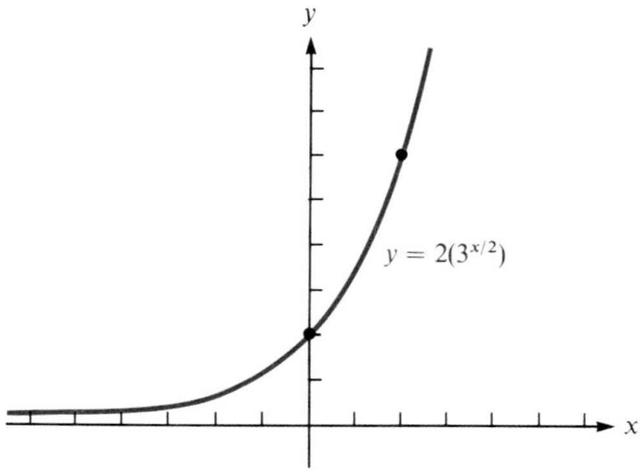

$y = 2(3^{x/2})$

Figure 12-4

see that the domain of the function is the set of real numbers, and the range is the set of positive real numbers. Note that the y-intercept is 2. ■

A mathematical description of an observed event is called a **model** of that event. Many observed events can be modeled by functions defined by equations of the form

$$y = f(x) = ab^{kx} \qquad \text{Remember that } ab^{kx} \text{ means } a(b^{kx}).$$

where a, b, and k are constants. If f is an increasing function such as the one in Example 4, then y is said to **grow exponentially**. If f is a decreasing function, then y **decays exponentially**.

A decreasing function determined by an equation of the form $y = ab^{kx}$ provides a model for a process called **radioactive decay**. The atomic structure of radioactive material changes as the material emits radiation. Uranium, for example, decays into thorium, then into radium, and eventually into lead.

Experiments have determined the time it takes for *half* of a given amount of radioactive material to decompose. This time, called the **half-life**, is constant for any given substance. The amount A of radioactive material present decays exponentially according to the model

Radioactive Decay Formula

$$A = A_0 2^{-t/h}$$

where A_0 is the amount present at $t = 0$ and h is the material's half-life.

Example 5 If the half-life of radium is 1600 years, how much of a 1-gram sample will remain after 660 years?

Solution In this example, $A_0 = 1$, $h = 1600$, and $t = 660$. Substitute these values into the equation $A = A_0 2^{-t/h}$ and simplify:

$$A = A_0 2^{-t/h}$$
$$A = 1 \cdot 2^{-660/1600}$$
$$= 1 \cdot 2^{-0.4125} \qquad \text{Use a calculator.}$$
$$\approx 0.75$$

After 660 years, approximately 0.75 gram of radium will remain. ■

One application of exponential growth in banking is **compound interest**. If the interest earned on money in a savings account is allowed to accumulate, then that interest also earns interest. The amount in the account grows exponentially according to the equation

Compound Interest Formula

$$A = A_0 \left(1 + \frac{r}{k}\right)^{kt}$$

where A represents the amount in the account after t years, with interest paid k times a year at an annual rate of r percent on an initial deposit A_0.

Example 6   If $1000 is deposited in an account that earns 12% interest compounded quarterly, how much will be in the account after 20 years?

Solution   Calculate A using the formula

$$A = A_0\left(1 + \frac{r}{k}\right)^{kt}$$

with $A_0 = 1000$, $r = 0.12$, and $t = 20$. Because quarterly interest payments occur four times a year, $k = 4$.

$$A = A_0\left(1 + \frac{r}{k}\right)^{kt}$$

$$A = 1000\left(1 + \frac{0.12}{4}\right)^{4 \cdot 20}$$

$$= 1000(1.03)^{80}$$

$$= 10{,}640.89 \qquad \text{Use a calculator.}$$

In 20 years, the account will contain $10,640.89.   ■

■ EXERCISE 12.1

In Exercises 1–8, graph each exponential function.

1. $y = 2^x$

2. $y = \left(\dfrac{1}{2}\right)^x$

3. $y = \left(\dfrac{1}{3}\right)^x$

4. $y = 3^x$

5. $y = 2.5^x$

6. $y = \left(\dfrac{2}{5}\right)^x$

7. $y = 10^x$

8. $y = (0.1)^x$

In Exercises 9–18, graph the function defined by each equation.

9. $y = 5(2^x)$

10. $y = 2(5^x)$

11. $y = 3(2^x)$

12. $y = 4(5^x)$

13. $y = 2^{x+1}$

14. $y = 2^{x-3}$

15. $y = 2 + 3^x$

16. $y = 3^x - 3$

17. $y = 2^{|x|}$

18. $y = 2^{-x}$

In Exercises 19–24, find the value of b, if any, that would cause the graph of $y = b^x$ to look like the graph indicated.

19.

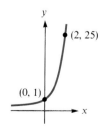

20.

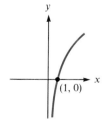

21.

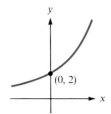

22.

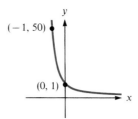

23.

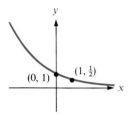

24.

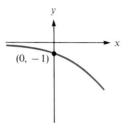

25. A radioactive material decays according to the formula $A = A_0(\frac{2}{3})^t$, where A_0 is the amount present initially and t is measured in years. What amount will be present in 5 years?

26. Tritium, a radioactive isotope of hydrogen, has a half-life of 12.4 years. Of an initial sample of 0.05 gram, how much will remain after 100 years?

27. The half-life of radioactive carbon-14 is 5700 years. How much of an initial sample will remain after 3000 years?

28. The **biological half-life** of the asthma medication theophylline is 4.5 hours for smokers and 8 hours for nonsmokers. Twelve hours after administering equal doses, what is the ratio of drug retained in a smoker's system to that in a nonsmoker's?

In Exercises 29–32, assume that there are no deposits or withdrawals.

29. An initial deposit of $500 earns 10% interest compounded quarterly. How much will be in the account in 10 years?

30. An initial deposit of $1000 earns 12% interest compounded monthly. How much will be in the account in $4\frac{1}{2}$ years?

31. If $1 had been invested in 1776 at 5% interest compounded annually, what would it be worth in 2076?

32. Some financial institutions pay daily interest, compounded by the **360/365 method**, by using the formula

$$A = A_0\left(1 + \frac{r}{360}\right)^{365t} \qquad (t \text{ is in years})$$

Using this method, what will an initial investment of $1000 be worth in 5 years assuming a 12% annual interest rate?

33. A colony of 6 million bacteria is growing in a culture medium. The population P after t hours is modeled by the formula $P = (6 \times 10^6)(2.3)^t$. What is the population after 4 hours?

34. The population of North Rivers is growing exponentially according to the model $P = 375(1.3)^t$, where t is measured in years from the present date. What will be the population in 3 years?

35. A bacteria culture grows exponentially according to the model $P = P_0 \, 2^{t/24}$, where P_0 is the initial population and t is measured in hours. By what factor will it have increased in 36 hours?

36. The charge remaining in a battery is decreasing exponentially according to the formula $C = C_0(0.7)^t$, where C is the charge remaining after t days, and C_0 is the initial charge. If a charge of 2.471×10^{-5} coulombs remains after 7 days, what was the battery's initial charge?

12.2 BASE-e EXPONENTIAL FUNCTIONS

In mathematical models of natural events, one number appears often as the base of an exponential function. This number is e. The symbol e was first used by Leonhard Euler (1707–1783). We introduce this important number by allowing k in the compound interest formula

$$A = A_0 \left(1 + \frac{r}{k} \right)^{kt}$$

to become very large. To see what happens, we let $k = rp$, where p is a new variable, and proceed as follows:

$$
\begin{aligned}
A &= A_0 \left(1 + \frac{r}{k} \right)^{kt} \\
&= A_0 \left(1 + \frac{r}{rp} \right)^{rpt} && \text{Substitute } rp \text{ for } k. \\
&= A_0 \left(1 + \frac{1}{p} \right)^{rpt} && \text{Simplify } \frac{r}{rp}. \\
&= A_0 \left[\left(1 + \frac{1}{p} \right)^{p} \right]^{rt} && \text{Remember that } (x^m)^n = x^{mn}.
\end{aligned}
$$

Because r is a positive constant and $k = rp$, it follows that as k becomes very large, then so does p. The question of what happens to the value of A becomes tied to the question: What happens to the value of $(1 + 1/p)^p$ as p becomes very large?

Some results calculated for increasing values of p appear in Table 12-1.

Table 12-1

p	$\left(1 + \dfrac{1}{p}\right)^{p}$
1	2
10	2.5937
1,000	2.7169
1,000,000	2.7182805
⋮	⋮

The results in the table suggest that as p increases, the value of $(1 + 1/p)^p$ approaches a fixed number. This number is e, an irrational number with a decimal representation of 2.71828182845904. . . .

If interest on an amount A_0 is compounded more and more often, the number p grows large without bound and the formula

$$A = A_0 \left[\left(1 + \frac{1}{p} \right)^p \right]^{rt}$$

becomes

Continuous
Compound Interest
Formula

$$A = A_0 e^{rt}$$

When the amount invested grows exponentially according to the formula $A = A_0 e^{rt}$, interest is said to be **compounded continuously**.

Example 1   If $1000 accumulates interest at an annual rate of 12% compounded continuously, how much money will be in the account in 20 years?

Solution $A = A_0 e^{rt}$

$A = 1000 e^{(0.12)(20)}$ Substitute 1000 for A_0, 0.12 for r, and 20 for t.

$\approx 1000(11.02318)$ Use a calculator.

$\approx 11{,}023.18$

In 20 years, the account will contain $11,023.18.   ∎

The exponential function $y = e^x$ is so important that it is often called *the* exponential function.

Example 2   Graph the exponential function.

Solution   Use a calculator to find several pairs (x, y) that satisfy the equation $y = e^x$. Plot them and join them with a smooth curve. The graph appears in Figure 12-5.

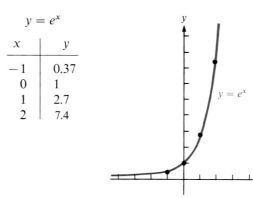

$y = e^x$

x	y
-1	0.37
0	1
1	2.7
2	7.4

Figure 12-5   ∎

Example 3   Graph $y = 3e^{-x/2}$.

Solution   Plot several pairs (x, y) that satisfy the equation $y = 3e^{-x/2}$ and join them with a smooth curve. The graph appears in Figure 12-6.

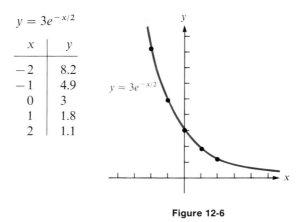

$y = 3e^{-x/2}$

x	y
-2	8.2
-1	4.9
0	3
1	1.8
2	1.1

$y = 3e^{-x/2}$

Figure 12-6   ■

A function similar to the exponential function provides a model for **population growth**. A population (of people, fish, bacteria, or other living organisms) changes with time. Many factors—such as birth and death rates, immigration, pollution, diet, wars, plagues, and famines—affect the population. Models of population growth that account for several factors are very complex. A simpler model, called the **Malthusian model of population growth**, assumes a constant birth rate B and constant death rate D and incorporates no other factors. In that model, the population P grows exponentially according to the formula

Population Growth Formula

$$P = P_0 e^{kt}$$

where P_0 is the population at $t = 0$, and $k = B - D$. If t is measured in years, then k is called the **annual growth rate**.

Example 4   The annual birth rate in a certain country is 19 per 1000 population, and the death rate is 7 per 1000. What would the Malthusian model predict the population of the country to be in 50 years if the current population is 2.3 million?

Solution   Use the Malthusian model of population growth

$$P = P_0 e^{kt}$$

The number k is the difference between the birth and death rates. The birth rate, B, is $\frac{19}{1000}$, or 0.019. The death rate, D, is $\frac{7}{1000}$, or 0.007. Thus

$$k = B - D$$
$$k = 0.019 - 0.007$$
$$= 0.012$$

Substitute 2.3×10^6 for P_0, 50 for t, and 0.012 for k in the equation $P = P_0 e^{kt}$ and simplify:

$$P = P_0 e^{kt}$$
$$P = (2.3 \times 10^6)e^{(0.012)(50)}$$
$$= (2.3 \times 10^6)(1.82)$$
$$= 4.2 \times 10^6$$

After 50 years, the population will exceed 4 million.   ∎

Example 5   A population of 1000 bacteria doubles in 8 hours. Assuming the Malthusian model, what will be the population in 12 hours?

Solution   The population P grows according to the formula $P = P_0 e^{kt}$. Let $P_0 = 1000$, $P = 2000$, and $t = 8$. Then proceed as follows:

$$P = P_0 e^{kt}$$
$$2000 = 1000e^{k8} \qquad \text{Substitute 2000 for } P, \text{ 1000 for } P_0, \text{ and 8 for } t.$$
$$2 = e^{k \cdot 8} \qquad \text{Divide both sides by 1000.}$$
$$2^{1/8} = (e^{k \cdot 8})^{1/8} \qquad \text{Raise both sides to the } \tfrac{1}{8} \text{ power.}$$
$$2^{1/8} = e^k$$

We know that the population grows according to the formula

$$P = 1000e^{kt}$$
$$= 1000(2^{1/8})^t \qquad \text{Substitute } 2^{1/8} \text{ for } e^k.$$
$$= 1000(2^{t/8})$$

To find the population after 12 hours, substitute 12 for t and simplify:

$$P = 1000(2^{t/8})$$
$$= 1000(2^{12/8})$$
$$= 1000(2^{3/2})$$
$$\approx 1000(2.8284) \qquad \text{Use a calculator.}$$
$$\approx 2800$$

After 12 hours, there are approximately 2800 bacteria.   ∎

▪ EXERCISE 12.2

In Exercises 1–8, graph the function defined by each equation. **Use a calculator.**

1. $y = -e^x$ **2.** $y = e^{-x}$ **3.** $y = e^{-0.5x}$ **4.** $y = -e^{2x}$

5. $y = 2e^{-x}$ **6.** $y = -3e^x$ **7.** $y = e^x + 1$ **8.** $y = 2 - e^x$

In Exercises 9–16, tell whether the graph of $y = e^x$ could look like the graph indicated.

9.

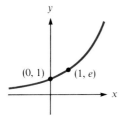

10.

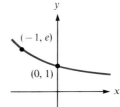

11.

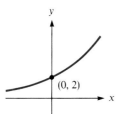

12.

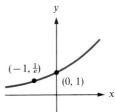

13.

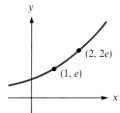

14.

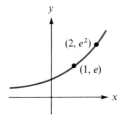

15.

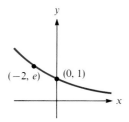

16.

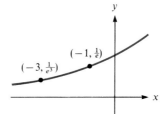

In Exercises 17–21, assume no deposits or withdrawals.

17. An initial investment of \$5000 earns 11.2% interest compounded continuously. What will the investment be worth in 12 years?

18. An initial deposit of \$2000 earns 8% interest compounded continuously. How much will be in the account in 15 years?

19. An account now contains \$11,180. It has been accumulating interest at 13%, compounded continuously, for 7 years. What was the initial deposit?

20. An account now contains \$3610. It has been accumulating interest at $10\frac{1}{2}\%$ compounded continuously. How much was in the account 1 year ago?

21. An initial deposit grows at a continuously compounded annual rate of 14%. If $5000 is in the account after 2 years, how much will be in the account after 6 years?

22. The growth of a population is modeled by

$$P = 173e^{0.03t}$$

How large will the population be when $t = 20$?

23. The decline of a population is modeled by

$$P = 1.2 \times 10^6 e^{-0.008t}$$

How large will the population be when $t = 30$?

24. The world population is approximately 5 billion and is growing at an annual rate of 1.9%. Assuming a Malthusian growth model, what will be the world's population in 30 years?

25. Assuming a Malthusian model and an annual growth rate of 1.9%, by what factor will the world's current population increase in 50 years?

26. A country's population is now 2×10^5 people and is expected to double every 20 years. Assuming a Malthusian model, what will be the population in 35 years?

27. The population of a small town is presently 140 and is expected to grow exponentially, tripling every 15 years. Assuming a Malthusian model, what can the city planners expect the population to be in 5 years?

28. The amount A of a drug remaining in a person's system after t hours is given by the formula

$$A = A_0 e^{kt}$$

where A_0 is the initial dose. After 2.3 hours, one-half of an initial dose of triazolam, a drug for treating insomnia, will remain. What percent will remain after 24 hours?

29. On a sheet of graph paper, graph the function $y = \frac{1}{2}(e^x + e^{-x})$ for values of x between -2 and 2. You'll need to calculate and plot about five or six points before joining them with a smooth curve. The graph looks like a parabola, but it is not. It is called a **catenary** and is important in the design of power distribution networks because it represents the shape of a cable drooping between its supporting poles.

30. The value of e can be calculated to any degree of accuracy by adding the first several terms of the following list.

$$1, 1, \frac{1}{2}, \frac{1}{2 \cdot 3}, \frac{1}{2 \cdot 3 \cdot 4}, \ldots, \frac{1}{2 \cdot 3 \cdot \cdots \cdot n - 1}, \ldots$$

The more terms that are added, the closer the sum is to the actual value of e. Calculate an approximation of the value of e by adding the first eight values in the preceding list. To how many decimal places is your sum accurate?

12.3 LOGARITHMIC FUNCTIONS

Because an exponential function defined by $y = b^x$ is one-to-one, it has an inverse that is defined by the equation $x = b^y$. To express this inverse function in the form $y = f^{-1}(x)$, we must solve the equation $x = b^y$ for y. To do so, we need the following definition.

Definition.   The **logarithmic function with base b** is defined by the equation

$$y = \log_b x$$

where $b > 0$ and $b \neq 1$. This equation is equivalent to the exponential equation

$$x = b^y$$

The domain of the logarithmic function is the set of positive real numbers. Its range is the set of real numbers.

Because the function $y = \log_b x$ is the inverse of the one-to-one exponential function $y = b^x$, the function $y = \log_b x$ is one-to-one also.

The previous definition implies that any pair (x, y) that satisfies the equation $x = b^y$ also satisfies the equation $y = \log_b x$ (or $\log_b x = y$). Thus,

$$\log_5 25 = 2 \quad \text{because} \quad 25 = 5^2$$
$$\log_7 1 = 0 \quad \text{because} \quad 1 = 7^0$$
$$\log_{16} 4 = \frac{1}{2} \quad \text{because} \quad 4 = 16^{1/2}$$

and

$$\log_2 \frac{1}{8} = -3 \quad \text{because} \quad \frac{1}{8} = 2^{-3}$$

Note that in each case, the logarithm of a number is an exponent.

Because the domain of the logarithmic function is the set of positive real numbers, it is impossible to find the logarithm of 0 or of a negative number.

Example 1   Find the value of y in each of the following equations: **a.** $\log_5 1 = y$, **b.** $\log_2 8 = y$, and   **c.** $\log_7 \frac{1}{7} = y$.

Solution   **a.**   Change the equation $\log_5 1 = y$ into the equivalent exponential form $1 = 5^y$. Because $1 = 5^0$, it follows that $y = 0$. Hence, $\log_5 1 = 0$.

b. $\log_2 8 = y$ is equivalent to $8 = 2^y$. Because $8 = 2^3$, it follows that $y = 3$. Hence, $\log_2 8 = 3$.

c. $\log_7 \frac{1}{7} = y$ is equivalent to $\frac{1}{7} = 7^y$. Because $\frac{1}{7} = 7^{-1}$, it follows that $y = -1$. Hence, $\log_7 \frac{1}{7} = -1$.   ■

Example 2   Find the value of a in each equation: **a.** $\log_3 \frac{1}{9} = a$,   **b.** $\log_a 32 = 5$, and   **c.** $\log_9 a = -\frac{1}{2}$.

Solution   a. $\log_3 \frac{1}{9} = a$ is equivalent to $\frac{1}{9} = 3^a$. Because $\frac{1}{9} = 3^{-2}$, it follows that $a = -2$.

b. $\log_a 32 = 5$ is equivalent to $a^5 = 32$. Because $2^5 = 32$, it follows that $a = 2$.

c. $\log_9 a = -\frac{1}{2}$ is equivalent to $9^{-1/2} = a$. Because $9^{-1/2} = \frac{1}{3}$, it follows that $a = \frac{1}{3}$.   ■

Example 3   Graph the logarithmic function defined by $y = \log_2 x$.

Solution   The equation $y = \log_2 x$ is equivalent to the equation $x = 2^y$. Calculate and plot pairs (x, y) that satisfy the equation $x = 2^y$ and connect them with a smooth curve. The graph appears in Figure 12-7.

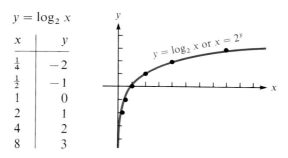

x	y
$\frac{1}{4}$	-2
$\frac{1}{2}$	-1
1	0
2	1
4	2
8	3

Figure 12-7   ■

Example 4   Graph the logarithmic function defined by $y = \log_{1/2} x$.

Solution   Rewrite $y = \log_{1/2} x$ as $x = (\frac{1}{2})^y$ and proceed as in Example 3. The graph appears in Figure 12-8.

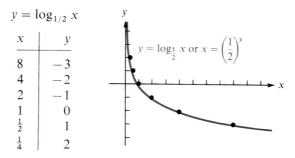

x	y
8	-3
4	-2
2	-1
1	0
$\frac{1}{2}$	1
$\frac{1}{4}$	2

Figure 12-8   ■

Just as $y = e^x$ represents an important exponential function, $y = \log_e x$, denoted as $y = \ln x$, represents an important logarithmic function.

Example 5   Graph the function determined by $y = \ln x$.

Solution   The equation $y = \ln x$ is equivalent to the equation $x = e^y$. Calculate and plot pairs (x, y) that satisfy the equation $x = e^y$ and connect them with a smooth curve. The graph appears in Figure 12-9.

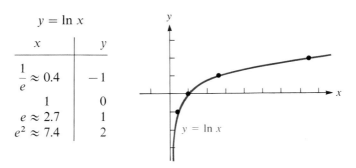

$y = \ln x$

x	y
$\dfrac{1}{e} \approx 0.4$	-1
1	0
$e \approx 2.7$	1
$e^2 \approx 7.4$	2

Figure 12-9   ■

Examples 3–5 suggest that the graphs of logarithmic functions are similar to those in Figure 12-10. If $b > 1$, the logarithmic function is *increasing* as in Figure 12-10a, and if $0 < b < 1$, the logarithmic function is *decreasing* as in Figure 12-10b. Note that each graph of $y = \log_b x$ passes through the points $(1, 0)$ and $(b, 1)$ and that the y-axis is an asymptote to the curve.

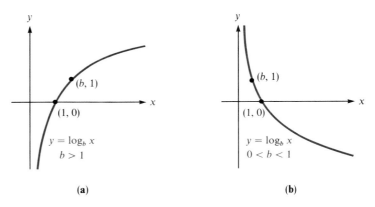

(a)   (b)

Figure 12-10

Because the logarithmic function is one-to-one, we have the following property of logarithms:

If $\log_b r = \log_b s$, then $r = s$.

Several other properties of logarithms can be found by expressing the properties of exponents in logarithmic form.

Properties of Logarithms.   If M, N, p, and b are positive numbers, and $b \neq 1$, then

1. $\log_b 1 = 0$ 2. $\log_b b = 1$

3. $\log_b b^x = x$ 4. $b^{\log_b x} = x$

5. $\log_b MN = \log_b M + \log_b N$ 6. $\log_b \dfrac{M}{N} = \log_b M - \log_b N$

7. $\log_b M^p = p \log_b M$

Proof   Properties 1 through 4 follow directly from the definition of logarithm. To prove Property 5, we let $x = \log_b M$ and $y = \log_b N$. Using the definition of logarithm, we write these equations in the form

$$M = b^x \qquad \text{and} \qquad N = b^y$$

We multiply equal quantities by equal quantities to get

$$MN = b^x b^y$$

or

$$MN = b^x$$

By the definition of a logarithm, this equation is equivalent to

$$\log_b MN = x + y$$

We substitute the values of x and y to complete the proof of Property 5.

$$\log_b MN = \log_b M + \log_b N$$

To prove Property 7, we let $x = \log_b M$, write this equation in exponential form, and raise both sides of the resulting equation to the pth power.

$$M = b^x$$
$$(M)^p = (b^x)^p$$
$$M^p = b^{px}$$

Using the definition of logarithms in reverse gives

$$\log_b M^p = px$$

Substituting the value for x completes the proof.

$$\log_b M^p = p \log_b M \qquad \qquad \square$$

The proof of Property 6 is similar to the proof of Property 5 and is left as an exercise.

Property 5 of logarithms asserts that the logarithm of the *product* of two numbers is equal to the *sum* of their logarithms. The logarithm of a *sum* or a *difference* usually does not simplify. In general,

$$\log_b(M + N) \neq \log_b M + \log_b N$$

Similarly,

$$\log_b(M - N) \neq \log_b M - \log_b N$$

Property 6 of logarithms asserts that the logarithm of the *quotient* of two numbers is equal to the *difference* of their logarithms. The logarithm of a quotient is not the quotient of the logarithms:

$$\log_b \frac{M}{N} \neq \frac{\log_b M}{\log_b N}$$

Example 6   Simplify each expression: **a.** $\log_3 1$,   **b.** $\log_4 4$,   **c.** $\log_7 7^3$, and
d. $b^{\log_b 3}$.

Solution   **a.**   By Property 1, $\log_3 1 = 0$.

b.   By Property 2, $\log_4 4 = 1$.

c.   By Property 3, $\log_7 7^3 = 3$.

d.   By Property 4, $b^{\log_b 3} = 3$.   ■

The properties of logarithms are often used to expand or condense a logarithmic expression, as in the following two examples.

Example 7   Assume that x, y, z, and b are positive numbers. Use the properties of logarithms to write each expression in terms of the logarithms of x, y, and z:

a. $\log_b \dfrac{xy}{z}$,   **b.** $\log_b(x^3 y^2 z)$, and   **c.** $\log_b \dfrac{y^2 \sqrt{z}}{x}$.

Solution   **a.** $\log_b \dfrac{xy}{z} = \log_b(xy) - \log_b z$ Use Property 6.

$= \log_b x + \log_b y - \log_b z$ Use Property 5.

b. $\log_b(x^3 y^2 z) = \log_b x^3 + \log_b y^2 + \log_b z$ Use Property 5 twice.

$= 3 \log_b x + 2 \log_b y + \log_b z$ Use Property 7 twice.

c. $\log_b \dfrac{y^2 \sqrt{z}}{x} = \log_b(y^2 \sqrt{z}) - \log_b x$ Use Property 6.

$= \log_b y^2 + \log_b \sqrt{z} - \log_b x$ Use Property 5.

$= \log_b y^2 + \log_b z^{1/2} - \log_b x$ Write $\sqrt{z}$ as $z^{1/2}$.

$= 2 \log_b y + \dfrac{1}{2} \log_b z - \log_b x$ Use Property 7 twice.   ■

Example 8 Assume that x, y, z, and b are positive numbers and $b \neq 1$. Use the properties of logarithms to write each expression as the logarithm of a single quantity:

a. $2 \log_b x + \dfrac{1}{3} \log_b y$

and

b. $\dfrac{1}{2} \log_b(x - 2) - \log_b y + 3 \log_b z$

Solution **a.** $2 \log_b x + \dfrac{1}{3} \log_b y = \log_b x^2 + \log_b y^{1/3}$ Use Property 7 twice.

$\qquad\qquad = \log_b(x^2 y^{1/3})$ Use Property 5.

$\qquad\qquad = \log_b(x^2 \sqrt[3]{y})$ Write $y^{1/3}$ as $\sqrt[3]{y}$.

b. $\dfrac{1}{2} \log_b(x - 2) - \log_b y + 3 \log_b z$

$\qquad = \log_b(x - 2)^{1/2} - \log_b y + \log_b z^3$ Use Property 7 twice.

$\qquad = \log_b \dfrac{(x - 2)^{1/2}}{y} + \log_b z^3$ Use Property 6.

$\qquad = \log_b \dfrac{z^3 \sqrt{x - 2}}{y}$ Use Property 5 and write $(x - 2)^{1/2}$ as $\sqrt{x - 2}$. ∎

Example 9 Given that $\log_{10} 2 \approx 0.3010$ and $\log_{10} 3 \approx 0.4771$, find approximate values for
a. $\log_{10} 18$ and   **b.** $\log_{10} 2.5$.

Solution **a.** $\log_{10} 18 = \log_{10}(2 \cdot 3^2)$ Factor 18.

$\qquad\qquad = \log_{10} 2 + \log_{10} 3^2$ Use Property 5.

$\qquad\qquad = \log_{10} 2 + 2 \log_{10} 3$ Use Property 7.

$\qquad\qquad \approx 0.3010 + 2(0.4771)$ Substitute the value of each logarithm.

$\qquad\qquad \approx 1.2552$ Simplify.

b. $\log_{10} 2.5 = \log_{10}\left(\dfrac{5}{2}\right)$ Write 2.5 as $\frac{5}{2}$.

$\qquad\qquad = \log_{10} 5 - \log_{10} 2$ Use Property 6.

$\qquad\qquad = \log_{10} \dfrac{10}{2} - \log_{10} 2$ Write 5 as $\frac{10}{2}$.

$\qquad\qquad = \log_{10} 10 - \log_{10} 2 - \log_{10} 2$ Use Property 6.

$\qquad\qquad = 1 - 2 \log_{10} 2$ Use Property 2 and combine terms.

$\qquad\qquad \approx 1 - 2(0.3010)$ Substitute 0.3010 for $\log_{10} 2$.

$\qquad\qquad \approx 0.3980$ Simplify. ∎

▪ EXERCISE 12.3

In Exercises 1–8, write each equation in exponential form.

1. $\log_3 81 = 4$ **2.** $\log_7 7 = 1$ **3.** $\log_{1/2} \dfrac{1}{8} = 3$ **4.** $\log_{1/5} 1 = 0$

5. $\log_4 \dfrac{1}{64} = -3$ **6.** $\log_6 \dfrac{1}{36} = -2$ **7.** $\log_x y = z$ **8.** $\log_m n = \dfrac{1}{2}$

In Exercises 9–16, write each equation in logarithmic form.

9. $8^2 = 64$ **10.** $10^3 = 1000$ **11.** $4^{-2} = \dfrac{1}{16}$ **12.** $3^{-4} = \dfrac{1}{81}$

13. $\left(\dfrac{1}{2}\right)^{-5} = 32$ **14.** $\left(\dfrac{1}{3}\right)^{-3} = 27$ **15.** $x^y = z$ **16.** $m^n = p$

In Exercises 17–40, find the value of x. A calculator is of no value.

17. $\log_2 8 = x$ **18.** $\log_{1/2} \dfrac{1}{8} = x$ **19.** $\log_{1/2} 8 = x$ **20.** $\log_{25} 5 = x$

21. $\log_5 25 = x$ **22.** $\log_8 x = 2$ **23.** $\log_x 8 = 3$ **24.** $\log_7 x = 0$

25. $\log_7 x = 1$ **26.** $\log_4 x = \dfrac{1}{2}$ **27.** $\log_x \dfrac{1}{16} = -2$ **28.** $\log_{125} x = \dfrac{2}{3}$

29. $\log_{100} \dfrac{1}{1000} = x$ **30.** $\log_{5/2} \dfrac{4}{25} = x$ **31.** $\log_{27} 9 = x$ **32.** $\log_{12} x = 0$

33. $\log_x 5^3 = 3$ **34.** $\log_x 5 = 1$ **35.** $\log_x \dfrac{9}{4} = 2$ **36.** $\log_x \dfrac{\sqrt{3}}{3} = \dfrac{1}{2}$

37. $\log_{\sqrt{3}} x = -4$ **38.** $\log_\pi x = 3$ **39.** $\log_{2\sqrt{2}} x = 2$ **40.** $\log_4 8 = x$

In Exercises 41–48, graph the function determined by each equation.

41. $y = \log_5 x$ **42.** $y = \log_{1/5} x$ **43.** $y = \log_{1/3} x$ **44.** $y = \log_3 x$

45. $y = \ln x^2$ **46.** $y = \ln 2x$ **47.** $y = (\ln x) - 1$ **48.** $y = \ln(x - 1)$

In Exercises 49–54, graph each pair of equations on one set of coordinate axes.

49. $y = \log_3 x$ and $y = \log_3(3x)$ **50.** $y = \log_3 x$ and $y = \log_3 \left(\dfrac{x}{3}\right)$

51. $y = \log_2 x$ and $y = \log_2(x + 1)$ **52.** $y = \log_2 x$ and $y = \log_2(-x)$

53. $y = \log_5 x$ and $y = 5^x$ **54.** $y = \ln x$ and $y = e^x$

In Exercises 55–60, find the value of b, if any, that would cause the graph of $y = \log_b x$ to look like the graph indicated.

55.

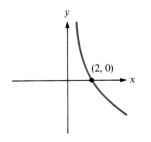

56.

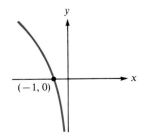

57.

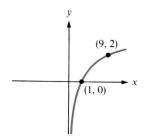

58.

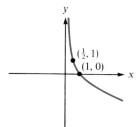

59.

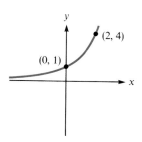

60.

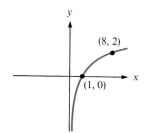

In Exercises 61–64, tell whether the graph of $y = \ln x$ could look like the graph indicated.

61.

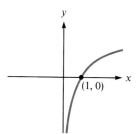

62.

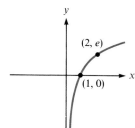

63.

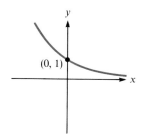

64.

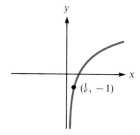

In Exercises 65–72, assume that x, y, z, and b are positive numbers. Use the properties of logarithms to write each expression in terms of the logarithms of x, y, and z.

65. $\log_b xyz$

66. $\log_b \dfrac{x}{yz}$

67. $\log_b \left(\dfrac{x}{y}\right)^2$

68. $\log_b (xz)^{1/3}$

69. $\log_b x\sqrt{z}$

70. $\log_b \dfrac{\sqrt[3]{x}}{\sqrt[3]{y-z}}$

71. $\log_b \sqrt[4]{\dfrac{x^3 y^2}{z^4}}$

72. $\log_b x\sqrt{\dfrac{\sqrt{y}}{z}}$

In Exercises 73–80, assume that x, y, and z are positive numbers. Use the properties of logarithms to write each expression as the logarithm of a single quantity.

73. $\log_b(x + 1) - \log_b x$

74. $\log_b x + \log_b(x + 2) - \log_b 8$

75. $2 \log_b x + \dfrac{1}{3} \log_b y$

76. $-2 \log_b x - 3 \log_b y + \log_b z$

77. $-3 \log_b x - 2 \log_b y + \dfrac{1}{2} \log_b z$

78. $3 \log_b(x + 1) - 2 \log_b(x + 2) + \log_b x$

79. $\log_b\left(\dfrac{x}{z} + x\right) - \log_b\left(\dfrac{y}{z} + y\right)$

80. $\log_b(xy + y^2) - \log_b(xz + yz) + \log_b x$

In Exercises 81–102, tell if the given statement is true. If it is not true, so indicate.

81. $\log_b ab = \log_b a + 1$

82. $\log_b \dfrac{1}{a} = -\log_b a$

83. $\log_b 0 = 1$

84. $\log_b 2 = \log_2 b$

85. $\log_b(x + y) \neq \log_b x + \log_b y$

86. $\log_b xy = (\log_b x)(\log_b y)$

87. If $\log_a b = c$, then $\log_b a = c$.

88. If $\log_a b = c$, then $\log_b a = \dfrac{1}{c}$.

89. $\log_7 7^7 = 7$

90. $7^{\log_7 7} = 7$

91. $\log_b(-x) = -\log_b x$

92. If $\log_b a = c$, then $\log_b a^p = pc$.

93. $\dfrac{\log A}{\log B} = \log A - \log B$

94. $\log(A - B) = \dfrac{\log A}{\log B}$

95. $\log \dfrac{1}{5} = -\log 5$

96. $3 \log_b \sqrt[3]{a} = \log_b a$

97. $\dfrac{1}{3} \log_b a^3 = \log_b a$

98. A logarithm cannot be negative.

99. $\log 10^3 = 3(10^{\log 3})$

100. If x lies between 0 and 1, $\log_b x$ is negative.

101. $\log_{4/3} y = -\log_{3/4} y$

102. $\log_b y + \log_{1/b} y = 0$

In Exercises 103–112, assume that $\log_{10} 4 \approx 0.6021$, $\log_{10} 7 \approx 0.8451$, and $\log_{10} 9 \approx 0.9542$. Use these values and the properties of logarithms to find the approximate value of each quantity.

103. $\log_{10} 28$

104. $\log_{10} \dfrac{7}{4}$

105. $\log_{10} 2.25$

106. $\log_{10} 36$

107. $\log_{10} \dfrac{63}{4}$

108. $\log_{10} \dfrac{4}{63}$

109. $\log_{10} 252$

110. $\log_{10} 49$

111. $\log_{10} 112$

112. $\log_{10} 324$

113. Prove Property 6 of logarithms: $\log_b \dfrac{M}{N} = \log_b M - \log_b N$.

114. Prove that $-\log_b x = \log_{1/b} x$.

115. Show that $e^{x \ln a} = a^x$.

116. Show that $e^{\ln x} = x$.

117.   Show that $\ln(e^x) = x$.

118.   Show that the equation $t = -\dfrac{1}{k} \ln\left(1 - \dfrac{C}{M}\right)$ can be written in the form $t = \ln\left(\dfrac{M}{M - C}\right)^{1/k}$.

12.4   APPLICATIONS OF LOGARITHMS

Before the widespread use of calculators, logarithms provided the only practical way to simplify many difficult computations. To use logarithms, mathematicians had to rely on extensive tables. Today, however, logarithms of numbers are easy to find with a calculator.

For computational purposes, base-10 logarithms are the most convenient. For this reason, base-10 logarithms have been called **common logarithms**. In this book, if the base b is not indicated in the notation $\log x$, always assume that b is 10;

$$\log A \quad \text{means} \quad \log_{10} A$$

Because the number e appears often in mathematical models of events in nature, base-e logarithms are called **natural logarithms**. They are also called **Napierian logarithms** after John Napier (1550–1617). As we have seen, natural logarithms are usually denoted by the symbol $\ln x$ rather than $\log_e x$.

$$\ln x \quad \text{means} \quad \log_e x$$

Example 1   Use a calculator to find   **a.** $\log 2.34$ and   **b.** $\ln 2$.

Solution   **a.**   To find $\log 2.34$, enter the number 2.34 and press the $\boxed{\log}$ key. (You may have to press a $\boxed{2^{\text{nd}}}$ function key first.) The display should read .3692158574. Hence,

$$\log 2.34 \approx 0.3692$$

b.   To find $\ln 2.34$, enter the number 2.34 and press the $\boxed{\ln x}$ key. The display should read .850150929. Hence,

$$\ln 2.34 \approx 0.8502 \qquad\qquad ■$$

Example 2   Find the value of x in each equation: **a.** $\log x = 0.7482$,   **b.** $\ln x = 1.335$, and   **c.** $\ln x = \log 5.5$.

Solution   **a.** $\log x = 0.7482$ is equivalent to $10^{0.7482} = x$. To find x, enter the number 10, press the $\boxed{y^x}$ key, enter the number .7482, and press $\boxed{=}$. The display reads 5.6001544. Hence,

$$x \approx 5.6$$

If your calculator has a $\boxed{10^x}$ key, simply enter .7482 and press it to get the same result. (You might have to press a $\boxed{2^{\text{nd}}}$ function key.)

b. $\ln x = 1.335$ is equivalent to $e^{1.335} = x$. To find x, enter the number 1.335 and press the $\boxed{e^x}$ key. The display reads 3.79999595. Hence,

$$x \approx 3.8$$

c. $\ln x = \log 5.5$ is equivalent to $e^{\log 5.5} = x$. To find x, enter 5.5 and press $\boxed{\log}$ followed by $\boxed{e^x}$. The display reads 2.0966958. Hence,

$$x \approx 2.1 \qquad \blacksquare$$

Example 3   Use a calculator to verify Property 5 of logarithms by showing that

$$\ln[(3.7)(15.9)] = \ln 3.7 + \ln 15.9$$

Solution   Calculate the left- and the right-hand sides of the equation separately, and compare the results. To calculate $\ln[(3.7)(15.9)]$, enter the number 3.7, press $\boxed{\times}$, enter 15.9, and press $\boxed{=}$. Then press $\boxed{\ln x}$. The display should read 4.0746519.
   To calculate $\ln 3.7 + \ln 15.9$, enter the number 3.7, press $\boxed{\ln x}$, press $\boxed{+}$, enter 15.9, press $\boxed{\ln x}$, and press $\boxed{=}$. The display should also read 4.0746519. Because the left- and the right-hand sides are equal, the equation is verified.

$$\blacksquare$$

Applications of Base-10 Logarithms

Example 4   In chemistry, common logarithms are used to express the acidity of solutions. The more acidic a solution, the greater the concentration of hydrogen ions. This concentration is indicated indirectly by the **pH scale**, or **hydrogen-ion index**. The pH of a solution is defined by the equation

$$pH = -\log[H^+]$$

where $[H^+]$ is the hydrogen-ion concentration in gram-ions per liter. Pure water has a few free hydrogen ions—$[H^+]$ is approximately 10^{-7} gram-ions per liter. The pH of pure water is

$$
\begin{aligned}
pH &= -\log 10^{-7} \\
&= -(-7)\log 10 &&\text{Use Property 7.} \\
&= -(-7) &&\text{Use Property 2.} \\
&= 7
\end{aligned}
$$

Seawater has a pH of approximately 8.5, and its hydrogen-ion concentration is found by solving the equation $8.5 = -\log_{10}[H^+]$ for $[H^+]$.

$$
\begin{aligned}
8.5 &= -\log[H^+] \\
-8.5 &= \log[H^+] \\
[H^+] &= 10^{-8.5} &&\text{Change the equation from logarithmic to} \\
& &&\text{exponential form.}
\end{aligned}
$$

Use a calculator to find that

$$[H^+] \approx 3.2 \times 10^{-9} \text{ gram-ions per liter} \qquad \blacksquare$$

Example 5 In electrical engineering, common logarithms are used to express the voltage gain (or loss) of an electronic device such as an amplifier or a length of transmission line. The unit of gain (or loss), called the **decibel**, is defined by a logarithmic relation. If E_O is the output voltage of a device, and E_I is the input voltage, the decibel voltage gain is defined as

$$\text{Decibel voltage gain} = 20 \log \frac{E_O}{E_I}$$

If, for example, the input to an amplifier is 0.5 volt and the output is 40 volts, the decibel voltage gain is calculated by substituting these values into the formula:

$$\text{Decibel voltage gain} = 20 \log \frac{E_O}{E_I}$$

$$\text{Decibel voltage gain} = 20 \log \frac{40}{0.5}$$

$$= 20 \log 80$$

$$\approx 20(1.9031)$$

$$\approx 38$$

The amplifier provides a 38-decibel voltage gain.   ■

Example 6 In seismology, common logarithms are used to measure the intensity of earthquakes on the **Richter scale**. The intensity R is given by

$$R = \log \frac{A}{P}$$

where A is the amplitude of the tremor (measured in micrometers) and P is the period of the tremor (the time of one oscillation of the earth's surface, measured in seconds). To calculate the intensity of an earthquake with an amplitude of 10,000 micrometers (1 centimeter) and a period of 0.1 second, substitute 10,000 for A and 0.1 for P in the formula and simplify:

$$R = \log \frac{A}{P}$$

$$R = \log \frac{10,000}{0.1}$$

$$= \log 100,000$$

$$= \log 10^5$$

$$= 5 \log 10 \qquad \text{Use Property 7.}$$

$$= 5 \qquad \text{Use Property 2.}$$

The earthquake measures 5 on the Richter scale.   ■

Applications of Base-e Logarithms

Example 7   In electronics, a mathematical model of the time required for charging a battery uses the natural logarithm function. A battery charges at a rate that depends on how close it is to being fully charged; it charges fastest when it is most discharged. The charge C at any instant t is modeled by the formula

$$C = M(1 - e^{-kt})$$

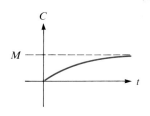

Figure 12-11

where M is the theoretical maximum charge that the battery can hold and k is a positive constant that depends on the battery and the charger. Plotting the variable C against t gives a curve like that in Figure 12-11. Notice that the full charge M is never attained; the actual charge can come very close to M, however, if the battery is charged long enough. To determine how long it will take a battery to reach a given charge C, solve the equation $C = M(1 - e^{-kt})$ for t as follows:

$$C = M(1 - e^{-kt})$$

$$\frac{C}{M} = 1 - e^{-kt} \qquad \text{Divide both sides by } M.$$

$$\frac{C}{M} - 1 = -e^{-kt} \qquad \text{Add } -1 \text{ to both sides.}$$

$$1 - \frac{C}{M} = e^{-kt} \qquad \text{Multiply both sides by } -1.$$

$$\ln\left(1 - \frac{C}{M}\right) = -kt \qquad \begin{array}{l}\text{Change the exponential equation to}\\ \text{logarithmic form.}\end{array}$$

$$-\frac{1}{k} \ln\left(1 - \frac{C}{M}\right) = t \qquad \text{Multiply both sides by } -\frac{1}{k}.$$

The formula that determines the time t required to charge a battery to a given level C is

$$t = -\frac{1}{k} \ln\left(1 - \frac{C}{M}\right)$$ ■

Example 8   In physiology, experiments suggest that the relationship of loudness and intensity of sound is a logarithmic one known as the **Weber-Fechner law**: the apparent loudness L of a sound is proportional to the natural logarithm of its actual intensity I. In symbols,

$$L = k \ln I$$

For example, what actual increase in intensity will cause a doubling of the apparent loudness? If the original loudness is L_0, caused by an actual intensity I_0, then $L_0 = k \ln I_0$. To double the apparent loudness, multiply both sides of the equation by 2 and use Property 7 of logarithms:

$$2L_0 = 2k \ln I_0$$
$$= k \ln(I_0)^2$$

Thus, to double the apparent volume of a sound, the actual intensity must be squared.   ■

Example 9   If a population grows exponentially at an annual rate r, the time t required for the population to double is called the **doubling time** and is given by the formula

$$t = \frac{\ln 2}{r}$$

The world's population is growing at the rate of approximately 2% per year. If this growth rate continues, when will the population be double its present size?

Solution   Because the population is growing at the rate 2%, substitute $r = 0.02$ into the formula and determine t.

$$t = \frac{\ln 2}{r}$$

$$t = \frac{\ln 2}{0.02}$$

$$\approx \frac{0.69315}{0.02}$$

$$\approx 31$$

At the current rate of growth, the world population is doubling every 31 years.
    ■

■ **EXERCISE 12.4**

In Exercises 1–12, use a calculator to find the value of the variable. Express all answers to four decimal places.

1. $\log 3.25 = x$ **2.** $\log 0.57 = y$ **3.** $\ln 0.93 = y$ **4.** $\ln 7.39 = x$

5. $\log(\ln 1.7) = x$ **6.** $\ln(\log 9.8) = y$ **7.** $\ln y = 4.24$ **8.** $\log y = 0.926$

9. $\log x = -3.71$ **10.** $\ln y = -0.28$ **11.** $\log x = \ln 8$ **12.** $\ln y = \log 7$

In Exercises 13–18, use a calculator to verify each equation.

13. $\log[(3.7)(2.9)] = \log 3.7 + \log 2.9$ **14.** $\ln \dfrac{9.3}{2.1} = \ln 9.3 - \ln 2.1$

15. $\ln(3.7)^3 = 3 \ln 3.7$ **16.** $\log 3.2 = \dfrac{\ln 3.2}{\ln 10}$

17. $\log \sqrt{14.1} = \frac{1}{2} \log 14.1$

18. $\ln 9.7 = \dfrac{\log 9.7}{\log 2.71828}$

19. Find the pH of a solution with a hydrogen-ion concentration of 1.7×10^{-5} gram-ions per liter.

20. What is the hydrogen-ion concentration of a saturated solution of calcium hydroxide whose pH is 13.2?

21. The pH of apples can range from 2.9 to 3.3. What is the range in the hydrogen-ion concentration?

22. The hydrogen-ion concentration of sour pickles is 6.31×10^{-4}. What is the pH?

23. The decibel voltage gain of an amplifier is 29. If the output is 20 volts, what is the input voltage?

24. The decibel voltage gain of an amplifier is 35. If the input signal is 0.05 volt, what is the output voltage?

25. The power output (or input) of an amplifier is directly proportional to the square of the voltage output (or input). Show that the formula for decibel voltage gain is

$$\text{Decibel voltage gain} = 10 \log \frac{P_O}{P_I}$$

where P_O is the power output and P_I is the power input.

26. An amplifier produces an output of 30 watts when driven by an input signal of 0.1 watt. What is the amplifier's voltage gain? See Exercise 25.

27. An earthquake has an amplitude of 5000 micrometers and a period of 0.2 second. What does it measure on the Richter scale?

28. An earthquake with amplitude of 8000 micrometers measures 6 on the Richter scale. What is its period?

29. An earthquake with a period of $\frac{1}{4}$ second measures 4 on the Richter scale. What is its amplitude?

30. By what factor must the period of an earthquake change to increase its severity by 1 point on the Richter scale? Assume that the amplitude remains constant.

31. If a battery can reach half of its full charge in 6 hours, how long will it take the battery to reach a 90% charge? Assume that the battery was fully discharged when it began charging.

32. A battery reaches 80% of a full charge in 8 hours. If it started charging when it was fully discharged, how long did it take to reach a 40% charge?

33. If the intensity of a sound is doubled, what is the apparent change in loudness?

34. What increase in intensity of sound will cause an apparent tripling of the loudness?

35. A town's population grows at the rate of 12% per year. How long will it take the population to double?

36. A population growing at an annual rate r will triple in a time t given by the formula

$$t = \frac{\ln 3}{r}$$

How long will it take the population of the town in Exercise 35 to triple?

37. In business, equipment is often depreciated using the double-declining balance method. A piece of equipment with a life expectancy of N years, costing C dollars, will depreciate to a value V dollars in n years, where n is given by the formula

$$n = \frac{\log V - \log C}{\log\left(1 - \dfrac{2}{N}\right)}$$

A computer with an expected life of 5 years cost $37,000. It has depreciated to $8000. How old is it?

38. A typewriter worth $470 when new has an expected life of 12 years. It is now worth $189. How old is the typewriter? See Exercise 37.

39. If P dollars are invested at the end of each year in an annuity earning annual interest at the rate r, then the amount in the account will be A dollars after n years, where

$$n = \frac{\log\left[\dfrac{Ar}{P} + 1\right]}{\log(1 + r)}$$

If $1000 is invested each year in an annuity bearing annual interest of 12%, when will the account contain $20,000?

40. If $5000 is invested each year in an annuity bearing annual interest of 8%, when will the account contain $50,000? See Exercise 39.

41. Use the formula $P = P_0 e^{rt}$ to verify that P will become double the initial population P_0 when $t = \dfrac{\ln 2}{r}$.

42. Use the formula $P = P_0 e^{rt}$ to verify that P will become triple the initial population P_0 when $t = \dfrac{\ln 3}{r}$.

43. Explain why it is impossible to calculate $\ln(\log 0.9)$.

44. Explain why it is impossible to calculate $\log(\ln 1)$.

12.5   EXPONENTIAL AND LOGARITHMIC EQUATIONS

An **exponential equation** is one that contains the variable in an exponent. A **logarithmic equation** is one that involves logarithms of expressions that contain the variable.

Example 1   Solve the exponential equation $3^x = 5$.

Solution   Because the logarithms of equal numbers are equal, you can take the common logarithm of both sides of the equation. Property 7 of logarithms then provides a means for moving the variable x from its position as an exponent to a position as a factor.

$$3^x = 5$$

$\log 3^x = \log 5$ Take the common logarithm of both sides.

$x \log 3 = \log 5$ Use Property 7 of logarithms.

1. $x = \dfrac{\log 5}{\log 3}$ Divide both sides by log 3.

$\approx \dfrac{0.6990}{0.4771}$ Substitute values for log 5 and log 3.

≈ 1.465

Thus, $x \approx 1.465$.

A careless reading of Equation 1 can lead to a common error. Because $\log \dfrac{A}{B} = \log A - \log B$, you may think that the expression $\dfrac{\log 5}{\log 3}$ also involves subtraction. It does not. The expression $\dfrac{\log 5}{\log 3}$ calls for division.   ■

Example 2   Solve the exponential equation $6^{x-3} = 2^x$.

Solution

$$6^{x-3} = 2^x$$

$\log 6^{x-3} = \log 2^x$	Take the common logarithm of both sides.
$(x - 3)\log 6 = x \log 2$	Use Property 7 of logarithms.
$x \log 6 - 3 \log 6 = x \log 2$	Remove parentheses.
$x \log 6 - x \log 2 = 3 \log 6$	Add $3 \log 6$ and $-x \log 2$ to both sides.
$x(\log 6 - \log 2) = 3 \log 6$	Factor out x from the left side.
$x = \dfrac{3 \log 6}{\log 6 - \log 2}$	Divide both sides by $\log 6 - \log 2$.
$x \approx 4.893$	Substitute values for $\log 6$ and $\log 2$ and simplify.

■

Example 3   Solve the logarithmic equation $\log x + \log(x - 3) = 1$.

Solution

$\log x + \log(x - 3) = 1$	
$\log x(x - 3) = 1$	Use Property 5 of logarithms.
$x(x - 3) = 10^1$	Use the definition of logarithm to change the equation to exponential form.
$x^2 - 3x - 10 = 0$	Remove parentheses and add -10 to both sides.
$(x + 2)(x - 5) = 0$	Factor $x^2 - 3x - 10$.

$$x + 2 = 0 \qquad \text{or} \qquad x - 5 = 0$$
$$x = -2 \qquad\qquad\quad x = 5$$

Check:

The number -2 is not a solution because it does not satisfy the equation: A negative number does not have a logarithm. Check the remaining number **5**:

$\log x + \log(x - 3) = 1$	
$\log 5 + \log(5 - 3) \stackrel{?}{=} 1$	Substitute 5 for x.
$\log 5 + \log 2 \stackrel{?}{=} 1$	
$\log(5 \cdot 2) \stackrel{?}{=} 1$	Use Property 5 of logarithms.
$\log 10 \stackrel{?}{=} 1$	
$1 = 1$	Use Property 2 of logarithms.

The solution 5 does check.   ■

Example 4   Solve the logarithmic equation $\log_b(3x + 2) - \log_b(2x - 3) = 0$.

Solution
$$\log_b(3x + 2) - \log_b(2x - 3) = 0$$
$$\log_b(3x + 2) = \log_b(2x - 3) \qquad \text{Add } \log_b(2x - 3) \text{ to both sides.}$$
$$3x + 2 = 2x - 3 \qquad \text{If } \log_b r = \log_b s, \text{ then } r = s.$$
$$x = -5 \qquad \text{Add } -2x - 2 \text{ to both sides.}$$

Check:

$$\log_b(3x + 2) - \log_b(2x - 3) = 0$$
$$\log_b[3(-5) + 2] - \log_b[2(-5) - 3] \overset{?}{=} 0$$
$$\log_b(-13) - \log_b(-13) \overset{?}{=} 0$$

Because the logarithm of a negative number does not exist, the number -5 is not a solution. The given equation has no solutions. ∎

If we know the base-a logarithm of a number, we can find the logarithm of that number to some other base b by using a formula called the **change-of-base formula**.

The Change-of-Base Formula.

$$\log_b x = \frac{\log_a x}{\log_a b}$$

Proof   We begin with the equation $\log_b x = y$ and proceed as follows:

1. $\log_b x = y$

$b^y = x$ Change the equation from logarithmic to exponential form.

$\log_a b^y = \log_a x$ Take the base-a logarithm of both sides.

$y \log_a b = \log_a x$ Use Property 7 of logarithms.

$y = \dfrac{\log_a x}{\log_a b}$ Divide both sides by $\log_a b$.

$\log_b x = \dfrac{\log_a x}{\log_a b}$ Refer to Equation 1 and substitute $\log_b x$ for y. □

If we know logarithms to base a (for example, $a = 10$), we can find the logarithm of x to a new base b. To do so, we divide the base-a logarithm of x by the base-a logarithm of b.

Example 5   Use the change-of-base formula to find $\log_3 5$.

Solution   Use the change-of-base formula with $b = 3$, $a = 10$, and $x = 5$:

$$\log_b x = \frac{\log_a x}{\log_a b}$$

$$\log_3 5 = \frac{\log_{10} 5}{\log_{10} 3} \qquad \text{Substitute 3 for } b, \text{ 10 for } a, \text{ and 5 for } x.$$

$$\approx \frac{0.6990}{0.4771} \qquad \text{Substitute values for log 5 and log 3.}$$

$$\approx 1.465 \qquad\qquad\qquad\qquad\qquad\qquad ■$$

Applications of Exponential and Logarithmic Equations

Example 6   When a living organism dies, the oxygen/carbon dioxide cycle common to all living things ceases and carbon-14, a radioactive isotope with a half-life of 5700 years, is no longer absorbed. By measuring the amount of carbon-14 present in an ancient object, archeologists can estimate the object's age and answer questions such as the following: How old is a wooden statue that contains only $\frac{1}{3}$ of its original carbon-14 content?

Solution   The amount A of radioactive material present at time t is given by the model

$$A = A_0 2^{-t/h}$$

where A_0 is the amount present initially and h is the material's half-life.

    To determine the time t when A is $\frac{1}{3}$ of A_0, substitute $A_0/3$ for A and **5700** for h and solve for t:

$$A = A_0 2^{-t/h}$$

$$\frac{A_0}{3} = A_0 2^{-t/5700} \qquad \text{Substitute } \frac{A_0}{3} \text{ for } A \text{ and 5700 for } h.$$

$$1 = 3 \cdot 2^{-t/5700} \qquad \text{Multiply both sides by } \frac{3}{A_0}.$$

$$\log 1 = \log(3 \cdot 2^{-t/5700}) \qquad \text{Take the common logarithm of both sides.}$$

$$0 = \log 3 + \log 2^{-t/5700} \qquad \text{Use Properties 1 and 5 of logarithms.}$$

$$-\log 3 = -\frac{t}{5700} \log 2 \qquad \begin{array}{l}\text{Add } -\log 3 \text{ to both sides and use}\\ \text{Property 7 of logarithms.}\end{array}$$

$$t = 5700 \left(\frac{\log 3}{\log 2} \right) \qquad \text{Multiply both sides by } -\frac{5700}{\log 2}.$$

$$\approx 9034.29$$

The wooden statue is approximately 9000 years old.   ■

Example 7   When there is sufficient food supply and space, populations of living organisms tend to increase exponentially according to the Malthusian population growth model

$$P = P_0 e^{kt}$$

where P_0 is the initial population (at $t = 0$), and k depends on the rate of growth.

The bacteria population in a laboratory culture increased from an initial population of 500 to 1500 in 3 hours. Determine the time it will take the population to reach 10,000.

Solution

$P = P_0 e^{kt}$	
$1500 = 500(e^{k \cdot 3})$	Substitute 1500 for P, 500 for P_0, and 3 for t.
$3 = e^{3k}$	Divide both sides by 500.
$3k = \ln 3$	Change the equation from exponential to logarithmic form.
$k = \dfrac{\ln 3}{3}$	Divide both sides by 3.

To find when the population will reach 10,000, substitute 10,000 for P, 500 for P_0, and $\dfrac{\ln 3}{3}$ for k in the equation $P = P_0 e^{kt}$ and solve for t:

$P = P_0 e^{kt}$	
$10,000 = 500 e^{(\ln 3/3)t}$	
$20 = e^{(\ln 3/3)t}$	Divide both sides by 500.
$\left(\dfrac{\ln 3}{3}\right) t = \ln 20$	Change the equation from exponential to logarithmic form.
$t = \dfrac{3 \ln 20}{\ln 3}$	Multiply both sides by $\dfrac{3}{\ln 3}$.
≈ 8.18	

The culture will reach the 10,000 mark in approximately 8 hours. ■

■ EXERCISE 12.5

In Exercises 1–12, solve each exponential equation.

1. $4^x = 5$ **2.** $7^x = 12$ **3.** $13^{x-1} = 2$ **4.** $5^{x+1} = 3$

5. $2^{x+1} = 3^x$ **6.** $5^{x-3} = 3^{2x}$ **7.** $2^x = 3^x$ **8.** $3^{2x} = 4^x$

9. $7^{x^2} = 10$ **10.** $8^{x^2} = 11$ **11.** $8^{x^2} = 9^x$ **12.** $5^{x^2} = 2^{5x}$

In Exercises 13–30, solve each logarithmic equation.

13. $\log(2x - 3) = \log(x + 4)$ **14.** $\log(3x + 5) - \log(2x + 6) = 0$

15. $\log \dfrac{4x + 1}{2x + 9} = 0$ **16.** $\log \dfrac{5x + 2}{2(x + 7)} = 0$ **17.** $\log x^2 = 2$ **18.** $\log x^3 = 3$

19. $\log x + \log(x - 48) = 2$

20. $\log x + \log(x + 9) = 1$

21. $\log x + \log(x - 15) = 2$

22. $\log x + \log(x + 21) = 2$

23. $\log(x + 90) = 3 - \log x$

24. $\log(x - 6) - \log(x - 2) = \log \dfrac{5}{x}$

25. $\log(x - 1) - \log 6 = \log(x - 2) - \log x$

26. $\log(2x - 3) - \log(x - 1) = 0$

27. $\log_{10} x^2 = (\log_{10} x)^2$

28. $\log_{10}(\log_{10} x) = 1$

29. $\log_3 x = \log_3 \left(\dfrac{1}{x}\right) + 4$

30. $\log_5(7 + x) + \log_5(8 - x) - \log_5 2 = 2$

In Exercises 31–34, find the logarithm with the indicated base.

31. $\log_3 7$ **32.** $\log_7 3$ **33.** $\log_{\sqrt{2}} \sqrt{5}$ **34.** $\log_\pi e$

35. The half-life of tritium is 12.4 years. How long will it take for 25% of a sample of tritium to decompose?

36. In 2 years 20% of a newly discovered radioactive element decays. What is its half-life?

37. An isotope of thorium, ^{227}Th, has a half-life of 18.4 days. How long will it take 80% of a sample to decompose?

38. An isotope of lead, ^{201}Pb, has a half-life of 8.4 hours. How many hours ago was there 30% more of the substance?

39. A parchment fragment is found in a newly discovered ancient tomb. It contains 60% of the carbon-14 that it is assumed to have had initially. Approximately how old is the fragment?

40. Only 10% of the carbon-14 in a small wooden bowl remains. How old is the bowl?

41. If $500 is deposited into an account paying 12% interest compounded semiannually, how long will it take for the account to increase to $800? How long will it take if the interest is compounded continuously?

42. If $1300 is deposited into an account paying 14% interest compounded quarterly, how long will it take to increase the amount to $2100?

43. A sum of $5000 deposited in an account grows to $7000 in 5 years. Assuming annual compounding, what interest rate is paid?

44. A quick rule of thumb for determining how long it takes an investment to double is known as the *rule of seventy*: Divide 70 by the rate (as a percent). At 5%, for example, it requires $\frac{70}{5} = 14$ years to double the capital. At 7%, it takes $\frac{70}{7} = 10$ years. Why does this formula work?

45. A bacteria culture grows according to the formula

$$P = P_0 a^t$$

If it takes 5 days for the culture to triple in size, how long does it take to double in size?

46. The intensity I of light a distance x meters beneath the surface of a lake decreases exponentially. If the light intensity at 6 meters is 70% of the intensity at the surface, at what depth will the intensity be 20%?

12.6 LOGARITHMIC CALCULATIONS (OPTIONAL)

Before calculators, logarithms provided the only reasonable way of performing certain calculations. In this section, we will show how to use logarithms as a computational aid. We begin by discussing the use of Table B in Appendix II.

Example 1   Use Table B to find the base-10 logarithm of 2.71.

Solution   To find log 2.71, run your finger down the left column of Table B until you reach 2.7. (A portion of Table B is reproduced below.) Then, slide your finger to the right until you reach entry .4330, which is in the column headed with 1. The number 0.4330 is the logarithm of 2.71. To verify that this is true, use a calculator to show that $10^{0.4330} \approx 2.71$.

N	0	1	2	3	4	5	6	7	8	9
2.6	.4150	.4166	.4183	.4200	.4216	.4232	.4249	.4265	.4281	.4298
2.7	.4314	**.4330**	.4346	.4362	.4378	.4393	.4409	.4425	.4440	.4456
2.8	.4472	.4487	.4502	.4518	.4533	.4548	.4564	.4579	.4594	.4609

∎

Example 2   Use Table B to find the base-10 logarithm of 2,710,000.

Solution   The logarithm of 2,710,000 cannot be found directly from the table. However, by using properties of logarithms, you can determine the logarithm of 2,710,000 as follows:

$$2,710,000 = 2.71 \times 10^6 \qquad \text{Write 2,710,000 in scientific notation.}$$
$$\log 2,710,000 = \log(2.71 \times 10^6) \qquad \text{Take the logarithm of both sides.}$$
$$= \log 2.71 + \log 10^6 \qquad \text{Use Property 5 of logarithms.}$$
$$= \log 2.71 + 6 \log 10 \qquad \text{Use Property 7 of logarithms.}$$
$$= \log 2.71 + 6 \qquad \text{Use Property 2 of logarithms.}$$
$$\approx 0.4330 + 6 \qquad \text{Substitute 0.4330 for log 2.71.}$$
$$\approx 6.4330 \qquad \text{Simplify.}$$

Hence, $\log 2,710,000 \approx 6.4330$. To verify that this is true, use a calculator to show that $10^{6.4330} \approx 2,710,000$. ∎

If a common logarithm is written as the sum of an integer and a positive decimal between 0 and 1, the positive decimal is called the **mantissa**, and the integer is called the **characteristic**. The characteristic of the value 0.4330 that was obtained in Example 1 is 0, and the mantissa is 0.4330. The characteristic of the value of 6.4330 that was obtained in Example 2 is 6, and the mantissa is 0.4330.

Example 3   Find log 0.000271.

Solution   Proceed as in Example 2.

$$0.000271 = 2.71 \times 10^{-4} \qquad \text{Write 0.000271 in scientific notation.}$$
$$\log 0.000271 = \log(2.71 \times 10^{-4}) \qquad \text{Take the logarithm of both sides.}$$
$$= \log 2.71 + \log 10^{-4} \qquad \text{Use Property 5 of logarithms.}$$
$$= \log 2.71 - 4 \log 10 \qquad \text{Use Property 7 of logarithms.}$$
$$= \log 2.71 - 4 \qquad \text{Use Property 2 of logarithms.}$$
$$\approx 0.4330 - 4 \qquad \text{Substitute 0.4330 for log 2.71.}$$

Hence, $\log 0.000271 \approx 0.4330 - 4$. The mantissa of $\log 0.000271$ is the positive decimal .4330 and the characteristic is -4. If the characteristic and the mantissa are combined, you have $\log 0.000271 \approx -3.5670$. To verify that this is true, use a calculator to show that $10^{-3.5670} \approx 0.000271$. ∎

From Examples 1, 2, and 3, it is apparent that the mantissa 0.4330 is determined by the digits 271, and the characteristic is determined by the location of the decimal point. The characteristic of the logarithm is the exponent of 10 used when expressing that number in scientific notation.

Example 4   If $\log N = -2.1180$, find N.

Solution   The negative number -2.1180 cannot be found in Table B. However, if you add and subtract 3 from -2.1180, you can establish a positive mantissa:

$$\log N = -2.1180$$
$$= (-2.1180 + 3) - 3 \qquad \text{Add and subtract 3.}$$
$$= 0.8820 - 3$$

The mantissa of this logarithm is 0.8820. Determine from Table B that $\log 7.62 \approx 0.8820$ or, equivalently, that $10^{0.8820} \approx 7.62$. To place the decimal point in the answer, write the equation $\log N \approx 0.8820 - 3$ in exponential form, and proceed as follows:

$$\log N \approx 0.8820 - 3$$
$$N \approx 10^{0.8820-3} \qquad \text{Change the equation from logarithmic to exponential form.}$$
$$\approx 10^{0.8820} \cdot 10^{-3} \qquad \text{Use the rule } x^{m+n} = x^m x^n.$$
$$\approx 7.62 \cdot 10^{-3} \qquad \text{Substitute 7.62 for } 10^{0.8820}$$
$$\approx 0.00762 \qquad \text{Write the number in standard form.}$$

Thus, $N \approx 0.00762$. The number 0.00762 is called the **antilogarithm** of -2.1180. ∎

Linear Interpolation

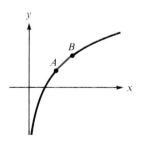

Figure 12-12

Table B in Appendix II gives values of N accurate to three significant digits, and values of the mantissas accurate to four significant digits. There is a process, called **linear interpolation**, that allows us to extend these estimates by one additional digit.

The method of linear interpolation is based on the fact that a small part of the graph of the logarithmic function appears to be a straight line. For example, the logarithmic curve in Figure 12-12 appears to be straight between points A and B. If AB is assumed to be a straight line, we can set up proportions involving points on the line AB. The following examples illustrate how.

Example 5   Use Table B to find log 3.974.

Solution   Table B does not give the value of log 3.974, but it does give the values for log 3.970 and log 3.980:

$$
\begin{array}{c}
\underset{\text{thousandths}}{10} \quad \left[\underset{\text{thousandths}}{4} \right. \left[\begin{array}{l} \log 3.970 = 0.5988 \\ \log 3.974 = ? \\ \log 3.980 = 0.5999 \end{array} \right] \underset{\text{thousandths}}{\underset{\text{ten-}}{x}} \quad \underset{\text{thousandths}}{\underset{\text{ten-}}{11}}
\end{array}
$$

Note that the difference between 3.970 and 3.980 is 10 thousandths, and that the difference between 3.970 and 3.974 is 4 thousandths. Also note that the difference between 0.5988 and 0.5999 is 11 ten-thousandths. If you assume that the graph of $y = \log x$ is a straight line between $x = 3.97$ and $x = 3.98$, then you can set up and solve the following proportion:

$$\frac{4 \text{ thousandths}}{10 \text{ thousandths}} = \frac{x \text{ ten-thousandths}}{11 \text{ ten-thousandths}}$$

$$\frac{4}{10} = \frac{x}{11}$$

$$10x = 44$$

$$x \approx 4$$

To get a good estimate of log 3.974, you must add 4 ten-thousandths to 0.5988. Hence,

$$\log 3.974 \approx 0.5992$$ ■

Example 6   Use linear interpolation to find N, where $\log N = 0.1514$.

Solution   You cannot find 0.1514 in the body of Table B, but you can find two consecutive values, 0.1492 and 0.1523, that straddle 0.1514. Hence, you can form the following chart:

$$
\begin{array}{c}
\underset{\text{thousandths}}{10} \quad \left[\underset{\text{thousandths}}{x} \right. \left[\begin{array}{l} \log 1.410 = 0.1492 \\ \log N = 0.1514 \\ \log 1.420 = 0.1523 \end{array} \right] \underset{\text{ten-thousandths}}{22} \quad \underset{\text{ten-thousandths}}{31}
\end{array}
$$

Set up the following proportion, and solve for x:

$$\frac{x}{10} = \frac{22}{31}$$

$$x = \frac{10 \cdot 22}{31}$$

$$x \approx 7$$

A good approximation for N is found by adding 7 thousandths to 1.410. Thus, $N \approx 1.417$.   ■

Example 7   Use logarithms to calculate $\dfrac{\sqrt{31.7}}{3.974}$.

Solution   First determine log 31.7 and log 3.974.

$$\log 31.7 = \log(3.17 \times 10^1) \qquad \text{Write 31.7 in scientific notation.}$$

$$= \log 3.17 + \log 10^1 \qquad \text{Use Property 5 of logarithms.}$$

$$\approx 0.5011 + 1 \log 10 \qquad \text{Find log 3.17 and use Property 7 of logarithms.}$$

$$\approx 1.5011 \qquad \text{Use Property 2 of logarithms and simplify.}$$

Finding log 3.974 requires interpolation. Refer to Example 5 to see that

$$\log 3.974 \approx 0.5992$$

Now form the equation

$$N = \frac{\sqrt{31.7}}{3.974}$$

and take the common logarithm of both sides:

$$\log N = \log \frac{\sqrt{31.7}}{3.974}$$

$$= \log \sqrt{31.7} - \log 3.974 \qquad \text{Use Property 6 of logarithms.}$$

$$= \log(31.7)^{1/2} - \log 3.974 \qquad \text{Write } \sqrt{31.7} \text{ as } (31.7)^{1/2}.$$

$$= \frac{1}{2} \log 31.7 - \log 3.974 \qquad \text{Use Property 7 of logarithms.}$$

$$\approx \frac{1}{2}(1.5011) - 0.5992 \qquad \text{Substitute the values of log 31.7 and log 3.974.}$$

$$\approx 0.1514$$

Finding the value of N requires linear interpolation. Refer to Example 6 to see that $N \approx 1.417$. Thus,

$$\frac{\sqrt{31.7}}{3.974} \approx 1.417 \qquad\blacksquare$$

Before calculators, mathematicians also relied on tables to find base-e logarithms. The next example uses a table of base-e logarithmic values.

Example 8   Use Table C in Appendix II to find the value of ln 2.34.

Solution   Look up 2.3 in the left column of Table C. (A portion of Table C is reproduced below.) Follow that row to the column headed by 4. From that position in the table, you can read that ln 2.34 ≈ 0.8502.

N	0	1	2	3	4	5	6	7	8	9
2.2	.7885	.7930	.7975	.8020	.8065	.8109	.8154	.8198	.8242	.8286
2.3	.8329	.8372	.8416	.8459	**.8502**	.8544	.8587	.8629	.8671	.8713
2.4	.8755	.8796	.8838	.8879	.8920	.8961	.9002	.9042	.9083	.9123

■

■ **EXERCISE 12.6**

In Exercises 1–8, use Table B in Appendix II to find each logarithm.

1. $\log 5.97$

2. $\log 3.15$

3. $\log 4.23$

4. $\log 9.83$

5. $\log 432,000$

6. $\log 57,900,000$

7. $\log 0.00137$

8. $\log 0.0823$

In Exercises 9–14, use Table B in Appendix II to find the value of N.

9. $\log N = 0.4969$

10. $\log N = 0.8785$

11. $\log N = 3.9232$

12. $\log N = 4.6149$

13. $\log N = -2.5467$

14. $\log N = -4.4377$

In Exercises 15–18, use linear interpolation and Table B in Appendix II to find each logarithm.

15. $\log 6.894$

16. $\log 37.43$

17. $\log 0.003456$

18. $\log 0.04376$

In Exercises 19–24, use linear interpolation and Table B in Appendix II to find N to four digits.

19. $\log N = 0.6315$

20. $\log N = 0.0437$

21. $\log N = 3.2036$

22. $\log N = 0.8508 - 4$

23. $\log N = -2.1134$

24. $\log N = -0.4467$

In Exercises 25–30, use Table B in Appendix II to calculate the approximate value of each indicated number. Do not use linear interpolation.

25. $\sqrt[3]{0.007}$

26. $(0.012)^{-0.03}$

27. $(1.05)^{25}$

28. $(\log 4.1)^{2.4}$

29. $4.3^{-5.2} + 3.1^{1.3}$

30. $(2.3 + 1.79)^{-0.157}$

In Exercises 31–34, use Table B in Appendix II to calculate each indicated value. Use linear interpolation.

31. $(34.41)(0.4455)$

32. $(0.0004519)^{2.5}$

33. $\sqrt[15]{38,670}$

34. $\dfrac{(8.034)(32.6)}{\sqrt{3.869}}$

In Exercises 35–38, use Table C in Appendix II to find x.

35. $\ln 4.65 = x$

36. $\ln 2.93 = x$

37. $\ln x = 2.0451$

38. $\ln x = 1.1969$

In Exercises 39–42, use Table C in Appendix II and the fact that $\ln 10 \approx 2.3026$ to calculate each value.

39. $\ln 29.4$

40. $\ln 751$

41. $\ln 0.00823$

42. $\ln 0.436$

CHAPTER SUMMARY

Key Words

change-of-base formula   (12.5)
characteristic   (12.6)
common logarithm   (12.4)
e   (12.2)
exponential decay   (12.1)
exponential function   (12.1)
exponential growth   (12.1)

exponential equation   (12.5)
linear interpolation   (12.6)
logarithmic equation   (12.5)
logarithmic function   (12.3)
mantissa   (12.6)
Napierian logarithm   (12.4)
natural logarithm   (12.4)

Key Ideas

(12.1)   The exponential function $y = b^x$, where $b > 0$, $b \neq 1$, and x is any real number, is one-to-one. Its domain is the set of real numbers, and its range is the set of positive real numbers.

(12.2) $e = 2.7182818\ldots$

The exponential function $y = e^x$ is one-to-one. Its domain is the set of real numbers, and its range is the set of positive real numbers.

(12.3)   The logarithmic function $y = \log_b x$, where $b > 0$, $b \neq 1$, and x is a positive real number, is one-to-one. Its domain is the set of positive real numbers and its range is the set of all real numbers.

The equation $y = \log_b x$ is equivalent to the equation $x = b^y$.

Logarithms of negative numbers do not exist.

The functions defined by $y = \log_b x$ and $y = b^x$ are inverse functions.

Properties of logarithms

1. $\log_b 1 = 0$

2. $\log_b b = 1$

3. $\log_b b^x = x$

4. $b^{\log_b x} = x$

5. $\log_b MN = \log_b M + \log_b N$

6. $\log_b \dfrac{M}{N} = \log_b M - \log_b N$

7. $\log_b M^p = p \log_b M$

(12.4)   Common logarithms are base-10 logarithms.

Natural logarithms are base-e logarithms.

(12.5)   **Change-of-base formula:** $\log_b y = \dfrac{\log_a y}{\log_a b}$

(12.6)   Logarithms can be used to simplify certain arithmetic calculations.

REVIEW EXERCISES

In Review Exercises 1–4, graph the function defined by each equation.

1. $y = \left(\dfrac{6}{5}\right)^x$ **2.** $y = \left(\dfrac{3}{4}\right)^x$ **3.** $y = \log x$ **4.** $y = \ln x$

In Review Exercises 5–8, graph each pair of equations on one set of coordinate axes.

5. $y = \left(\dfrac{1}{3}\right)^x$ and $y = \log_{1/3} x$ **6.** $y = \left(\dfrac{2}{5}\right)^x$ and $y = \log_{2/5} x$

7. $y = 4^x$ and $y = \log_4 x$ **8.** $y = 3^x$ and $y = \log_3 x$

In Review Exercises 9–30, solve each equation for x.

9. $\log_2 x = 3$ **10.** $\log_3 x = -2$ **11.** $\log_x 9 = 2$ **12.** $\log_x 0.125 = -3$

13. $\log_7 7 = x$ **14.** $\log_3 \sqrt{3} = x$ **15.** $\log_8 \sqrt{2} = x$ **16.** $\log_6 36 = x$

17. $\log_{1/3} 9 = x$ **18.** $\log_{1/2} 1 = x$ **19.** $\log_x 3 = \dfrac{1}{3}$ **20.** $\log_x 25 = -2$

21. $\log_2 x = 5$ **22.** $\log_{\sqrt{3}} x = 4$ **23.** $\log_{\sqrt{3}} x = 6$ **24.** $\log_{0.1} 10 = x$

25. $\log_x 2 = -\dfrac{1}{3}$ **26.** $\log_x 32 = 5$ **27.** $\log_{0.25} x = -1$ **28.** $\log_{0.125} x = -\dfrac{1}{3}$

29. $\log_{\sqrt{2}} 32 = x$ **30.** $\log_{\sqrt{5}} x = -4$

31. Write the following expression in terms of the logarithms of x, y, and z: $\log_b \sqrt{\dfrac{x}{yz^2}}$

32. Write the following expression as the logarithm of a single quantity:

$\dfrac{1}{2} \log_b x + 3 \log_b y - 7 \log_b z$

In Review Exercises 33–34, assume that $\log a = 0.6$, $\log b = 0.36$, and $\log c = 2.4$. Find the value of each expression.

33. $\log \dfrac{ac}{b}$ **34.** $\log a^2 b^{1/2}$

In Review Exercises 35–44, solve for x, if possible.

35. $3^x = 7$ **36.** $1.2 = (3.4)^{5.6x}$

37. $2^x = 3^{x-1}$ **38.** $\log x + \log(29 - x) = 2$

39. $\log_2 x + \log_2(x - 2) = 3$ **40.** $\log_2(x + 2) + \log_2(x - 1) = 2$

41. $e^{x \ln 2} = 9$ **42.** $\ln x = \ln(x - 1)$

43. $\ln x = \ln(x - 1) + 1$

44. $\ln x = \log_{10} x$ (*Hint:*   Use the change-of-base formula.)

45. A wooden statue excavated from the sands of Egypt has a carbon-14 content that is $\frac{1}{3}$ of that found in living wood. The half-life of carbon-14 is 5700 years. How old is the statue?

46. The pH of grapefruit juice is approximately 3.1. What is its hydrogen-ion concentration?

47. Some chemistry texts define the pH of a solution as the common logarithm of the reciprocal of the hydrogen-ion concentration:

$$pH = \log_{10} \frac{1}{[H^+]}$$

Show that this definition is equivalent to the one given in the text.

48. What is the half-life of a radioactive material if $\frac{1}{3}$ of it decays in 20 years?

In Review Exercises 49–52, use Table B in Appendix II and perform the indicated calculations. Use linear interpolation, if necessary.

49. $(34.5)(0.236)$ **50.** $\sqrt[5]{456,000}$ **51.** $\dfrac{(0.00235)^3}{(0.00896)^2}$ **52.** $\dfrac{(3.476)(0.003456)}{3.45}$

CHAPTER TWELVE TEST

1. Graph the equation $y = 3^x$.

2. A deposit of \$5000 earns 7% annual interest compounded semiannually. How much will be on deposit after 6 years? $\left(Hint:\ A = A_0 \left(1 + \dfrac{r}{k} \right)^{kt}. \right)$

In Problems 3–8, find each value of x.

3. $\log_4 16 = x$ **4.** $\log_x 32 = 5$ **5.** $\log_{16} x = \dfrac{1}{2}$ **6.** $\log 100 = x$

7. $\ln e^2 = x$ **8.** $\log(\log 10) = x$

9. Graph the equation $y = \log_3 x$.   **10.** Graph the equation $y = \ln x$.

11. Write the following expression in terms of the logarithms of x, y, and z:

$$\log_b \frac{x\sqrt{y}}{z^2}$$

12. Write the following expression as the logarithm of a single quantity:

$$2 \log_b x - \frac{1}{3} \log_b y + \log_b z$$

In Problems 13–14, assume that $\log a = 0.8$, $\log b = 3.2$, and $\log c = 1.6$. Find the value of each expression.

13. $\log(ab)$ **14.** $\log \dfrac{c}{a}$

In Problems 15–18, assume that $\log a = 1.2$, $\log b = 0.6$, and $\log c = 2.4$. Find the value of each expression.

15. $\log b^2$ **16.** $\dfrac{\log a}{\log b}$ **17.** $\log(abc)$ **18.** $\log \dfrac{ac}{b}$

In Problems 19–22, solve each equation for x.

19. $5^x = 3$

20. $3^{x-1} = 100^x$

21. $\log(5x + 2) = \log(2x + 5)$

22. $\log x + \log(x - 9) = 1$

23. Given that $\log 2 = 0.30$ and $\log 10 = 1$, find the value of $\log_2 10$.

24. Recall the formula db gain $= 20 \log \dfrac{E_O}{E_I}$. Find the db gain of an amplifier if E_O is 60 volts and E_I is 0.6 volts.

CUMULATIVE REVIEW EXERCISES (CHAPTERS 10–12)

1. Solve the system $\begin{cases} 2x + y = 5 \\ x - 2y = 0 \end{cases}$ by graphing.

2. Solve the system $\begin{cases} 3x + y = 4 \\ 2x - 3y = -1 \end{cases}$ by substitution.

3. Solve the system $\begin{cases} x + 2y = -2 \\ 2x - y = 6 \end{cases}$ by addition.

4. Solve the system $\begin{cases} \dfrac{x}{10} + \dfrac{y}{5} = \dfrac{1}{2} \\ \dfrac{x}{2} - \dfrac{y}{5} = \dfrac{13}{10} \end{cases}$ by any method.

5. Evaluate $\begin{vmatrix} 3 & -2 \\ 1 & -1 \end{vmatrix}$.

6. Use Cramer's Rule to solve the system $\begin{cases} 4x - 3y = -1 \\ 3x + 4y = -7 \end{cases}$ for y.

7. Use any method to solve the system $\begin{cases} x + y + z = 1 \\ 2x - y - z = -4 \\ x + 2y + z = 3 \end{cases}$.

8. Use Cramer's Rule to solve the system $\begin{cases} x + 2y + 3z = 6 \\ 3x + 2y + z = 6 \\ 2x + 3y + z = 6 \end{cases}$.

9. Use Gaussian elimination to solve the system $\begin{cases} x + y + z = 2 \\ x - y + 2z = 5 \\ x + 2y - z = -1 \end{cases}$.

10. Use graphing to solve the system $\begin{cases} 3x - 2y < 6 \\ y < -x + 2 \end{cases}$.

11. Use the factor theorem to decide whether $x - 2$ is a factor of $x^3 + 4x^2 - 2x + 4$.

12. Find the polynomial of lowest degree with zeros of 1, -2, and 3.

13. Find all of the solutions of the equation $2x^3 + 17x^2 + 41x + 30 = 0$.

14. Find all of the solutions of the equation $6x^4 + 11x^3 - 19x^2 + 6x = 0$.

15. Graph the function determined by $y = (\frac{1}{2})^x$.

16. Write $y = \log_2 x$ as an exponential expression.

In Exercises 17–20, find x.

17. $\log_x 25 = 2$ **18.** $\log_5 125 = x$ **19.** $\log_7 x = 0$ **20.** $\log_{11} x = 0$

21. Find the inverse of $y = \log_2 x$.   **22.** If $\log_{10} 10^x = y$, then what is the value of y?

In Exercises 23–26, assume that $\log 7 = 0.8451$ *and* $\log 14 = 1.1461$. *Evaluate each expression without using a calculator or tables. Remember that* $\log 10 = 1$.

23. $\log 98$ **24.** $\log 2$ **25.** $\log 49$ **26.** $\log \dfrac{7}{5}$

27. Solve the equation $2^{x+2} = 3^x$.   **28.** Solve the equation $2 \log 5 + \log x - \log 4 = 2$.

In Exercises 29–30, use a calculator.

29. A boat depreciates 12% each year. How much will it be worth in 9 years if its original value was $9000?

30. Find $\log_6 8$.

Conic Sections and Quadratic Systems

The graphs of second-degree equations in x and y represent figures that have interested mathematicians since the time of the ancient Greeks. However, the equations of those graphs were not carefully studied until the seventeenth century, when René Descartes (1596–1650) and Blaise Pascal (1623–1662) began investigating them.

Definition. If A, B, C, D, E, and F are real numbers, and if at least one of A, B, and C is not 0, then

$$Ax^2 + Bxy + Cy^2 + Dx + Ey + F = 0$$

is called the **general form of a second-degree equation in x and y**.

Descartes discovered that the graphs of second-degree equations always fall into one of seven categories: a single point, a pair of straight lines, a circle, a parabola, an ellipse, a hyperbola, or no graph at all. These graphs are called **conic sections** because each is the intersection of a plane and a right-circular cone. See Figure 13-1.

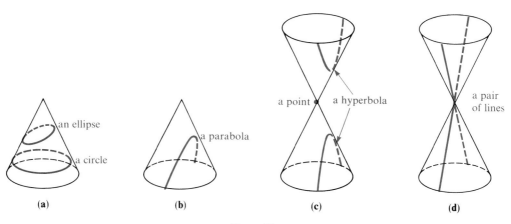

Figure 13-1

The conic sections have many practical applications. For example, the properties of parabolas are used in building flashlights, satellite antennas, and solar furnaces. The orbits of the planets around the sun are ellipses. Hyperbolas are used in navigation and the design of gears.

13.1 THE CIRCLE

The most familiar of the conic sections is the circle.

Definition.   A **circle** is the set of all points in a plane that are a fixed distance from a point called its **center**. The fixed distance is called the **radius of the circle**.

To find the general equation of a circle with radius r and center at the point $C(h, k)$, we must find all points $P(x, y)$ such that the length of the line segment PC is r. See Figure 13-2. We can use the distance formula to find the length of CP, which is r:

$$r = \sqrt{(x - h)^2 + (y - k)^2}$$

We square both sides to get

$$r^2 = (x - h)^2 + (y - k)^2$$

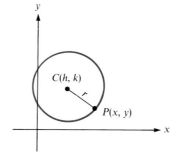

Figure 13-2

This equation is called the **standard form of the equation of a circle**.

Theorem.   Any equation that can be written in the form

$$(x - h)^2 + (y - k)^2 = r^2$$

has a graph that is a circle with radius r and center at the point (h, k).

If $r = 0$, the circle reduces to a single point called a **point circle**. If the center of the circle is the origin, then $(h, k) = (0, 0)$, and we have the following result.

> **Theorem.**   Any equation that can be written in the form
>
> $$x^2 + y^2 = r^2$$
>
> has a graph that is a circle with radius r and with center at the origin.

We can use the previous theorems to write the equations of many circles.

Example 1   Find the equation of the circle with radius 5 and center $(3, 2)$. Express the equation in general form.

Solution   Substitute **5** for r, **3** for h, and **2** for k in the standard form of the equation of the circle and simplify:

$$(x - h)^2 + (y - k)^2 = r^2$$
$$(x - 3)^2 + (y - 2)^2 = 5^2$$
$$x^2 - 6x + 9 + y^2 - 4y + 4 = 25$$
$$x^2 + y^2 - 6x - 4y - 12 = 0$$

This final equation is a special case of the general form of a second-degree equation. The coefficient of the xy-term equals 0, and the coefficients of x^2 and y^2 are both 1.   ■

Example 2   Find the equation of the circle with endpoints of its diameter at $(8, -3)$ and $(-4, 13)$.

Solution   First find the center (h, k) of the circle by finding the midpoint of its diameter. Use the midpoint formulas with $(x_1, y_1) = (8, -3)$ and $(x_2, y_2) = (-4, 13)$:

$$h = \frac{x_1 + x_2}{2} \qquad k = \frac{y_1 + y_2}{2}$$
$$h = \frac{8 + (-4)}{2} \qquad k = \frac{-3 + 13}{2}$$
$$= \frac{4}{2} \qquad\qquad = \frac{10}{2}$$
$$= 2 \qquad\qquad = 5$$

Thus, the center of the circle is the point $(h, k) = (2, 5)$.

To find the radius of the circle, use the distance formula to find the distance between the center and one endpoint of the diameter. Because one endpoint is $(8, -3)$, substitute **8** for x_1, **−3** for y_1, **2** for x_2, and **5** for y_2 in the distance formula and simplify:

$$r = \sqrt{(x_2 - x_1)^2 + (y_2 - y_1)^2}$$
$$r = \sqrt{(2 - 8)^2 + [5 - (-3)]^2}$$
$$= \sqrt{(-6)^2 + (8)^2}$$
$$= \sqrt{36 + 64}$$
$$= \sqrt{100}$$
$$= 10$$

Thus, the radius of the circle is 10.

To find the equation of the circle with radius 10 and center at the point (2, 5), substitute 2 for h, 5 for k, and 10 for r in the standard form of the equation of the circle and simplify:

$$(x - h)^2 + (y - k)^2 = r^2$$
$$(x - 2)^2 + (y - 5)^2 = 10^2$$
$$x^2 - 4x + 4 + y^2 - 10y + 25 = 100 \qquad \text{Remove parentheses.}$$
$$x^2 + y^2 - 4x - 10y - 71 = 0 \qquad \text{Simplify.} \qquad ■$$

Example 3   Graph the circle $x^2 + y^2 - 4x + 2y = 20$.

Solution   To find the coordinates of the center and the radius, write the equation in standard form by completing the square on both x and y and then simplifying:

$$x^2 + y^2 - 4x + 2y = 20$$
$$x^2 - 4x + y^2 + 2y = 20$$
$$x^2 - 4x + 4 + y^2 + 2y + 1 = 20 + 4 + 1 \qquad \text{Add 4 and 1 to both sides to complete the square.}$$
$$(x - 2)^2 + (y + 1)^2 = 25 \qquad \text{Factor } x^2 - 4x + 4 \text{ and } y^2 + 2y + 1.$$
$$(x - 2)^2 + [y - (-1)]^2 = 5^2$$

Note that the radius of the circle is 5 and the coordinates of its center are $h = 2$ and $k = -1$. Plot the center of the circle and construct the circle with a radius of 5 units, as shown in Figure 13-3.   ■

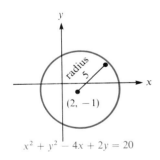

$x^2 + y^2 - 4x + 2y = 20$

Figure 13-3

■ EXERCISE 13.1

In Exercises 1–26, write an equation for the circle with the given properties.

1.   Center at the origin; $r = 1$

2.   Center at the origin; $r = 4$

3.   Center at (6, 8); $r = 4$

4.   Center at (5, 3); $r = 2$

5.   Center at $(-5, 3)$ and tangent to the y-axis

6.   Center at $(-7, -2)$ and tangent to the x-axis

7.   Center at $(3, -4)$; $r = \sqrt{2}$

8.   Center at $(-9, 8)$; $r = 2\sqrt{3}$

9.   Ends of diameter at $(3, -2)$ and $(3, 8)$

10.   Ends of diameter at $(5, 9)$ and $(-5, -9)$

11.   Ends of diameter at $(-6, 9)$ and $(-4, -7)$ **12.**   Ends of diameter at $(17, 0)$ and $(-3, -3)$

13.   Center at $(-3, 4)$ and circle passing through the origin

14.   Center at $(4, 0)$ and circle passing through the origin

15.   Center at $(-2, -6)$ and circle passing through the origin

16.   Center at $(-19, -13)$ and circle passing through the origin

17.   Center at $(0, -3)$ and circle passing through $(6, 8)$

18.   Center at $(2, 4)$ and circle passing through $(1, 1)$

19.   Center at $(5, 8)$ and circle passing through $(-2, -9)$

20.   Center at $(7, -5)$ and circle passing through $(-3, -7)$

21.   Center at $(-4, -2)$ and circle passing through $(3, 5)$

22.   Center at $(0, -7)$ and circle passing through $(0, 7)$

23.   Radius of 6 and center at the intersection of $3x + y = 1$ and $-2x - 3y = 4$

24.   Radius of 8 and center at the intersection of $x + 2y = 8$ and $2x - 3y = -5$

25.   Radius of $\sqrt{10}$ and center at the intersection of $x - y = 12$ and $3x - y = 12$

26.   Radius of $2\sqrt{2}$ and center at the intersection of $6x - 4y = 8$ and $2x + 3y = 7$

27.   Can a circle with a radius of 10 have endpoints of its diameter at $(6, 8)$ and $(-2, -2)$?

28.   Can a circle with radius 25 have endpoints of its diameter at $(0, 0)$ and $(6, 24)$?

In Exercises 29–38, graph each equation.

29. $x^2 + y^2 - 25 = 0$ **30.** $x^2 + y^2 - 8 = 0$

31. $(x - 1)^2 + (y + 2)^2 = 4$ **32.** $(x + 1)^2 + (y - 2)^2 = 9$

33. $x^2 + y^2 + 2x - 26 = 0$ **34.** $x^2 + y^2 - 4y = 12$

35. $9x^2 + 9y^2 - 12y = 5$ **36.** $4x^2 + 4y^2 + 4y = 15$

37. $4x^2 + 4y^2 - 4x + 8y + 1 = 0$ **38.** $9x^2 + 9y^2 - 6x + 18y + 1 = 0$

39.   Write the equation of the circle passing through $(0, 8)$, $(5, 3)$, and $(4, 6)$.

40.   Write the equation of the circle passing through $(-2, 0)$, $(2, 8)$, and $(5, -1)$.

41.   Find the area of the circle $3x^2 + 3y^2 + 6x + 12y = 0$. (*Hint:* $A = \pi r^2$.)

42.   Find the circumference of the circle $x^2 + y^2 + 4x - 10y - 20 = 0$. (*Hint:* $C = 2\pi r$.)

13.2   THE PARABOLA

We have encountered parabolas in the discussion of quadratic functions. We now examine their equations in greater detail.

> **Definition.**   A **parabola** is the set of all points in a plane such that each point in the set is equidistant from a line l, called the **directrix**, and a fixed point F, called the **focus**. The point on the parabola that is closest to the directrix is called the **vertex**. The line passing through the vertex and the focus is called the **axis**.

We will consider parabolas that open to the left, to the right, upward, and downward and that have a vertex at point (h, k). There is a standard form for the equation of each of these parabolas.

Consider the parabola in Figure 13-4, which opens to the right and has its vertex at the point $V(h, k)$. Let $P(x, y)$ be any point on the parabola. Because each point on the parabola is the same distance from the focus (point F) and from the directrix, we can let $DV = VF = p$, where p is some positive constant.

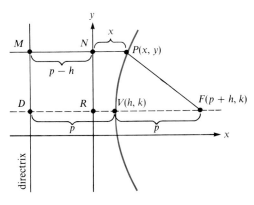

Figure 13-4

Because of the geometry of the figure,

$$MP = p - h + x$$

Because of the distance formula,

$$PF = \sqrt{[x - (p + h)]^2 + (y - k)^2}$$

By the definition of the parabola, $MP = PF$. Thus,

$$p - h + x = \sqrt{[x - (p + h)]^2 + (y - k)^2}$$
$$(p - h + x)^2 = [x - (p + h)]^2 + (y - k)^2 \qquad \text{Square both sides.}$$

Finally, we expand the expression on each side of the equation and simplify:

$$p^2 - ph + px - ph + h^2 - hx + px - hx + x^2$$
$$= x^2 - 2px - 2hx + p^2 + 2ph + h^2 + (y - k)^2$$
$$-2ph + 2px = -2px + 2ph + (y - k)^2$$
$$4px - 4ph = (y - k)^2$$
$$4p(x - h) = (y - k)^2$$

The above argument proves the following theorem.

> **Theorem.**   The standard form of the equation of a parabola with vertex at point (h, k) and opening to the right is
>
> $$(y - k)^2 = 4p(x - h)$$
>
> where p is the distance from the vertex to the focus.

If the parabola has its vertex at the origin, both h and k are equal to zero, and we have the following theorem.

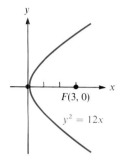

$F(3, 0)$

$y^2 = 12x$

Figure 13-5

> **Theorem.**   The standard form of the equation of a parabola with vertex at the origin and opening to the right is
>
> $$y^2 = 4px$$
>
> where p is the distance from the vertex to the focus.

Equations of parabolas that open to the right, left, upward, and downward are summarized in Table 13-1. If $p > 0$, then

Table 13-1

Parabola opening	Vertex at origin	Vertex at $V(h, k)$
Right	$y^2 = 4px$	$(y - k)^2 = 4p(x - h)$
Left	$y^2 = -4px$	$(y - k)^2 = -4p(x - h)$
Upward	$x^2 = 4py$	$(x - h)^2 = 4p(y - k)$
Downward	$x^2 = -4py$	$(x - h)^2 = -4p(y - k)$

Example 1   Find the equation of the parabola with vertex at the origin and focus at $(3, 0)$.

Solution   Sketch the parabola as in Figure 13-5. Because the focus is to the right of the vertex, the parabola opens to the right. Because the vertex is the origin, the standard form of the equation is $y^2 = 4px$. The distance between the focus and the vertex is 3, which is p. Therefore, the equation of the parabola is $y^2 = 4(3)x$, or

$$y^2 = 12x$$ ∎

Example 2   Find the equation of the parabola that opens upward, has vertex at the point $(4, 5)$, and passes through the point $(0, 7)$.

Solution   Because the parabola opens upward, use the standard form $(x - h)^2 = 4p(y - k)$. Because the point $(0, 7)$ is on the curve, substitute **0** for x and **7** for y in the equation. Because the vertex (h, k) is $(4, 5)$, also substitute **4** for h and **5** for k.

Then solve the equation to determine p:

$$(x - h)^2 = 4p(y - k)$$
$$(0 - 4)^2 = 4p(7 - 5)$$
$$16 = 8p$$
$$2 = p$$

To find the equation of the parabola, substitute 4 for h, 5 for k, and 2 for p in the standard form of the equation and simplify:

$$(x - h)^2 = 4p(y - k)$$
$$(x - 4)^2 = 4 \cdot 2(y - 5)$$
$$(x - 4)^2 = 8(y - 5)$$

The graph of this equation appears in Figure 13-6.

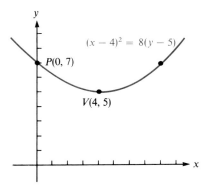

Figure 13-6

Example 3 Find the equations of the two parabolas each having its vertex at $(2, 4)$ and passing through the point $(0, 0)$.

Solution Sketch the two possible parabolas, as shown in Figure 13-7.

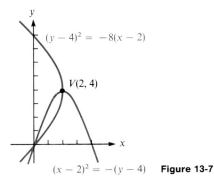

Figure 13-7

Part 1.   To find the parabola that opens to the left, use the standard form of the equation $(y - k)^2 = -4p(x - h)$. Because the curve passes through the point $(x, y) = (0, 0)$ and the vertex is $(h, k) = (2, 4)$, substitute **0** for x, **0** for y, **2** for h, and **4** for k in the equation $(y - k)^2 = -4p(x - h)$ and solve for p:

$$(y - k)^2 = -4p(x - h)$$
$$(0 - 4)^2 = -4p(0 - 2)$$
$$16 = 8p$$
$$2 = p$$

Because $h = 2$, $k = 4$, and $p = 2$ and because the parabola opens to the left, its equation is

$$(y - k)^2 = -4p(x - h)$$
$$(y - 4)^2 = -4(2)(x - 2)$$
$$(y - 4)^2 = -8(x - 2)$$

Part 2.   To find the equation of the parabola that opens downward, use the standard form $(x - h)^2 = -4p(y - k)$. Substitute **2** for h, **4** for k, **0** for x, and **0** for y in the equation and solve for p:

$$(x - h)^2 = -4p(y - k)$$
$$(0 - 2)^2 = -4p(0 - 4)$$
$$4 = 16p$$
$$\frac{1}{4} = p$$

Because $h = 2$, $k = 4$, and $p = \dfrac{1}{4}$, and the parabola opens downward, its equation is

$$(x - h)^2 = -4p(y - k)$$
$$(x - 2)^2 = -4\left(\frac{1}{4}\right)(y - 4)$$
$$(x - 2)^2 = -(y - 4)$$ ∎

Example 4   Find the vertex and y-intercepts of the parabola $y^2 + 8x - 4y = 28$. Then graph the parabola.

Solution   Complete the square on y to write the equation in standard form:

$$y^2 + 8x - 4y = 28$$
$$y^2 - 4y = -8x + 28 \qquad \text{Add } -8x \text{ to both sides.}$$
$$y^2 - 4y + 4 = -8x + 28 + 4 \qquad \text{Add 4 to both sides.}$$
$$(y - 2)^2 = -8(x - 4) \qquad \text{Factor both sides.}$$

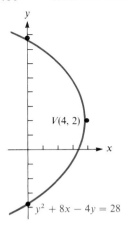

Figure 13-8

Observe that this equation represents a parabola opening to the left with vertex at (4, 2). To find the points where the graph intersects the y-axis, substitute 0 for x in the equation of the parabola.

$$(y - 2)^2 = -8(x - 4)$$
$$(y - 2)^2 = -8(0 - 4) \qquad \text{Substitute 0 for } x.$$
$$y^2 - 4y + 4 = 32 \qquad \text{Remove parentheses.}$$
$$y^2 - 4y - 28 = 0$$

Use the quadratic formula to determine that the roots of this quadratic equation are $y \approx 7.7$ and $y \approx -3.7$.

The points with coordinates of approximately (0, 7.7) and (0, −3.7) are on the graph of the parabola. Using this information and the knowledge that the graph opens to the left and has a vertex at (4, 2), draw the curve as shown in Figure 13-8. ∎

Example 5   A stone is thrown straight up. The equation $s = 128t - 16t^2$ expresses the height of the stone in feet t seconds after it was thrown. Find the maximum height reached by the stone.

Solution   The stone goes straight up and then straight down. The graph of $s = 128t - 16t^2$, expressing the height of the stone t seconds after it was thrown, is a parabola (see Figure 13-9). To find the maximum height reached by the stone, calculate the y-coordinate, k, of the vertex of the parabola. To find k, write the equation of the parabola, $s = 128t - 16t^2$, in standard form. To change this equation into standard form, complete the square on t:

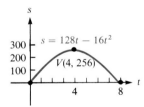

Figure 13-9

$$s = 128t - 16t^2$$
$$16t^2 - 128t = -s \qquad \text{Multiply both sides by } -1.$$
$$t^2 - 8t = \frac{-s}{16} \qquad \text{Divide both sides by 16.}$$
$$t^2 - 8t + 16 = \frac{-s}{16} + 16 \qquad \text{Add 16 to both sides.}$$
$$(t - 4)^2 = \frac{-s + 256}{16} \qquad \text{Factor } t^2 - 8t + 16 \text{ and combine terms.}$$
$$(t - 4)^2 = -\frac{1}{16}(s - 256) \qquad \text{Factor out } -\frac{1}{16}.$$

■ EXERCISE 13.2

In Exercises 1–16, find the equation of each parabola.

1. Vertex at (0, 0) and focus at (0, 3)

2. Vertex at (0, 0) and focus at (0, −3)

3. Vertex at (0, 0) and focus at (3, 0)

4. Vertex at (0, 0) and focus at (−3, 0)

5. Vertex at $(3, 5)$ and focus at $(3, 2)$

6. Vertex at $(3, 5)$ and focus at $(-3, 5)$

7. Vertex at $(3, 5)$ and focus at $(3, -2)$

8. Vertex at $(3, 5)$ and focus at $(6, 5)$

9. Vertex at $(2, 2)$ and the parabola passing through $(0, 0)$

10. Vertex at $(-2, -2)$ and the parabola passing through $(0, 0)$

11. Vertex at $(-4, 6)$ and the parabola passing through $(0, 3)$

12. Vertex at $(-2, 3)$ and the parabola passing through $(0, -3)$

13. Vertex at $(6, 8)$ and the parabola passing through $(5, 10)$ and $(5, 6)$

14. Vertex at $(2, 3)$ and the parabola passing through $(1, \frac{13}{4})$ and $(-1, \frac{21}{4})$

15. Vertex at $(3, 1)$ and the parabola passing through $(4, 3)$ and $(2, 3)$

16. Vertex at $(-4, -2)$ and the parabola passing through $(-3, 0)$ and $(\frac{9}{4}, 3)$

In Exercises 17–26, change each equation to standard form and graph it.

17. $y = x^2 + 4x + 5$

18. $2x^2 - 12x - 7y = 10$

19. $y^2 + 4x - 6y = -1$

20. $x^2 - 2y - 2x = -7$

21. $y^2 + 2x - 2y = 5$

22. $y^2 - 4y = -8x + 20$

23. $x^2 - 6y + 22 = -4x$

24. $4y^2 - 4y + 16x = 7$

25. $4x^2 - 4x + 32y = 47$

26. $4y^2 - 16x + 17 = 20y$

27. A parabolic arch spans 30 meters and has a maximum height of 10 meters. Derive the equation of the arch using the vertex of the arch as the origin.

28. Find the maximum value of y in the parabola $x^2 + 8y - 8x = 8$.

29. A resort owner plans to build and rent n cabins for d dollars per week. The price, d, that she can charge for each cabin depends on the number of cabins she builds, where $d = -45\left(\dfrac{n}{32} - \dfrac{1}{2}\right)$. Find the number of cabins that she should build to maximize her weekly income.

30. A toy rocket is s meters above the earth at the end of t seconds, where $s = -16t^2 + 80\sqrt{3}\,t$. Find the maximum height of the rocket.

31. An engineer plans to build a tunnel whose arch is in the shape of a parabola. The tunnel will span a two-lane highway that is 8 meters wide. To allow safe passage for most vehicles, the tunnel must be 5 meters high at a distance of 1 meter from the tunnel's edge. What will be the maximum height of the tunnel?

32. The towers of a suspension bridge are 900 feet apart and rise 120 feet above the roadway. The cable between the towers has the shape of a parabola with a vertex 15 feet above the roadway. Find the equation of the parabola with respect to the indicated coordinate system. See Illustration 1.

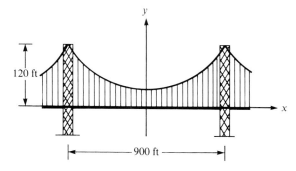

Illustration 1

33. A satellite antenna with a parabolic cross section is a dish 6 feet in diameter and 1 foot deep at its center. How far is the focus from the center of the dish?

34. A stone tossed upward is s meters above the earth after t seconds, where $s = -16t^2 + 128t$. Show that the stone's height x seconds *after* it is thrown is equal to its height x seconds *before* it returns to the ground.

35. Derive the standard form of the equation of a parabola that opens downward and has vertex at the origin.

36. Show that the result in Example 1 is a special case of the general form of the equation of second degree.

In Exercises 37–38, find the equation of the form $y = ax^2 + bx + c$ that determines a parabola passing through the three given points.

37. $(1, 8), (-2, -1)$, and $(2, 15)$ **38.** $(1, -3), (-2, 12)$, and $(-1, 3)$

13.3   THE ELLIPSE

A third important conic is the ellipse.

> **Definition.**   An **ellipse** is the set of all points P in a plane such that the sum of the distances from P to two other fixed points F and F' is a positive constant.

In the ellipse shown in Figure 13-10, the two fixed points F and F' are called **foci** of the ellipse, the midpoint of the chord FF' is called the **center**, the chord VV' is called the **major axis**, and each endpoint of the major axis is called a **vertex**. The chord BB', perpendicular to the major axis and passing through the center C, is called the **minor axis**.

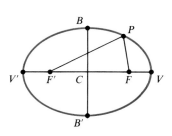

Figure 13-10

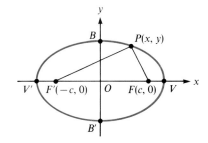

Figure 13-11

To keep the algebra manageable, we will derive the equation of the ellipse shown in Figure 13-11, which has its center at $(0, 0)$. Because the origin is the midpoint of the chord FF', we can let $OF = OF' = c$, where $c > 0$. Then the coordinates of point F are $(c, 0)$, and the coordinates of F' are $(-c, 0)$. We also let $P(x, y)$ be any point on the ellipse.

The definition of an ellipse requires that the sum of $F'P$ and PF be a positive constant, which we will call $2a$. Thus,

1. $F'P + PF = 2a$

We use the distance formula to compute the lengths of $F'P$ and PF:

$$F'P = \sqrt{[x - (-c)]^2 + y^2}$$

$$PF = \sqrt{(x - c)^2 + y^2}$$

and substitute these values into Equation 1 to obtain

$$\sqrt{[x - (-c)]^2 + y^2} + \sqrt{(x - c)^2 + y^2} = 2a$$

or

$$\sqrt{[x + c]^2 + y^2} = 2a - \sqrt{(x - c)^2 + y^2}$$

We square both sides of this equation and simplify to get

$$(x + c)^2 + y^2 = 4a^2 - 4a\sqrt{(x - c)^2 + y^2} + [(x - c)^2 + y^2]$$
$$x^2 + 2cx + c^2 + y^2 = 4a^2 - 4a\sqrt{(x - c)^2 + y^2} + x^2 - 2cx + c^2 + y^2$$
$$4cx = 4a^2 - 4a\sqrt{(x - c)^2 + y^2}$$
$$cx = a^2 - a\sqrt{(x - c)^2 + y^2}$$
$$cx - a^2 = -a\sqrt{(x - c)^2 + y^2}$$

We square both sides again and simplify to obtain

$$c^2x^2 - 2a^2cx + a^4 = a^2[(x - c)^2 + y^2]$$
$$c^2x^2 - 2a^2cx + a^4 = a^2(x^2 - 2cx + c^2 + y^2)$$
$$c^2x^2 - 2a^2cx + a^4 = a^2x^2 - 2a^2cx + a^2c^2 + a^2y^2$$
$$c^2x^2 + a^4 = a^2x^2 + a^2c^2 + a^2y^2$$
$$a^4 - a^2c^2 = a^2x^2 - c^2x^2 + a^2y^2$$

2. $$a^2(a^2 - c^2) = (a^2 - c^2)x^2 + a^2y^2$$

Because the shortest path between two points is a line segment, $F'P + PF > F'F$. Therefore, $2a > 2c$. This implies that $a > c$ and that $a^2 - c^2$ is a positive number, which we will call b^2. Letting $b^2 = a^2 - c^2$ and substituting into Equation 2, we have

$$a^2b^2 = b^2x^2 + a^2y^2$$

Dividing both sides of this equation by a^2b^2 gives the standard form of the equation for an ellipse with center at the origin and major axis on the x-axis:

$$\frac{x^2}{a^2} + \frac{y^2}{b^2} = 1 \quad \text{where } a > b > 0$$

To find the coordinates of the vertices V and V', we substitute $\mathbf{0}$ for y and solve for x:

$$\frac{x^2}{a^2} + \frac{y^2}{b^2} = 1$$

$$\frac{x^2}{a^2} + \frac{\mathbf{0}^2}{b^2} = 1$$

$$\frac{x^2}{a^2} = 1$$

$$x^2 = a^2$$

$$x = a \qquad \text{or} \qquad x = -a$$

Thus, the coordinates of V are $(a, 0)$, and the coordinates of V' are $(-a, 0)$. In other words, a is the distance between the center of the ellipse, $(0, 0)$, and either of its vertices, and the center of the ellipse is the midpoint of the major axis.

To find the coordinates of B and B', we substitute $\mathbf{0}$ for x and solve for y:

$$\frac{x^2}{a^2} + \frac{y^2}{b^2} = 1$$

$$\frac{\mathbf{0}^2}{a^2} + \frac{y^2}{b^2} = 1$$

$$y^2 = b^2$$

$$y = b \qquad \text{or} \qquad y = -b$$

Thus, the coordinates of B are $(0, b)$, and the coordinates of B' are $(0, -b)$. The distance between the center of the ellipse and either endpoint of the minor axis is b.

Theorem.   The standard form of the equation of an ellipse with center at the origin and major axis on the x-axis is

$$\frac{x^2}{a^2} + \frac{y^2}{b^2} = 1 \quad \text{where } a > b > 0$$

If the major axis of an ellipse with center at $(0, 0)$ lies on the y-axis, the standard form of the equation of the ellipse is

$$\frac{y^2}{a^2} + \frac{x^2}{b^2} = 1 \quad \text{where } a > b > 0$$

In either case, the length of the major axis is $2a$, and the length of the minor axis is $2b$.

If we develop the equation of the ellipse with center at (h, k), we obtain the following results.

Theorem.   The standard form of the equation of an ellipse with center at (h, k) and major axis parallel to the x-axis is

$$\frac{(x - h)^2}{a^2} + \frac{(y - k)^2}{b^2} = 1 \quad \text{where } a > b > 0$$

If the major axis of an ellipse with center at (h, k) is parallel to the y-axis, the standard form of the equation of the ellipse is

$$\frac{(y - k)^2}{a^2} + \frac{(x - h)^2}{b^2} = 1 \quad \text{where } a > b > 0$$

In either case, the length of the major axis is $2a$, and the length of the minor axis is $2b$.

Example 1   Find the equation of the ellipse with center at the origin, major axis of length 6 units located on the x-axis, and minor axis of length 4 units.

Solution   Because the center of the ellipse is the origin and the length of the major axis is 6, $a = 3$ and the coordinates of the vertices of the ellipse are $(3, 0)$ and $(-3, 0)$, as shown in Figure 13-12.

Because the length of the minor axis is 4, the value of b is 2 and the coordinates of B and B' are $(0, 2)$ and $(0, -2)$. To find the desired equation, substitute **3** for a and **2** for b in the standard form of the equation of an ellipse with center at the origin and major axis on the x-axis. Then simplify the equation:

$$\frac{x^2}{a^2} + \frac{y^2}{b^2} = 1$$

$$\frac{x^2}{3^2} + \frac{y^2}{2^2} = 1$$

$$\frac{x^2}{9} + \frac{y^2}{4} = 1$$

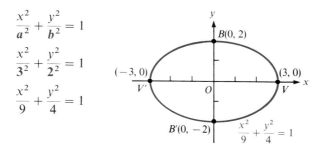

Figure 13-12   ■

Example 2   Find the equation of the ellipse with focus $(0, 3)$ and vertices V and V' at $(3, 3)$ and $(-5, 3)$.

Solution   Because the midpoint of the major axis is the center of the ellipse, the coordinates of the center are $(-1, 3)$. Look at Figure 13-13 and note that the major axis is parallel to the x-axis. The standard form of the equation to use is

$$\frac{(x - h)^2}{a^2} + \frac{(y - k)^2}{b^2} = 1 \quad \text{where } a > b > 0$$

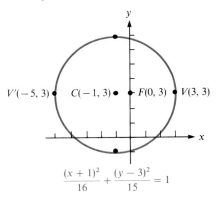

Figure 13-13

The distance between the center of the ellipse and a vertex is $a = 4$; the distance between the focus and the center is $c = 1$. In the ellipse, $b^2 = a^2 - c^2$. From this equation, compute b^2:

$$b^2 = a^2 - c^2$$
$$= 4^2 - 1^2$$
$$= 15$$

To find the equation of the ellipse, substitute -1 for h, **3** for k, **16** for a^2, and **15** for b^2 in the standard form of the equation for an ellipse and simplify:

$$\frac{(x - h)^2}{a^2} + \frac{(y - k)^2}{b^2} = 1$$
$$\frac{[x - (-1)]^2}{16} + \frac{(y - 3)^2}{15} = 1$$
$$\frac{(x + 1)^2}{16} + \frac{(y - 3)^2}{15} = 1 \qquad\qquad\blacksquare$$

Example 3   The orbit of the earth is approximately an ellipse, with the sun at one focus. The ratio of c to a (called the *eccentricity* of the ellipse) is about $\frac{1}{62}$, and the length of the major axis is approximately 186,000,000 miles. How close does the earth get to the sun?

Solution   Assume that this ellipse has its center at the origin and vertices V' and V at $(-93{,}000{,}000, 0)$ and $(93{,}000{,}000, 0)$, as shown in Figure 13-14. This implies that $a = 93{,}000{,}000$.

$$\frac{c}{a} = \frac{1}{62} \qquad \text{or} \qquad c = \frac{1}{62}a$$

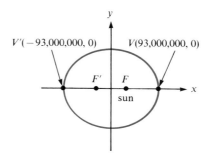

Figure 13-14

Because $a = 93,000,000$,

$$c = \frac{1}{62}(93,000,000)$$

$$= 1,500,000$$

FV represents the shortest possible distance between the earth and the sun. (You'll be asked to prove this in the exercises.) Thus,

$$FV = a - c = 93,000,000 - 1,500,000 = 91,500,000 \text{ miles}$$

The earth's point of closest approach to the sun (called the *perigee*) is approximately 91.5 million miles.   ■

Example 4   Graph the ellipse $\dfrac{(x + 2)^2}{4} + \dfrac{(y - 2)^2}{9} = 1$.

Solution   The center of the ellipse is at $(-2, 2)$, and the major axis is parallel to the y-axis. Because $a = 3$, the vertices are 3 units above and below the center at points $(-2, 5)$ and $(-2, -1)$. Because $b = 2$, the endpoints of the minor axis are 2 units to the right and left of the center at points $(0, 2)$ and $(-4, 2)$. Using these four points as guides, sketch the ellipse, as shown in Figure 13-15.

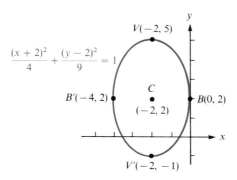

Figure 13-15   ■

Example 5   Graph the equation $4x^2 + 9y^2 - 16x - 18y = 11$.

Solution   Write the equation in standard form by completing the square on x and y as follows:

$$4x^2 + 9y^2 - 16x - 18y = 11$$
$$4x^2 - 16x + 9y^2 - 18y = 11$$
$$4(x^2 - 4x) + 9(y^2 - 2y) = 11$$
$$4(x^2 - 4x + 4) + 9(y^2 - 2y + 1) = 11 + 16 + 9$$
$$4(x - 2)^2 + 9(y - 1)^2 = 36$$
$$\frac{(x - 2)^2}{9} + \frac{(y - 1)^2}{4} = 1$$

You can now see that the graph of the given equation is an ellipse with center at $(2, 1)$ and major axis parallel to the x-axis. Because $a = 3$, the vertices are at $(-1, 1)$ and $(5, 1)$. Because $b = 2$, the endpoints of the minor axis are at $(2, -1)$ and $(2, 3)$. Using these four points as guides, sketch the ellipse, as shown in Figure 13-16.

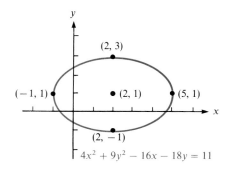

Figure 13-16

■ EXERCISE 13.3

In Exercises 1–6, write the equation of the ellipse that has its center at the origin.

1. Focus at $(3, 0)$ and a vertex at $(5, 0)$
2. Focus at $(0, 4)$ and a vertex at $(0, 7)$
3. Focus at $(0, 1)$; $\frac{4}{3}$ is one-half the length of the minor axis.
4. Focus at $(1, 0)$; $\frac{4}{3}$ is one-half the length of the minor axis.
5. Focus at $(0, 3)$ and major axis equal to 8
6. Focus at $(5, 0)$ and major axis equal to 12

In Exercises 7–16, write the equation of each ellipse.

7. Center at $(3, 4)$; $a = 3$, $b = 2$; the major axis is parallel to the y-axis.
8. Center at $(3, 4)$; the curve passes through $(3, 10)$ and $(3, -2)$; $b = 2$.
9. Center at $(3, 4)$; $a = 3$, $b = 2$; the major axis is parallel to the x-axis.

10.   Center at $(3, 4)$; the curve passes through $(8, 4)$ and $(-2, 4)$; $b = 2$.

11.   Foci at $(-2, 4)$ and $(8, 4)$; $b = 4$

12.   Foci at $(-8, 5)$ and $(4, 5)$; $b = 3$

13.   Vertex at $(6, 4)$ and foci at $(-4, 4)$ and $(4, 4)$

14.   Center at $(-4, 5)$; $\dfrac{c}{a} = \dfrac{1}{3}$; vertex at $(-4, -1)$

15.   Foci at $(6, 0)$ and $(-6, 0)$; $\dfrac{c}{a} = \dfrac{3}{5}$

16.   Vertices at $(2, 0)$ and $(-2, 0)$; $\dfrac{2b^2}{a} = 2$

In Exercises 17–24, graph each equation.

17. $\dfrac{x^2}{25} + \dfrac{y^2}{49} = 1$

18. $4x^2 + y^2 = 4$

19. $\dfrac{x^2}{16} + \dfrac{(y+2)^2}{36} = 1$

20. $(x-1)^2 + \dfrac{4y^2}{25} = 4$

21. $x^2 + 4y^2 - 4x + 8y + 4 = 0$

22. $x^2 + 4y^2 - 2x - 16y = -13$

23. $16x^2 + 25y^2 - 160x - 200y + 400 = 0$

24. $3x^2 + 2y^2 + 7x - 6y = -1$

25.   The moon has an orbit that is an ellipse with the earth at one focus. If the major axis of the orbit is 378,000 miles and the ratio of c to a is approximately $\frac{11}{200}$, how far does the moon get from earth? (This farthest point in an orbit is called the *apogee*.)

26.   An arch is a semiellipse 10 meters wide and 5 meters high. Write the equation of the ellipse if the ellipse is centered at the origin.

27.   A track is built in the shape of an ellipse and has a maximum length of 100 meters and a maximum width of 60 meters. Write the equation of the ellipse and find its focal width; that is, find the length of a chord that is perpendicular to the major axis and that passes through either focus of the ellipse.

28.   An arch has the shape of a semiellipse and has a maximum height of 5 meters. The foci are on the ground with a distance between them of 24 meters. Find the total distance from one focus to any point on the arch and back to the other focus.

29.   Consider the ellipse in Illustration 1. If F is a focus of the ellipse and B is an endpoint of the minor axis, use the distance formula to prove that the length of segment FB is a. (*Hint:*   Remember that in an ellipse $a^2 - c^2 = b^2$.)

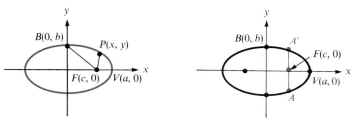

Illustration 1   **Illustration 2**

30.   Consider the ellipse in Illustration 1. If F is a focus of the ellipse and P is any point on the ellipse, use the distance formula to show that the length of segment FP is $a - \dfrac{c}{a} x$. (*Hint:*   Remember that in an ellipse $a^2 - c^2 = b^2$.)

31.   Consider the ellipse in Illustration 2. Chord AA' passes through the focus F and is perpendicular to the major axis. Show that the length of AA' (called the focal width of the ellipse) is $\dfrac{2b^2}{a}$.

32. Prove that the segment FV in Example 3 does represent the shortest distance between the earth and the sun. (*Hint:* You might find the result of Exercise 30 helpful.)

33. The ends of a piece of string 6 meters long are attached to two thumbtacks that are 2 meters apart. A pencil catches the loop and draws it tight. As the pencil is moved about the thumbtacks (always keeping the tension), an ellipse is produced with the thumbtacks as foci. Write the equation of the ellipse. (*Hint:* You will have to establish a coordinate system.)

34. Prove that $a > b$ in the development of the standard form of the equation of an ellipse.

35. Show that the expansion of the standard equation of an ellipse is a special case of the general second-degree equation.

36. The distance between point $P(x, y)$ and the point $(0, 2)$ is $\frac{1}{3}$ of the distance of point P from the line $y = 18$. Find the equation of the curve on which point P lies.

13.4   THE HYPERBOLA

The definition of the hyperbola is similar to the definition of the ellipse except that we demand a constant *difference* of $2a$ instead of a constant sum.

> **Definition.**   A **hyperbola** is the set of all points P in a plane such that the difference of the distances from point P to two other points in the plane, F and F', is a positive constant.

Points F and F' (see Figure 13-17) are called the **foci** of the hyperbola, and the midpoint of chord FF' is called the **center** of the hyperbola. The points V and V', where the hyperbola intersects the line segment FF', are called the **vertices** of the hyperbola, and the line segment VV' is called the **transverse axis**.

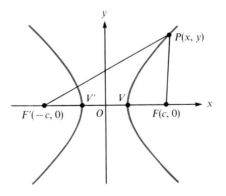

Figure 13-17

As with the ellipse, we will develop the equation of the hyperbola centered at the origin. Because the origin is the midpoint of chord FF', we can let $F'O = OF = c > 0$. Therefore, F is at $(c, 0)$ and F' is at $(-c, 0)$. The definition requires that $|F'P - PF| = 2a$, where $2a$ is a positive constant. Using the distance formula to compute the lengths of $F'P$ and PF gives

$$F'P = \sqrt{[x - (-c)]^2 + y^2}$$
$$PF = \sqrt{(x - c)^2 + y^2}$$

Substituting these values into the equation $F'P - PF = 2a$ gives

$$\sqrt{(x + c)^2 + y^2} - \sqrt{(x - c)^2 + y^2} = 2a$$

or

$$\sqrt{(x + c)^2 + y^2} = 2a + \sqrt{(x - c)^2 + y^2}$$

Squaring both sides of this equation and simplifying gives

$$(x + c)^2 + y^2 = 4a^2 + 4a\sqrt{(x - c)^2 + y^2} + (x - c)^2 + y^2$$
$$x^2 + 2cx + c^2 + y^2 = 4a^2 + 4a\sqrt{(x - c)^2 + y^2} + x^2 - 2cx + c^2 + y^2$$
$$4cx = 4a^2 + 4a\sqrt{(x - c)^2 + y^2}$$
$$cx - a^2 = a\sqrt{(x - c)^2 + y^2}$$

Squaring both sides again and simplifying gives

$$c^2x^2 - 2a^2cx + a^4 = a^2(x^2 - 2cx + c^2 + y^2)$$
$$c^2x^2 - 2a^2cx + a^4 = a^2x^2 - 2a^2cx + a^2c^2 + a^2y^2$$
$$c^2x^2 + a^4 = a^2x^2 + a^2c^2 + a^2y^2$$

1. $(c^2 - a^2)x^2 - a^2y^2 = a^2(c^2 - a^2)$

Because $c > a$ (you will be asked to prove this in the exercises), $c^2 - a^2$ is a positive number. Thus, we can let $b^2 = c^2 - a^2$ and substitute b^2 for $c^2 - a^2$ in Equation 1 to get

$$b^2x^2 - a^2y^2 = a^2b^2$$

Dividing both sides of the previous equation by a^2b^2 gives the standard form of the equation for a hyperbola with center at the origin and foci on the x-axis:

$$\frac{x^2}{a^2} - \frac{y^2}{b^2} = 1$$

If $y = 0$, the equation above becomes

$$\frac{x^2}{a^2} = 1 \qquad \text{or} \qquad x^2 = a^2$$

Solving this equation for x gives

$$x = a \qquad \text{or} \qquad x = -a$$

This implies that the coordinates of V and V' are $(a, 0)$ and $(-a, 0)$ and that the distance between the center of the hyperbola and either vertex is a. This, in turn, implies that the center of the hyperbola is the midpoint of the segment $V'V$ as well as of the segment FF'.

If $x = 0$, the equation becomes

$$\frac{-y^2}{b^2} = 1 \qquad \text{or} \qquad y^2 = -b^2$$

Because this equation has no real solutions, the hyperbola cannot intersect the y-axis. These results suggest the following theorem.

Theorem.   The standard form of the equation of a hyperbola with center at the origin and foci on the x-axis is

$$\frac{x^2}{a^2} - \frac{y^2}{b^2} = 1$$

The standard form of the equation of a hyperbola with center at the origin and foci on the y-axis is

$$\frac{y^2}{a^2} - \frac{x^2}{b^2} = 1$$

As with the ellipse, the standard equation of the hyperbola can be developed with center at (h, k). We state the results without proof.

Theorem.   The standard form of the equation of a hyperbola with center at (h, k) and foci on a line parallel to the x-axis is

$$\frac{(x - h)^2}{a^2} - \frac{(y - k)^2}{b^2} = 1$$

The standard form of the equation of a hyperbola with center at (h, k) and foci on a line parallel to the y-axis is

$$\frac{(y - k)^2}{a^2} - \frac{(x - h)^2}{b^2} = 1$$

Example 1   Write the equation of the hyperbola with vertices $(3, -3)$ and $(3, 3)$ and with a focus at $(3, 5)$.

Solution   First, plot the vertices and focus, as shown in Figure 13-18. Note that the foci lie on a vertical line. Therefore, the standard form to use is

$$\frac{(y - k)^2}{a^2} - \frac{(x - h)^2}{b^2} = 1$$

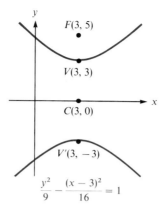

Figure 13-18

Because the center of the hyperbola is midway between the vertices V and V', the center is point $(3, 0)$, so $h = 3$, and $k = 0$. The distance between the vertex and the center of the hyperbola is $a = 3$, and the distance between the focus and the center is $c = 5$. Also, in a hyperbola, $b^2 = c^2 - a^2$. Therefore, $b^2 = 5^2 - 3^2 = 16$. Substituting the values for h, k, a^2, and b^2 into the standard form of the equation gives the desired result:

$$\frac{(y - 0)^2}{9} - \frac{(x - 3)^2}{16} = 1$$

$$\frac{y^2}{9} - \frac{(x - 3)^2}{16} = 1$$

∎

Asymptotes of a Hyperbola

The values of a and b play an important role in graphing hyperbolas. To see their significance, we consider the hyperbola

$$\frac{x^2}{a^2} - \frac{y^2}{b^2} = 1$$

The center of this hyperbola is the origin, and the vertices are at $V(a, 0)$ and $V'(-a, 0)$. We plot points V, V', $B(0, b)$, and $B'(0, -b)$ and form rectangle $RSQP$, called the **fundamental rectangle**, as in Figure 13-19. The extended diagonals of this rectangle are asymptotes of the hyperbola. In the exercises, you will be asked to show that the equations of these two lines are

$$y = \frac{b}{a} x \qquad \text{and} \qquad y = -\frac{b}{a} x$$

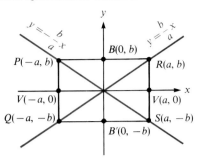

Figure 13-19

To show that the extended diagonals are asymptotes of the hyperbola, we solve the equation

$$\frac{x^2}{a^2} - \frac{y^2}{b^2} = 1$$

for y and modify its form:

$$\frac{x^2}{a^2} - \frac{y^2}{b^2} = 1$$

$$b^2x^2 - a^2y^2 = a^2b^2 \qquad \text{Multiply both sides by } a^2b^2.$$

$$y^2 = \frac{b^2x^2 - a^2b^2}{a^2} \qquad \begin{array}{l}\text{Add } -b^2x^2 \text{ to both sides and} \\ \text{divide both sides by } -a^2.\end{array}$$

$$y^2 = \frac{b^2x^2}{a^2}\left(1 - \frac{a^2}{x^2}\right) \qquad \text{Factor out a } b^2x^2 \text{ from the numerator.}$$

$$y = \pm\frac{bx}{a}\sqrt{1 - \frac{a^2}{x^2}} \qquad \text{Take the square root of both sides.}$$

If $|x|$ grows large without bound, the fraction $\dfrac{a^2}{x^2}$ in the previous equation approaches 0 and $\sqrt{1 - \dfrac{a^2}{x^2}}$ approaches 1. Hence, the hyperbola approaches the lines

$$y = \frac{b}{a}x \qquad \text{or} \qquad y = -\frac{b}{a}x$$

This fact makes it easy to sketch a hyperbola. We convert the equation into standard form, find the coordinates of its vertices, and plot them. Then, we construct the fundamental rectangle and its extended diagonals. Using the vertices and the asymptotes as guides, we make a quick and relatively accurate sketch, as in Figure 13-20. The segment BB' is called the **conjugate axis** of the hyperbola.

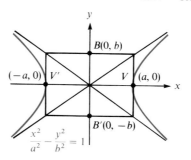

Figure 13-20

Example 2   Graph the hyperbola $x^2 - y^2 - 2x + 4y = 12$.

Solution   First complete the square on x and y to convert the equation into standard form:

$$x^2 - 2x - y^2 + 4y = 12$$
$$x^2 - 2x - (y^2 - 4y) = 12$$
$$x^2 - 2x + 1 - (y^2 - 4y + 4) = 12 - 3$$
$$(x - 1)^2 - (y - 2)^2 = 9$$
$$\frac{(x - 1)^2}{9} - \frac{(y - 2)^2}{9} = 1$$

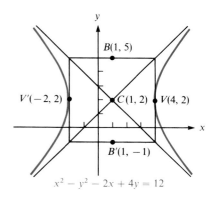

Figure 13-21

From the standard form of the equation of a hyperbola, observe that the center is (1, 2), that $a = 3$ and $b = 3$, and that the vertices are on a line segment parallel to the x-axis, as shown in Figure 13-21. Therefore, the vertices V and V' are 3 units to the right and left of the center and have coordinates of (4, 2) and (−2, 2). Points B and B', 3 units above and below the center, have coordinates (1, 5) and (1, −1). After plotting points V, V', B, and B', construct the fundamental rectangle and its extended diagonals. Using the vertices as points on the hyperbola and the extended diagonals as asymptotes, sketch the graph. ■

This discussion of the hyperbola has considered only cases where the segment that joins the foci is horizontal or vertical. However, there are hyperbolas where this is not true. For example, the graph of the equation $xy = 4$ is a hyperbola with vertices at (2, 2) and (−2, −2), as shown in Figure 13-22.

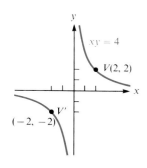

Figure 13-22

▪ EXERCISE 13.4

In Exercises 1–12, write the equation of each hyperbola.

1. Vertices at $(5, 0)$ and $(-5, 0)$ and focus at $(7, 0)$

2. Focus at $(3, 0)$, vertex at $(2, 0)$, and center at $(0, 0)$

3. Center at $(2, 4)$; $a = 2$, $b = 3$; transverse axis is horizontal

4. Center at $(-1, 3)$, vertex at $(1, 3)$, and focus at $(2, 3)$

5. Center at $(5, 3)$, vertex at $(5, 6)$, hyperbola passes through $(1, 8)$

6. Foci at $(0, 10)$ and $(0, -10)$; $\dfrac{c}{a} = \dfrac{5}{4}$

7. Vertices at $(0, 3)$ and $(0, -3)$; $\dfrac{c}{a} = \dfrac{5}{3}$

8. Focus at $(4, 0)$, vertex at $(2, 0)$, and center at the origin

9. Center at $(1, -3)$; $a^2 = 4$, $b^2 = 16$

10. Center at $(1, 4)$, focus at $(7, 4)$, and vertex at $(3, 4)$

11. Center at the origin; hyperbola passes through points $(4, 2)$ and $(8, -6)$

12. Center at $(3, -1)$, y-intercept of -1, x-intercept of $3 + \dfrac{3\sqrt{5}}{2}$

In Exercises 13–16, find the area of the fundamental rectangle of each hyperbola.

13. $4(x - 1)^2 - 9(y + 2)^2 = 36$

14. $x^2 - y^2 - 4x - 6y = 6$

15. $x^2 + 6x - y^2 + 2y = -11$

16. $9x^2 - 4y^2 = 18x + 24y + 63$

In Exercises 17–20, write the equation of each hyperbola.

17. Center at $(-2, -4)$; $a = 2$; area of fundamental rectangle is 36 square units

18. Center at $(3, -5)$; $b = 6$; area of fundamental rectangle is 24 square units

19. One vertex at $(6, 0)$, one end of conjugate axis at $\left(0, \dfrac{5}{4}\right)$

20. One vertex at $(3, 0)$, one focus at $(-5, 0)$, center at $(0, 0)$

In Exercises 21–29, graph each equation.

21. $\dfrac{x^2}{9} - \dfrac{y^2}{4} = 1$

22. $\dfrac{y^2}{4} - \dfrac{x^2}{9} = 1$

23. $4x^2 - 3y^2 = 36$

24. $x^2 + 6x - y^2 + 2y = -11$

25. $y^2 - x^2 = 1$

26. $x^2 - y^2 - 4x - 6y = 6$

27. $4x^2 - 2y^2 + 8x - 8y = 8$

28. $9(y + 2)^2 - 4(x - 1)^2 = 36$

29. $y^2 - 4x^2 + 6y + 32x = 59$

In Exercises 30–32, graph each hyperbola by plotting points.

30. $xy = 9$

31. $-xy = 6$

32. $-xy = 20$

In Exercises 33–36, find the equation of each curve on which point P lies.

33.   The difference of the distances between $P(x, y)$ and the points $(-2, 1)$ and $(8, 1)$ is 6.

34.   The difference of the distances between $P(x, y)$ and the points $(3, -1)$ and $(3, 5)$ is 5.

35.   The distance between point $P(x, y)$ and the point $(0, 3)$ is $\frac{3}{2}$ of the distance between P and the line $y = -2$.

36.   The distance between point $P(x, y)$ and the point $(5, 4)$ is $\frac{5}{3}$ of the distance between P and the line $x = -3$.

37.   Prove that $c > a$ for a hyperbola with center at the origin and line segment FF' on the x-axis.

38.   Show that the equations of the extended diagonals of the fundamental rectangle of the hyperbola with equation $\dfrac{x^2}{a^2} - \dfrac{y^2}{b^2} = 1$ are $y = \dfrac{b}{a}x$ and $y = -\dfrac{b}{a}x$.

39.   Show that the expansion of the standard form of the equation of a hyperbola is a special case of the general equation of second degree with $B = 0$.

13.5   SOLVING SIMULTANEOUS SECOND-DEGREE EQUATIONS

We now discuss techniques for solving systems of two equations in two variables where at least one of the equations is of second degree.

Example 1   Solve this system of equations by graphing:

$$\begin{cases} x^2 + y^2 = 25 \\ 2x + y = 10 \end{cases}$$

Solution   The graph of the equation $x^2 + y^2 = 25$ is a circle with center at the origin and radius of 5. The graph of the equation $2x + y = 10$ is a straight line. Depending on whether the line is a secant (intersecting the circle at two points) or a tangent (intersecting the circle at one point) or does not intersect the circle at all, there are two, one, or no solutions to the system, respectively. After graphing the circle and the line, as shown in Figure 13-23, note that there are two intersection points, P and P', with the coordinates of $(3, 4)$ and $(5, 0)$. Thus, the solutions to the given system of equations are

$$\begin{cases} x = 3 \\ y = 4 \end{cases} \quad \text{and} \quad \begin{cases} x = 5 \\ y = 0 \end{cases}$$

Verify that these are *exact* solutions.

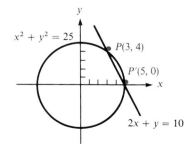

Figure 13-23

Graphical solutions of systems of equations usually give only approximate solutions. A second method, using algebra, can be used to find exact solutions.

Example 2   Solve the following system of equations algebraically:

$$\begin{cases} x^2 + y^2 = 25 \\ 2x + y = 10 \end{cases}$$

Solution   This system contains one equation of second degree and another of first degree. Solve systems of this kind by the substitution method. Solving the linear equation for y gives

$$2x + y = 10$$
$$y = -2x + 10$$

Substitute the expression $-2x + 10$ for y in the second-degree equation, and solve the resulting quadratic equation for x:

$$x^2 + y^2 = 25$$
$$x^2 + (-2x + 10)^2 = 25$$
$$x^2 + 4x^2 - 40x + 100 = 25 \qquad \text{Remove parentheses.}$$
$$5x^2 - 40x + 75 = 0 \qquad \text{Combine terms.}$$
$$x^2 - 8x + 15 = 0 \qquad \text{Divide both sides by 5.}$$
$$(x - 5)(x - 3) = 0 \qquad \text{Factor } x^2 - 8x + 15 = 0.$$
$$x = 5 \quad \text{or} \quad x = 3$$

Because $y = -2x + 10$, if $x = 5$ then $y = 0$, and if $x = 3$ then $y = 4$. The two solutions are

$$\begin{cases} x = 5 \\ y = 0 \end{cases} \quad \text{or} \quad \begin{cases} x = 3 \\ y = 4 \end{cases}$$

Example 3   Solve the following system of equations algebraically:

$$\begin{cases} 4x^2 + 9y^2 = 5 \\ y = x^2 \end{cases}$$

Solution   Solve this system by substitution.

$$4x^2 + 9y^2 = 5$$
$$4y + 9y^2 = 5 \qquad \text{Substitute } y \text{ for } x^2.$$
$$9y^2 + 4y - 5 = 0 \qquad \text{Add } -5 \text{ to both sides.}$$
$$(9y - 5)(y + 1) = 0 \qquad \text{Factor } 9y^2 + 4y^2 - 5.$$
$$9y - 5 = 0 \quad \text{or} \quad y + 1 = 0$$
$$y = \frac{5}{9} \qquad\qquad y = -1$$

Because $y = x^2$, the values of x are found by solving the equations

$$x^2 = \frac{5}{9} \qquad \text{and} \qquad x^2 = -1$$

Because the equation $x^2 = -1$ has no real solutions, this possibility is discarded. The solutions of the equation $x^2 = \frac{5}{9}$ are

$$x = \frac{\sqrt{5}}{3} \qquad \text{or} \qquad x = \frac{-\sqrt{5}}{3}$$

Thus, the solutions of the system are

$$\left(\frac{\sqrt{5}}{3}, \frac{5}{9} \right) \qquad \text{and} \qquad \left(\frac{-\sqrt{5}}{3}, \frac{5}{9} \right) \qquad\qquad \blacksquare$$

Example 4 Solve the following system of equations algebraically:

$$\begin{cases} 3x^2 + 2y^2 = 36 \\ 4x^2 - y^2 = 4 \end{cases}$$

Solution In this system, both equations are of second degree and in the form $ax^2 + by^2 = c$. Solve systems like this by eliminating one of the variables by addition. Copy the first equation and multiply the second equation by 2 to obtain the equivalent system of equations

$$\begin{cases} 3x^2 + 2y^2 = 36 \\ 8x^2 - 2y^2 = 8 \end{cases}$$

Add the equations to eliminate the variable y, and solve the resulting equation for x:

$$11x^2 = 44$$
$$x^2 = 4$$
$$x = 2 \qquad \text{or} \qquad x = -2$$

To find y, substitute **2** for x and then $-\mathbf{2}$ for x in the first equation and proceed as follows:

For $x = 2$	For $x = -2$
$3x^2 + 2y^2 = 36$	$3x^2 + 2y^2 = 36$
$3(2)^2 + 2y^2 = 36$	$3(-2)^2 + 2y^2 = 36$
$12 + 2y^2 = 36$	$12 + 2y^2 = 36$
$2y^2 = 24$	$2y^2 = 24$
$y^2 = 12$	$y^2 = 12$
$y = +\sqrt{12} \quad \text{or} \quad y = -\sqrt{12}$	$y = +\sqrt{12} \quad \text{or} \quad y = -\sqrt{12}$
$y = 2\sqrt{3} \qquad\qquad y = -2\sqrt{3}$	$y = 2\sqrt{3} \qquad\qquad y = -2\sqrt{3}$

The four solutions of this system are

$$(2, 2\sqrt{3}), \quad (2, -2\sqrt{3}), \quad (-2, 2\sqrt{3}), \quad \text{and} \quad (-2, -2\sqrt{3}) \qquad\qquad \blacksquare$$

▪ EXERCISE 13.5

In Exercises 1–10, solve each system of equations by graphing.

1. $\begin{cases} 8x^2 + 32y^2 = 256 \\ x = 2y \end{cases}$
  2. $\begin{cases} x^2 + y^2 = 2 \\ x + y = 2 \end{cases}$
  3. $\begin{cases} x^2 + y^2 = 90 \\ y = x^2 \end{cases}$
  4. $\begin{cases} x^2 + y^2 = 5 \\ x + y = 3 \end{cases}$

5. $\begin{cases} x^2 + y^2 = 25 \\ 12x^2 + 64y^2 = 768 \end{cases}$
  6. $\begin{cases} x^2 + y^2 = 13 \\ y = x^2 - 1 \end{cases}$
  7. $\begin{cases} x^2 - 13 = -y^2 \\ y = 2x - 4 \end{cases}$
  8. $\begin{cases} x^2 + y^2 = 20 \\ y = x^2 \end{cases}$

9. $\begin{cases} x^2 - 6x - y = -5 \\ x^2 - 6x + y = -5 \end{cases}$
  10. $\begin{cases} x^2 - y^2 = -5 \\ 3x^2 + 2y^2 = 30 \end{cases}$

In Exercises 11–36, solve each system of equations algebraically for real values of x and y.

11. $\begin{cases} 25x^2 + 9y^2 = 225 \\ 5x + 3y = 15 \end{cases}$
  12. $\begin{cases} x^2 + y^2 = 20 \\ y = x^2 \end{cases}$

13. $\begin{cases} x^2 + y^2 = 2 \\ x + y = 2 \end{cases}$
  14. $\begin{cases} x^2 + y^2 = 36 \\ 49x^2 + 36y^2 = 1764 \end{cases}$

15. $\begin{cases} x^2 + y^2 = 5 \\ x + y = 3 \end{cases}$
  16. $\begin{cases} x^2 - x - y = 2 \\ 4x - 3y = 0 \end{cases}$
  17. $\begin{cases} x^2 + y^2 = 13 \\ y = x^2 - 1 \end{cases}$
  18. $\begin{cases} x^2 + y^2 = 25 \\ 2x^2 - 3y^2 = 5 \end{cases}$

19. $\begin{cases} x^2 + y^2 = 30 \\ y = x^2 \end{cases}$
  20. $\begin{cases} 9x^2 - 7y^2 = 81 \\ x^2 + y^2 = 9 \end{cases}$
  21. $\begin{cases} x^2 + y^2 = 13 \\ x^2 - y^2 = 5 \end{cases}$
  22. $\begin{cases} 2x^2 + y^2 = 6 \\ x^2 - y^2 = 3 \end{cases}$

23. $\begin{cases} x^2 + y^2 = 20 \\ x^2 - y^2 = -12 \end{cases}$
  24. $\begin{cases} xy = -\dfrac{9}{2} \\ 3x + 2y = 6 \end{cases}$

25. $\begin{cases} y^2 = 40 - x^2 \\ y = x^2 - 10 \end{cases}$
  26. $\begin{cases} x^2 - 6x - y = -5 \\ x^2 - 6x + y = -5 \end{cases}$

27. $\begin{cases} y = x^2 - 4 \\ x^2 - y^2 = -16 \end{cases}$
  28. $\begin{cases} 6x^2 + 8y^2 = 182 \\ 8x^2 - 3y^2 = 24 \end{cases}$
  29. $\begin{cases} x^2 - y^2 = -5 \\ 3x^2 + 2y^2 = 30 \end{cases}$
  30. $\begin{cases} \dfrac{1}{x} + \dfrac{1}{y} = 5 \\ \dfrac{1}{x} - \dfrac{1}{y} = -3 \end{cases}$

31. $\begin{cases} \dfrac{1}{x} + \dfrac{2}{y} = 1 \\ \dfrac{2}{x} - \dfrac{1}{y} = \dfrac{1}{3} \end{cases}$
  32. $\begin{cases} \dfrac{1}{x} + \dfrac{3}{y} = 4 \\ \dfrac{2}{x} - \dfrac{1}{y} = 7 \end{cases}$

33. $\begin{cases} 3y^2 = xy \\ 2x^2 + xy - 84 = 0 \end{cases}$
  34. $\begin{cases} x^2 + y^2 = 10 \\ 2x^2 - 3y^2 = 5 \end{cases}$

35. $\begin{cases} xy = \dfrac{1}{6} \\ y + x = 5xy \end{cases}$
  36. $\begin{cases} xy = \dfrac{1}{12} \\ y + x = 7xy \end{cases}$

37. The area of a rectangle is 63 square centimeters, and its perimeter is 32 centimeters. Find the dimensions of the rectangle.

38. The product of two integers is 32 and their sum is 12. Find the integers.

39. The sum of the squares of two numbers is 221, and the sum of the numbers is 212 less. Find the numbers.

40. Grant receives $225 annual income from one investment. Jeff invested $500 more than Grant, but at an annual rate of 1% less. Jeff's annual income is $240. What is the amount and rate of Grant's investment?

41. Carol receives $67.50 annual income from one investment. John invested $150 more than Carol at an annual rate of $1\frac{1}{2}\%$ more. John's annual income is $94.50. What is the amount and rate of Carol's investment? (*Hint:* There are two answers.)

42. Jim drove 306 miles. Jim's brother made the same trip at a speed 17 miles per hour slower than Jim did and required an extra $1\frac{1}{2}$ hours. What was Jim's rate and time?

13.6   TRANSLATION OF COORDINATE AXES

The graph of the equation

$$(x - 3)^2 + (y - 1)^2 = 4$$

is a circle with radius of 2 and with center at the point (3, 1). See Figure 13-24. If we were to shift the black xy-coordinate system 3 units to the right and 1 unit up, we would establish the colored $x'y'$-coordinate system. With respect to this new $x'y'$-system, the center of the circle is the origin and its equation is

$$x'^2 + y'^2 = 4$$

In this section, we will discuss how to change the equation of a graph by shifting the position of the x- and y-axes. A shift to the left, right, up, or down is called a **translation of the coordinate axes**.

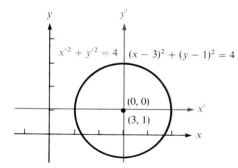

Figure 13-24

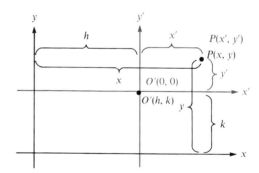

Figure 13-25

Figure 13-25 shows both an xy- and an $x'y'$-coordinate system. The colored x'- and y'-axes are parallel to the black x- and y-axes, respectively, and the unit distance on each is the same. The origin of the $x'y'$-system is the point O' with $x'y'$-coordinates of (0, 0) and with xy-coordinates of (h, k). The $x'y'$-system is called a **translated coordinate system**.

Relative to the xy-system in Figure 13-25, the coordinates of point P are (x, y). Relative to the $x'y'$-system, the coordinates of point P are (x', y'). By the geometry of the figure,

1. $\begin{cases} x = x' + h \\ y = y' + k \end{cases}$ or   **2.** $\begin{cases} x' = x - h \\ y' = y - k \end{cases}$

Equations 1 and Equations 2 are called the **translation-of-axes formulas**. They enable us to determine the coordinates of any point with respect to any translated coordinate system.

Example 1   The $x'y'$-coordinates of point P in Figure 13-26 are $(-3, -2)$, and the xy-coordinates of point O' are $(2, 1)$. Find the xy-coordinates of point P.

Solution   Because you want to find xy-coordinates, use Equations 1 with $(h, k) = (2, 1)$ and $(x', y') = (-3, -2)$:

$$x = x' + h \qquad y = y' + k$$
$$x = -3 + 2 \qquad y = -2 + 1$$
$$= -1 \qquad\qquad = -1$$

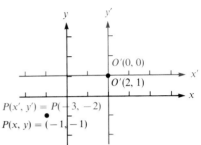

Figure 13-26

The xy-coordinates of point P are $(-1, -1)$.   ■

Example 2   The xy-coordinates of point O' in Figure 13-27 are $(-3, -5)$, and the xy-coordinates of point Q are $(1, -2)$. Find the $x'y'$-coordinates of point Q.

Solution   Because you want to find $x'y'$-coordinates, use Equations 2 with $(h, k) = (-3, -5)$ and $(x, y) = (1, -2)$:

$$x' = x - h \qquad y' = y - k$$
$$x' = 1 - (-3) \qquad y' = -2 - (-5)$$
$$= 4 \qquad\qquad = 3$$

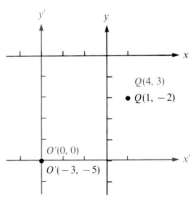

Figure 13-27

The $x'y'$-coordinates of point Q are $(4, 3)$.   ■

Example 3   The xy-coordinates of point O' in Figure 13-28 are $(1, 5)$. Find the equation of the line determined by $y = 2x + 3$ in the variables x' and y'.

Solution   Because the xy-coordinates of point O' are $(h, k) = (1, 5)$, substitute **1** for h and **5** for k in Equations 1 to obtain

$$x = x' + h \qquad y = y' + k$$
$$x = x' + 1 \qquad y = y' + 5$$

Then substitute $x' + 1$ for x and $y' + 5$ for y in the equation $y = 2x + 3$ and simplify:

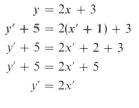

$$y = 2x + 3$$
$$y' + 5 = 2(x' + 1) + 3$$
$$y' + 5 = 2x' + 2 + 3$$
$$y' + 5 = 2x' + 5$$
$$y' = 2x'$$

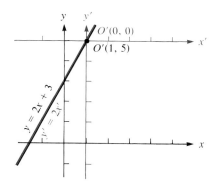

Figure 13-28

In the variables x' and y', the equation of the line is $y' = 2x'$. Note that graphing $y = 2x + 3$ with respect to the black xy-coordinate system gives the same line as graphing $y' = 2x'$ with respect to the colored $x'y'$-coordinate system.   ■

Example 4   Find the equation of the parabola $y + 3 = (x - 2)^2$ with respect to a translated coordinate system with origin at $O'(2, -3)$. Graph the resulting equation with respect to the translated coordinate system.

Solution   Because the origin is translated to the point $(h, k) = (2, -3)$, substitute **2** for h and -3 for k in the translation-of-axes formulas:

$$x = x' + h \qquad y = y' + k$$
$$x = x' + 2 \qquad y = y' + (-3)$$
$$\qquad\qquad\qquad y = y' - 3$$

To obtain the equation of the same parabola with respect to the translated axes, substitute $x' + 2$ for x and $y' - 3$ for y in the given equation:

$$y + 3 = (x - 2)^2$$
$$(y' - 3) + 3 = [(x' + 2) - 2]^2$$
$$y' = x'^2 \qquad\qquad \text{Simplify.}$$

The graph of the equation $y' = x'^2$ is a parabola with vertex at the origin of the $x'y'$-system. See Figure 13-29.

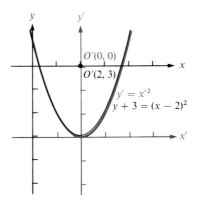

Figure 13-29   ■

Example 5   To what point should the origin of the xy-coordinate system be translated to remove the first-degree terms in the equation

$$4x^2 + y^2 + 8x - 6y + 9 = 0$$

Graph the resulting equation with respect to the translated coordinate system.

Solution   Begin by completing the square in both x and y and simplifying:

$$4x^2 + y^2 + 8x - 6y + 9 = 0$$
$$4x^2 + 8x + y^2 - 6y = -9 \qquad \text{Rearrange terms and add } -9 \text{ to both sides.}$$
$$4(x^2 + 2x) + y^2 - 6y = -9 \qquad \text{Factor 4 from } 4x^2 + 8x.$$
$$4(x^2 + 2x + 1) + y^2 - 6y + 9 = -9 + 4 + 9 \qquad \text{Add 4 and 9 to both sides.}$$
$$4(x + 1)^2 + (y - 3)^2 = 4 \qquad \text{Factor both trinomials.}$$
$$\frac{(x + 1)^2}{1} + \frac{(y - 3)^2}{4} = 1 \qquad \text{Divide both sides by 4.}$$

To transform this equation into one that involves no first-degree terms, substitute x' for $x + 1$ and y' for $y - 3$ as follows:

$$\frac{(x + 1)^2}{1} + \frac{(y - 3)^2}{4} = 1$$
$$\frac{x'^2}{1} + \frac{y'^2}{4} = 1$$

The graph of the final equation is an ellipse, centered at the origin of an $x'y'$-coordinate system. Because the substitutions

$$x' = x + 1 = x - (-1) \quad \text{and} \quad y' = y - 3$$

represent a translation of axes, the origin of the $x'y'$-system is located at the point $(-1, 3)$ of the xy-system. See Figure 13-30.

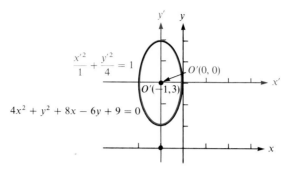

Figure 13-30

Example 6   Show that the slope of a nonvertical line is not affected by a translation of axes.

Solution   In the xy-system, the slope-intercept form of the equation of a nonvertical line with slope m is

$$y = mx + b$$

Use the translation-of-axes formulas to find the equation of the *same* line with respect to an $x'y'$-system whose origin has been translated to the point (h, k) of the xy-system. Substitute $x' + h$ for x and $y' + k$ for y and simplify. Proceed as follows:

$$y = mx + b$$
$$y' + k = m(x' + h) + b$$
$$y' + k = mx' + mh + b \qquad \text{Remove parentheses.}$$
$$y' = mx' + mh + b - k \qquad \text{Add } -k \text{ to both sides.}$$

This final equation is in slope-intercept form and represents a line with y'-intercept of $mh + b - k$ and a slope of m. Thus, the translation does not change the slope of the line.   ■

▪ EXERCISE 13.6

In Exercises 1–4, the origin of the $x'y'$-system is at the point $(1, -3)$ of the xy-system. Find the xy-coordinates of the point whose $x'y'$-coordinates are given.

1. $P(2, 4)$ **2.** $Q(-1, 3)$ **3.** $R(0, 0)$ **4.** $S(1, -3)$

In Exercises 5–8, the origin of the $x'y'$-system is at the point $(-2, 4)$ of the xy-system. Find the $x'y'$-coordinates of the point whose xy-coordinates are given.

5. $P(2, -4)$ **6.** $Q(-2, 4)$ **7.** $R(0, 0)$ **8.** $S(4, 2)$

In Exercises 9–12, the origin of the x′y′-system is at the point (0, −5) of the xy-system. Express each equation in terms of the variables x′ and y′. Draw a sketch that shows the relation of the graphs of the equations to both coordinate systems.

9. $y = 3x - 2$ **10.** $y = -3x - 4$ **11.** $y = x^2 - 5$ **12.** $x = y^2 + 10y + 25$

In Exercises 13–16, the origin of the x′y′-system is at the point (3, −2) of the xy-system. Express each equation in terms of the variables x′ and y′. Draw a sketch that shows the relation of the graphs of the equations to both coordinate systems.

13. $x^2 + y^2 = 9$ **14.** $2x^2 + 3y^2 = 12$ **15.** $x^2 - 6x + 7 = y$ **16.** $y^2 + 4y + 7 = x$

In Exercises 17–22, determine the point to which the origin of the x′y′-system should be translated to eliminate the first-degree terms of the given equation. Draw a sketch that shows the relation of the graphs of the equations to both coordinate systems.

17. $x^2 + y^2 + 4x - 10y - 6 = 0$ **18.** $x^2 + y^2 - 8x - 2y + 1 = 0$

19. $2x^2 + y^2 + 4x + 2y - 1 = 0$ **20.** $4x^2 + 9y^2 + 24x - 18y + 9 = 0$

21. $x^2 - y^2 - 6x - 4y + 4 = 0$ **22.** $4x^2 - 9y^2 + 8x - 36y = 68$

23. Show that the radius of a circle is not affected by a translation of axes.

24. Show that no translation of axes will remove the xy-term of the equation $xy = 1$.

In Exercises 25–26, suppose that the equation $Ax^2 + Bxy + Cy^2 + Dx + Ey + F = 0$ is changed into $A'x'^2 + B'x'y' + C'y'^2 + D'x' + E'y' + F' = 0$ by substituting $x' + h$ for x and $y' + k$ for k and then simplifying.

25. Show that $A + C = A' + C'$. **26.** Show that $B^2 - 4AC = B'^2 - 4A'C'$.

CHAPTER SUMMARY

Key Words

center of a circle (13.1)
center of an ellipse (13.3)
center of a hyperbola (13.4)
circle (13.1)
conjugate axis of a hyperbola (13.4)
directrix of a parabola (13.2)
ellipse (13.3)
foci of an ellipse (13.3)
foci of a hyperbola (13.4)
focus of a parabola (13.2)
fundamental rectangle (13.4)

hyperbola (13.4)
major axis of an ellipse (13.3)
minor axis of an ellipse (13.3)
parabola (13.2)
translation of axes (13.6)
transverse axis of a hyperbola (13.4)
vertices of an ellipse (13.3)
vertices of a hyperbola (13.4)
vertex of a parabola (13.2)

Key Ideas

(13.1) Any equation that can be written in the form

$$(x - h)^2 + (y - k)^2 = r^2$$

has a graph that is a circle with center at point $C(h, k)$ and with a radius of r.

Any equation that can be written in the form

$$x^2 + y^2 = r^2$$

has a graph that is a circle with center at the origin and with radius r.

(13.2) The standard forms of the equations of parabolas that open to the right, left, upward, and downward are as follows (consider $p > 0$):

Parabola opening	Vertex at origin	Vertex at $V(h, k)$
Right	$y^2 = 4px$	$(y - k)^2 = 4p(x - h)$
Left	$y^2 = -4px$	$(y - k)^2 = -4p(x - h)$
Upward	$x^2 = 4py$	$(x - h)^2 = 4p(y - k)$
Downward	$x^2 = -4py$	$(x - h)^2 = -4p(y - k)$

(13.3) The standard form of the equation of an ellipse with center at the origin and major axis on the x-axis is

$$\frac{x^2}{a^2} + \frac{y^2}{b^2} = 1 \quad \text{where } a > b > 0$$

If the major axis of the ellipse with center at the origin lies on the y-axis, the standard form of the equation of an ellipse is

$$\frac{y^2}{a^2} + \frac{x^2}{b^2} = 1 \quad \text{where } a > b > 0$$

In either case, the length of the major axis is $2a$, and the length of the minor axis is $2b$.

The standard form of the equation of an ellipse with center at (h, k) and major axis parallel to the x-axis is

$$\frac{(x - h)^2}{a^2} + \frac{(y - k)^2}{b^2} = 1 \quad \text{where } a > b > 0$$

If the major axis of an ellipse with center (h, k) is parallel to the y-axis, the standard form of the equation of the ellipse is

$$\frac{(y - k)^2}{a^2} + \frac{(x - h)^2}{b^2} = 1 \quad \text{where } a > b > 0$$

In either case, the length of the major axis is $2a$, and the length of the minor axis is $2b$.

(13.4) The standard form of the equation of a hyperbola with center at the origin and foci on the x-axis is

$$\frac{x^2}{a^2} - \frac{y^2}{b^2} = 1$$

The standard form of the equation of a hyperbola with center at the origin and foci on the y-axis is

$$\frac{y^2}{a^2} - \frac{x^2}{b^2} = 1$$

The standard form of the equation of a hyperbola with center at (h, k) and foci on a line parallel to the x-axis is

$$\frac{(x - h)^2}{a^2} - \frac{(y - k)^2}{b^2} = 1$$

The standard form of the equation of a hyperbola with center at (h, k) and foci on a line parallel to the y-axis is

$$\frac{(y - k)^2}{a^2} - \frac{(x - h)^2}{b^2} = 1$$

The extended diagonals of the fundamental rectangle are asymptotes of the graph of a hyperbola.

(13.5)   Good estimates for solutions to systems of simultaneous second-degree equations can be found by graphing.

Exact solutions to systems of simultaneous second-degree equations can often be found by algebraic techniques.

(13.6)   Equations in two variables x and y can often be simplified by using the translation-of-axes formulas

$$\begin{cases} x = x' + h \\ y = y' + k \end{cases} \quad \text{or} \quad \begin{cases} x' = x - h \\ y' = y - k \end{cases}$$

REVIEW EXERCISES

1. Write the equation of the circle with center at the origin and passing through point $(5, 5)$.

2. Write the equation of the circle with center at the origin and passing through point $(6, 8)$.

3. Write the equation of a circle with endpoints of its diameter at $(-2, 4)$ and $(12, 16)$.

4. Write the equation of a circle with endpoints of its diameter at $(-3, -6)$ and $(7, 10)$.

5. Write in standard form the equation of the circle $x^2 + y^2 - 6x + 4y = 3$ and graph the circle.

6. Write in standard form the equation of the circle $x^2 + 4x + y^2 - 10y = -13$ and graph the circle.

7. Write the equation of the parabola with vertex at the origin and curve passing through $(-8, 4)$ and $(-8, -4)$.

8. Write the equation of the parabola with vertex at the origin and curve passing through $(-8, 4)$ and $(8, 4)$.

9. Write the equation of the parabola $y = ax^2 + bx + c$ in standard form to show that the x-coordinate of the vertex of the parabola is $-\frac{b}{2a}$.

10. Find the equation of the parabola with vertex at $(-2, 3)$, curve passing through point $(-4, -8)$, and opening downward.

11. Graph the parabola $x^2 - 4y - 2x + 9 = 0$.

12. Graph the parabola $y^2 - 6y = 4x - 13$.

13. Graph $y^2 - 4x - 2y + 13 = 0$.

14. Write the equation of the ellipse with center at the origin, major axis that is horizontal and 12 units long, and minor axis 8 units long.

15. Write the equation of the ellipse with center at point $(-2, 3)$ and curve passing through points $(-2, 0)$ and $(2, 3)$.

16. Graph the ellipse $4x^2 + y^2 - 16x + 2y = -13$.

17. Graph the curve $x^2 + 9y^2 - 6x - 18y + 9 = 0$.

18. Write the equation of the hyperbola with vertices at points $(-3, 3)$ and $(3, 3)$ and a focus at point $(5, 3)$.

19. Graph the hyperbola $9x^2 - 4y^2 - 16y - 18x = 43$.

20. Graph the hyperbola $-2xy = 9$.

21. Solve the following system of equations by graphing:

$$\begin{cases} 3x^2 + y^2 = 52 \\ x^2 - y^2 = 12 \end{cases}$$

22. Solve the system in Review Exercise 21 algebraically.

23. Solve the following system of equations by graphing:

$$\begin{cases} x^2 + y^2 = 16 \\ -\sqrt{3}y + 4\sqrt{3} = 3x \end{cases}$$

24. Solve the system in Review Exercise 23 algebraically.

25. Solve the following system of equations by graphing:

$$\begin{cases} \dfrac{x^2}{16} + \dfrac{y^2}{12} = 1 \\ \dfrac{x^2}{1} - \dfrac{y^2}{3} = 1 \end{cases}$$

26. Solve the system in Review Exercise 25 algebraically.

In Review Exercises 27–30, the origin of the $x'y'$-system is at the point $(2, -3)$ of the xy-system. Express each equation in terms of the variables x' and y'. Draw a sketch that shows the relation of the graphs to both coordinate systems.

27. $x^2 + y^2 = 25$

28. $x^2 - y^2 = 4$

29. $4x^2 + 9y^2 = 36$

30. $x^2 - 4x - 3y = 5$

In Review Exercises 31–32, determine the point at which the origin of the $x'y'$-system should be located to eliminate the first-degree terms of the given equation. Draw a sketch that shows the relation of the graphs of the equations to both coordinate systems.

31. $x^2 + y^2 - 6x - 4y + 12 = 0$

32. $4x^2 - y^2 - 8x + 4y = 4$

CHAPTER THIRTEEN TEST

In Problems 1–9, find the equations of the conics with the following properties. Write all answers in standard form.

1. A circle with center at the origin and radius 2

2. A circle with endpoints of its diameter at points $P(2, 4)$ and $Q(10, 8)$

3. A circle with center at $(3, 4)$ and passing through the origin

4. A parabola with vertex at the origin and focus at $(5, 0)$

5. A parabola with vertex at $(2, 3)$, passing through the origin, and with a horizontal axis

6. An ellipse with center at the origin, major axis of 10 units and horizontal, and minor axis of 8 units

7. An ellipse with center at the origin, focus at $(0, 5)$, and vertex at $(0, -13)$

8. A hyperbola with center at the origin, vertex at $(0, 6)$, and focus at $(0, 10)$

9. A hyperbola with center at $(2, 4)$, vertex at $(4, 4)$, and a fundamental rectangle with area of 32 square units

10. Find the coordinates of the center of the circle with an equation of

$$x^2 - 4x + y^2 - 10y + 17 = 0$$

11. Find the area of the fundamental rectangle of the hyperbola with an equation of $\dfrac{x^2}{9} - \dfrac{y^2}{25} = 1$.

12. Find the coordinates of the focus located on the positive x-axis of the ellipse with an equation of $\dfrac{x^2}{225} + \dfrac{y^2}{144} = 1$.

13. Find the vertex of the parabola with equation of $y^2 + 8x - 4y = 28$.

In Problems 14–15, solve each system of equations.

14. $\begin{cases} 2x - y = -2 \\ x^2 + y^2 = 16 + 4y \end{cases}$

15. $\begin{cases} x^2 + y^2 = 25 \\ 4x^2 - 9y = 0 \end{cases}$

16. Graph the equation $x^2 + y^2 - 2x - 6y + 6 = 0$.

17. Determine the point at which the origin of an $x'y'$-coordinate system should be placed to eliminate the first-degree terms of the equation $x^2 + 6x + y^2 - 4y = -4$. Then, graph the resulting equation on the $x'y'$-coordinate system.

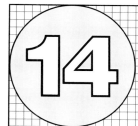

14 Natural Number Functions and Probability

The brilliant German mathematician Carl Friedrich Gauss (1777–1855) was once a student in the class of a very strict teacher. To keep the class busy one day, the teacher asked the students to add together all the natural numbers from 1 through 100. Gauss immediately wrote the sum on his slate and put it on the teacher's desk.

Gauss's solution was relatively simple. He recognized that in the sum $1 + 2 + 3 + \cdots + 98 + 99 + 100$, the first number (1) added to the last number (100) was 101. Similarly, the second number (2) added to the second from the last number (99) was 101. The third number (3) added to the third from the last number (98) was 101 also. Gauss realized that this pattern continued, and because there were fifty pairs of numbers there were fifty sums of 101. He multiplied 101 by 50 and obtained the correct answer of 5050.

This story illustrates a group of problems involving long strings of numbers called *sequences*. We begin a discussion of sequences by considering a method of proof that is used to prove sequence formulas. This method of proof, called **mathematical induction**, was first used extensively by Giuseppe Peano (1858–1932).

14.1 MATHEMATICAL INDUCTION

Suppose we ask a theatergoer whether everyone in line for a movie gained admittance. The theatergoer answers that "the first person in line was admitted." Does this response answer our question? Certainly more than one person was admitted, but this does not mean that everyone was admitted. As a matter of fact, we know little more now than before we asked the question.

Meeting a second theatergoer, we ask the question again. This time the answer is "they promised that if anyone was admitted, the person next in line would also be admitted." On the basis of this response we know that if anyone was admitted, the person behind was admitted also. But a promise that begins with "if someone is admitted" does not guarantee that anyone actually was admitted.

However, when we consider both the first and second answers, we know that everyone in line gained admittance. The first theatergoer said that the first person got in; the second theatergoer said that if anyone got in, the next person in line got in also. Because the first person was admitted, the second person was admitted also. And, if the second person was admitted, then so was the third. This pattern would have continued until everyone was admitted to the theater.

This situation is very similar to a children's game played with dominoes. The dominoes are placed on end fairly close together in a row. When the first domino is pushed over, it falls against the second, knocking it down. The second domino, in turn, knocks down the third, which topples the fourth, and so on until all of the dominoes fall. Two things must happen to guarantee that all the dominoes fall: (1) The first domino must be knocked over, and (2) every domino that falls must topple the next one. When both of these conditions are met, it is certain that all of the dominoes will fall.

The preceding examples illustrate the basic idea that underlies the principle of mathematical induction.

The Axiom of Mathematical Induction.   If a statement involving the natural number n has the two properties that

1.   the statement is true for $n = 1$, and
2.   the statement is true for $n = k + 1$ whenever it is true for $n = k$,

then the statement is true for all natural numbers.

The axiom of mathematical induction provides a method for proving many theorems. Note that any such proof by induction involves two parts: We must first show that the formula is true for the natural number 1, and then show that, *if* the formula is true for any natural number k, then it also is true for the natural number $k + 1$. A proof by induction is complete only if both of the required properties are established.

Let us return to Gauss's problem of finding the sum of the first 100 natural numbers. There is a formula for finding the sum of the first n natural numbers:

$$1 + 2 + 3 + \cdots + n = \frac{n(n + 1)}{2}$$

To show that this formula is correct, we will prove it by using the axiom of mathematical induction.

Example 1   Use mathematical induction to prove that the formula

$$1 + 2 + 3 + \cdots + n = \frac{n(n + 1)}{2}$$

is true for every natural number n.

Solution   The proof has two parts.

Part 1.   Verify that the formula is true for the value $n = 1$. Substituting $n = 1$ into the term n on the left side of the equation yields a single term, the number 1. Substituting the number 1 for n on the right side, the formula becomes

$$1 = \frac{n(n + 1)}{2}$$

$$1 = \frac{(1)(1 + 1)}{2}$$

$$1 = 1$$

Thus, the formula is true for $n = 1$, and part 1 of the proof is complete.

Part 2.   Assume that the given formula is true when n is replaced by *some* natural number k. By this assumption, called the **induction hypothesis**, you accept that

1. $1 + 2 + 3 + \cdots + k = \dfrac{k(k + 1)}{2}$

is a true statement. The plan is to show that the given formula is true for the next natural number, $k + 1$. Do this by verifying the equation

2. $1 + 2 + 3 + \cdots + k + (k + 1) = \dfrac{(k + 1)[(k + 1) + 1]}{2}$

obtained from the given formula by replacing n with $k + 1$.
    Compare the left sides of Equations 1 and 2 and note that the left side of Equation 2 contains an extra term of $k + 1$. Hence, add $k + 1$ to both sides of Equation 1 (which was assumed to be true) to obtain the equation

$$1 + 2 + 3 + \cdots + k + (k + 1) = \frac{k(k + 1)}{2} + (k + 1)$$

Because both terms on the right side of this equation have a common factor of $k + 1$, the right side factors and the equation can be rewritten as follows:

$$1 + 2 + 3 + \cdots + k + (k + 1) = (k + 1)\left(\frac{k}{2} + 1\right)$$

$$= \frac{(k + 1)(k + 2)}{2}$$

$$= \frac{(k + 1)[(k + 1) + 1]}{2}$$

This final result is Equation 2. Because the truth of Equation 1 implies the truth of Equation 2, part 2 of the proof is complete. Parts 1 and 2 together establish that the formula

$$1 + 2 + 3 + \cdots + n = \frac{n(n + 1)}{2}$$

is true for any natural number n.   ■

Here is a brief overview of Example 1.

1. Did the first domino fall? That is, is the formula

$$1 + 2 + 3 + \cdots + n = \frac{n(n + 1)}{2}$$

    true for $n = 1$? Yes, part 1 verified this.
2. Will toppling any domino knock over the next domino? If the given formula is true for the value $n = k$, is it also true for the value $n = k + 1$? Yes, part 2 of the proof verified this.

Because both of the induction requirements were verified, the formula is true for all natural numbers n.

Example 2   Use mathematical induction to prove the formula

$$1 + 5 + 9 + \cdots + (4n - 3) = n(2n - 1)$$

for all natural numbers n.

Solution   The proof has two parts.

Part 1.   First verify the formula for the value $n = 1$. Substituting the value $n = 1$ into the term $4n - 3$ on the left side of the formula gives the single term 1. After substituting the same value into the right side, the equation becomes

$$1 = 1[2(1) - 1]$$
$$1 = 1$$

Thus, the formula is true for $n = 1$, and part 1 of the proof is complete.

Part 2.   The induction hypothesis is the assumption that the formula is true for $n = k$. Hence, you assume that

$$1 + 5 + 9 + \cdots + (4k - 3) = k(2k - 1)$$

is a true statement. Because the truth of this assumption must guarantee the truth of the formula for $k + 1$ terms, add the $(k + 1)$th term to both sides of the induction hypothesis formula. In this example, the terms on the left side increase by 4, so the $(k + 1)$th term is $(4k - 3) + 4$, or $4k + 1$. Adding $4k + 1$ to both sides of the induction hypothesis formula gives

$$1 + 5 + 9 + \cdots + (4k - 3) + (4k + 1) = k(2k - 1) + (4k + 1)$$

Simplify the right side and rewrite the equation as follows:

$$1 + 5 + 9 + \cdots + (4k - 3) + [4(k + 1) - 3] = 2k^2 + 3k + 1$$
$$= (k + 1)(2k + 1)$$
$$= (k + 1)[2(k + 1) - 1]$$

Because the preceding equation has the same form as the given formula, except that $k + 1$ appears in place of n, the truth of the formula for $n = k$ implies the truth of the formula for $n = k + 1$. Part 2 of the proof is complete.

Because both of the induction requirements have been verified, the given formula is proved for all natural numbers.   ■

Example 3   Prove that $\dfrac{1}{2} + \dfrac{1}{4} + \dfrac{1}{8} + \cdots + \dfrac{1}{2^n} < 1$.

Solution   The proof is by induction.

Part 1.   Verify the formula for $n = 1$. Substituting 1 for n on the left side of the inequality gives $\frac{1}{2} < 1$. Thus, the formula is true for $n = 1$, and part 1 of the proof is complete.

Part 2.   The induction hypothesis is the assumption that the inequality is true for $n = k$. Thus, assume that

$$\frac{1}{2} + \frac{1}{4} + \frac{1}{8} + \cdots + \frac{1}{2^k} < 1$$

Multiply both sides of the above inequality by $\frac{1}{2}$ to obtain the inequality

$$\frac{1}{2}\left(\frac{1}{2} + \frac{1}{4} + \frac{1}{8} + \cdots + \frac{1}{2^k}\right) < 1\left(\frac{1}{2}\right)$$

or

$$\frac{1}{4} + \frac{1}{8} + \frac{1}{16} + \cdots + \frac{1}{2^{k+1}} < \frac{1}{2}$$

Now add $\frac{1}{2}$ to both sides of this inequality to obtain

$$\frac{1}{2} + \frac{1}{4} + \frac{1}{8} + \frac{1}{16} + \cdots + \frac{1}{2^{k+1}} < \frac{1}{2} + \frac{1}{2}$$

or

$$\frac{1}{2} + \frac{1}{4} + \frac{1}{8} + \frac{1}{16} + \cdots + \frac{1}{2^{k+1}} < 1$$

The resulting inequality is the same as the original except that $k + 1$ appears in place of n. The truth of the inequality for $n = k$ implies the truth of the inequality for $n = k + 1$. Part 2 of the proof is complete.

Because both of the induction requirements have been verified, this inequality is true for all natural numbers. ∎

There are statements that are not true when $n = 1$ but that are true for all natural numbers equal to or greater than some given natural number, say q. In these cases, verify the given statements for $n = q$ in part 1 of the induction proof. After establishing part 2 of the induction proof, the given statement is proved for all natural numbers that are greater than or equal to q.

■ EXERCISE 14.1

In Exercises 1–4, verify each given formula for $n = 1, 2, 3,$ and 4.

1. $5 + 10 + 15 + \cdots + 5n = \dfrac{5n(n+1)}{2}$

2. $1^2 + 2^2 + 3^2 + \cdots + n^2 = \dfrac{n(n+1)(2n+1)}{6}$

3. $7 + 10 + 13 + \cdots + (3n + 4) = \dfrac{n(3n+11)}{2}$

4. $1(3) + 2(4) + 3(5) + \cdots + n(n+2) = \dfrac{n}{6}(n+1)(2n + 7)$

In Exercises 5–20, prove each of the following formulas by mathematical induction, if possible.

5. $2 + 4 + 6 + \cdots + 2n = n(n + 1)$

6. $1 + 3 + 5 + \cdots + (2n - 1) = n^2$

7. $3 + 7 + 11 + \cdots + (4n - 1) = n(2n + 1)$

8. $4 + 8 + 12 + \cdots + 4n = 2n(n + 1)$

9. $10 + 6 + 2 + \cdots + (14 - 4n) = 12n - 2n^2$

10. $8 + 6 + 4 + \cdots + (10 - 2n) = 9n - n^2$

11. $2 + 5 + 8 + \cdots + (3n - 1) = \dfrac{n(3n+1)}{2}$

12. $3 + 6 + 9 + \cdots + 3n = \dfrac{3n(n+1)}{2}$

13. $1^2 + 2^2 + 3^2 + \cdots + n^2 = \dfrac{n(n+1)(2n+1)}{6}$

14. $1 + 2 + 3 + \cdots + (n - 1) + n + (n - 1) + \cdots + 3 + 2 + 1 = n^2$

15. $\dfrac{1}{3} + 2 + \dfrac{11}{3} + \cdots + \left(\dfrac{5}{3}n - \dfrac{4}{3}\right) = n\left(\dfrac{5}{6}n - \dfrac{1}{2}\right)$

16. $\dfrac{1}{1 \cdot 2} + \dfrac{1}{2 \cdot 3} + \dfrac{1}{3 \cdot 4} + \cdots + \dfrac{1}{n(n+1)} = \dfrac{n}{n+1}$

17. $\dfrac{1}{2} + \dfrac{1}{4} + \dfrac{1}{8} + \cdots + \left(\dfrac{1}{2}\right)^n = 1 - \left(\dfrac{1}{2}\right)^n$

18. $\dfrac{1}{3} + \dfrac{2}{9} + \dfrac{4}{27} + \cdots + \dfrac{1}{3}\left(\dfrac{2}{3}\right)^{n-1} = 1 - \left(\dfrac{2}{3}\right)^n$

19. $2^0 + 2^1 + 2^2 + 2^3 + \cdots + 2^{n-1} = 2^n - 1$

20. $1^3 + 2^3 + 3^3 + \cdots + n^3 = \left[\dfrac{n(n+1)}{2}\right]^2$

21. Prove that $x - y$ is a factor of $x^n - y^n$. (*Hint:* Consider subtracting and adding xy^k to the binomial $x^{k+1} - y^{k+1}$.)

22. Prove that $n < 2^n$.

23. There are 180° in the sum of the angles of any triangle. Prove by induction that $(n - 2)180°$ gives the sum of the angles of any simple polygon when n is the number of sides of that polygon. (*Hint:* If a polygon has $k + 1$ sides, it has $k - 2$ sides plus three more sides.)

24. Consider the equation $1 + 3 + 5 + \cdots + 2n - 1 = 3n - 2$.
    a. Is the equation true for $n = 1$?
    b. Is the equation true for $n = 2$?
    c. Is the equation true for all natural numbers n?

25. If $1 + 2 + 3 + \cdots + n = \dfrac{n}{2}(n + 1) + 1$ were true for $n = k$, show that it would be true for $n = k + 1$. Is it true for $n = 1$?

26. Prove that $n + 1 = 1 + n$ for each natural number n.

27. If n is any natural number, prove that $7^n - 1$ is divisible by 6.

28. Prove that $1 + 2n < 3^n$ for $n > 1$.

29. Prove that, if r is a real number where $r \neq 1$, then $1 + r + r^2 + \cdots + r^n = \dfrac{1 - r^{n+1}}{1 - r}$.

30. The expression a^m where m is a natural number was defined in Section 2.1. An alternative definition of a^m, useful in proofs by induction, is (part 1) $a^1 = a$ and (part 2) $a^{m+1} = a^m \cdot a$. Use mathematical induction on n to prove the familiar law of exponents, $a^m a^n = a^{m+n}$.

14.2 SEQUENCES, SERIES, AND SUMMATION NOTATION

We now formally define a **sequence**.

Definition.   A **sequence** is a function whose domain is the set of natural numbers.

Since a sequence is a function whose domain is the set of natural numbers, we can write its values as a list of numbers. For example, if n is a natural number, the function defined by $f(n) = 2n - 1$ generates the list

$$1, 3, 5, \ldots, 2n - 1, \ldots$$

It is common to call such a list, as well as the function, a sequence. The number 1 is the first term of this sequence, the number 3 is the second term, and the expression $2n - 1$ represents the **general**, or **nth**, **term** of the sequence. Likewise, if n is a natural number, then the function defined by $f(n) = 3n^2 + 1$ generates the list

$$4, 13, 28, \ldots, 3n^2 + 1, \ldots$$

The number 4 is the first term, 13 is the second term, 28 is the third term, and $3n^2 + 1$ is the general term.

Because the domain of any sequence is the infinite set of natural numbers, the sequence itself is an unending list of numbers. Note that a constant function such as $g(n) = 1$ is a sequence also; it generates the list $1, 1, 1, \ldots$.

Many times, sequences do not lend themselves to functional notation because it is difficult or even impossible to write the general term—the expression that shows how the terms are constructed. In such cases, if there is a pattern that is assumed to be continued, it is acceptable simply to list several terms of the sequence. Some examples of sequences follow:

$$1^2, 2^2, 3^2, \ldots, n^2, \ldots$$

$$3, 9, 19, 33, \ldots, 2n^2 + 1, \ldots$$

$$1, 3, 6, 10, 15, 21, \ldots, \frac{n(n + 1)}{2}, \ldots$$

$$1, 1, 2, 3, 5, 8, 13, 21, \ldots \text{ (Fibonacci sequence)}$$

$$2, 3, 5, 7, 11, 13, 17, 19, 23, \ldots \text{ (prime numbers)}$$

The fourth example listed is called the Fibonacci sequence, after the twelfth-century mathematician Leonardo of Pisa—known as Fibonacci. After the two 1s in the Fibonacci sequence, each term is the sum of the two terms that immediately precede it. The Fibonacci sequence occurs in the study of botany, for example, in the growth patterns of certain plants.

To add the terms of a sequence, we replace each comma between the terms with a plus sign, forming what is called a **series**. Because each sequence is infinite, the number of terms in the series associated with it is infinite also.

Two examples of infinite series are

$$1^2 + 2^2 + 3^2 + \cdots + n^2 + \cdots$$

and

$$1 + 2 + 3 + 5 + 8 + 13 + 21 + \cdots$$

There is a shorthand method of indicating the sum of the first n terms, or the **nth partial sum** of a sequence. This method, called **summation notation**, involves the symbol $\sum$, which is capital sigma in the Greek alphabet. The expression

$$\sum_{n=1}^{3} (2n^2 + 1)$$

designates the sum of the three terms obtained if we successively substitute the natural numbers 1, 2, and 3 for n in the expression $2n^2 + 1$. Hence,

$$\sum_{n=1}^{3} (2n^2 + 1) = [2(1)^2 + 1] + [2(2)^2 + 1] + [2(3)^2 + 1]$$
$$= 3 + 9 + 19$$
$$= 31$$

Example 1   Evaluate $\displaystyle\sum_{n=1}^{4} (n^2 - 1)$.

Solution   In this example, n is said to run from 1 to 4. Hence, substitute 1, 2, 3, and 4 for n in the expression $n^2 - 1$, and find the sum of the resulting values:

$$\sum_{n=1}^{4} (n^2 - 1) = (1^2 - 1) + (2^2 - 1) + (3^2 - 1) + (4^2 - 1)$$

$$= 0 + 3 + 8 + 15$$

$$= 26$$ ■

Example 2 Evaluate $\sum_{n=3}^{5} (3n + 2)$.

Solution In this example, n runs from 3 to 5. Hence, substitute 3, 4, and 5 for n in the expression $3n + 2$ and find the sum of the resulting values:

$$\sum_{n=3}^{5} (3n + 2) = [3(3) + 2] + [3(4) + 2] + [3(5) + 2]$$

$$= 11 + 14 + 17$$

$$= 42$$ ■

The following theorems give three properties of summations.

Theorem. If c is a constant, then $\sum_{k=1}^{n} c = nc$.

Proof Because c is a constant, each term is c for each value of k as k runs from 1 to n.

$$\sum_{k=1}^{n} c = \overbrace{c + c + c + c + \cdots + c}^{n \text{ number of } c\text{'s}} = nc$$ □

In words, this theorem states that the summation of a constant as k runs from 1 to n is n times that constant.

Example 3 Evaluate $\sum_{n=1}^{5} 13$.

Solution
$$\sum_{n=1}^{5} 13 = 13 + 13 + 13 + 13 + 13$$

$$= 5(13)$$

$$= 65$$ ■

Theorem. If c is a constant, then $\sum_{k=1}^{n} cf(k) = c \sum_{k=1}^{n} f(k)$.

Proof

$$\sum_{k=1}^{n} cf(k) = cf(1) + cf(2) + cf(3) + \cdots + cf(n)$$

$$= c[f(1) + f(2) + f(3) + \cdots + f(n)] \qquad \text{Factor out } c.$$

$$= c \sum_{k=1}^{n} f(k) \qquad \qquad \square$$

In words, this theorem states that a constant factor may be brought outside a summation sign.

Example 4   Show that $\displaystyle\sum_{k=1}^{3} 5k^2 = 5 \sum_{k=1}^{3} k^2$.

Solution

$$\sum_{k=1}^{3} 5k^2 = 5(1)^2 + 5(2)^2 + 5(3)^2$$

$$= 5 + 20 + 45$$

$$= 70$$

$$5 \sum_{k=1}^{3} k^2 = 5[(1)^2 + (2)^2 + (3)^2]$$

$$= 5[1 + 4 + 9]$$

$$= 5(14)$$

$$= 70 \qquad \blacksquare$$

Theorem. $\displaystyle\sum_{k=1}^{n} [f(k) + g(k)] = \sum_{k=1}^{n} f(k) + \sum_{k=1}^{n} g(k)$

Proof

$$\sum_{k=1}^{n} [f(k) + g(k)] = [f(1) + g(1)] + [f(2) + g(2)]$$

$$+ [f(3) + g(3)] + \cdots + [f(n) + g(n)]$$

$$= [f(1) + f(2) + f(3) + \cdots + f(n)]$$

$$+ [g(1) + g(2) + g(3) + \cdots + g(n)]$$

$$= \sum_{k=1}^{n} f(k) + \sum_{k=1}^{n} g(k) \qquad \square$$

In words, this theorem states that the summation of a sum is equal to the sum of the summations.

Example 5   Show that $\displaystyle\sum_{k=1}^{3} (k + k^2) = \sum_{k=1}^{3} k + \sum_{k=1}^{3} k^2$.

Solution
$$\sum_{k=1}^{3} (k + k^2) = (1 + 1^2) + (2 + 2^2) + (3 + 3^2)$$
$$= 2 + 6 + 12$$
$$= 20$$

$$\sum_{k=1}^{3} k + \sum_{k=1}^{3} k^2 = (1 + 2 + 3) + (1^2 + 2^2 + 3^2)$$
$$= 6 + 14$$
$$= 20$$ ∎

Example 6 Evaluate $\sum_{k=1}^{5} (2k - 1)^2$ directly. Then expand the binomial, apply the previous theorems, and evaluate the expression again.

Solution *Part 1.* $\sum_{k=1}^{5} (2k - 1)^2 = 1 + 9 + 25 + 49 + 81 = 165$

Part 2. $\sum_{k=1}^{5} (2k - 1)^2 = \sum_{k=1}^{5} (4k^2 - 4k + 1)$

$$= \sum_{k=1}^{5} 4k^2 + \sum_{k=1}^{5} (-4k) + \sum_{k=1}^{5} 1$$
The summation of a sum is the sum of the summations.

$$= 4 \sum_{k=1}^{5} k^2 - 4 \sum_{k=1}^{5} k + \sum_{k=1}^{5} 1$$
Bring the constant factors outside the summation sign.

$$= 4 \sum_{k=1}^{5} k^2 - 4 \sum_{k=1}^{5} k + 5$$
The summation of a constant as k runs from 1 to 5 is 5 times that constant.

$$= 4(1 + 4 + 9 + 16 + 25) - 4(1 + 2 + 3 + 4 + 5) + 5$$
$$= 4(55) - 4(15) + 5$$
$$= 220 - 60 + 5$$
$$= 165$$

Note that the sum is 165, regardless of the method used. ∎

▪ EXERCISE 14.2

1. Write the first eight terms of the sequence defined by the function $f(n) = 5n(n - 1)$.

2. Write the first six terms of the sequence defined by the function $f(n) = n\left(\dfrac{n - 1}{2}\right)\left(\dfrac{n - 2}{3}\right)$.

In Exercises 3–8, write the fifth term in each of the given sequences.

3. $1, 6, 11, 16, \ldots$

4. $1, 8, 27, 64, \ldots$

5. $a, a + d, a + 2d, a + 3d, \ldots$

6. $a, ar, ar^2, ar^3, \ldots$

7. $1, 3, 6, 10, \ldots$

8. $20, 17, 13, 8, \ldots$

In Exercises 9–16, find the sum of the first five terms of the sequence with the given general term.

9. n

10. $2k$

11. 3

12. $4k^0$

13. $2\left(\dfrac{1}{3}\right)^n$

14. $(-1)^n$

15. $3n - 2$

16. $2k + 1$

In Exercises 17–28, evaluate each sum.

17. $\displaystyle\sum_{k=1}^{5} 2k$

18. $\displaystyle\sum_{k=3}^{6} 3k$

19. $\displaystyle\sum_{k=3}^{4} (-2k^2)$

20. $\displaystyle\sum_{k=1}^{100} 5$

21. $\displaystyle\sum_{k=1}^{5} (3k - 1)$

22. $\displaystyle\sum_{n=2}^{5} (n^2 + 3n)$

23. $\displaystyle\sum_{k=1}^{1000} \dfrac{1}{2}$

24. $\displaystyle\sum_{x=4}^{5} \dfrac{2}{x}$

25. $\displaystyle\sum_{x=3}^{4} \dfrac{1}{x}$

26. $\displaystyle\sum_{x=2}^{6} (3x^2 + 2x) - 3\sum_{x=2}^{6} x^2$

27. $\displaystyle\sum_{x=1}^{4} (4x + 1)^2 - \sum_{x=1}^{4} (4x - 1)^2$

28. $\displaystyle\sum_{x=0}^{10} (2x - 1)^2 + 4\sum_{x=0}^{10} x(1 - x)$

In Exercises 29–31, use mathematical induction to prove each statement.

29. $\displaystyle\sum_{k=1}^{n} (4k - 3) = n(2n - 1)$

30. $\displaystyle\sum_{k=1}^{n} (5k - 3) = \dfrac{n(5n - 1)}{2}$

31. $\displaystyle\sum_{k=1}^{n} (6k + 4) = n(3n + 7)$

32. Construct an example to disprove the proposition that the summation of a product is the product of the summations. In other words, prove that

$$\sum_{k=1}^{n} f(k)g(k) \qquad \text{is not always equal to} \qquad \sum_{k=1}^{n} f(k) \sum_{k=1}^{n} g(k)$$

14.3 ARITHMETIC AND GEOMETRIC PROGRESSIONS

Some important sequences are called **progressions**. One of these is the arithmetic progression.

Definition.   An **arithmetic progression** is a sequence of the form

$$a, a + d, a + 2d, a + 3d, \ldots, a + (n - 1)d, \ldots$$

where a is the first term, $a + (n - 1)d$ is the nth term, and d is the common difference.

In this definition, note that the second term of the progression has an addend of d, the third term has an addend of $2d$, the fourth term has an addend of $3d$, and so on. This is why the nth term has an addend of $(n-1)d$.

Example 1   For an arithmetic progression that has a first term of 7 and a common difference of 5, write the first six terms and the 21st term of the progression.

Solution   Because the first term, a, is 7 and the common difference, d, is 5, the first six terms are

$$7, \quad 7+5, \quad 7+2(5), \quad 7+3(5), \quad 7+4(5), \quad 7+5(5)$$

or

$$7, \quad 12, \quad 17, \quad 22, \quad 27, \quad 32$$

The nth term is $a+(n-1)d$, and, because you are looking for the 21st term, $n = \mathbf{21}$.

$$n\text{th term} = a + (n-1)d$$
$$21\text{st term} = 7 + (\mathbf{21}-1)5$$
$$= 7 + (20)5$$
$$= 107$$

The 21st term is 107.   ∎

Example 2   For an arithmetic progression with the first three terms 2, 6, and 10, find the 98th term.

Solution   In this example, $a = \mathbf{2}$, $n = \mathbf{98}$, and $d = 6 - 2 = 10 - 6 = 4$. The nth term is given by the formula $a + (n-1)d$. Therefore, the 98th term is

$$n\text{th term} = a + (n-1)d$$
$$98\text{th term} = \mathbf{2} + (\mathbf{98}-1)4$$
$$= 2 + (97)4$$
$$= 390$$ ∎

Numbers inserted between a first and last term to form a segment of an arithmetic progression are called **arithmetic means**. In this type of problem, the last term, l, is considered the nth term:

$$l = a + (n-1)d$$

Example 3   Insert three arithmetic means between the numbers -3 and 12.

Solution   Begin by finding the common difference d. In this example the first term is -3 and the last term is 12. Because you are inserting three terms, the total number of terms is five. Thus, $a = -3$, $l = 12$, and $n = 5$. The formula for the nth (or last) term is

$$l = a + (n - 1)d$$

Substituting 12 for l, -3 for a, and 5 for n in the formula and solving for d gives

$$12 = -3 + (5 - 1)d$$

$$15 = 4d$$

$$\frac{15}{4} = d$$

Once the common difference has been found, the arithmetic means are the second, third, and fourth terms of the arithmetic progression with a first term of -3 and a fifth term of 12:

$$a + d = -3 + \frac{15}{4} = \frac{3}{4}$$

$$a + 2d = -3 + \frac{30}{4} = 4\frac{1}{2}$$

$$a + 3d = -3 + \frac{45}{4} = 8\frac{1}{4}$$

The three arithmetic means are $\frac{3}{4}$, $4\frac{1}{2}$, and $8\frac{1}{4}$.   ■

The formula stated in the following theorem gives the sum of the first n terms of an arithmetic progression.

Theorem.   The formula

$$S_n = \frac{n(a + l)}{2}$$

gives the sum of the first n terms of an arithmetic progression. In this formula, a is the first term, l is the last (or nth) term, and n is the number of terms.

Proof   We write the first n terms of an arithmetic progression letting S_n represent their sum, rewrite the same sum in reverse order, and add the equations together term by term:

$$
\begin{aligned}
S_n &= \quad\quad a \quad\quad + \quad (a + d) \quad + \cdots + [a + (n - 2)d] + [a + (n - 1)d] \\
S_n &= [a + (n - 1)d] + [a + (n - 2)d] + \cdots + \quad (a + d) \quad + \quad\quad a \\
\hline
2S_n &= [2a + (n - 1)d] + [2a + (n - 1)d] + \cdots + [2a + (n - 1)d] + [2a + (n - 1)d]
\end{aligned}
$$

Because there are n equal terms on the right side of the previous equation,

$$2S_n = n[2a + (n - 1)d]$$

or

$$2S_n = n\{a + [a + (n - 1)d]\}$$

Because $a + (n - 1)d = l$, we make that substitution in the right side of the above equation and divide both sides by 2 to obtain

$$S_n = \frac{n(a + l)}{2}$$

The theorem is proved. (Exercise 45 will ask you to prove this theorem again using mathematical induction.)   □

Example 4   Find the sum of the first 30 terms of the arithmetic progression 5, 8, 11, ...

Solution   In this example, $a = 5$, $n = 30$, $d = 3$, and $l = 5 + 29(3) = 92$. Substituting these values into the formula $S_n = \dfrac{n(a + l)}{2}$ and simplifying gives

$$S_{30} = \frac{30(5 + 92)}{2} = 15(97) = 1455$$

The sum of the first 30 terms is 1455.   ■

Another important sequence is the **geometric progression.**

Definition.   A **geometric progression** is a sequence of the form

$$a,\ ar,\ ar^2,\ ar^3,\ \ldots,\ ar^{n-1},\ \ldots$$

where a is the first term, ar^{n-1} is the nth term, and r is the common ratio.

In this definition, note that the second term of the progression has a factor of r^1, the third term has a factor of r^2, the fourth term has a factor of r^3, and so on. This explains why the nth term has a factor of r^{n-1}.

Example 5   For a geometric progression with a first term of 3 and a common ratio of 2, write the first six terms and the 15th term of the progression.

Solution   Write the first six terms of the geometric progression:

$$3,\ 3(2),\ 3(2)^2,\ 3(2)^3,\ 3(2)^4,\ 3(2)^5$$

or

$$3,\ 6,\ 12,\ 24\ 48,\ 96$$

To obtain the 15th term, substitute **15** for n, **3** for a, and **2** for r in the formula for the nth term:

$$n\text{th term} = ar^{n-1}$$
$$15\text{th term} = 3(2)^{15-1}$$
$$= 3(2)^{14}$$
$$= 3(16{,}384)$$
$$= 49{,}152$$

■

Example 6   For a geometric progression with the first three terms 9, 3, and 1, find the eighth term.

Solution   In this example, $a = 9$, $r = \frac{1}{3}$, $n = 8$, and the nth term is ar^{n-1}. To obtain the eighth term, substitute these values into the expression for the nth term:

$$n\text{th term} = ar^{n-1}$$
$$8\text{th term} = 9\left(\frac{1}{3}\right)^{8-1}$$
$$= 9\left(\frac{1}{3}\right)^{7}$$
$$= \frac{1}{243}$$

■

As with arithmetic progressions, numbers may be inserted between a first and last term to form a segment of a geometric progression. The numbers inserted are called **geometric means**. In this type of problem, the last term, l, is considered to be the nth term: $l = ar^{n-1}$.

Example 7   Insert two geometric means between the numbers 4 and 256.

Solution   Begin by finding the common ratio. The first term, a, is **4**. Because 256 is to be the fourth term, $n = 4$ and $l = 256$. Substituting these values into the formula for the nth term of a geometric progression, and solving for r gives

$$ar^{n-1} = l$$
$$4r^{4-1} = 256$$
$$r^3 = 64$$
$$r = 4$$

The common ratio is 4. The two geometric means are the second and third terms of the geometric progression:

$$ar = 4 \cdot 4 = 16$$
$$ar^2 = 4 \cdot 4^2 = 4 \cdot 16 = 64$$

The first four terms of the geometric progression are 4, 16, 64, and 256; 16 and 64 are geometric means between 4 and 256.

■

There is a formula that gives the sum of the first n terms of a geometric progression.

> **Theorem.**   The formula
>
> $$S_n = \frac{a - ar^n}{1 - r} \quad (r \neq 1)$$
>
> gives the sum of the first n terms of a geometric progression. In this formula, S_n is the sum, a is the first term, r is the common ratio, and n is the number of terms.

Proof   We write out the sum of the first n terms of the geometric progression:

1. $S_n = a + ar + ar^2 + \cdots + ar^{n-3} + ar^{n-2} + ar^{n-1}$

Multiplying both sides of this equation by r gives

2. $S_n r = \quad ar + ar^2 + \quad \cdots \quad + ar^{n-2} + ar^{n-1} + ar^n$

We now subtract Equation 2 from Equation 1 and solve for S_n:

$$S_n - S_n r = a - ar^n$$
$$S_n(1 - r) = a - ar^n$$
$$S_n = \frac{a - ar^n}{1 - r}$$

The theorem is proved. (Exercise 46 will ask you to prove this theorem using mathematical induction.)   □

Example 8   Find the sum of the first six terms of the geometric progression $8, 4, 2, \ldots$.

Solution   In this example, $a = 8$, $n = 6$, and $r = \frac{1}{2}$. Substituting these values into the formula for the sum of the first n terms of a geometric progression gives

$$S_n = \frac{a - ar^n}{1 - r}$$

$$S_6 = \frac{8 - 8\left(\frac{1}{2}\right)^6}{1 - \frac{1}{2}}$$

$$= 2\left(\frac{63}{8}\right)$$

$$= \frac{63}{4}$$

The sum of the first six terms is $\frac{63}{4}$.   ∎

Under certain conditions, it is possible to find the sum of all the terms in an infinite geometric progression. To define this sum, we consider the geometric progression

$$a_1, a_2, a_3, \ldots$$

The first partial sum, S_1, of the progression is a_1. Hence,

$$S_1 = a_1$$

The second partial sum, S_2, of this progression is $a_1 + a_2$. Hence,

$$S_2 = a_1 + a_2$$

In general, the nth partial sum, S_n, of this progression is

$$S_n = a_1 + a_2 + a_3 + \cdots + a_n$$

If the nth partial sum, S_n, of an infinite geometric progression approaches some number S as n becomes large without bound, then S is called the **sum of the infinite geometric progression**. The symbol $\sum\limits_{n=1}^{\infty} a_n$, where ∞ is the symbol for infinity, denotes the sum, S, of the infinite geometric progression: $S = \sum\limits_{n=1}^{\infty} a_n$, provided that sum exists.

To develop a formula for finding the sum of all the terms in an infinite geometric progression, we consider the formula

$$S_n = \frac{a - ar^n}{1 - r} \quad (r \neq 1)$$

If $|r| < 1$ and a is a constant, then the term ar^n, or $a(r^n)$, approaches 0 as n becomes large without bound. Hence, when n is very large, the value of ar^n is extremely small, and the term ar^n in the formula can be ignored. This argument leads to the following theorem.

Theorem.   If $|r| < 1$, then the sum of the terms of an infinite geometric progression is given by the formula

$$S = \frac{a}{1 - r}$$

where a is the first term and r is the common ratio.

Example 9   Change $0.444\ldots$ to a common fraction.

Solution   Write the decimal as an infinite geometric series and find its sum:

$$S = \frac{4}{10} + \frac{4}{100} + \frac{4}{1000} + \frac{4}{10,000} + \cdots$$

$$S = \frac{4}{10} + \frac{4}{10}\left(\frac{1}{10}\right) + \frac{4}{10}\left(\frac{1}{10}\right)^2 + \frac{4}{10}\left(\frac{1}{10}\right)^3 + \cdots$$

Because the common ratio is $\frac{1}{10}$ and $\left|\frac{1}{10}\right| < 1$, use the formula for the sum of an infinite geometric series:

$$S = \frac{a}{1 - r} = \frac{\dfrac{4}{10}}{1 - \dfrac{1}{10}} = \frac{\dfrac{4}{10}}{\dfrac{9}{10}} = \frac{4}{9}$$

Long division will verify that changing $\frac{4}{9}$ to a decimal fraction gives $0.444\ldots$.

■

■ EXERCISE 14.3

In Exercises 1–6, write the first six terms of the arithmetic progressions with the given properties.

1. $a = 1$ and $d = 2$ **2.** $a = -12$ and $d = -5$

3. $a = 5$ and the third term is 2.   **4.** $a = 4$ and the fifth term is 12.

5. The seventh term is 24, and the common difference is $\frac{5}{2}$.

6. The 20th term is -49, and the common difference is -3.

In Exercises 7–10, find the sum of the first n terms of each arithmetic progression.

7. $5 + 7 + 9 + \cdots$ (to 15 terms)   **8.** $\displaystyle\sum_{n=1}^{10} (-n - 2)$

9. $\displaystyle\sum_{n=1}^{20} \left(\frac{3}{2}n + 12\right)$ **10.** $\displaystyle\sum_{n=1}^{10} \left(\frac{2}{3}n + \frac{1}{3}\right)$

11. In an arithmetic progression, the 25th term is 10 and the common difference is $\frac{1}{2}$. Find the sum of the first 30 terms.

12. In an arithmetic progression, the 15th term is 86 and the first term is 2. Find the sum of the first 100 terms.

13. If the fifth term of an arithmetic progression is 14 and the second term is 5, find the 15th term.

14. Can an arithmetic progression have a first term of 4, a 25th term of 126, and a common difference of $4\frac{1}{4}$? If not, explain why.

15. Insert three arithmetic means between 10 and 20.

16. Insert five arithmetic means between 5 and 15.

17. Insert four arithmetic means between -7 and $\frac{2}{3}$.

18. Insert three arithmetic means between -11 and -2.

In Exercises 19–26, write the first four terms of each geometric progression with the given properties.

19. $a = 10$ and $r = 2$ **20.** $a = -3$ and $r = 2$

21. $a = -2$ and $r = 3$ **22.** $a = 64$ and $r = \frac{1}{2}$

23. $a = 3$ and $r = \sqrt{2}$ **24.** $a = 2$ and $r = \sqrt{3}$

25. $a = 2$, and the fourth term is 54.   **26.** The third term is 4, and $r = \frac{1}{2}$.

In Exercises 27–32, find the sum of the indicated terms of each geometric progression.

27. $4, 8, 16, \ldots$ (to 5 terms)   **28.** $9, 27, 81, \ldots$ (to 6 terms)

29. $2, -6, 18, \ldots$ (to 10 terms)

30. $\dfrac{1}{8}, \dfrac{1}{4}, \dfrac{1}{2}, \ldots$ (to 12 terms)

31. $\displaystyle\sum_{n=1}^{6} 3\left(\dfrac{3}{2}\right)^{n-1}$

32. $\displaystyle\sum_{n=1}^{6} 12\left(-\dfrac{1}{2}\right)^{n-1}$

In Exercises 33–36, find the sum of each infinite geometric progression.

33. $6 + 4 + \dfrac{8}{3} + \cdots$

34. $8 + 4 + 2 + 1 + \cdots$

35. $\displaystyle\sum_{n=1}^{\infty} 12\left(-\dfrac{1}{2}\right)^{n-1}$

36. $\displaystyle\sum_{n=1}^{\infty} 1\left(\dfrac{1}{3}\right)^{n-1}$

37. Insert three positive geometric means between 10 and 20.

38. Insert five geometric means between -5 and 5, if possible.

39. Insert four geometric means between 2 and 2048.

40. Insert three positive geometric means between 162 and 2.

In Exercises 41–44, change each decimal to a common fraction.

41. $0.555 \ldots$ **42.** $0.666 \ldots$ **43.** $0.252525 \ldots$ **44.** $0.373737 \ldots$

45. Use mathematical induction to prove the formula for finding the sum of the first n terms of an arithmetic progression.

46. Use mathematical induction to prove the formula for finding the sum of the first n terms of a geometric progression.

47. If Justin earns 1¢ on the first day of May, 2¢ on the second day, 4¢ on the third day, and the pay continues to double each day throughout the month, what will his total earnings be for the month?

48. A single arithmetic mean between two numbers is called *the* arithmetic mean of the two numbers. Similarly, a single positive geometric mean between two numbers is called *the* geometric mean of the two numbers. Find the arithmetic mean and the geometric mean between the numbers 4 and 64. Which is larger, the arithmetic or the geometric mean?

49. Use the definitions in Exercise 48 to compute the arithmetic mean and the geometric mean between $\frac{1}{2}$ and $\frac{7}{8}$. Which is larger, the arithmetic or geometric mean?

50. If a and b are positive numbers and $a \neq b$, prove that their arithmetic mean is greater than their geometric mean. (*Hint:* See Exercises 48 and 49.)

51. Find the indicated sum: $\displaystyle\sum_{n=1}^{100} \dfrac{1}{n(n+1)}$. (*Hint:* Use partial fractions first.)

52. Find the indicated sum: $\displaystyle\sum_{k=1}^{100} \ln\left(\dfrac{k}{k+1}\right)$.

14.4 APPLICATIONS OF PROGRESSIONS

The following examples illustrate some applications of arithmetic and geometric progressions.

Example 1   A town with a population of 3500 people has a predicted growth rate of 6% over the preceding year for the next 20 years. How many people are expected to live in the town 20 years from now?

Solution   Let p_0 be the initial population of the town. After 1 year, there will be a different population, p_1. The initial population (p_0) plus the growth (the product of p_0 and the rate of growth, r) will equal the new population after 1 year (p_1):

$$p_1 = p_0 + p_0 r = p_0(1 + r)$$

The population of the town at the end of 2 years will be p_2, and

$$p_2 = p_1 + p_1 r$$
$$p_2 = p_1(1 + r)$$
$$p_2 = p_0(1 + r)(1 + r)$$
$$p_2 = p_0(1 + r)^2$$

The population at the end of the third year will be $p_3 = p_0(1 + r)^3$. Writing the terms in a sequence yields

$$p_0, \quad p_0(1 + r), \quad p_0(1 + r)^2, \quad p_0(1 + r)^3, \quad p_0(1 + r)^4, \ldots$$

This is a geometric progression with p_0 as the first term and $1 + r$ as the common ratio. Recall that the nth term is given by the formula $l = ar^{n-1}$. In this example $p_0 = 3500$, $1 + r = 1.06$, and, because the population after 20 years will be the value of the 21st term of the geometric progression, $n = 21$. The population after 20 years is $p = 3500(1.06)^{20}$. Use a calculator to find that $p \approx 11,225$.   ∎

Example 2   A women deposits $2500 in a bank at 9% annual interest compounded daily. If the investment is left untouched for 6 years, how much money will be in the account?

Solution   This problem is similar to that of Example 1. Let the initial amount in the account be A_0. At the end of the first day, the amount in the account is

$$A_1 = A_0 + A_0\left(\frac{r}{365}\right) = A_0\left(1 + \frac{r}{365}\right)$$

The amount in the bank after the second day is

$$A_2 = A_1 + A_1\left(\frac{r}{365}\right) = A_1\left(1 + \frac{r}{365}\right) = A_0\left(1 + \frac{r}{365}\right)^2$$

Just as in Example 1, the amounts in the account each day form a geometric progression.

$$A_0, \quad A_0\left(1 + \frac{r}{365}\right), \quad A_0\left(1 + \frac{r}{365}\right)^2, \quad A_0\left(1 + \frac{r}{365}\right)^3, \ldots$$

where A_0 is the initial deposit and r is the annual rate of interest.

Because the interest is compounded daily for 6 years, the amount in the bank at the end of 6 years will be the 2191th term $(6 \cdot 365 + 1)$ of the progression. The amount in the account at the end of 6 years is

$$A_{2191} = 2500\left(1 + \frac{0.09}{365}\right)^{2190}$$

Use a calculator to find that $A_{2191} \approx \$4289.73$.   ∎

Example 3   The equation $S = 16t^2$ represents the distance in feet, S, that an object will fall in t seconds. After 1 second, the object has fallen 16 feet. After 2 seconds, the object has fallen 64 feet. After 3 seconds the object has fallen 144 feet. In other words, the object fell 16 feet during the first second, 48 feet during the next second, and 80 feet during the third second. Thus, the sequence 16, 48, 80, ... represents the distance an object will fall during the first second, second second, third second, and so forth. Find the distance the object falls during the 12th second.

Solution   The sequence 16, 48, 80, ... is an arithmetic progression with $a = 16$ and $d = 32$. To find the 12th term, substitute these values into the formula $l = a + (n - 1)d$ and simplify:

$$l = a + (n - 1)d$$
$$l = 16 + 11(32)$$
$$l = 16 + 352$$
$$l = 368$$

During the 12th second, the object falls 368 feet.   ∎

Example 4   A pump can remove 20% of the gas in a container with each stroke. What percent of the gas will remain in the container after six strokes?

Solution   Let V represent the volume of the container. Because each stroke of the pump removes 20% of the gas, 80% of the gas remains after each stroke, and you have the sequence

$$V, \quad 0.80\,V, \quad 0.80(0.80\,V), \quad 0.80[0.80(0.80\,V)], \ldots$$

This can be written as the geometric progression

$$V, \quad 0.8\,V, \quad (0.8)^2 V, \quad (0.8)^3 V, \quad (0.8)^4 V, \ldots$$

You wish to know the amount of gas remaining after six strokes. This amount is the seventh term, l, of the progression:

$$l = ar^{n-1}$$
$$l = V(0.8)^6$$

Use a calculator to find that approximately 26% of the gas remains after six strokes of the pump.   ∎

■ EXERCISE 14.4

Decide whether each of the following exercises involves an arithmetic or geometric progression and then solve each problem. **You may use a calculator.**

1. The number of students studying college algebra this year at State College is 623. If a trend has been established that the following year's enrollment is always 10% higher than the preceding year, how many professors will be needed in 8 years to teach college algebra if one professor can handle 60 students?

2. If Amelia borrows $5500 interest free from her mother to buy a new car and agrees to pay her mother back at the rate of $105 per month, how much does she still owe after 4 years?

3. A Super Ball can always rebound to 95% of the height from which it was dropped. How high will the ball rise after the 13th bounce if it was dropped from a height of 10 meters?

4. If Philip invests $1000 in a 1-year certificate of deposit at $6\frac{3}{4}\%$ annual interest compounded daily, how much interest will be earned that year?

5. If a single cell divides into two cells every 30 minutes, how many cells will there be at the end of 10 hours?

6. If a lawn tractor, which cost c dollars when new, depreciates 20% of its previous year's value each year, how much is the lawn tractor worth after 5 years?

7. Maria can invest $1000 at $7\frac{1}{2}\%$ compounded annually or at $7\frac{1}{4}\%$ compounded daily. If she invests the money for a year, which is the best investment?

8. Find how many feet a brick will travel during the 10th second of its fall.

9. If the population of the world were to double every 30 years, approximately how many people would be on Earth in the year 3000? (Consider the population in 1980 to be 4 billion, and use 1980 as the base year.)

10. If Linda deposits $1300 in a bank at 7% interest compounded annually, how much will be in the bank 17 years later? (Assume that there are no other transactions on the account.)

11. If a house purchased for $50,000 in 1978 appreciates in value by 6% each year, how much will the house be worth in the year 2000?

12. Calculate the value of $1000 left on deposit for 10 years at an annual rate of 7% compounded annually.

13. Calculate the value of $1000 left on deposit for 10 years at an annual rate of 7% compounded quarterly.

14. Calculate the value of $1000 left on deposit for 10 years at an annual rate of 7% compounded monthly.

15. Calculate the value of $1000 left on deposit for 10 years at an annual rate of 7% compounded daily.

16. Calculate the value of $1000 left on deposit for 10 years at an annual rate of 7% compounded hourly.

17. When John was 20 years old, he opened an individual retirement account by investing $2000 that will earn 11% interest compounded quarterly. How much will his investment be worth when John is 65 years old?

18. One lone bacterium divides to form two bacteria every 5 minutes. If two bacteria multiply enough to fill a petri dish completely in 2 hours, how long will it take one bacterium to fill the dish?

19. A legend tells of an ancient king who was grateful to the inventor of the game of chess and offered to grant him any request. The man was shrewd, and he said, "My request is modest, Your Majesty. Simply place one grain of wheat on the first square on the chessboard, two grains on the second, four on the third, and so on, with each square holding double that of the square before. Do this until the board is full." The king, thinking he'd gotten off lightly, readily agreed. How many grains did the king need to fill the chessboard?

20. Estimate the size of the wheat pile in Exercise 19. (*Hint:* There are about one-half million grains of wheat in a bushel.)

21. Does 0.999999 = 1? Explain.

22. Does 0.999 . . . = 1? Explain.

14.5 THE BINOMIAL THEOREM

In this section we discuss a method to raise binomials to positive integral powers. To this end, we consider the following binomial expansions:

$(a + b)^0 = 1$

$(a + b)^1 = a + b$

$(a + b)^2 = a^2 + 2ab + b^2$

$(a + b)^3 = a^3 + 3a^2b + 3ab^2 + b^3$

$(a + b)^4 = a^4 + 4a^3b + 6a^2b^2 + 4ab^3 + b^4$

$(a + b)^5 = a^5 + 5a^4b + 10a^3b^2 + 10a^2b^3 + 5ab^4 + b^5$

$(a + b)^6 = a^6 + 6a^5b + 15a^4b^2 + 20a^3b^3 + 15a^2b^4 + 6ab^5 + b^6$

Four patterns are apparent in the preceding expansions.

1. Each expansion has one more term than the power of the binomial.
2. The degree of each term in each expansion equals the exponent of the binomial.
3. The first term in each expansion is a raised to the power of the binomial.
4. The exponents of a decrease by one in each successive term, and the exponents of b, beginning with b^0 in the first term, increase by one in each successive term.

To make another pattern apparent, we write the coefficients of each of the binomial expansions in a triangular array:

$(a + b)^0$						1						
$(a + b)^1$					1		1					
$(a + b)^2$				1		2		1				
$(a + b)^3$			1		3		3		1			
$(a + b)^4$		1		4		6		4		1		
$(a + b)^5$	1		5		10		10		5		1	
$(a + b)^6$	1	6		15		20		15		6		1

In this triangular array, each entry other than the 1s is the sum of the closest pair of numbers in the line immediately above it. For example, the 6 in the bottom row is the sum of the 1 and the 5 above it, and the 20 is the sum of the two 10s above it.

The triangular array, named after the French mathematician Blaise Pascal (1623–1662), continues with the same pattern forever. The next two lines are shown below.

$(a + b)^7$		1	7	21	35	35	21	7	1
$(a + b)^8$	1	8	28	56	70	56	28	8	1

Example 1   Expand $(x + y)^6$.

Solution   The first term in the expansion is x^6, and the exponents of x decrease by one in each successive term. The y will appear in the second term, and the exponents of y will increase in each successive term, concluding when the term y^6 is reached. The variables in the expansion are

$$x^6 \qquad x^5y \qquad x^4y^2 \qquad x^3y^3 \qquad x^2y^4 \qquad xy^5 \qquad y^6$$

Using Pascal's triangle, you can find the coefficients of these variables. Because the binomial is raised to the sixth power, choose the row in Pascal's triangle whose second entry is 6. The coefficients of the variables are the numbers in that row:

$$1 \qquad 6 \qquad 15 \qquad 20 \qquad 15 \qquad 6 \qquad 1$$

Putting these two pieces of information together, the expansion is

$$(x + y)^6 = x^6 + 6x^5y + 15x^4y^2 + 20x^3y^3 + 15x^2y^4 + 6xy^5 + y^6 \qquad \blacksquare$$

Example 2   Expand $(x - y)^6$.

Solution   To expand $(x - y)^6$, rewrite the binomial in the form

$$[x + (-y)]^6$$

The expansion is

$$\begin{aligned}
[x + (-y)]^6 &= x^6 + 6x^5(-y) + 15x^4(-y)^2 + 20x^3(-y)^3 + 15x^2(-y)^4 \\
&\quad + 6x(-y)^5 + (-y)^6 \\
&= x^6 - 6x^5y + 15x^4y^2 - 20x^3y^3 + 15x^2y^4 - 6xy^5 + y^6
\end{aligned}$$

In general, in the binomial expansion of $(x - y)^n$, the sign of the first term, x^n, is $+$, the sign of the second term is $-$, and the signs continue to alternate. $\blacksquare$

Another method for expanding a binomial, called the **binomial theorem**, uses **factorial notation**.

Definition.   The symbol $n!$ (read either as "n factorial" or as "factorial n") is defined as

$$n! = n(n - 1)(n - 2)(n - 3) \cdots (3)(2)(1)$$

where n is a natural number.

Example 3   Evaluate   **a.** $3!$,   **b.** $6!$, and   **c.** $10!$.

Solution   **a.** $3! = 3 \cdot 2 \cdot 1 = 6$

b. $6! = 6 \cdot 5 \cdot 4 \cdot 3 \cdot 2 \cdot 1 = 720$

c. $10! = 10 \cdot 9 \cdot 8 \cdot 7 \cdot 6 \cdot 5 \cdot 4 \cdot 3 \cdot 2 \cdot 1 = 3,628,800$ $\blacksquare$

There are two fundamental properties of factorials.

Property 1. By definition, $0! = 1$.
Property 2. $n \cdot (n - 1)! = n!$

Example 4   Show that   **a.** $6 \cdot 5! = 6!$ and that   **b.** $8 \cdot 7! = 8!$

Solution   **a.** $6 \cdot 5! = 6(5 \cdot 4 \cdot 3 \cdot 2 \cdot 1) = 6 \cdot 5 \cdot 4 \cdot 3 \cdot 2 \cdot 1 = 6!$

   b. $8 \cdot 7! = 8(7 \cdot 6 \cdot 5 \cdot 4 \cdot 3 \cdot 2 \cdot 1) = 8 \cdot 7 \cdot 6 \cdot 5 \cdot 4 \cdot 3 \cdot 2 \cdot 1 = 8!$ ■

We now state the binomial theorem without proof.

The Binomial Theorem.   If n is any positive integer, then

$$(a + b)^n = a^n + \frac{n!}{1!(n - 1)!} a^{n-1}b + \frac{n!}{2!(n - 2)!} a^{n-2}b^2$$

$$+ \frac{n!}{3!(n - 3)!} a^{n-3}b^3 + \cdots + \frac{n!}{r!(n - r)!} a^{n-r}b^r + \cdots + b^n$$

In the binomial theorem, the exponents of the variables in each term on the right side follow familiar patterns: The sum of the exponents of a and b in each term is n, the exponents of a decrease, and the exponents of b increase. Only the method of finding the coefficients is different. Except for the first and last term, $n!$ is the numerator of each coefficient. If the exponent of b is r in a particular term, the two factors $r!$ and $(n - r)!$ form the denominator of the fractional coefficient.

Example 5   Use the binomial theorem to expand $(a + b)^5$.

Solution   Substituting directly into the binomial theorem gives

$$(a + b)^5 = a^5 + \frac{5!}{1!(5 - 1)!} a^4b + \frac{5!}{2!(5 - 2)!} a^3b^2 + \frac{5!}{3!(5 - 3)!} a^2b^3$$

$$+ \frac{5!}{4!(5 - 4)!} ab^4 + b^5$$

$$= a^5 + \frac{5 \cdot 4!}{1 \cdot 4!} a^4b + \frac{5 \cdot 4 \cdot 3!}{2 \cdot 1 \cdot 3!} a^3b^2 + \frac{5 \cdot 4 \cdot 3!}{3! \cdot 2 \cdot 1} a^2b^3$$

$$+ \frac{5 \cdot 4!}{4! \cdot 1} ab^4 + b^5$$

$$= a^5 + 5a^4b + 10a^3b^2 + 10a^2b^3 + 5ab^4 + b^5$$

Note that the coefficients in this example are the same numbers that appear in the sixth row of Pascal's triangle (the row whose second entry is 5).   ■

Example 6   Find the expansion of $(2x - 3y)^4$.

Solution   Note that $(2x - 3y)^4 = (2x + [-3y])^4$. To find the expansion of $(2x + [-3y])^4$, let $a = 2x$ and $b = -3y$. Then find the expansion of $(a + b)^4$. Substituting 4 for n in the binomial theorem gives

$$(a + b)^4 = a^4 + \frac{4!}{1!(4-1)!} a^3b + \frac{4!}{2!(4-2)!} a^2b^2 + \frac{4!}{3!(4-3)!} ab^3 + b^4$$

$$= a^4 + \frac{4 \cdot 3!}{3!} a^3b + \frac{4 \cdot 3 \cdot 2!}{2 \cdot 1 \cdot 2!} a^2b^2 + \frac{4 \cdot 3!}{3!} ab^3 + b^4$$

$$= a^4 + 4a^3b + 6a^2b^2 + 4ab^3 + b^4$$

In this expansion, substitute $2x$ for a and $-3y$ for b, and simplify to obtain

$$(2x - 3y)^4 = (2x)^4 + 4(2x)^3(-3y) + 6(2x)^2(-3y)^2 + 4(2x)(-3y)^3 + (-3y)^4$$

$$= 16x^4 - 96x^3y + 216x^2y^2 - 216xy^3 + 81y^4 \qquad ■$$

Suppose we wish to find the fifth term of the expansion of $(a + b)^{11}$. It is possible to raise the binomial $a + b$ to the 11th power and then look at the fifth term, but that would be tedious. However, this task is easy if we use the binomial theorem.

Example 7   Find the fifth term of the expansion of $(a + b)^{11}$.

Solution   The exponent of b in the fifth term of this expansion is 4, because the exponent for b is always 1 less than the number of the term. Because the exponent of b added to the exponent of a must equal 11, the exponent of a must be 7. The variables of the fifth term appear as a^7b^4.

Because of the binomial theorem, the number in the numerator of the coefficient is $n!$, which in this case is 11!. The factors in the denominator are 4! and $(11 - 4)!$. Thus, the complete fifth term of the expansion of $(a + b)^{11}$ is

$$\frac{11!}{4!7!} a^7b^4 = \frac{11 \cdot 10 \cdot 9 \cdot 8 \cdot 7!}{4 \cdot 3 \cdot 2 \cdot 1 \cdot 7!} a^7b^4 = 330a^7b^4 \qquad ■$$

Example 8   Find the sixth term of the expansion of $(a + b)^9$.

Solution   The exponent of b is 5, and the exponent of a is $9 - 5$ or 4 in the sixth term. The factors in the denominator of the coefficient are 5! and $(9 - 5)!$, and 9! is the numerator. Thus, the sixth term of the expansion of $(a + b)^9$ is

$$\frac{9!}{5!(9-5)!} a^4b^5 = \frac{9 \cdot 8 \cdot 7 \cdot 6 \cdot 5!}{5!4!} a^4b^5 = \frac{9 \cdot 8 \cdot 7 \cdot 6}{4 \cdot 3 \cdot 2 \cdot 1} a^4b^5 = 126a^4b^5 \qquad ■$$

Example 9   Find the third term of the expansion of $(3x - 2y)^6$.

Solution   Let $a = 3x$ and $b = -2y$ and use the binomial theorem to find the third term in the expansion of $(a + b)^6$:

$$\frac{6!}{2!(6 - 2)!} a^4 b^2 = \frac{6 \cdot 5 \cdot 4!}{2 \cdot 1 \cdot 4!} a^4 b^2 = 15 a^4 b^2$$

Replacing a with $3x$ and b with $-2y$ in the term $15 a^4 b^2$ gives the third term of the expansion of $(3x - 2y)^6$.

$$15 a^4 b^2 = 15(3x)^4(-2y)^2$$
$$= 15(3)^4(-2)^2 x^4 y^2$$
$$= 4860 x^4 y^2$$ ∎

■ EXERCISE 14.5

In Exercises 1–10, evaluate each expression.

1. $4!$ **2.** $-5!$ **3.** $3! \cdot 5!$ **4.** $0! \cdot 7!$

5. $6! + 6!$ **6.** $5! - 2!$ **7.** $\dfrac{9!}{12!}$ **8.** $\dfrac{8!}{5!}$

9. $\dfrac{18!}{6!(18 - 6)!}$ **10.** $\dfrac{15!}{9!(15 - 9)!}$

In Exercises 11–22, use the binomial theorem to expand each binomial.

11. $(a + b)^4$ **12.** $(a + b)^3$ **13.** $(a - b)^5$ **14.** $(x - y)^6$
15. $(2x - y)^3$ **16.** $(x + 2y)^5$ **17.** $(2x + y)^4$ **18.** $(2x - y)^4$
19. $(4x - 3y)^4$ **20.** $(5x + 2y)^5$ **21.** $(6x - 3y)^2$ **22.** $\left(\dfrac{x}{2} + \dfrac{y}{3}\right)^4$

In Exercises 23–38, find the required term in the expansion of the given expression.

23. $(a + b)^4$; third term   **24.** $(a - b)^4$; second term
25. $(a + b)^7$; fifth term   **26.** $(a + b)^5$; fourth term
27. $(a - b)^5$; sixth term   **28.** $(a + b)^{12}$; twelfth term
29. $(x - y)^8$; seventh term   **30.** $(2x - y)^4$; second term
31. $(\sqrt{2}x + y)^5$; third term   **32.** $(\sqrt{2}x - 3y)^5$; third term
33. $(x + 2y)^9$; eighth term   **34.** $(3x - 5y)^6$; fourth term
35. $(a + b)^r$; fourth term   **36.** $(a - b)^r$; fifth term
37. $(a + b)^n$; rth term   **38.** $(a + b)^n$; $(r + 1)$th term

39.   Find the sum of the numbers in each row of the first 10 rows of Pascal's triangle. What is the pattern?

40.   Show that the sum of the coefficients in the binomial expansion of $(x + y)^n$ is 2^n. (*Hint:*   Let $x = y = 1$.)

41. Find the constant term in the expansion of $\left(a - \dfrac{1}{a} \right)^{10}$.

42. Find the coefficient of x^5 in the expansion of $\left(x + \dfrac{1}{x} \right)^{9}$.

43. Find the coefficient of x^8 in the expansion of $\left(\sqrt{x} + \dfrac{1}{2x} \right)^{25}$.

44. Find the constant term in the expansion of $\left(\dfrac{1}{a} + a \right)^{8}$.

14.6   PERMUTATIONS AND COMBINATIONS

Lydia plans to go to dinner and then attend a movie. If she has a choice of four restaurants and three movies, in how many ways can Lydia spend her evening? There are four choices of restaurants and, for any one of these options, there are three choices of movies. The choices are shown in the tree diagram in Figure 14-1.

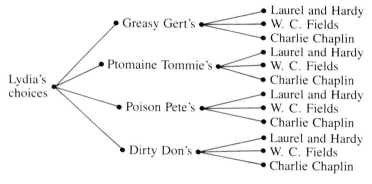

Figure 14-1

This diagram shows that Lydia has 12 ways to spend her evening. One possibility is to visit Ptomaine Tommie's and see W. C. Fields. Another is to dine at Dirty Don's and enjoy Laurel and Hardy.

Any situation that can have several outcomes is called an **event**. Lydia's first event (choosing a restaurant) can occur in 4 ways. Her second event (choosing a movie) can occur in 3 ways. Lydia has 4 times 3, or 12, ways to spend her evening. This example illustrates the **multiplication principle for events**.

The Multiplication Principle for Events.   Let E_1 and E_2 be two events. If E_1 can be done in a_1 ways, and if—after E_1 has occurred—E_2 can be done in a_2 ways, then the event "E_1 followed by E_2" can be done in $a_1 \cdot a_2$ ways.

The multiplication principle can be extended to n events.

Example 1   If Frank has four ways to travel from New York to Chicago, three ways to travel from Chicago to Denver, and six ways to travel from Denver to San Francisco, in how many ways can he go from New York to San Francisco?

Solution   Let E_1 be the event "going from New York to Chicago," let E_2 be the event "going from Chicago to Denver," and let E_3 be the event "going from Denver to San Francisco." Because there are 4 ways to accomplish E_1, 3 ways to accomplish E_2, and 6 ways to accomplish E_3, the number of routes that Frank can follow is

$$4 \cdot 3 \cdot 6 = 72$$ ∎

Permutations

Suppose we wish to arrange 7 books on a shelf. We can fill the first space with any of the 7 books, the second space with any of the remaining 6 books, the third space with any of the remaining 5 books, and so on, until there is only one space to fill with the last book. According to the multiplication principle, the number of ways that we can arrange the books is

$$7 \cdot 6 \cdot 5 \cdot 4 \cdot 3 \cdot 2 \cdot 1 = 5040$$

When computing the number of possible arrangements of the elements in a set such as books on a shelf, we are determining the number of **permutations** of the elements in the set. The number of permutations of 7 books, using all the books, is 5040. The symbol $_nP_r$, which is used in expressing permutation problems, is read as "the number of permutations of n things r at a time."

Example 2   If there are 7 flags of 7 different colors to hang on a flagpole, how many different signals can be sent if only 3 flags are used?

Solution   You are asked to find $_7P_3$, the number of permutations of 7 things using only 3 of them. Any one of the 7 flags can hang in the top position on the flagpole. In the middle position, any one of the 6 remaining flags can hang, and in the bottom position can hang any one of the remaining 5 flags. Therefore, according to the multiplication principle,

$$_7P_3 = 7 \cdot 6 \cdot 5 = 210$$

It is possible to send 210 different signals.   ∎

Although it is acceptable to write $_7P_3 = 7 \cdot 6 \cdot 5$, there is an advantage in changing the form of this answer to obtain a convenient formula. To get this formula, we will multiply both the numerator and denominator of $\dfrac{7 \cdot 6 \cdot 5}{1}$ by 4!.

$$_7P_3 = 7 \cdot 6 \cdot 5 = \frac{7 \cdot 6 \cdot 5 \cdot 4 \cdot 3 \cdot 2 \cdot 1}{4 \cdot 3 \cdot 2 \cdot 1} = \frac{7!}{4!} = \frac{7!}{(7-3)!}$$

This idea is generalized in the following theorem.

Theorem.   The formula for computing the number of permutations of n things r at a time is

$$_nP_r = \frac{n!}{(n-r)!}$$

If $r = n$, then

$$_nP_n = n!$$

The second part of the previous theorem is true because

$$_nP_n = \frac{n!}{(n-n)!} = \frac{n!}{0!} = n! \qquad \text{Remember } 0! = 1.$$

Example 3   In how many ways can a baseball manager arrange the batting order if there are 25 players on the team?

Solution   To find the number of permutations of 25 things 9 at a time, $_{25}P_9$, use the formula $_nP_r = \frac{n!}{(n-r)!}$.

$$_{25}P_9 = \frac{25!}{(25-9)!}$$

$$= \frac{25!}{16!}$$

$$= \frac{25 \cdot 24 \cdot 23 \cdot 22 \cdot 21 \cdot 20 \cdot 19 \cdot 18 \cdot 17 \cdot \cancel{16!}}{\cancel{16!}}$$

$$\approx 741,354,768,000$$

The number of permutations is approximately 741,354,768,000.   ■

Example 4   In how many ways can 5 people stand in a line if 2 people refuse to stand next to each other?

Solution   The total number of ways that 5 people can stand in line is

$$_5P_5 = 5! = 5 \cdot 4 \cdot 3 \cdot 2 \cdot 1 = 120$$

Now find the number of ways that five people can stand in line if two people *insist* on standing together by considering those two people as a single person. Then, there are 4 people to stand in line, and this can be done in $_4P_4 = 4! = 24$ ways. However, there are two arrangements for the pair that insist on standing together, because either could be first. Hence, there are $2 \cdot 4!$ ways that the 5 people can stand in line if 2 people insist on standing together.

The number of ways that 5 people can stand in line if two people *refuse* to stand together is $5! = 120$ (the total number of ways to arrange 5 people) minus

$2 \cdot 4! = 48$ (the number of ways to arrange five people if two must stand together):

$$120 - 48 = 72$$

There are 72 ways to stand 5 people in a line if 2 people refuse to stand next to each other. ■

Example 5   In how many ways can 5 people be seated at a round table?

Solution   If you were to seat 5 people in a row, there would be 5! possible arrangements. However, the situation is different when seating people at a round table. At a round table, each person has a neighbor to the left and to the right. If each person moves one place to the left, everyone will still have the same neighbors as before. This same situation applies if everyone moves two, three, four, or five places. Hence, you must divide 5! by 5 to get rid of these duplications. The number of ways that 5 people can be seated at a round table is

$$\frac{5!}{5} = 4! = 4 \cdot 3 \cdot 2 \cdot 1 = 24$$ ■

The results of Example 5 can be generalized into the following theorem.

Theorem.   There are $(n - 1)!$ ways to place n things in a circle.

Combinations

Suppose a class of 12 students selects a committee of 3 to plan a party. A possible committee is John, Sally, and Joe. In this situation, the order of the 3 is not important, because the committee of John, Sally, and Joe is the same as the committee of Sally, Joe, and John. For the moment, however, we assume that order is important and compute the number of permutations of 12 things 3 at a time:

$$_{12}P_3 = \frac{12!}{(12 - 3)!} = \frac{12 \cdot 11 \cdot 10 \cdot \cancel{9!}}{\cancel{9!}} = 1320$$

This result indicates the number of ways of arranging 3 people if there are 12 people to choose from. However, in this situation we do not care about the order of the trio. Because there are six ways (3!) of ordering the committee of 3 students, the calculation of $_{12}P_3 = 1320$ provides an answer that is 6 times too big. Actually, the number of possible committees that could plan the party is the number of permutations of 12 things taken 3 at a time divided by 6:

$$\frac{_{12}P_3}{6} = \frac{1320}{6} = 220$$

When choosing committee members and in other cases of selection where order is not important, we are interested in **combinations**, not permutations.

The symbols $_nC_r$ and $\binom{n}{r}$ both mean the number of combinations of n things r at a time. If a committee of r people is chosen from a total of n people, the number of committees is $_nC_r$, and there will be $r!$ arrangements of each committee. If we consider the committee as an ordered grouping, the number of orderings of r people selected from a group of n people is $_nP_r$. Therefore, the number of *combinations* of n things r at a time multiplied by $r!$ is equal to the number of *permutations* of n things r at a time. This relationship is shown by the equation

$$r! \, _nC_r = {_nP_r}$$

We divide both sides of this equation by $r!$ to obtain the formula for computing $_nC_r$, or $\binom{n}{r}$.

$$_nC_r = \binom{n}{r} = \frac{_nP_r}{r!} = \frac{n!}{r!(n-r)!}$$

This reasoning leads to the following theorem.

Theorem.   The formula for computing the number of combinations of n things r at a time is

$$_nC_r = \binom{n}{r} = \frac{n!}{r!(n-r)!}$$

In the exercises, you will be asked to prove the following theorem.

Theorem.   If n is a whole number, then

$$_nC_n = 1 \qquad \text{and} \qquad _nC_0 = 1$$

Example 6   If Carla must read 4 books from a reading list of 10 books, how many choices does she have?

Solution   Because the order in which the books are read is unimportant, calculate the number of combinations of 10 things 4 at a time:

$$_{10}C_4 = \frac{10!}{4!(10-4)!} = \frac{10 \cdot 9 \cdot 8 \cdot 7 \cdot 6!}{4 \cdot 3 \cdot 2 \cdot 1 \cdot 6!}$$

$$= \frac{10 \cdot 9 \cdot 8 \cdot 7}{4 \cdot 3 \cdot 2}$$

$$= 210$$

Carla has 210 options.   ∎

Example 7   A class consists of 15 boys and 8 girls. In how many ways can a debate team be chosen that will have 3 boys and 3 girls on the team?

Solution   There are $_{15}C_3$ ways of choosing the three boys and $_8C_3$ ways of choosing the three girls. By the multiplication principle, there are $_{15}C_3 \cdot {}_8C_3$ ways of choosing members of the debate team:

$$_{15}C_3 \cdot {}_8C_3 = \frac{15!}{3!(15-3)!} \cdot \frac{8!}{3!(8-3)!}$$

$$= \frac{15 \cdot 14 \cdot 13 \cdot 12!}{6 \cdot 12!} \cdot \frac{8 \cdot 7 \cdot 6 \cdot 5!}{6 \cdot 5!}$$

$$= \frac{15 \cdot 14 \cdot 13}{6} \cdot \frac{8 \cdot 7 \cdot 6}{6}$$

$$= 25{,}480$$

There are 25,480 ways to place 3 boys and 3 girls on the debate team.   ■

Note that the formula $_nC_r = n!/[r!(n-r)!]$ gives the coefficient of the $(r+1)$st term of the binomial expansion of $(a+b)^n$. This implies that the coefficients of a binomial expansion can be used to solve problems involving combinations. The binomial theorem is restated below, this time using combination notation.

The Binomial Theorem.   If n is any positive integer, then

$$(a+b)^n = \binom{n}{0}a^n + \binom{n}{1}a^{n-1}b + \binom{n}{2}a^{n-2}b^2 + \cdots$$

$$+ \binom{n}{r}a^{n-r}b^r + \cdots + \binom{n}{n}b^n$$

Example 8   Use Pascal's triangle to compute $_7C_5$.

Solution   Consider the eighth row of Pascal's triangle and the corresponding combinations:

$$\begin{array}{cccccccc} 1 & 7 & 21 & 35 & 35 & 21 & 7 & 1 \\ \binom{7}{0} & \binom{7}{1} & \binom{7}{2} & \binom{7}{3} & \binom{7}{4} & \binom{7}{5} & \binom{7}{6} & \binom{7}{7} \end{array}$$

$$_7C_5 = \binom{7}{5} = 21$$ ■

When discussing permutations and combinations, a "word" is a distinguishable arrangement of letters. For example, 6 words can be formed with the letters a, b, and c if all 3 letters are used exactly once. The six words are *abc*, *acb*, *bac*, *bca, cab,* and *cba.* If there are *n* distinct letters and each letter is used once, the number of distinct words that can be formed is $n! = {}_nP_n$. It is more complicated to compute the number of distinguishable words that can be formed with *n* letters if some of the letters are duplicates.

Example 9   Find the number of "words" that can be formed if each of the 6 letters of the word *little* is used once.

Solution   For the moment, pretend that all of the letters of the word *little* are distinguishable: "LitTle." The number of words that can be formed using each letter once is $6! = {}_6P_6$. However, in reality you cannot tell the *l*'s or the *t*'s apart. Therefore, divide by an appropriate number to get rid of these duplications; because there are 2! orderings of the two *l*'s and 2! orderings of the two *t*'s, divide by 2! · 2!. The number of words that can be formed using each letter of the word *little* is

$$\frac{{}_6P_6}{2!2!} = \frac{6!}{2!2!} = \frac{6 \cdot 5 \cdot 4 \cdot 3 \cdot 2 \cdot 1}{2 \cdot 1 \cdot 2 \cdot 1} = 180 \qquad \blacksquare$$

Example 9 illustrates the following general principle.

Theorem.   If a word with *n* letters has *a* of one letter, *b* of another letter, and so on, then the number of distinguishable words that can be formed using each of the *n* letters exactly once is

$$\frac{n!}{a!b! \cdots}$$

EXERCISE 14.6

1. A lunch room has a machine with 8 kinds of sandwiches, a machine with 4 kinds of soda, a machine with both white and chocolate milk, and a machine with 3 kinds of ice cream. How many different lunches can be chosen? (Consider a lunch to be 1 sandwich, 1 drink, and 1 ice cream.)

2. How many six-digit license plates can be manufactured if no license plate number begins with 0?

3. How many different seven-digit phone numbers can be used in one area code if no phone number begins with 0 or 1?

4. In how many ways can the letters of the word *number* be arranged?

5. In how many ways can the letters of the word *number* be arranged if the *e* and *r* must remain next to each other?

6. In how many ways can the letters of the word *number* be arranged if the *e* and *r* cannot be side by side?

7. How many ways can five Scrabble tiles bearing the letters *F, F, F, L,* and *U* be arranged to spell the word *fluff?*

8. How many ways can six Scrabble tiles bearing the letters *B*, *E*, *E*, *E*, *F*, and *L* be arranged to spell the word *feeble*?

In Exercises 9–24, evaluate each expression.

9. $_7P_4$

10. $_8P_3$

11. $_7C_4$

12. $_8C_3$

13. $_5P_5$

14. $_5P_0$

15. $\binom{5}{4}$

16. $\binom{8}{4}$

17. $\binom{5}{0}$

18. $\binom{5}{5}$

19. $_5P_4 \cdot {_5C_3}$

20. $_3P_2 \cdot {_4C_3}$

21. $\binom{5}{3}\binom{4}{3}\binom{3}{3}$

22. $\binom{5}{5}\binom{6}{6}\binom{7}{7}\binom{8}{8}$

23. $\binom{68}{66}$

24. $\binom{100}{99}$

25. In how many arrangements can 8 girls be placed in a line?

26. In how many arrangements can 5 girls and 5 boys be placed in a line if the girls and boys alternate?

27. In how many arrangements can 5 girls and 5 boys be placed in a line if all the boys line up first?

28. In how many arrangements can 5 girls and 5 boys be placed in a line if all the girls line up first?

29. How many permutations does a combination lock have if each combination has 3 numbers, no two numbers of the combination are the same, and the lock dial has 30 notches? Wouldn't it be better to call these locks "permutation locks"? Explain.

30. How many permutations does a combination lock have if each combination has 3 numbers, no two numbers of the combination are the same, and the lock has 100 notches?

31. In how many ways can 8 people be seated at a round table?

32. In how many ways can 7 people be seated at a round table?

33. In how many ways can 6 people be seated at a round table if 2 of the people insist on sitting together?

34. In how many ways can 6 people be seated at a round table if 2 of the people refuse to sit together?

35. In how many ways can 7 children be arranged in a circle if Sally and John must be kept apart and Martha and Peter want to be together?

36. In how many ways can 8 children be arranged in a circle if Laura and Scott want to be together but Billy and Paula don't?

37. In how many ways can 4 candy bars be selected from 10 different candy bars? (*Hint:* Order is not important.)

38. How many hands of 5 cards can be selected from a deck of 52 cards?

39. How many possible bridge hands are there? (*Hint:* There are 13 cards in a bridge hand and 52 cards in a deck.)

40. How many words can be formed from the letters of the word *igloo* if each of the 5 letters is to be used once?

41. How many words can be formed from the letters of the word *parallel* if each letter is to be used once?

42. How many words can be formed from the letters of the word *banana* if each letter is to be used once?

43. How many license plates can be made using two different letters followed by four different digits if the first digit cannot be 0 and the letter *O* is not used?

44. If there are 7 class periods in a school day and a typical student takes 5 classes, how many different time patterns are possible for the student?

45. From a bucket containing 6 red and 8 white golf balls, in how many ways can we draw 6 golf balls of which 3 are red and 3 are white?

46. In how many ways can you select a committee of 3 Republicans and 3 Democrats from a group containing 18 Democrats and 11 Republicans?

47. In how many ways can you select a committee of 4 Democrats and 3 Republicans from a group containing 12 Democrats and 10 Republicans?

48. In how many ways can you select a group of 5 red cards and 2 black cards from a deck containing 10 red cards and 8 black cards?

49. In how many ways can a husband and wife choose 2 different dinners from a menu of 17 dinners?

50. In how many ways can 7 people stand in a row if 2 of the people refuse to stand together?

51. How many lines are determined by 8 points if no 3 points lie on a straight line?

52. How many lines are determined by 10 points if no 3 points lie on a straight line?

53. Use Pascal's triangle to find $_8C_5$.

54. Use Pascal's triangle to find $_{10}C_8$.

55. How many teams can a baseball manager put on the field if the entire squad consists of 25 players? (There are 9 players on the field at a time. Assume that all players can play all positions.)

56. Prove that $_nC_n = 1$ and that $_nC_0 = 1$.

57. Prove that $\binom{n}{r} = \binom{n}{n-r}$.

58. Show that the binomial theorem can be expressed in the form

$$(a + b)^n = \sum_{k=0}^{n} \binom{n}{k} a^{n-k} b^k$$

14.7 PROBABILITY

> **Definition.**   If an experiment can have n distinct and equally likely outcomes and if E is an event that can occur in f of these ways, then the probability of E is
>
> $$P(E) = \frac{f}{n}$$

Because $0 \le f \le n$, it follows that $0 \le f/n \le 1$ and that all probabilities must have values from 0 to 1. An event that cannot happen has probability 0, and an event that is certain to happen has probability 1.

Saying that the probability of tossing heads with a single toss of a coin is $\frac{1}{2}$ means that, if a fair coin is tossed a very large number of times, the ratio of the number of heads to the total number of tosses is very nearly $\frac{1}{2}$. As the number of tosses approaches infinity, this ratio approaches $\frac{1}{2}$ more and more closely. To say that the probability of rolling a 5 with a single roll of a die is

$\frac{1}{6}$ is to say that, as the number of rolls approaches infinity, the ratio of the number of favorable outcomes (rolling a 5) to the total number of outcomes approaches $\frac{1}{6}$.

In order to calculate probabilities, we sometimes need to exhibit the total list of possible outcomes. Such a listing is called a **sample space**.

Example 1   Exhibit the sample space of the event "rolling two dice a single time."

Solution   The sample space is the listing of all possible outcomes. Use ordered-pair notation, and let the first number of the pair be the result on the first die and the second number the result on the second die:

$$
\begin{array}{cccccc}
(1, 1) & (1, 2) & (1, 3) & (1, 4) & (1, 5) & (1, 6) \\
(2, 1) & (2, 2) & (2, 3) & (2, 4) & (2, 5) & (2, 6) \\
(3, 1) & (3, 2) & (3, 3) & (3, 4) & (3, 5) & (3, 6) \\
(4, 1) & (4, 2) & (4, 3) & (4, 4) & (4, 5) & (4, 6) \\
(5, 1) & (5, 2) & (5, 3) & (5, 4) & (5, 5) & (5, 6) \\
(6, 1) & (6, 2) & (6, 3) & (6, 4) & (6, 5) & (6, 6)
\end{array}
$$

This sample space contains 36 ordered pairs. Because there are 6 possible outcomes with the first die and 6 possible outcomes with the second die, the multiplication principle for events tells you to expect $6 \cdot 6$, or 36 total possible outcomes. ∎

Example 2   On a single toss of two dice, what is the probability of tossing a sum of seven?

Solution   The sample space for this event is listed in Example 1. The favorable outcomes are the ones that give a sum of 7: (1, 6), (2, 5), (3, 4), (4, 3), (5, 2), and (6, 1). Because there are 6 favorable outcomes among the 36 possible outcomes

$$P(\text{tossing a 7}) = \frac{6}{36} = \frac{1}{6}$$ ∎

Example 3   What is the probability of being dealt 5 cards, all hearts, from an ordinary deck of cards?

Solution   The number of ways to draw 5 hearts from the 13 hearts is $_{13}C_5$. The number of ways of drawing 5 cards from the complete deck is $_{52}C_5$. The desired probability is the ratio of the number of favorable outcomes to the number of possible outcomes.

$$P(\text{5 hearts}) = \frac{_{13}C_5}{_{52}C_5}$$

$$P(5 \text{ hearts}) = \frac{\dfrac{13!}{5!8!}}{\dfrac{52!}{5!47!}}$$

$$= \frac{13!}{5!8!} \cdot \frac{5!47!}{52!}$$

$$= \frac{13 \cdot 12 \cdot 11 \cdot 10 \cdot 9 \cdot 8!}{8!} \cdot \frac{47!}{52 \cdot 51 \cdot 50 \cdot 49 \cdot 48 \cdot 47!}$$

$$= \frac{13 \cdot 12 \cdot 11 \cdot 10 \cdot 9}{52 \cdot 51 \cdot 50 \cdot 49 \cdot 48}$$

$$= \frac{33}{66,640} \qquad \blacksquare$$

There is a multiplication property for probabilities that is similar to the multiplication principle for events that occur in succession.

> **Multiplication Property of Probabilities.**   If $P(A)$ represents the probability of event A, and $P(B|A)$ represents the probability that event B will occur after event A, then $P(A \text{ and } B) = P(A) \cdot P(B|A)$.

Example 4   A box contains 40 cubes of the same size. Of these cubes, 17 are red, 13 are blue, and the rest are yellow. If 2 cubes are drawn at random, without replacement, what is the probability that 2 yellow cubes will be drawn?

Solution   Of the 40 cubes in the box, 10 are yellow. Thus, the probability of getting a yellow cube on the first draw is

$$P(\text{yellow cube on first draw}) = \frac{10}{40} = \frac{1}{4}$$

Because there is no replacement after the first draw, 39 cubes remain in the box, and 9 of these are yellow. The probability of getting a yellow cube on the second draw is

$$P(\text{yellow cube on the second draw}) = \frac{9}{39} = \frac{3}{13}$$

The probability of drawing 2 yellow cubes in succession is the product of the probability of drawing a yellow cube on the first draw and the probability of drawing a yellow cube on the second draw.

$$P(\text{drawing two yellow cubes}) = \frac{1}{4} \cdot \frac{3}{13} = \frac{3}{52} \qquad \blacksquare$$

Example 5   Repeat Example 3 using the multiplication property of probabilities.

Solution   The probability of drawing a heart on the first draw is $\frac{13}{52}$, on the second draw $\frac{12}{51}$, on the third draw $\frac{11}{50}$, on the fourth draw $\frac{10}{49}$, and on the fifth draw $\frac{9}{48}$. By the multiplication property of probabilities,

$$P(5 \text{ hearts in a row}) = \frac{13}{52} \cdot \frac{12}{51} \cdot \frac{11}{50} \cdot \frac{10}{49} \cdot \frac{9}{48}$$

$$= \frac{33}{66,640}$$

■

■ EXERCISE 14.7

In Exercises 1–4, an ordinary die is tossed. Find the probability of each event.

1. Tossing a 2

2. Tossing a number greater than 4

3. Tossing a number larger than 1 but less than 6

4. Tossing an odd number

In Exercises 5–8, balls numbered from 1 to 42 are placed in a container and stirred. If one is drawn at random, find the probability of each event.

5. The number is less than 20.

6. The number is less than 50.

7. The number is a prime number.

8. The number is less than 10 or greater than 40.

In Exercises 9–12, refer to the spinner in Illustration 1. If the spinner is spun, find the probability of each event. Assume that the spinner never stops on a line.

9. The spinner stops on red.

10. The spinner stops on green.

11. The spinner stops on orange.

12. The spinner stops on yellow.

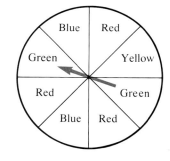

Illustration 1

In Exercises 13–30, find the probability of each given event.

13. Rolling a sum of 4 on one roll of two dice

14. Drawing a diamond on one draw from a card deck

15. Drawing two aces in succession from a card deck if the card is replaced and the deck shuffled after the first draw

16. Drawing two aces from a card deck without replacing the card after the first draw

17. Drawing a red egg from a basket containing 5 red eggs and 7 azure eggs

18.   Getting 2 red eggs in a single scoop from a bucket containing 5 red eggs and 7 cyan eggs

19.   Drawing a bridge hand of 13 cards, all of one suit

20.   Drawing 6 diamonds from a card deck without replacing the cards after each draw

21.   Drawing 5 aces from a card deck without replacing the cards after each draw

22.   Drawing 5 clubs from the black cards in a card deck

23.   Drawing a face card from à card deck

24.   Drawing 6 face cards in a row from a card deck without replacing the cards after each draw

25.   Drawing 5 fuchsia cubes from a bowl containing 5 fuchsia cubes and 1 beige cube

26.   Rolling a sum of 4 with one roll of three dice

27.   Rolling a sum of 11 with one roll of three dice

28.   Picking, at random, 5 Republicans from a group containing 8 Republicans and 10 Democrats

29.   Tossing 3 heads in 5 tosses of a fair coin   **30.**   Tossing 5 heads in 5 tosses of a fair coin

In Exercises 31–37, assume that the probability that an airplane engine will fail during a torture test is $\frac{1}{2}$ and that the aircraft in question has 4 engines.

31.   Construct a sample space showing each of the possible outcomes after the torture test.

32.   Find the probability that all of the engines will survive the test.

33.   Find the probability that exactly 1 engine will survive.

34.   Find the probability that exactly 2 engines will survive.

35.   Find the probability that exactly 3 engines will survive.

36.   Find the probability that no engines will survive.

37.   Find the sum of the probabilities in Exercises 32 through 36.

In Exercises 38–40, assume that a survey of 282 people is taken to determine the opinions of blacks, whites, and Orientals on a proposed piece of legislation, with the following results:

	Number that favor	Number that oppose	Number with no opinion	Total
Black	70	32	17	119
White	83	24	10	117
Oriental	23	15	8	46
Total	176	71	35	282

A person is chosen at random from those surveyed. Refer to the chart to find each probability.

38.   What is the probability that the person favors the legislation?

39.   If a black is chosen, what is the probability that he or she opposes the legislation?

40.   If the person opposes the legislation, what is the probability that the person is Oriental?

14.8   COMPUTATION OF COMPOUND PROBABILITIES

Sometimes we need to compute the probability of one event *or* another, or one event *and* another. Such events are called **compound events**.

Suppose we wish to find the probability of drawing an ace *or* a heart from an ordinary card deck. The probability of drawing an ace is $\frac{4}{52}$, and the probability of drawing a heart is $\frac{13}{52}$. However, the probability of drawing an ace *or* a heart is not the sum of these two probabilities. Because the ace of hearts was counted twice, once as an ace and once as a heart, and the probability of drawing the ace of hearts is $\frac{1}{52}$, we must subtract $\frac{1}{52}$ from the sum of $\frac{4}{52}$ and $\frac{13}{52}$. Thus,

$$P(\text{ace } or \text{ heart}) = P(\text{ace}) + P(\text{heart}) - P(\text{ace of hearts})$$

$$= \frac{4}{52} + \frac{13}{52} - \frac{1}{52}$$

$$= \frac{16}{52}$$

$$= \frac{4}{13}$$

This example suggests the following theorem.

Theorem.   If A and B are two events, then

$$P(A \text{ or } B) = P(A) + P(B) - P(A \text{ and } B)$$

If event A and event B are **mutually exclusive** (that is, if one event occurs, the other cannot), then $P(A \text{ and } B) = 0$ and we have another theorem.

Theorem.   If A and B cannot occur simultaneously, then

$$P(A \text{ or } B) = P(A) + P(B)$$

Because the events A and $\bar{A}$ (read as "not A") are mutually exclusive,

$$P(A \text{ or } \bar{A}) = P(A) + P(\bar{A})$$

Because either event A or event $\bar{A}$ must happen, $P(A \text{ or } \bar{A}) = 1$. Thus,

$$P(A \text{ or } \bar{A}) = 1$$
$$P(A) + P(\bar{A}) = 1$$
$$P(\bar{A}) = 1 - P(A) \qquad \text{Add } -P(A) \text{ to both sides.}$$

This result gives a third theorem about compound probabilities.

> **Theorem.**   If A is any event, then
>
> $$P(\bar{A}) = 1 - P(A)$$

Example 1   A guidance counselor tells a student that his probability of earning a grade of D in algebra is $\frac{1}{5}$, and his probability of failing is $\frac{1}{25}$. What is the probability that the student earns a C or better?

Solution   The probability of earning a D or F is given by

$$P(D \text{ or } F) = P(D) + P(F) \qquad \text{Note that } P(D \text{ and } F) = 0.$$

$$= \frac{1}{5} + \frac{1}{25}$$

$$= \frac{6}{25}$$

The probability that the student will receive a C or better is given by

$$P(C \text{ or better}) = 1 - P(D \text{ or } F)$$

$$= 1 - \frac{6}{25}$$

$$= \frac{19}{25}$$

The student's probability of earning a C or better is $\frac{19}{25}$.   ∎

If two events do not influence each other, they are called **independent events**.

> **Definition.**   The events A and B are said to be **independent events** if and only if $P(B) = P(B|A)$.

Substituting $P(B)$ for $P(B|A)$ in the multiplication property for probabilities gives a formula for computing probabilities of compound independent events.

> **Theorem.**   If A and B are independent events, then
>
> $$P(A \text{ and } B) = P(A) \cdot P(B)$$

For example, if one card is drawn at random from a card deck and one coin is tossed, then $P(\text{drawing an ace and tossing a head}) = P(\text{drawing an ace}) \cdot P(\text{tossing a head})$. This is true because neither event influences the other.

Consequently,

$$P(\text{drawing an ace and tossing a head}) = \frac{4}{52} \cdot \frac{1}{2} = \frac{1}{26}$$

Example 2   The probability that a baseball player can get a hit is $\frac{1}{3}$. What is the probability that she will bat safely three times in a row?

Solution   Assume that the three events, each time at bat, are independent: one time at bat does not influence the player's chances of getting a hit on another turn at bat. Because $P(E_1) = \frac{1}{3}$, $P(E_2) = \frac{1}{3}$, and $P(E_3) = \frac{1}{3}$,

$$P(E_1 \text{ and } E_2 \text{ and } E_3) = \frac{1}{3} \cdot \frac{1}{3} \cdot \frac{1}{3} = \frac{1}{27}$$

The probability that the baseball player bats safely three times in a row is $\frac{1}{27}$.   ∎

Example 3   A die is tossed three times. What is the probability that the outcome is a six on the first toss, an even number on the second toss, and an odd prime number on the third toss?

Solution   The probability of a six on any toss is $P(\text{six}) = \frac{1}{6}$. Because there are three even integers represented on the faces of a die, the probability of tossing an even number is $P(\text{even number}) = \frac{3}{6} = \frac{1}{2}$. The numbers 3 and 5 are the only odd prime numbers on the faces of a die, so the probability of tossing an odd prime is $P(\text{odd prime}) = \frac{2}{6} = \frac{1}{3}$. Because these three events are independent, the probability of the three events happening in succession is the product of the probabilities:

$$P(\text{six and even number and odd prime}) = \frac{1}{6} \cdot \frac{1}{2} \cdot \frac{1}{3} = \frac{1}{36}$$ ∎

Example 4   The probability that the drug Flake Off will cure dandruff is $\frac{1}{8}$. If the drug is used, the probability that the patient will have side effects is $\frac{1}{6}$. What is the probability that a patient who uses the drug will be cured and will suffer no side effects?

Solution   The probability that Flake Off will work is $P(\text{works}) = \frac{1}{8}$, and the probability that the patient will have no side effects is $P(\text{no side effects}) = 1 - P(\text{side effects}) = 1 - \frac{1}{6} = \frac{5}{6}$. These events are independent, so $P(\text{cure and no side effects}) = \frac{1}{8} \cdot \frac{5}{6} = \frac{5}{48}$.   ∎

■ EXERCISE 14.8

In Exercises 1–4, assume that you draw one card from a card deck. Find the probability of the given event.

1. Drawing a black card
2. Drawing a jack
3. Drawing a black card or an ace
4. Drawing a red card or a face card

In Exercises 5–8, assume that you draw two cards from a card deck without replacement. Find the probability of the given event.

5. Drawing two aces
6. Drawing three aces
7. Drawing a club and then drawing another black card
8. Drawing a heart and then drawing a spade

In Exercises 9–12, assume that you roll two dice once.

9. What is the probability of rolling a sum of 7 or 6?
10. What is the probability of rolling a sum of 5 or an even sum?
11. What is the probability of rolling a sum of 10 or an odd sum?
12. What is the probability of rolling a sum of 12 or 1?

In Exercises 13–16, assume that you are dealing with a bucket that contains 7 beige capsules, 3 cyan capsules, and 6 magenta capsules. You make a single draw from the bucket, taking one capsule.

13. What is the probability of drawing a beige or a cyan capsule?
14. What is the probability of drawing a magenta capsule?
15. What is the probability of not drawing a cyan capsule?
16. What is the probability of not drawing either a beige or a cyan capsule?

In Exercises 17–19, assume that you are using the same bucket of capsules as in Exercises 13–16.

17. On two draws from the bucket, what is the probability of drawing a beige capsule followed by a magenta capsule? (Assume that the capsule is returned to the bucket after the first draw.)

18. On two draws from the bucket, what is the probability of drawing one cyan and one magenta capsule? (Assume that the capsule is not returned to the bucket after the first draw.)

19. On three successive draws from the bucket (without replacement), what is the probability of failing to draw a beige capsule?

20. Jeff rolls a die and draws one card from a card deck. What is the probability of his rolling a four and drawing a four?

21. Three people are in an elevator together. What is the probability that all three were born on the same day of the week?

22. Three people are on a bus together. What is the probability that at least one was born on a different day of the week than the others?

23. Five people are in a room together. What is the probability that all five were born on a different day of the year?

24. Five people are on a bus together. What is the probability that at least two of them were born on the same day of the year?

25. If the probability that Rick will solve a problem is $\frac{1}{4}$ and the probability that Dinah will solve it is $\frac{2}{5}$, what is the probability that at least one of them will solve the problem?

26. A certain bugle call is based on four pitches and is five notes long. If a child can play these four pitches on a bugle, what is the probability that the first five notes that the child plays will be the bugle call? (Assume that the child is equally likely to play any of the four pitches each time a note is blown.)

27. Valerie visits her cabin in Canada. The probability that her lawn mower will start is $\frac{1}{2}$, the probability that her gas power saw will start is $\frac{1}{3}$, and the probability that her outboard motor will start is $\frac{3}{4}$. What is the probability that all three will start and that Valerie will have a nice vacation? What is the probability that none will start? That exactly one will start? That exactly two will start? What is the sum of your answers?

28. Three children will leave Thailand to start a new life in either the United States or France. The probability that May Xao will go to France is $\frac{1}{3}$, that Tou Lia will go to France is $\frac{1}{2}$, and that May Moua will go to France is $\frac{1}{6}$. What is the probability that exactly two of them will end up in the United States?

CHAPTER SUMMARY

Key Words

arithmetic means   (14.3)
arithmetic progression   (14.3)
binomial theorem   (14.5)
combinations   (14.6)
compound events   (14.8)
event   (14.6)
factorial notation   (14.5)
general term of a sequence   (14.2)
geometric means   (14.3)
geometric progression   (14.3)
independent events   (14.8)
induction hypothesis   (14.1)
mathematical induction   (14.1)

multiplication principle for events
(14.6)
multiplication property of
probabilities   (14.7)
Pascal's triangle   (14.5)
permutations   (14.6)
probability   (14.7)
progression   (14.3)
sample space   (14.7)
sequence   (14.2)
series   (14.2)
summation notation   (14.2)

Key Ideas

(14.1)   **The Axiom of Mathematical Induction.**   If a statement involving the natural number n has the two properties that

1.   the statement is true for $n = 1$ and
2.   the statement is true for $n = k + 1$ whenever it is true for $n = k$,

then the statement is true for all natural numbers.

(14.2)   If c is a constant, then $\sum_{k=1}^{n} c = nc$.

If c is a constant, then $\sum_{k=1}^{n} cf(k) = c \sum_{k=1}^{n} f(k)$.

$$\sum_{k=1}^{n} [f(k) + g(k)] = \sum_{k=1}^{n} f(k) + \sum_{k=1}^{n} g(k)$$

(14.3) The formula $S_n = \dfrac{n(a + l)}{2}$ gives the sum of the first n terms of an arithmetic progression. In this formula, a is the first term, l is the last (or nth) term, and n is the number of terms.

(14.4) The formula $S_n = \dfrac{a - ar^n}{1 - r}$ gives the sum of the first n terms of a geometric progression. In this formula, S_n is the sum, a is the first term, r is the common ratio, and n is the number of terms. Assume that $r \neq 1$.

If $|r| < 1$, the sum of the terms of an infinite geometric progression is given by the formula $S = \dfrac{a}{1 - r}$, where S is the sum, a is the first term, and r is the common ratio.

(14.5) $n! = n(n - 1)(n - 2) \cdots 3 \cdot 2 \cdot 1$ $0! = 1$ $n(n - 1)! = n!$

The Binomial Theorem.   If n is any positive integer, then

$$(a + b)^n = a^n + \frac{n!}{1!(n - 1)!} a^{n-1}b + \frac{n!}{2!(n - 2)!} a^{n-2}b^2$$

$$+ \frac{n!}{3!(n - 3)!} a^{n-3}b^3 + \cdots + \frac{n!}{r!(n - r)!} a^{n-r}b^r + \cdots + b^n$$

(14.6) The formula for computing the number of permutations of n things r at a time is $_nP_r = \dfrac{n!}{(n - r)!}$. $(_nP_n = n!)$

There are $(n - 1)!$ ways to place n things in a circle.

The formula for computing the number of combinations of n things r at a time is $_nC_r = \dbinom{n}{r} = \dfrac{n!}{r!(n - r)!}$. $(_nC_0 = 1$ and $_nC_n = 1)$

If an n-lettered word has a of one letter, b of another letter, and so on, then the number of distinguishable words that can be formed using each letter of the n-lettered word is $\dfrac{n!}{a!b! \cdots}$.

(14.7) An event that cannot happen has a probability of 0. An event that is certain to happen has a probability of 1. All other events have probabilities between 0 and 1.

(14.8) If A and B are two events, then

$$P(A \text{ or } B) = P(A) + P(B) - P(A \text{ and } B)$$

If A and B cannot occur simultaneously, then

$$P(A \text{ or } B) = P(A) + P(B)$$

If A is any event, then

$$P(\bar{A}) = 1 - P(A)$$

If A and B are independent events, then

$$P(A \text{ and } B) = P(A) \cdot P(B)$$

REVIEW EXERCISES

1. Verify the following formula for $n = 1$, $n = 2$, $n = 3$, and $n = 4$, and then prove the formula by mathematical induction:

$$1^3 + 2^3 + 3^3 + \cdots + n^3 = \frac{n^2(n + 1)^2}{4}$$

2. Evaluate $\displaystyle\sum_{k=1}^{4} 3k^2$.

3. Evaluate $\displaystyle\sum_{k=5}^{8} (k^3 + 3k^2)$.   4. Evaluate $\displaystyle\sum_{k=1}^{30} \left(\frac{3}{2}k - 12\right) - \frac{3}{2}\sum_{k=1}^{30} k$.

In Review Exercises 5–8, find the required term of each arithmetic progression.

5. $5, 9, 13, \ldots$; 29th term   6. $8, 15, 22, \ldots$; 40th term

7. $6, -1, -8, \ldots$; 15th term   8. $\dfrac{1}{2}, -\dfrac{3}{2}, -\dfrac{7}{2}, \ldots$; 35th term

In Review Exercises 9–12, find the required term of each geometric progression.

9. $81, 27, 9, \ldots$; 11th term   10. $2, 6, 18, \ldots$; 9th term

11. $9, \dfrac{9}{2}, \dfrac{9}{4}, \ldots$; 15th term   12. $8, -\dfrac{8}{5}, \dfrac{8}{25}, \ldots$; 7th term

In Review Exercises 13–16, find the sum of the first 40 terms in each progression.

13. $5, 9, 13, \ldots$ 14. $8, 15, 22, \ldots$ 15. $6, -1, -8, \ldots$ 16. $\dfrac{1}{2}, -\dfrac{3}{2}, -\dfrac{7}{2}, \ldots$

In Review Exercises 17–20, find the sum of the first eight terms in each progression.

17. $81, 27, 9, \ldots$ 18. $2, 6, 18, \ldots$ 19. $9, \dfrac{9}{2}, \dfrac{9}{4}, \ldots$ 20. $8, -\dfrac{8}{5}, \dfrac{8}{25}, \ldots$

In Review Exercises 21–24, find the sum of each infinite progression, if possible.

21. $\dfrac{1}{3}, \dfrac{1}{6}, \dfrac{1}{12}, \ldots$ 22. $\dfrac{1}{5}, -\dfrac{2}{15}, \dfrac{4}{45}, \ldots$ 23. $1, \dfrac{3}{2}, \dfrac{9}{4}, \ldots$ 24. $0.5, 0.25, 0.125, \ldots$

In Review Exercises 25–28, use the formula for the sum of the terms of an infinite geometric progression to change each decimal into a common fraction.

25. $0.333\ldots$ **26.** $0.999\ldots$ **27.** $0.171717\ldots$ **28.** $0.454545\ldots$

29. Insert three arithmetic means between 2 and 8.

30. Insert five arithmetic means between 10 and 100.

31. Insert three geometric means between 2 and 8.

32. Insert four geometric means between -2 and 64.

33. Find the sum of the first 8 terms of the progression $\frac{1}{3}, 1, 3, \ldots$.

34. Find the seventh term of the progression $2\sqrt{2}, 4, 4\sqrt{2}, \ldots$.

35. Find the positive geometric mean between 4 and 64.

36. If Leonard invests \$3000 in a 6-year certificate of deposit at the annual rate of 7.75% compounded daily, how much money will be in the account when it matures?

37. The enrollment at Hometown College is growing at the rate of 5% over each previous year's enrollment. If the enrollment is currently 4000 students, what will the enrollment be 10 years from now? What was it 5 years ago?

38. A house trailer that originally cost \$10,000 depreciates in value at the rate of 10% per year. How much will the trailer be worth after 10 years?

In Review Exercises 39–42, use the binomial theorem to find the expansion of each expression.

39. $(x - y)^3$ **40.** $(u + 2v)^3$ **41.** $(4a - 5b)^5$ **42.** $(\sqrt{7}r + \sqrt{3}s)^4$

In Review Exercises 43–46, find the required term of each expansion.

43. $(a + b)^8$; fourth term   **44.** $(2x - y)^5$; third term

45. $(x - y)^9$; seventh term   **46.** $(4x + 7)^6$; fourth term

In Review Exercises 47–58, evaluate each expression.

47. $_6P_6$ **48.** $\binom{7}{4}$ **49.** $0!$ **50.** $_{10}P_2 \cdot {}_{10}C_2$

51. $_8P_6 \cdot {}_8C_6$ **52.** $\binom{8}{5}\binom{6}{2}$ **53.** $_7C_5 \cdot {}_4P_0$ **54.** $_{12}C_0 \cdot {}_{11}C_0$

55. $\dfrac{_8P_5}{_8C_5}$ **56.** $\dfrac{_8C_5}{_{13}C_5}$ **57.** $\dfrac{_6C_3}{_{10}C_3}$ **58.** $\dfrac{_{13}C_5}{_{52}C_5}$

59. Make a tree diagram to illustrate the possible results of tossing a coin four times.

60. State the multiplication principle for events.

61. State the multiplication property for probabilities.

62. In how many ways can you draw a five-card poker hand of 3 aces and 2 kings?

63. What is the probability of drawing the hand described in Review Exercise 62?

64. What is the probability of *not* drawing the hand described in Review Exercise 62?

65. In how many ways can 10 teenagers be seated at a round table if 2 girls wish to sit with their boyfriends?

66. How many distinguishable words can be formed from the letters of the word *casserole* if each of the nine letters is used once?

67. What is the probability of having a 13-card bridge hand consisting of 4 aces, 4 kings, 4 queens, and 1 jack?

68. Find the probability of choosing a committee of 3 boys and 2 girls from a group of 8 boys and 6 girls.

69. Find the probability of drawing a club or a spade on one draw from a card deck.

70. Find the probability of drawing a black card or a king on one draw from a card deck.

71. What is the probability of getting an ace-high royal flush (ace, king, queen, jack, and ten of hearts) in poker?

72. What is the probability of being dealt 13 cards of one suit in a bridge hand?

73. What is the probability of getting 3 heads or fewer on 4 tosses of a fair coin?

CHAPTER FOURTEEN TEST

1. Use mathematical induction to prove the formula

$$5 + 10 + 15 + \cdots + 5n = \frac{5n}{2}(n + 1)$$

In Problems 2–3, supply the next term in each sequence.

2. 2, 7, 12, ?

3. 1, 1, 1, 3, 5, 9, 17, ?

In Problems 4–5, evaluate each sum.

4. $\displaystyle\sum_{n=2}^{4} (2n^2 - 3)$

5. $\displaystyle\sum_{n=1}^{8} 32n - 32 \sum_{n=1}^{8} n + 32 \sum_{n=1}^{8} 1$

6. Write the 75th term of the arithmetic progression with a first term of 2 and a common difference of 3.

7. The third term in an arithmetic progression is 1 and the sixth term is 13. What is the second term?

8. Find the sum of the first 29 terms of the sequence

$$-5, -\frac{1}{2}, 4, \ldots$$

9. Find three arithmetic means between 10 and 26.

10. Find the seventh term of the progression 2, −6, 18, ...

11. Find the positive geometric mean between 5 and 20.

12. Find the sum of the first six terms of a geometric progression with third, fourth, and fifth terms of −2, 6, and −18.

13. Find the sum of the infinite geometric progression $\frac{1}{2}, \frac{1}{6}, \frac{1}{18}, \ldots$.

14. Evaluate $\dfrac{10!}{8!}$.

15. Find the 3rd term in the expansion of

$$(x + y)^6.$$

16. Find the 2nd term in the expansion of

$$(2x + y)^6.$$

17. Evaluate $_9P_4$.

18. Evaluate $_8C_5$.

19. In how many ways can 6 children be placed in a row?

20. In how many ways can a committee of 3 people be chosen from a group of 8 people?

21. On a roll of two dice, what is the probability of getting a sum of 3?

22. On a roll of one die, what is the probability of obtaining a 2 or a 3?

23. If the probability that Sally passes a test is $\frac{1}{3}$ and that John passes the same test is $\frac{1}{4}$, what is the probability that both fail?

24. In Problem 23, what is the probability that neither person fails?

CUMULATIVE REVIEW EXERCISES (CHAPTERS 13–14)

1. Write the equation of the circle with center at the origin and passing through the point $(7, 7)$.

2. Write the equation of the circle with center at $O(-2, 4)$ and radius of 4 units.

3. Write the equation $x^2 - 6x + y^2 + 4y = 3$ in standard form. Then graph it.

4. Find the equation of the parabola with vertex at $(-2, 3)$, passing through point $(-4, -8)$, and opening downward.

5. Graph the parabola $x^2 - 2x = 4y - 9$.

6. Write the equation of the ellipse with center at the origin, major axis that is horizontal and 12 units long, and the minor axis 8 units long.

7. Write the equation of the ellipse with foci at $(-6, 4)$ and $(2, 4)$ and $b = 2$.

8. Write the equation of the hyperbola with vertices at points $(-3, 3)$ and $(3, 3)$ and a focus at point $(5, 3)$.

9. Use any method to solve the system $\begin{cases} 3x^2 + 4y^2 = 43 \\ x^2 - 2y^2 = 1 \end{cases}$

10. To what point should the origin of the xy-coordinate system be translated to remove the first-degree term in the equation

$$x^2 + 4x + y^2 - 6y + 11 = 0$$

11. Use mathematical induction to prove that

$$1 + 4 + 7 + \cdots + (3n - 2) = \frac{n(3n - 1)}{2}$$

for all natural numbers n.

12. Evaluate $\sum\limits_{k=1}^{3} 3k^2$.

13. Evaluate $\sum\limits_{k=3}^{5} (2k + 1)$

14. Find the 20th term of an arithmetic progression with a first term of -11 and a common difference of 6.

15. Find the sum of the first 20 terms of an arithmetic progression with a first term of 6 and a common difference of 3.

16. Insert two arithmetic means between -3 and 30.

17. Find the seventh term of a geometric progression with a first term of $\frac{1}{27}$ and a common ratio of 3.

18. Find the sum of the first 10 terms of the progression $\frac{1}{64}, \frac{1}{32}, \frac{1}{16}, \ldots$.

19. Insert two geometric means between -3 and 192.

20. Find the sum of all the terms of the progression $9, 3, 1, \ldots$.

21. Evaluate $\dfrac{6!7!}{5!}$.

22. Use the binomial theorem to expand $(3a - b)^4$.

23. Find the seventh term of the expansion of $(2x - y)^8$.

24. In how many ways can 7 people stand in line?

25. Evaluate $_6P_3$.

26. Evaluate $_6C_3$.

27. In how many ways can a committee of 3 people be chosen from a group containing 9 people?

28. If $n > 1$, which of $_nP_n$ or $_nC_n$ is the smaller?

29. What is the probability of being dealt two aces in succession from a well-shuffled card deck?

30. What is the probability of tossing exactly 3 heads in 4 tosses of a fair coin?

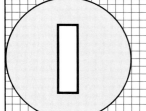

APPENDIX: MATRIX ALGEBRA

I.1 MATRIX ALGEBRA

In this section we discuss how to add, subtract, and multiply matrices.

> **Definition.** An **$m \times n$ matrix** is a rectangular array of $m \cdot n$ numbers arranged in m rows and n columns.

We will use any of the following notations to denote the matrix A:

$$A_{m \times n}, \quad A, \quad [a_{ij}], \quad \begin{bmatrix} a_{11} & a_{12} & a_{13} & \cdots & a_{1n} \\ a_{21} & a_{22} & a_{23} & \cdots & a_{2n} \\ \vdots & & & & \vdots \\ a_{m1} & a_{m2} & a_{m3} & \cdots & a_{mn} \end{bmatrix}$$

The symbol a_{23} represents the entry in row two, column three, of the matrix A. Similarly, the symbol a_{ij} represents the entry in the ith row and the jth column.

> **Definition of Equal Matrices.** If $A = [a_{ij}]$ and $B = [b_{ij}]$ are both $m \times n$ matrices, then
>
> $$A = B \text{ if and only if } a_{ij} = b_{ij}$$
>
> for all i and j, where $i = 1, 2, 3, \ldots, m$ and $j = 1, 2, 3, \ldots, n$.

The previous definition points out that two matrices must be identical to be equal. They must be the same size and have the same corresponding entries.

> **The Sum of Two Matrices.** Let $A = [a_{ij}]$ and $B = [b_{ij}]$ be two $m \times n$ matrices. The sum, $A + B$, is the $m \times n$ matrix C, found by adding the corresponding entries of matrices A and B:
>
> $$A + B = C = [c_{ij}]$$
>
> where $c_{ij} = a_{ij} + b_{ij}$, for $i = 1, 2, 3, \ldots, m$ and $j = 1, 2, 3, \ldots, n$.

Example 1   Add the matrices

$$\begin{bmatrix} 2 & 1 & 3 \\ 1 & -1 & 0 \end{bmatrix} \quad \text{and} \quad \begin{bmatrix} 1 & -1 & 2 \\ -1 & 1 & 5 \end{bmatrix}$$

Solution   Because each matrix is 2×3, their sum is defined and can be calculated by adding their corresponding elements:

$$\begin{bmatrix} 2 & 1 & 3 \\ 1 & -1 & 0 \end{bmatrix} + \begin{bmatrix} 1 & -1 & 2 \\ -1 & 1 & 5 \end{bmatrix} = \begin{bmatrix} 2+1 & 1-1 & 3+2 \\ 1-1 & -1+1 & 0+5 \end{bmatrix}$$
$$= \begin{bmatrix} 3 & 0 & 5 \\ 0 & 0 & 5 \end{bmatrix} \qquad \blacksquare$$

Example 2   If possible, add the matrices

$$\begin{bmatrix} 2 & 4 & 3 \\ 1 & 1 & 1 \end{bmatrix} \quad \text{and} \quad \begin{bmatrix} 1 & 2 \\ 2 & 3 \end{bmatrix}$$

Solution   The first matrix is 2×3 and the second is 2×2. Because these matrices are of different sizes, they cannot be added. $\blacksquare$

Several of the field properties discussed in Chapter 1 apply to matrices also.

Theorem.   The addition of two $m \times n$ matrices is commutative.

Proof   Let $A = [a_{ij}]$ and $B = [b_{ij}]$ be $m \times n$ matrices. Then $A + B = C = [c_{ij}]$, where $c_{ij} = a_{ij} + b_{ij}$ for each $i = 1, 2, 3, \ldots, m$ and $j = 1, 2, 3, \ldots, n$. On the other hand, $B + A = D = [d_{ij}]$, where $d_{ij} = b_{ij} + a_{ij}$ for each i and j.

Because each entry in each matrix is a real number and the addition of real numbers is commutative, it follows that

$$c_{ij} = a_{ij} + b_{ij} = b_{ij} + a_{ij} = d_{ij}$$

for all i and j, $i = 1, 2, 3, \ldots, m$ and $j = 1, 2, 3, \ldots, n$.

By the definition of equality of matrices, $C = D$, and therefore $A + B = B + A$. $\square$

Theorem.   The addition of three $m \times n$ matrices is associative.

The proof of the previous theorem is left as an exercise.

In the collection of all $m \times n$ matrices, there is a matrix called the **zero matrix**.

Definition.   Let A be any $m \times n$ matrix. There is an $m \times n$ matrix **0**, called the **zero matrix**, or the **additive identity matrix**, for which

$$A + \mathbf{0} = \mathbf{0} + A = A$$

The matrix **0** consists of m rows and n columns of 0s.

To illustrate the above definition, we note that the matrix

$$\begin{bmatrix} 0 & 0 & 0 \\ 0 & 0 & 0 \\ 0 & 0 & 0 \end{bmatrix}$$

is the 3×3 zero matrix, and that

$$\begin{bmatrix} 0 & 0 & 0 \\ 0 & 0 & 0 \\ 0 & 0 & 0 \end{bmatrix} + \begin{bmatrix} 1 & 2 & 3 \\ 4 & 5 & 6 \\ 7 & 8 & 9 \end{bmatrix} = \begin{bmatrix} 1 & 2 & 3 \\ 4 & 5 & 6 \\ 7 & 8 & 9 \end{bmatrix}$$

Matrices are similar to real numbers in another respect: every matrix has an additive inverse.

Definition.   Any $m \times n$ matrix A has an **additive inverse**, an $m \times n$ matrix $-A$ with the property that the sum of A and $-A$ is the zero matrix:

$$A + (-A) = (-A) + A = \mathbf{0}$$

The entries of $-A$ are the negatives of the corresponding entries of A.

The additive inverse of the 2×3 matrix $A = \begin{bmatrix} 1 & -3 & 2 \\ 0 & 1 & -5 \end{bmatrix}$ is the matrix

$$-A = \begin{bmatrix} -1 & 3 & -2 \\ 0 & -1 & 5 \end{bmatrix}$$

because their sum is the zero matrix:

$$\begin{aligned} A + (-A) &= \begin{bmatrix} 1 & -3 & 2 \\ 0 & 1 & -5 \end{bmatrix} + \begin{bmatrix} -1 & 3 & -2 \\ 0 & -1 & 5 \end{bmatrix} \\ &= \begin{bmatrix} 1-1 & -3+3 & 2-2 \\ 0+0 & 1-1 & -5+5 \end{bmatrix} \\ &= \begin{bmatrix} 0 & 0 & 0 \\ 0 & 0 & 0 \end{bmatrix} \end{aligned}$$

> **The Difference of Two Matrices.** If A and B are $m \times n$ matrices, their difference, $A - B$, is the sum of A and the additive inverse of B:
>
> $$A - B = A + (-B)$$

Example 3

$$\begin{bmatrix} 2 & -5 \\ 3 & 1 \end{bmatrix} - \begin{bmatrix} 4 & -5 \\ -3 & 9 \end{bmatrix} = \begin{bmatrix} 2 & -5 \\ 3 & 1 \end{bmatrix} + \begin{bmatrix} -4 & 5 \\ 3 & -9 \end{bmatrix}$$

$$= \begin{bmatrix} -2 & 0 \\ 6 & -8 \end{bmatrix}$$

■

We illustrate how to find the product of two matrices by computing the product of a 2×3 matrix A and a 3×3 matrix B. The result is the 2×3 matrix C.

$$A \cdot B = \begin{bmatrix} 1 & 2 & 3 \\ 4 & 5 & 6 \end{bmatrix} \cdot \begin{bmatrix} a & b & c \\ d & e & f \\ g & h & i \end{bmatrix} = C$$

Each entry of matrix C is the result of a calculation that involves a row of A and a column of B. For example, the first-row, third-column entry of matrix C is found by keeping a running total of the products of corresponding entries of the first row of A and the third column of B:

$$\begin{bmatrix} \mathbf{1} & \mathbf{2} & \mathbf{3} \\ 4 & 5 & 6 \end{bmatrix}\begin{bmatrix} a & b & c \\ d & e & f \\ g & h & i \end{bmatrix} = \begin{bmatrix} ? & ? & 1c + 2f + 3i \\ ? & ? & ? \end{bmatrix}$$

Similarly, the second-row, second-column entry of matrix C is formed by a calculation involving the second row of A and the second column of B.

$$\begin{bmatrix} 1 & 2 & 3 \\ \mathbf{4} & \mathbf{5} & \mathbf{6} \end{bmatrix}\begin{bmatrix} a & b & c \\ d & e & f \\ g & h & i \end{bmatrix} = \begin{bmatrix} ? & ? & 1c + 2f + 3i \\ ? & 4b + 5e + 6h & ? \end{bmatrix}$$

To calculate the first-row, first-column entry of matrix C, we use the first row of A and the first column of B.

$$\begin{bmatrix} \mathbf{1} & \mathbf{2} & \mathbf{3} \\ 4 & 5 & 6 \end{bmatrix} \cdot \begin{bmatrix} a & b & c \\ d & e & f \\ g & h & i \end{bmatrix} = \begin{bmatrix} 1a + 2d + 3g & ? & 1c + 2f + 3i \\ ? & 4b + 5e + 6h & ? \end{bmatrix}$$

The complete product C is

$$\begin{bmatrix} 1 & 2 & 3 \\ 4 & 5 & 6 \end{bmatrix} \begin{bmatrix} a & b & c \\ d & e & f \\ g & h & i \end{bmatrix} = \begin{bmatrix} 1a + 2d + 3g & 1b + 2e + 3h & 1c + 2f + 3i \\ 4a + 5d + 6g & 4b + 5e + 6h & 4c + 5f + 6i \end{bmatrix}$$

For the product $A \cdot B$ to exist, the number of columns of A must equal the number of rows of B. If the product exists, it will have as many rows as A and as many columns as B:

$$\begin{array}{ccccc} A & \cdot & B & = & C \\ m \times n & & n \times p & & m \times p \end{array}$$

These must
agree.

The product is $m \times p$.

More formally, we have the following definition.

The Product of Two Matrices.   Let $A = [a_{ij}]$ be an $m \times n$ matrix and $B = [b_{ij}]$ be an $n \times p$ matrix. The product, AB, is the $m \times p$ matrix C found as follows:

$AB = C = [c_{ij}]$, where c_{ij} is the sum of the products of the corresponding entries in ith row of A and the jth column of B, where $i = 1, 2, 3, \ldots, m$ and $j = 1, 2, 3, \ldots, p$

Example 4   Find C if $A \cdot B = \begin{bmatrix} 1 & 2 \\ 3 & 4 \\ 5 & 6 \end{bmatrix} \begin{bmatrix} a & b \\ c & d \end{bmatrix} = C.$

Solution   Because the first matrix is 3×2 and the second matrix is 2×2, the product C exists, and it is a 3×2 matrix. The first-row, first-column entry of C is the total of the products of corresponding entries in the first row of A and the first column of B: $c_{11} = 1a + 2c$. Similarly, c_{12} is computed by using the first row of A and the second column of B: $c_{12} = 1b + 2d$. The entire product is

$$\begin{bmatrix} 1 & 2 \\ 3 & 4 \\ 5 & 6 \end{bmatrix} \begin{bmatrix} a & b \\ c & d \end{bmatrix} = \begin{bmatrix} 1a + 2c & 1b + 2d \\ 3a + 4c & 3b + 4d \\ 5a + 6c & 5b + 6d \end{bmatrix}$$ ∎

Example 5   Find the product $\begin{bmatrix} 1 & -1 & 2 \\ 1 & 3 & 0 \\ 0 & 1 & 1 \end{bmatrix} \begin{bmatrix} 2 & 1 \\ 1 & 3 \\ 0 & 1 \end{bmatrix}.$

Solution   Because the matrices are 3×3 and 3×2, the product is a 3×2 matrix.

$$\begin{bmatrix} 1 & -1 & 2 \\ 1 & 3 & 0 \\ 0 & 1 & 1 \end{bmatrix} \begin{bmatrix} 2 & 1 \\ 1 & 3 \\ 0 & 1 \end{bmatrix}$$

$$= \begin{bmatrix} 1 \cdot 2 + (-1) \cdot 1 + 2 \cdot 0 & 1 \cdot 1 + (-1) \cdot 3 + 2 \cdot 1 \\ 1 \cdot 2 + 3 \cdot 1 + 0 \cdot 0 & 1 \cdot 1 + 3 \cdot 3 + 0 \cdot 1 \\ 0 \cdot 2 + 1 \cdot 1 + 1 \cdot 0 & 0 \cdot 1 + 1 \cdot 3 + 1 \cdot 1 \end{bmatrix}$$

$$= \begin{bmatrix} 1 & 0 \\ 5 & 10 \\ 1 & 4 \end{bmatrix}$$ ∎

Example 6   Find the product $\begin{bmatrix} 1 & 2 & 3 \end{bmatrix} \begin{bmatrix} 4 \\ 5 \\ 6 \end{bmatrix}$.

Solution   Because the first matrix is 1×3 and the second matrix is 3×1, the product is a 1×1 matrix:

$$\begin{bmatrix} 1 & 2 & 3 \end{bmatrix} \begin{bmatrix} 4 \\ 5 \\ 6 \end{bmatrix} = \begin{bmatrix} 1 \cdot 4 + 2 \cdot 5 + 3 \cdot 6 \end{bmatrix} = \begin{bmatrix} 32 \end{bmatrix}$$ ∎

Example 7   If $A = \begin{bmatrix} 1 & 1 \\ 0 & 0 \end{bmatrix}$ and $B = \begin{bmatrix} 0 & 1 \\ 0 & 1 \end{bmatrix}$, calculate AB and BA and thereby show that multiplication of matrices is not commutative.

Solution $$AB = \begin{bmatrix} 1 & 1 \\ 0 & 0 \end{bmatrix} \begin{bmatrix} 0 & 1 \\ 0 & 1 \end{bmatrix} = \begin{bmatrix} 0 & 2 \\ 0 & 0 \end{bmatrix}$$

$$BA = \begin{bmatrix} 0 & 1 \\ 0 & 1 \end{bmatrix} \begin{bmatrix} 1 & 1 \\ 0 & 0 \end{bmatrix} = \begin{bmatrix} 0 & 0 \\ 0 & 0 \end{bmatrix}$$

Because the products are not equal, matrix multiplication is not commutative.   ∎

Example 8   Find values for x, y, and z such that

$$\begin{bmatrix} 1 & 2 & 3 \\ 2 & -1 & -2 \\ 1 & -3 & -3 \end{bmatrix} \begin{bmatrix} x \\ y \\ z \end{bmatrix} = \begin{bmatrix} 4 \\ 0 \\ -2 \end{bmatrix}$$

Solution   Find the product of the first two matrices and set it equal to the third matrix.

$$\begin{bmatrix} 1 & 2 & 3 \\ 2 & -1 & -2 \\ 1 & -3 & -3 \end{bmatrix} \begin{bmatrix} x \\ y \\ z \end{bmatrix} = \begin{bmatrix} 1x + 2y + 3z \\ 2x - 1y - 2z \\ 1x - 3y - 3z \end{bmatrix} = \begin{bmatrix} 4 \\ 0 \\ -2 \end{bmatrix}$$

The product will be equal to the third matrix if and only if their corresponding components are equal. Set the corresponding components equal to get

$$\begin{cases} x + 2y + 3z = 4 \\ 2x - y - 2z = 0 \\ x - 3y - 3z = -2 \end{cases}$$

Solve this system for x, y, and z to obtain $x = 1$, $y = 0$, and $z = 1$. ∎

The number 1 is called the identity for multiplication because multiplying a number by 1 does not change that number. There is a **multiplicative identity matrix** with a similar property.

Definition.   Let A be an $n \times n$ matrix. There is an $n \times n$ **identity matrix** I for which

$$AI = IA = A$$

The matrix I consists of 1s on its diagonal and 0s elsewhere.

$$I = \begin{bmatrix} 1 & 0 & 0 & \cdots & 0 \\ 0 & 1 & 0 & \cdots & 0 \\ 0 & 0 & 1 & \cdots & 0 \\ \vdots & \vdots & \vdots & & \vdots \\ 0 & 0 & 0 & \cdots & 1 \end{bmatrix}$$

Note that an identity matrix is a square matrix—it has the same number of rows and columns.

Example 9 illustrates the previous definition for the 3×3 identity matrix.

Example 9   Find **a.** $\begin{bmatrix} 1 & 0 & 0 \\ 0 & 1 & 0 \\ 0 & 0 & 1 \end{bmatrix}\begin{bmatrix} 1 & 2 & 3 \\ 4 & 5 & 6 \\ 7 & 8 & 9 \end{bmatrix}$ and **b.** $\begin{bmatrix} 1 & 2 & 3 \\ 4 & 5 & 6 \\ 7 & 8 & 9 \end{bmatrix}\begin{bmatrix} 1 & 0 & 0 \\ 0 & 1 & 0 \\ 0 & 0 & 1 \end{bmatrix}$.

Solution   **a.** $\begin{bmatrix} 1 & 0 & 0 \\ 0 & 1 & 0 \\ 0 & 0 & 1 \end{bmatrix}\begin{bmatrix} 1 & 2 & 3 \\ 4 & 5 & 6 \\ 7 & 8 & 9 \end{bmatrix}$

$$= \begin{bmatrix} 1 \cdot 1 + 0 \cdot 4 + 0 \cdot 7 & 1 \cdot 2 + 0 \cdot 5 + 0 \cdot 8 & 1 \cdot 3 + 0 \cdot 6 + 0 \cdot 9 \\ 0 \cdot 1 + 1 \cdot 4 + 0 \cdot 7 & 0 \cdot 2 + 1 \cdot 5 + 0 \cdot 8 & 0 \cdot 3 + 1 \cdot 6 + 0 \cdot 9 \\ 0 \cdot 1 + 0 \cdot 4 + 1 \cdot 7 & 0 \cdot 2 + 0 \cdot 5 + 1 \cdot 8 & 0 \cdot 3 + 0 \cdot 6 + 1 \cdot 9 \end{bmatrix}$$

$$= \begin{bmatrix} 1 & 2 & 3 \\ 4 & 5 & 6 \\ 7 & 8 & 9 \end{bmatrix}$$

b.
$$\begin{bmatrix} 1 & 2 & 3 \\ 4 & 5 & 6 \\ 7 & 8 & 9 \end{bmatrix} \begin{bmatrix} 1 & 0 & 0 \\ 0 & 1 & 0 \\ 0 & 0 & 1 \end{bmatrix} = \begin{bmatrix} 1 & 2 & 3 \\ 4 & 5 & 6 \\ 7 & 8 & 9 \end{bmatrix}$$ ∎

▬ EXERCISE I.1 ▬

In Exercises 1–8, find values of x and y, if any, that will make the two matrices equal.

1. $\begin{bmatrix} x & y \\ 1 & 3 \end{bmatrix} = \begin{bmatrix} 2 & 5 \\ 1 & 3 \end{bmatrix}$

2. $\begin{bmatrix} x & 5 \\ 3 & y \end{bmatrix} = \begin{bmatrix} 0 & 5 \\ 3 & 2 \end{bmatrix}$

3. $\begin{bmatrix} x & y \\ 1 & 3 \end{bmatrix} = \begin{bmatrix} 2 & 5 \\ 1 & 4 \end{bmatrix}$

4. $\begin{bmatrix} x & y \\ 1 & x+y \end{bmatrix} = \begin{bmatrix} 2 & 1 \\ 1 & 2 \end{bmatrix}$

5. $\begin{bmatrix} x+y & 3+x \\ -2 & 5y \end{bmatrix} = \begin{bmatrix} 3 & 4 \\ -2 & 10 \end{bmatrix}$

6. $\begin{bmatrix} x+y & x-y \\ 2x & 3y \end{bmatrix} = \begin{bmatrix} -x & x-2 \\ -y & 8-y \end{bmatrix}$

7. $\begin{bmatrix} x & 3x \\ y & x+1 \end{bmatrix} = \begin{bmatrix} y & 6 \\ 2 & 3 \end{bmatrix}$

8. $\begin{bmatrix} x \\ y \end{bmatrix} = \begin{bmatrix} 1 & 2 \\ 3 & 4 \end{bmatrix}$

In Exercises 9–18, perform the indicated operation, if possible.

9. $\begin{bmatrix} 2 & 1 & -1 \\ -3 & 2 & 5 \end{bmatrix} + \begin{bmatrix} -3 & 1 & 2 \\ -3 & -2 & -5 \end{bmatrix}$

10. $\begin{bmatrix} 3 & 1 \\ 2 & 2 \end{bmatrix} + \begin{bmatrix} 2 & 1 \\ -1 & 0 \end{bmatrix} + \begin{bmatrix} -5 & -2 \\ -1 & -2 \end{bmatrix}$

11. $\begin{bmatrix} 3 & 2 & 1 \\ -2 & 3 & -3 \\ -4 & -2 & -1 \end{bmatrix} - \begin{bmatrix} -2 & 6 & -2 \\ 5 & 7 & -1 \\ -4 & -6 & 7 \end{bmatrix}$

12. $\begin{bmatrix} -2 & 7 & -3 \\ 3 & 6 & -7 \\ -9 & -2 & -5 \end{bmatrix} + \begin{bmatrix} -5 & -4 & -3 \\ -1 & 2 & 10 \\ -1 & -3 & -4 \end{bmatrix}$

13. $\begin{bmatrix} 1 & 3 & -1 \\ 2 & 1 & 5 \\ 1 & 3 & 0 \end{bmatrix} + \begin{bmatrix} 2 \\ 0 \\ -3 \end{bmatrix}$

14. $\begin{bmatrix} 3 \\ 2 \\ 3 \end{bmatrix} - \begin{bmatrix} -3 & 5 & -6 \\ -3 & -5 & -6 \\ 4 & 6 & -6 \end{bmatrix}$

15. $\begin{bmatrix} 1 & 2 & 3 \end{bmatrix} + \begin{bmatrix} 4 & 5 & 6 \end{bmatrix}$

16. $\begin{bmatrix} 1 \\ 2 \\ 3 \end{bmatrix} + \begin{bmatrix} 4 & -5 & -6 \end{bmatrix}$

17. $\begin{bmatrix} 1 & 3 & -4 \\ 2 & -1 & 3 \\ 1 & 5 & 7 \end{bmatrix} + \begin{bmatrix} 3 & 2 & -8 \\ 9 & 11 & 17 \\ 2 & 1 & 3 \end{bmatrix} - \begin{bmatrix} 1 & 3 & -5 \\ 2 & -9 & 5 \\ 3 & 10 & 11 \end{bmatrix}$

18. $\begin{bmatrix} -3 & -2 & 15 \\ 2 & -5 & 9 \end{bmatrix} - \begin{bmatrix} 3 & 2 & -15 \\ -2 & 5 & -9 \end{bmatrix} + \begin{bmatrix} 6 & 4 & -30 \\ -3 & 12 & -15 \end{bmatrix}$

In Exercises 19–30, find each product, if possible.

19. $\begin{bmatrix} 2 & 3 \\ 3 & -2 \end{bmatrix} \begin{bmatrix} 1 & 2 \\ 0 & -2 \end{bmatrix}$

20. $\begin{bmatrix} -2 & 3 \\ 3 & -2 \end{bmatrix} \begin{bmatrix} 2 & 4 \\ -5 & 7 \end{bmatrix}$

21. $\begin{bmatrix} -4 & -2 \\ 21 & 0 \end{bmatrix} \begin{bmatrix} -5 & 6 \\ 21 & -1 \end{bmatrix}$

22. $\begin{bmatrix} -5 & 4 \\ 4 & -5 \end{bmatrix} \begin{bmatrix} 6 & -2 \\ 1 & 3 \end{bmatrix}$

23. $\begin{bmatrix} 2 & 1 & 3 \\ 1 & 2 & -1 \\ 0 & 1 & 0 \end{bmatrix} \begin{bmatrix} 1 & 2 & 3 \\ 2 & -2 & 1 \\ 0 & 0 & 1 \end{bmatrix}$

24. $\begin{bmatrix} 2 & 1 & 1 \\ 1 & 1 & 2 \\ 1 & -2 & -1 \end{bmatrix} \begin{bmatrix} 1 & 2 & 3 \\ 1 & 2 & -3 \\ -1 & -1 & 3 \end{bmatrix}$

25. $\begin{bmatrix} 1 & -2 & -3 \end{bmatrix} \begin{bmatrix} 4 \\ -5 \\ -6 \end{bmatrix}$

26. $\begin{bmatrix} 1 \\ -2 \\ -3 \end{bmatrix} \begin{bmatrix} 4 & -5 & -6 \end{bmatrix}$

27. $\begin{bmatrix} 1 & 2 & 3 \end{bmatrix} \begin{bmatrix} 4 & 5 & 6 \end{bmatrix}$

28. $\begin{bmatrix} 2 & 3 & 4 \\ 1 & 2 & 3 \\ -2 & 2 & 2 \end{bmatrix} \begin{bmatrix} -1 \\ 2 \\ 3 \end{bmatrix}$

29. $\begin{bmatrix} 1 & 2 & 3 \end{bmatrix} \begin{bmatrix} 1 & 2 & 3 \\ 4 & 5 & 6 \\ 7 & 8 & 9 \end{bmatrix}$

30. $\begin{bmatrix} 1 & 2 & 3 \\ 1 & 2 & 1 \\ 1 & -1 & -1 \end{bmatrix} \begin{bmatrix} 1 & 2 \\ 2 & 1 \\ 1 & 1 \end{bmatrix}$

In Exercises 31–36, perform the indicated operations.

31. $\begin{bmatrix} 1 & 2 \\ 2 & 3 \end{bmatrix} \left(\begin{bmatrix} 2 & 1 & -5 \\ 1 & 1 & 2 \end{bmatrix} + \begin{bmatrix} -2 & -1 & 6 \\ 0 & -1 & -1 \end{bmatrix} \right)$

32. $\begin{bmatrix} 1 & 2 \\ 2 & 3 \end{bmatrix} \begin{bmatrix} 2 & 1 & -5 \\ 1 & 1 & 2 \end{bmatrix} + \begin{bmatrix} 1 & 2 \\ 2 & 3 \end{bmatrix} \begin{bmatrix} -2 & -1 & 6 \\ 0 & -1 & -1 \end{bmatrix}$

33. $\begin{bmatrix} 1 & 2 & 3 \\ 2 & 3 & 1 \\ 1 & 2 & 1 \end{bmatrix} \begin{bmatrix} 2 & 1 & 1 \\ 3 & -1 & -1 \\ 2 & -2 & 2 \end{bmatrix} + \begin{bmatrix} -2 & 3 & 4 \\ 1 & 1 & 1 \\ 0 & 1 & 0 \end{bmatrix}$

34. $\begin{bmatrix} 2 & 1 & 0 \\ 1 & -2 & -1 \\ 1 & 1 & -1 \end{bmatrix} \left(\begin{bmatrix} 1 & 0 & 1 \\ 1 & 1 & 2 \\ 1 & 2 & -1 \end{bmatrix} + \begin{bmatrix} -1 & -1 & 2 \\ 0 & 0 & 1 \\ 1 & 0 & -1 \end{bmatrix} \right)$

35. $\left(\begin{bmatrix} 1 & 2 \\ 2 & 3 \end{bmatrix} \begin{bmatrix} 1 \\ -3 \end{bmatrix} + \begin{bmatrix} -2 \\ 1 \end{bmatrix} \right) \left(\begin{bmatrix} 1 & 2 \end{bmatrix} \begin{bmatrix} 1 \\ -3 \end{bmatrix} + \begin{bmatrix} 4 \end{bmatrix} \right)$

36. $\begin{bmatrix} 1 \\ 2 \end{bmatrix} \begin{bmatrix} -3 & -4 \end{bmatrix} - \begin{bmatrix} 0 & 3 \\ 2 & 1 \end{bmatrix} \begin{bmatrix} 2 & 0 \\ 1 & -1 \end{bmatrix}$

In Exercises 37–42, let $A = \begin{bmatrix} 1 & 3 \\ 2 & 5 \end{bmatrix}$, $B = \begin{bmatrix} -1 \\ 3 \end{bmatrix}$, *and* $C = \begin{bmatrix} 3 & 2 \end{bmatrix}$. *Perform, if possible, the indicated operations.*

37. $A - BC$　　　**38.** $AB + B$　　　**39.** $CB - AB$　　　**40.** CAB

41. ABC　　　　　　　　　　　　　　　**42.** $CA + C$

43. Let $A = \begin{bmatrix} 1 & 1 \\ 1 & 1 \end{bmatrix}$. Find A^7. (*Hint:* Calculate A^2 and A^3. Do you see a pattern?)

44. Let a, b, and c be real numbers. If $ab = ac$ and $a \neq 0$, then $b = c$. Find 2×2 matrices A, B, and C, where $A \neq 0$, to show that such a law does not hold for all matrices.

45. In the real number system the numbers 0 and 1 are the only numbers that equal their own squares: if $a^2 = a$, then $a = 0$ or $a = 1$. Find a 2×2 matrix A that is neither the zero matrix nor the identity matrix, such that $A^2 = A \cdot A = A$.

46. Another property of the real numbers is that, if $ab = 0$, then either $a = 0$ or $b = 0$. To show that this property is not true for matrices, find two nonzero 2×2 matrices, A and B, such that $AB = 0$.

47. Multiplication of three $n \times n$ matrices is associative: $(AB)C = A(BC)$. Verify this by an example chosen from the set of 2×2 matrices.

48. If A is an $m \times n$ matrix and B and C are each $n \times p$ matrices, then $A(B + C) = AB + AC$. Illustrate this with an example showing that matrix multiplication distributes over matrix addition.

49. Prove that the addition of matrices is associative.

I.2 MATRIX INVERSION

Two real numbers are called **multiplicative inverses** if their product is the multiplicative identity 1. Some matrices have multiplicative inverses also.

Definition.   If A and B are $n \times n$ matrices, I is the $n \times n$ identity matrix, and

$$A \cdot B = B \cdot A = I$$

then A and B are called **multiplicative inverses**. Matrix A is the **inverse** of B, and B is the **inverse** of A.

It can be shown that the inverse of a matrix A, if it exists, is unique. The inverse of A is denoted by A^{-1}.

Example 1   If $A = \begin{bmatrix} 1 & 1 & 0 \\ 4 & 3 & 0 \\ 2 & 1 & -1 \end{bmatrix}$ and $B = \begin{bmatrix} -3 & 1 & 0 \\ 4 & -1 & 0 \\ -2 & 1 & -1 \end{bmatrix}$, show that A and B are inverses.

Solution   Multiply the matrices in each order to show that the product is the identity matrix.

$$AB = \begin{bmatrix} 1 & 1 & 0 \\ 4 & 3 & 0 \\ 2 & 1 & -1 \end{bmatrix}\begin{bmatrix} -3 & 1 & 0 \\ 4 & -1 & 0 \\ -2 & 1 & -1 \end{bmatrix}$$

$$= \begin{bmatrix} -3+4 & 1-1 & 0 \\ -12+12 & 4-3 & 0 \\ -6+4+2 & 2-1-1 & 1 \end{bmatrix} = \begin{bmatrix} 1 & 0 & 0 \\ 0 & 1 & 0 \\ 0 & 0 & 1 \end{bmatrix}$$

$$BA = \begin{bmatrix} -3 & 1 & 0 \\ 4 & -1 & 0 \\ -2 & 1 & -1 \end{bmatrix}\begin{bmatrix} 1 & 1 & 0 \\ 4 & 3 & 0 \\ 2 & 1 & -1 \end{bmatrix} = \begin{bmatrix} 1 & 0 & 0 \\ 0 & 1 & 0 \\ 0 & 0 & 1 \end{bmatrix}$$ ■

If a matrix has an inverse, it is called a **nonsingular matrix**. Otherwise, it is called a **singular matrix**. The following theorem, stated without proof, provides a way of calculating the inverse of a nonsingular matrix.

> **Theorem.**   If a sequence of elementary row operations performed on the $n \times n$ matrix A reduces A to the $n \times n$ identity matrix I, then those same row operations, performed in the same order on the identity matrix I, will transform I into A^{-1}. Furthermore, if *no* sequence of row operations will reduce A to I, then A is singular.

To use the previous theorem, we perform elementary row operations on matrix A to change it to the identity matrix I. At the same time, we perform these elementary row operations on the identity matrix I. This changes I into A^{-1}.

A notation for this process uses an n-row by $2n$-column matrix, with matrix A as the left half and matrix I as the right half. If A is nonsingular, the proper row operations performed on $[A \mid I]$ will transform it into $[I \mid A^{-1}]$.

Example 2   Find the inverse of matrix A if $A = \begin{bmatrix} 2 & -4 \\ 4 & -7 \end{bmatrix}$.

Solution   Set up a 2×4 matrix with A on the left and I on the right of the broken line:

$$[A \mid I] = \begin{bmatrix} 2 & -4 & \vdots & 1 & 0 \\ 4 & -7 & \vdots & 0 & 1 \end{bmatrix}$$

Perform row operations on the entire matrix to transform the left half into I. Begin by multiplying row 1 by $\frac{1}{2}$ to obtain a new row 1 ($\frac{1}{2}R1 \to R1$) and add -2 times row 1 to row 2 to obtain a new row 2 ($-2R1 + R2 \to R2$).

$$\begin{matrix} (\frac{1}{2})R1 \to R1 \\ (-2)R1 + R2 \to R2 \end{matrix}$$

$$\begin{bmatrix} 2 & -4 & \vdots & 1 & 0 \\ 4 & -7 & \vdots & 0 & 1 \end{bmatrix} \Leftrightarrow \begin{bmatrix} 1 & -2 & \vdots & \frac{1}{2} & 0 \\ 0 & 1 & \vdots & -2 & 1 \end{bmatrix}$$

$$(2)R2 + R1 \to R1$$

$$\Leftrightarrow \begin{bmatrix} 1 & 0 & \vdots & -\frac{7}{2} & 2 \\ 0 & 1 & \vdots & -2 & 1 \end{bmatrix}$$

Matrix A has been transformed into I. Thus, the right side of the previous matrix is A^{-1}. Verify this by finding AA^{-1} and $A^{-1}A$ and showing that each product is I:

$$AA^{-1} = \begin{bmatrix} 2 & -4 \\ 4 & -7 \end{bmatrix} \begin{bmatrix} -\frac{7}{2} & 2 \\ -2 & 1 \end{bmatrix} = \begin{bmatrix} 1 & 0 \\ 0 & 1 \end{bmatrix}$$

$$A^{-1}A = \begin{bmatrix} -\frac{7}{2} & 2 \\ -2 & 1 \end{bmatrix} \begin{bmatrix} 2 & -4 \\ 4 & -7 \end{bmatrix} = \begin{bmatrix} 1 & 0 \\ 0 & 1 \end{bmatrix}$$

■

Example 3   Find the inverse of matrix A if $A = \begin{bmatrix} 1 & 1 & 0 \\ 1 & 2 & 1 \\ 2 & 3 & 2 \end{bmatrix}$.

Solution   Set up a 3×6 matrix with A on the left and I on the right of the broken line:

$$[A \mid I] = \begin{bmatrix} 1 & 1 & 0 & \mid & 1 & 0 & 0 \\ 1 & 2 & 1 & \mid & 0 & 1 & 0 \\ 2 & 3 & 2 & \mid & 0 & 0 & 1 \end{bmatrix}$$

Perform row operations on the entire matrix to transform the left half into I.

$$(-1)R1 + R2 \rightarrow R2$$
$$(-2)R1 + R3 \rightarrow R3$$

$$\begin{bmatrix} 1 & 1 & 0 & \mid & 1 & 0 & 0 \\ 1 & 2 & 1 & \mid & 0 & 1 & 0 \\ 2 & 3 & 2 & \mid & 0 & 0 & 1 \end{bmatrix} \Leftrightarrow \begin{bmatrix} 1 & 1 & 0 & \mid & 1 & 0 & 0 \\ 0 & 1 & 1 & \mid & -1 & 1 & 0 \\ 0 & 1 & 2 & \mid & -2 & 0 & 1 \end{bmatrix}$$

$$(-1)R2 + R1 \rightarrow R1$$
$$(-1)R2 + R3 \rightarrow R3$$

$$\Leftrightarrow \begin{bmatrix} 1 & 0 & -1 & \mid & 2 & -1 & 0 \\ 0 & 1 & 1 & \mid & -1 & 1 & 0 \\ 0 & 0 & 1 & \mid & -1 & -1 & 1 \end{bmatrix}$$

$$R3 + R1 \rightarrow R1$$
$$(-1)R3 + R2 \rightarrow R2$$

$$\Leftrightarrow \begin{bmatrix} 1 & 0 & 0 & \mid & 1 & -2 & 1 \\ 0 & 1 & 0 & \mid & 0 & 2 & -1 \\ 0 & 0 & 1 & \mid & -1 & -1 & 1 \end{bmatrix}$$

The left half has been transformed into the identity matrix, and the right half has become A^{-1}. Thus,

$$A^{-1} = \begin{bmatrix} 1 & -2 & 1 \\ 0 & 2 & -1 \\ -1 & -1 & 1 \end{bmatrix}$$ ∎

Example 4   Find the inverse of $A = \begin{bmatrix} 1 & 2 \\ 2 & 4 \end{bmatrix}$, if possible.

Solution   Form the 2×4 matrix

$$[A \mid I] = \begin{bmatrix} 1 & 2 & \mid & 1 & 0 \\ 2 & 4 & \mid & 0 & 1 \end{bmatrix}$$

and begin to transform the left side of the matrix into the identity matrix I:

$$(-2)R1 + R2 \rightarrow R2$$

$$\begin{bmatrix} 1 & 2 & \mid & 1 & 0 \\ 2 & 4 & \mid & 0 & 1 \end{bmatrix} \Leftrightarrow \begin{bmatrix} 1 & 2 & \mid & 1 & 0 \\ 0 & 0 & \mid & -2 & 1 \end{bmatrix}$$

In obtaining the second-row, first-column position of A, the entire second row of A is "zeroed out." Because it is impossible to transform A to the identity, matrix A is singular and has no inverse. ∎

The next example shows how the inverse of a nonsingular matrix can be used to solve a system of equations.

Example 5   Solve the system

$$\begin{cases} x + y = 3 \\ x + 2y + z = -2 \\ 2x + 3y + 2z = 1 \end{cases}$$

Solution   This system can be written as a single equation involving three matrices.

$$\mathbf{1.} \quad \begin{bmatrix} 1 & 1 & 0 \\ 1 & 2 & 1 \\ 2 & 3 & 2 \end{bmatrix} \begin{bmatrix} x \\ y \\ z \end{bmatrix} = \begin{bmatrix} 3 \\ -2 \\ 1 \end{bmatrix}$$

The 3×3 matrix on the left is the matrix whose inverse was found in Example 3. Multiply each side of Equation 1 on the left by this inverse to obtain an equivalent system of equations. The solution of this system can be read directly from the matrix to the right of the equals sign:

$$\begin{bmatrix} 1 & -2 & 1 \\ 0 & 2 & -1 \\ -1 & -1 & 1 \end{bmatrix} \begin{bmatrix} 1 & 1 & 0 \\ 1 & 2 & 1 \\ 2 & 3 & 2 \end{bmatrix} \begin{bmatrix} x \\ y \\ z \end{bmatrix} = \begin{bmatrix} 1 & -2 & 1 \\ 0 & 2 & -1 \\ -1 & -1 & 1 \end{bmatrix} \begin{bmatrix} 3 \\ -2 \\ 1 \end{bmatrix}$$

$$\begin{bmatrix} 1 & 0 & 0 \\ 0 & 1 & 0 \\ 0 & 0 & 1 \end{bmatrix} \begin{bmatrix} x \\ y \\ z \end{bmatrix} = \begin{bmatrix} 8 \\ -5 \\ 0 \end{bmatrix}$$

$$\begin{bmatrix} x \\ y \\ z \end{bmatrix} = \begin{bmatrix} 8 \\ -5 \\ 0 \end{bmatrix}$$

The solution of this system of equations is $x = 8$, $y = -5$, $z = 0$. Verify that these results satisfy all three of the original equations. ∎

The equations of Example 5 can be thought of as the matrix equation $AX = B$, where A is the coefficient matrix,

$$A = \begin{bmatrix} 1 & 1 & 0 \\ 1 & 2 & 1 \\ 2 & 3 & 2 \end{bmatrix}$$

X is a column matrix of the variables,

$$X = \begin{bmatrix} x \\ y \\ z \end{bmatrix}$$

and B is a column matrix of the constants from the right sides of the equations.

$$B = \begin{bmatrix} 3 \\ -2 \\ 1 \end{bmatrix}$$

When each side of $AX = B$ is multiplied on the left by A^{-1}, the solution of the system appears as the column of numbers in the matrix that is the product of A^{-1} and B:

$$A^{-1}AX = A^{-1}B$$
$$IX = A^{-1}B$$
$$X = A^{-1}B$$

This method is especially useful for finding solutions of several systems of equations that differ from each other *only* in the column matrix B. If the coefficient matrix A remains unchanged from one system of equations to the next, then A^{-1} needs to be found only once. The solution of each system is found by a single matrix multiplication, $A^{-1}B$.

■ EXERCISE I.2

In Exercises 1–16, find the inverse of each given matrix, if possible.

1. $\begin{bmatrix} 3 & -4 \\ -2 & 3 \end{bmatrix}$ **2.** $\begin{bmatrix} 2 & 3 \\ 3 & 5 \end{bmatrix}$ **3.** $\begin{bmatrix} 3 & 7 \\ 2 & 5 \end{bmatrix}$ **4.** $\begin{bmatrix} 1 & -2 \\ 2 & -5 \end{bmatrix}$

5. $\begin{bmatrix} 1 & 2 & 3 \\ 2 & 5 & 3 \\ 1 & 0 & 8 \end{bmatrix}$ **6.** $\begin{bmatrix} 2 & 1 & -1 \\ 2 & 2 & -1 \\ -1 & -1 & 1 \end{bmatrix}$

7. $\begin{bmatrix} 3 & 2 & 1 \\ 1 & 1 & -1 \\ 4 & 3 & 1 \end{bmatrix}$ **8.** $\begin{bmatrix} -2 & 1 & -3 \\ 2 & 3 & 0 \\ 1 & 0 & 1 \end{bmatrix}$

9. $\begin{bmatrix} 1 & 3 & 5 \\ 0 & 1 & 6 \\ 1 & 4 & 11 \end{bmatrix}$ **10.** $\begin{bmatrix} 1 & 1 & 1 \\ 2 & 2 & 2 \\ 3 & 3 & 3 \end{bmatrix}$

11. $\begin{bmatrix} 1 & 2 & 3 \\ 0 & 1 & 2 \\ 0 & 0 & 1 \end{bmatrix}$ **12.** $\begin{bmatrix} 1 & 2 & 3 \\ 0 & 1 & 1 \\ 0 & -1 & 0 \end{bmatrix}$

13. $\begin{bmatrix} 1 & 6 & 4 \\ 1 & -2 & -5 \\ 2 & 4 & -1 \end{bmatrix}$ **14.** $\begin{bmatrix} 1 & 1 & 1 \\ 1 & 0 & -1 \\ 1 & 2 & 3 \end{bmatrix}$

15. $\begin{bmatrix} 1 & 2 & 3 & 4 \\ 0 & 1 & 2 & 3 \\ 0 & 0 & 1 & 2 \\ 0 & 0 & 0 & 1 \end{bmatrix}$ **16.** $\begin{bmatrix} 1 & 0 & 0 & 0 \\ 1 & 1 & 0 & 0 \\ 1 & 1 & 1 & 0 \\ 1 & 2 & 2 & 1 \end{bmatrix}$

In Exercises 17–26, use the method of Example 5 to solve each system of equations.

17. $\begin{cases} 3x - 4y = 1 \\ -2x + 3y = 5 \end{cases}$ **18.** $\begin{cases} 2x + 3y = 7 \\ 3x + 5y = -5 \end{cases}$ **19.** $\begin{cases} 3x + 7y = 0 \\ 2x + 5y = -10 \end{cases}$ **20.** $\begin{cases} x - 2y = 12 \\ 2x - 5y = 13 \end{cases}$

21. $\begin{cases} x + 2y + 3z = 1 \\ 2x + 5y + 3z = 3 \\ x \quad\quad + 8z = -2 \end{cases}$ **22.** $\begin{cases} 2x + y - z = 3 \\ 2x + 2y - z = -1 \\ -x - y + z = 4 \end{cases}$

23. $\begin{cases} 3x + 2y + z = 2 \\ x + y - z = -1 \\ 4x + 3y + z = 0 \end{cases}$ **24.** $\begin{cases} -2x + y - 3z = 5 \\ 2x + 3y \quad\quad = 1 \\ x \quad\quad + z = -2 \end{cases}$

25. $\begin{cases} x + 2y + 3z = 1 \\ 2x + 2y + 2z = 2x + y \\ \quad\quad\quad z = 3 \end{cases}$ **26.** $\begin{cases} x + 2y + 3z = 2 \\ x + y + z = x \\ x - y \quad\quad = x \end{cases}$

27. If the $n \times n$ matrix A is nonsingular, and if B and C are $n \times n$ matrices such that $AB = AC$, prove that $B = C$.

28. If B is an $n \times n$ matrix that behaves as an identity ($AB = BA = A$, for any $n \times n$ matrix A), prove that $B = I$.

29. If $A = \begin{bmatrix} 0 & 1 \\ 1 & 0 \end{bmatrix}$, compute A^2, A^3, A^4, ... Give a general rule for A^n, where n is a natural number.

30. If A and B are 2×2 matrices, is $(AB)^2 = A^2B^2$? Support your answer.

31. Prove that $\begin{bmatrix} a & b \\ c & d \end{bmatrix}$ has an inverse if and only if $ad - bc \neq 0$.

32. If $A = \begin{bmatrix} 1 & 1 \\ 0 & 1 \end{bmatrix}$, compute A^n for various values of n ($n = 2, 3, 4, \ldots$). What do you notice?

33. If $A = \begin{bmatrix} 1 & 0 \\ 1 & 1 \end{bmatrix}$, compute A^n for various values of n ($n = 2, 3, 4, \ldots$). What do you notice?

34. For what value of x will $\begin{bmatrix} 3 & 8 \\ 6 & x \end{bmatrix}$ not have a multiplicative inverse? (*Hint:*   See Exercise 31.)

35. For what values of x will $\begin{bmatrix} x & 8 \\ 2 & x \end{bmatrix}$ not have a multiplicative inverse?

36. Does $(AB)^{-1} = A^{-1}B^{-1}$? Support your answer with an example chosen from 2×2 matrices.

37. Use an example chosen from 2×2 matrices to illustrate that $(AB)^{-1} = B^{-1}A^{-1}$.

38. Let A be any 3×3 matrix. Find a 3×3 matrix E such that the product EA is the result of performing the row operation $R1 \leftrightarrow R2$ on matrix A (the row operation that exchanges rows one and two of matrix A). What is E^{-1}?

39. Let A be any 3×3 matrix. Find another 3×3 matrix E such that the product EA is the result of performing the row operation $(3)R1 + R3 \to R3$ on matrix A. What is E^{-1}?

APPENDIX: TABLES

Table A Powers and Roots

n	n^2	$\sqrt{n}$	n^3	$\sqrt[3]{n}$	n	n^2	$\sqrt{n}$	n^3	$\sqrt[3]{n}$
1	1	1.000	1	1.000	51	2,601	7.141	132,651	3.708
2	4	1.414	8	1.260	52	2,704	7.211	140,608	3.733
3	9	1.732	27	1.442	53	2,809	7.280	148,877	3.756
4	16	2.000	64	1.587	54	2,916	7.348	157,464	3.780
5	25	2.236	125	1.710	55	3,025	7.416	166,375	3.803
6	36	2.449	216	1.817	56	3,136	7.483	175,616	3.826
7	49	2.646	343	1.913	57	3,249	7.550	185,193	3.849
8	64	2.828	512	2.000	58	3,364	7.616	195,112	3.871
9	81	3.000	729	2.080	59	3,481	7.681	205,379	3.893
10	100	3.162	1,000	2.154	60	3,600	7.746	216,000	3.915
11	121	3.317	1,331	2.224	61	3,721	7.810	226,981	3.936
12	144	3.464	1,728	2.289	62	3,844	7.874	238,328	3.958
13	169	3.606	2,197	2.351	63	3,969	7.937	250,047	3.979
14	196	3.742	2,744	2.410	64	4,096	8.000	262,144	4.000
15	225	3.873	3,375	2.466	65	4,225	8.062	274,625	4.021
16	256	4.000	4,096	2.520	66	4,356	8.124	287,496	4.041
17	289	4.123	4,913	2.571	67	4,489	8.185	300,763	4.062
18	324	4.243	5,832	2.621	68	4,624	8.246	314,432	4.082
19	361	4.359	6,859	2.668	69	4,761	8.307	328,509	4.102
20	400	4.472	8,000	2.714	70	4,900	8.367	343,000	4.121
21	441	4.583	9,261	2.759	71	5,041	8.426	357,911	4.141
22	484	4.690	10,648	2.802	72	5,184	8.485	373,248	4.160
23	529	4.796	12,167	2.844	73	5,329	8.544	389,017	4.179
24	576	4.899	13,824	2.884	74	5,476	8.602	405,224	4.198
25	625	5.000	15,625	2.924	75	5,625	8.660	421,875	4.217
26	676	5.099	17,576	2.962	76	5,776	8.718	438,976	4.236
27	729	5.196	19,683	3.000	77	5,929	8.775	456,533	4.254
28	784	5.292	21,952	3.037	78	6,084	8.832	474,552	4.273
29	841	5.385	24,389	3.072	79	6,241	8.888	493,039	4.291
30	900	5.477	27,000	3.107	80	6,400	8.944	512,000	4.309
31	961	5.568	29,791	3.141	81	6,561	9.000	531,441	4.327
32	1,024	5.657	32,768	3.175	82	6,724	9.055	551,368	4.344
33	1,089	5.745	35,937	3.208	83	6,889	9.110	571,787	4.362
34	1,156	5.831	39,304	3.240	84	7,056	9.165	592,704	4.380
35	1,225	5.916	42,875	3.271	85	7,225	9.220	614,125	4.397
36	1,296	6.000	46,656	3.302	86	7,396	9.274	636,056	4.414
37	1,369	6.083	50,653	3.332	87	7,569	9.327	658,503	4.431
38	1,444	6.164	54,872	3.362	88	7,744	9.381	681,472	4.448
39	1,521	6.245	59,319	3.391	89	7,921	9.434	704,969	4.465
40	1,600	6.325	64,000	3.420	90	8,100	9.487	729,000	4.481
41	1,681	6.403	68,921	3.448	91	8,281	9.539	753,571	4.498
42	1,764	6.481	74,088	3.476	92	8,464	9.592	778,688	4.514
43	1,849	6.557	79,507	3.503	93	8,649	9.644	804,357	4.531
44	1,936	6.633	85,184	3.530	94	8,836	9.695	830,584	4.547
45	2,025	6.708	91,125	3.557	95	9,025	9.747	857,375	4.563
46	2,116	6.782	97,336	3.583	96	9,216	9.798	884,736	4.579
47	2,209	6.856	103,823	3.609	97	9,409	9.849	912,673	4.595
48	2,304	6.928	110,592	3.634	98	9,604	9.899	941,192	4.610
49	2,401	7.000	117,649	3.659	99	9,801	9.950	970,299	4.626
50	2,500	7.071	125,000	3.684	100	10,000	10.000	1,000,000	4.642

Table B Base-10 Logarithms

N	0	1	2	3	4	5	6	7	8	9
1.0	.0000	.0043	.0086	.0128	.0170	.0212	.0253	.0294	.0334	.0374
1.1	.0414	.0453	.0492	.0531	.0569	.0607	.0645	.0682	.0719	.0755
1.2	.0792	.0828	.0864	.0899	.0934	.0969	.1004	.1038	.1072	.1106
1.3	.1139	.1173	.1206	.1239	.1271	.1303	.1335	.1367	.1399	.1430
1.4	.1461	.1492	.1523	.1553	.1584	.1614	.1644	.1673	.1703	.1732
1.5	.1761	.1790	.1818	.1847	.1875	.1903	.1931	.1959	.1987	.2014
1.6	.2041	.2068	.2095	.2122	.2148	.2175	.2201	.2227	.2253	.2279
1.7	.2304	.2330	.2355	.2380	.2405	.2430	.2455	.2480	.2504	.2529
1.8	.2553	.2577	.2601	.2625	.2648	.2672	.2695	.2718	.2742	.2765
1.9	.2788	.2810	.2833	.2856	.2878	.2900	.2923	.2945	.2967	.2989
2.0	.3010	.3032	.3054	.3075	.3096	.3118	.3139	.3160	.3181	.3201
2.1	.3222	.3243	.3263	.3284	.3304	.3324	.3345	.3365	.3385	.3404
2.2	.3424	.3444	.3464	.3483	.3502	.3522	.3541	.3560	.3579	.3598
2.3	.3617	.3636	.3655	.3674	.3692	.3711	.3729	.3747	.3766	.3784
2.4	.3802	.3820	.3838	.3856	.3874	.3892	.3909	.3927	.3945	.3962
2.5	.3979	.3997	.4014	.4031	.4048	.4065	.4082	.4099	.4116	.4133
2.6	.4150	.4166	.4183	.4200	.4216	.4232	.4249	.4265	.4281	.4298
2.7	.4314	.4330	.4346	.4362	.4378	.4393	.4409	.4425	.4440	.4456
2.8	.4472	.4487	.4502	.4518	.4533	.4548	.4564	.4579	.4594	.4609
2.9	.4624	.4639	.4654	.4669	.4683	.4698	.4713	.4728	.4742	.4757
3.0	.4771	.4786	.4800	.4814	.4829	.4843	.4857	.4871	.4886	.4900
3.1	.4914	.4928	.4942	.4955	.4969	.4983	.4997	.5011	.5024	.5038
3.2	.5051	.5065	.5079	.5092	.5105	.5119	.5132	.5145	.5159	.5172
3.3	.5185	.5198	.5211	.5224	.5237	.5250	.5263	.5276	.5289	.5302
3.4	.5315	.5328	.5340	.5353	.5366	.5378	.5391	.5403	.5416	.5428
3.5	.5441	.5453	.5465	.5478	.5490	.5502	.5514	.5527	.5539	.5551
3.6	.5563	.5575	.5587	.5599	.5611	.5623	.5635	.5647	.5658	.5670
3.7	.5682	.5694	.5705	.5717	.5729	.5740	.5752	.5763	.5775	.5786
3.8	.5798	.5809	.5821	.5832	.5843	.5855	.5866	.5877	.5888	.5899
3.9	.5911	.5922	.5933	.5944	.5955	.5966	.5977	.5988	.5999	.6010
4.0	.6021	.6031	.6042	.6053	.6064	.6075	.6085	.6096	.6107	.6117
4.1	.6128	.6138	.6149	.6160	.6170	.6180	.6191	.6201	.6212	.6222
4.2	.6232	.6243	.6253	.6263	.6274	.6284	.6294	.6304	.6314	.6325
4.3	.6335	.6345	.6355	.6365	.6375	.6385	.6395	.6405	.6415	.6425
4.4	.6435	.6444	.6454	.6464	.6474	.6484	.6493	.6503	.6513	.6522
4.5	.6532	.6542	.6551	.6561	.6571	.6580	.6590	.6599	.6609	.6618
4.6	.6628	.6637	.6646	.6656	.6665	.6675	.6684	.6693	.6702	.6712
4.7	.6721	.6730	.6739	.6749	.6758	.6767	.6776	.6785	.6794	.6803
4.8	.6812	.6821	.6830	.6839	.6848	.6857	.6866	.6875	.6884	.6893
4.9	.6902	.6911	.6920	.6928	.6937	.6946	.6955	.6964	.6972	.6981
5.0	.6990	.6998	.7007	.7016	.7024	.7033	.7042	.7050	.7059	.7067
5.1	.7076	.7084	.7093	.7101	.7110	.7118	.7126	.7135	.7143	.7152
5.2	.7160	.7168	.7177	.7185	.7193	.7202	.7210	.7218	.7226	.7235
5.3	.7243	.7251	.7259	.7267	.7275	.7284	.7292	.7300	.7308	.7316
5.4	.7324	.7332	.7340	.7348	.7356	.7364	.7372	.7380	.7388	.7396

Table B (Continued)

N	0	1	2	3	4	5	6	7	8	9
5.5	.7404	.7412	.7419	.7427	.7435	.7443	.7451	.7459	.7466	.7474
5.6	.7482	.7490	.7497	.7505	.7513	.7520	.7528	.7536	.7543	.7551
5.7	.7559	.7566	.7574	.7582	.7589	.7597	.7604	.7612	.7619	.7627
5.8	.7634	.7642	.7649	.7657	.7664	.7672	.7679	.7686	.7694	.7701
5.9	.7709	.7716	.7723	.7731	.7738	.7745	.7752	.7760	.7767	.7774
6.0	.7782	.7789	.7796	.7803	.7810	.7818	.7825	.7832	.7839	.7846
6.1	.7853	.7860	.7868	.7875	.7882	.7889	.7896	.7903	.7910	.7917
6.2	.7924	.7931	.7938	.7945	.7952	.7959	.7966	.7973	.7980	.7987
6.3	.7993	.8000	.8007	.8014	.8021	.8028	.8035	.8041	.8048	.8055
6.4	.8062	.8069	.8075	.8082	.8089	.8096	.8102	.8109	.8116	.8122
6.5	.8129	.8136	.8142	.8149	.8156	.8162	.8169	.8176	.8182	.8189
6.6	.8195	.8202	.8209	.8215	.8222	.8228	.8235	.8241	.8248	.8254
6.7	.8261	.8267	.8274	.8280	.8287	.8293	.8299	.8306	.8312	.8319
6.8	.8325	.8331	.8338	.8344	.8351	.8357	.8363	.8370	.8376	.8382
6.9	.8388	.8395	.8401	.8407	.8414	.8420	.8426	.8432	.8439	.8445
7.0	.8451	.8457	.8463	.8470	.8476	.8482	.8488	.8494	.8500	.8506
7.1	.8513	.8519	.8525	.8531	.8537	.8543	.8549	.8555	.8561	.8567
7.2	.8573	.8579	.8585	.8591	.8597	.8603	.8609	.8615	.8621	.8627
7.3	.8633	.8639	.8645	.8651	.8657	.8663	.8669	.8675	.8681	.8686
7.4	.8692	.8698	.8704	.8710	.8716	.8722	.8727	.8733	.8739	.8745
7.5	.8751	.8756	.8762	.8768	.8774	.8779	.8785	.8791	.8797	.8802
7.6	.8808	.8814	.8820	.8825	.8831	.8837	.8842	.8848	.8854	.8859
7.7	.8865	.8871	.8876	.8882	.8887	.8893	.8899	.8904	.8910	.8915
7.8	.8921	.8927	.8932	.8938	.8943	.8949	.8954	.8960	.8965	.8971
7.9	.8976	.8982	.8987	.8993	.8998	.9004	.9009	.9015	.9020	.9025
8.0	.9031	.9036	.9042	.9047	.9053	.9058	.9063	.9069	.9074	.9079
8.1	.9085	.9090	.9096	.9101	.9106	.9112	.9117	.9122	.9128	.9133
8.2	.9138	.9143	.9149	.9154	.9159	.9165	.9170	.9175	.9180	.9186
8.3	.9191	.9196	.9201	.9206	.9212	.9217	.9222	.9227	.9232	.9238
8.4	.9243	.9248	.9253	.9258	.9263	.9269	.9274	.9279	.9284	.9289
8.5	.9294	.9299	.9304	.9309	.9315	.9320	.9325	.9330	.9335	.9340
8.6	.9345	.9350	.9355	.9360	.9365	.9370	.9375	.9380	.9385	.9390
8.7	.9395	.9400	.9405	.9410	.9415	.9420	.9425	.9430	.9435	.9440
8.8	.9445	.9450	.9455	.9460	.9465	.9469	.9474	.9479	.9484	.9489
8.9	.9494	.9499	.9504	.9509	.9513	.9518	.9523	.9528	.9533	.9538
9.0	.9542	.9547	.9552	.9557	.9562	.9566	.9571	.9576	.9581	.9586
9.1	.9590	.9595	.9600	.9605	.9609	.9614	.9619	.9624	.9628	.9633
9.2	.9638	.9643	.9647	.9652	.9657	.9661	.9666	.9671	.9675	.9680
9.3	.9685	.9689	.9694	.9699	.9703	.9708	.9713	.9717	.9722	.9727
9.4	.9731	.9736	.9741	.9745	.9750	.9754	.9759	.9763	.9768	.9773
9.5	.9777	.9782	.9786	.9791	.9795	.9800	.9805	.9809	.9814	.9818
9.6	.9823	.9827	.9832	.9836	.9841	.9845	.9850	.9854	.9859	.9863
9.7	.9868	.9872	.9877	.9881	.9886	.9890	.9894	.9899	.9903	.9908
9.8	.9912	.9917	.9921	.9926	.9930	.9934	.9939	.9943	.9948	.9952
9.9	.9956	.9961	.9965	.9969	.9974	.9978	.9983	.9987	.9991	.9996

Table C (Continued)

N	0	1	2	3	4	5	6	7	8	9
5.5	1.7047	.7066	.7084	.7102	.7120	.7138	.7156	.7174	.7192	.7210
5.6	.7228	.7246	.7263	.7281	.7299	.7317	.7334	.7352	.7370	.7387
5.7	.7405	.7422	.7440	.7457	.7475	.7492	.7509	.7527	.7544	.7561
5.8	.7579	.7596	.7613	.7630	.7647	.7664	.7681	.7699	.7716	.7733
5.9	.7750	.7766	.7783	.7800	.7817	.7834	.7851	.7867	.7884	.7901
6.0	1.7918	.7934	.7951	.7967	.7984	.8001	.8017	.8034	.8050	.8066
6.1	.8083	.8099	.8116	.8132	.8148	.8165	.8181	.8197	.8213	.8229
6.2	.8245	.8262	.8278	.8294	.8310	.8326	.8342	.8358	.8374	.8390
6.3	.8405	.8421	.8437	.8453	.8469	.8485	.8500	.8516	.8532	.8547
6.4	.8563	.8579	.8594	.8610	.8625	.8641	.8656	.8672	.8687	.8703
6.5	1.8718	.8733	.8749	.8764	.8779	.8795	.8810	.8825	.8840	.8856
6.6	.8871	.8886	.8901	.8916	.8931	.8946	.8961	.8976	.8991	.9006
6.7	.9021	.9036	.9051	.9066	.9081	.9095	.9110	.9125	.9140	.9155
6.8	.9169	.9184	.9199	.9213	.9228	.9242	.9257	.9272	.9286	.9301
6.9	.9315	.9330	.9344	.9359	.9373	.9387	.9402	.9416	.9430	.9445
7.0	1.9459	.9473	.9488	.9502	.9516	.9530	.9544	.9559	.9573	.9587
7.1	.9601	.9615	.9629	.9643	.9657	.9671	.9685	.9699	.9713	.9727
7.2	.9741	.9755	.9769	.9782	.9796	.9810	.9824	.9838	.9851	.9865
7.3	.9879	.9892	.9906	.9920	.9933	.9947	.9961	.9974	.9988	2.0001
7.4	2.0015	.0028	.0042	.0055	.0069	.0082	.0096	.0109	.0122	.0136
7.5	2.0149	.0162	.0176	.0189	.0202	.0215	.0229	.0242	.0255	.0268
7.6	.0281	.0295	.0308	.0321	.0334	.0347	.0360	.0373	.0386	.0399
7.7	.0412	.0425	.0438	.0451	.0464	.0477	.0490	.0503	.0516	.0528
7.8	.0541	.0554	.0567	.0580	.0592	.0605	.0618	.0631	.0643	.0656
7.9	.0669	.0681	.0694	.0707	.0719	.0732	.0744	.0757	.0769	.0782
8.0	2.0794	.0807	.0819	.0832	.0844	.0857	.0869	.0882	.0894	.0906
8.1	.0919	.0931	.0943	.0956	.0968	.0980	.0992	.1005	.1017	.1029
8.2	.1041	.1054	.1066	.1078	.1090	.1102	.1114	.1126	.1138	.1150
8.3	.1163	.1175	.1187	.1199	.1211	.1223	.1235	.1247	.1258	.1270
8.4	.1282	.1294	.1306	.1318	.1330	.1342	.1353	.1365	.1377	.1389
8.5	2.1401	.1412	.1424	.1436	.1448	.1459	.1471	.1483	.1494	.1506
8.6	.1518	.1529	.1541	.1552	.1564	.1576	.1587	.1599	.1610	.1622
8.7	.1633	.1645	.1656	.1668	.1679	.1691	.1702	.1713	.1725	.1736
8.8	.1748	.1759	.1770	.1782	.1793	.1804	.1815	.1827	.1838	.1849
8.9	.1861	.1872	.1883	.1894	.1905	.1917	.1928	.1939	.1950	.1961
9.0	2.1972	.1983	.1994	.2006	.2017	.2028	.2039	.2050	.2061	.2072
9.1	.2083	.2094	.2105	.2116	.2127	.2138	.2148	.2159	.2170	.2181
9.2	.2192	.2203	.2214	.2225	.2235	.2246	.2257	.2268	.2279	.2289
9.3	.2300	.2311	.2322	.2332	.2343	.2354	.2364	.2375	.2386	.2396
9.4	.2407	.2418	.2428	.2439	.2450	.2460	.2471	.2481	.2492	.2502
9.5	2.2513	.2523	.2534	.2544	.2555	.2565	.2576	.2586	.2597	.2607
9.6	.2618	.2628	.2638	.2649	.2659	.2670	.2680	.2690	.2701	.2711
9.7	.2721	.2732	.2742	.2752	.2762	.2773	.2783	.2793	.2803	.2814
9.8	.2824	.2834	.2844	.2854	.2865	.2875	.2885	.2895	.2905	.2915
9.9	.2925	.2935	.2946	.2956	.2966	.2976	.2986	.2996	.3006	.3016

Use the properties of logarithms and ln 10 ≈ 2.3026 to find logarithms of numbers less than 1 or greater than 10.

Table C   Base e Logarithms

N	0	1	2	3	4	5	6	7	8	9
1.0	0.0000	.0100	.0198	.0296	.0392	.0488	.0583	.0677	.0770	.0862
1.1	.0953	.1044	.1133	.1222	.1310	.1398	.1484	.1570	.1655	.1740
1.2	.1823	.1906	.1989	.2070	.2151	.2231	.2311	.2390	.2469	.2546
1.3	.2624	.2700	.2776	.2852	.2927	.3001	.3075	.3148	.3221	.3293
1.4	.3365	.3436	.3507	.3577	.3646	.3716	.3784	.3853	.3920	.3988
1.5	.4055	.4121	.4187	.4253	.4318	.4383	.4447	.4511	.4574	.4637
1.6	.4700	.4762	.4824	.4886	.4947	.5008	.5068	.5128	.5188	.5247
1.7	.5306	.5365	.5423	.5481	.5539	.5596	.5653	.5710	.5766	.5822
1.8	.5878	.5933	.5988	.6043	.6098	.6152	.6206	.6259	.6313	.6366
1.9	.6419	.6471	.6523	.6575	.6627	.6678	.6729	.6780	.6831	.6881
2.0	.6931	.6981	.7031	.7080	.7129	.7178	.7227	.7275	.7324	.7372
2.1	.7419	.7467	.7514	.7561	.7608	.7655	.7701	.7747	.7793	.7839
2.2	.7885	.7930	.7975	.8020	.8065	.8109	.8154	.8198	.8242	.8286
2.3	.8329	.8372	.8416	.8459	.8502	.8544	.8587	.8629	.8671	.8713
2.4	.8755	.8796	.8838	.8879	.8920	.8961	.9002	.9042	.9083	.9123
2.5	.9163	.9203	.9243	.9282	.9322	.9361	.9400	.9439	.9478	.9517
2.6	.9555	.9594	.9632	.9670	.9708	.9746	.9783	.9821	.9858	.9895
2.7	.9933	.9969	1.0006	.0043	.0080	.0116	.0152	.0188	.0225	.0260
2.8	1.0296	.0332	.0367	.0403	.0438	.0473	.0508	.0543	.0578	.0613
2.9	.0647	.0682	.0716	.0750	.0784	.0818	.0852	.0886	.0919	.0953
3.0	1.0986	.1019	.1053	.1086	.1119	.1151	.1184	.1217	.1249	.1282
3.1	.1314	.1346	.1378	.1410	.1442	.1474	.1506	.1537	.1569	.1600
3.2	.1632	.1663	.1694	.1725	.1756	.1787	.1817	.1848	.1878	.1909
3.3	.1939	.1969	.2000	.2030	.2060	.2090	.2119	.2149	.2179	.2208
3.4	.2238	.2267	.2296	.2326	.2355	.2384	.2413	.2442	.2470	.2499
3.5	1.2528	.2556	.2585	.2613	.2641	.2669	.2698	.2726	.2754	.2782
3.6	.2809	.2837	.2865	.2892	.2920	.2947	.2975	.3002	.3029	.3056
3.7	.3083	.3110	.3137	.3164	.3191	.3218	.3244	.3271	.3297	.3324
3.8	.3350	.3376	.3403	.3429	.3455	.3481	.3507	.3533	.3558	.3584
3.9	.3610	.3635	.3661	.3686	.3712	.3737	.3762	.3788	.3813	.3838
4.0	1.3863	.3888	.3913	.3938	.3962	.3987	.4012	.4036	.4061	.4085
4.1	.4110	.4134	.4159	.4183	.4207	.4231	.4255	.4279	.4303	.4327
4.2	.4351	.4375	.4398	.4422	.4446	.4469	.4493	.4516	.4540	.4563
4.3	.4586	.4609	.4633	.4656	.4679	.4702	.4725	.4748	.4770	.4793
4.4	.4816	.4839	.4861	.4884	.4907	.4929	.4951	.4974	.4996	.5019
4.5	1.5041	.5063	.5085	.5107	.5129	.5151	.5173	.5195	.5217	.5239
4.6	.5261	.5282	.5304	.5326	.5347	.5369	.5390	.5412	.5433	.5454
4.7	.5476	.5497	.5518	.5539	.5560	.5581	.5602	.5623	.5644	.5665
4.8	.5686	.5707	.5728	.5748	.5769	.5790	.5810	.5831	.5851	.5872
4.9	.5892	.5913	.5933	.5953	.5974	.5994	.6014	.6034	.6054	.6074
5.0	1.6094	.6114	.6134	.6154	.6174	.6194	.6214	.6233	.6253	.6273
5.1	.6292	.6312	.6332	.6351	.6371	.6390	.6409	.6429	.6448	.6467
5.2	.6487	.6506	.6525	.6544	.6563	.6582	.6601	.6620	.6639	.6658
5.3	.6677	.6696	.6715	.6734	.6752	.6771	.6790	.6808	.6827	.6845
5.4	.6864	.6882	.6901	.6919	.6938	.6956	.6974	.6993	.7011	.7029

Exercise 1.1   (page 6)

1. $\subseteq$ **3.** $\in$ **5.** $\subseteq$ **7.** 2, 3, 5, 7   **9.** No such numbers
11. {2, 3, 4, 5, 6, 7, 8, 10}   **13.** $\varnothing$ **15.** $\varnothing$ **17.** {3, 5, 7}   **19.** infinite   **21.** finite
23. infinite   **25.** natural number, whole number, integer, rational number, real number
27. whole number, integer, rational number, real number   **29.** rational number, real number
31. rational number, real number   **33.** natural number, whole number, integer, rational number, real number
35. irrational number, real number   **37.** even integer, composite number   **39.** odd integer
41. even integer, prime number   **43.** even integer   **45.** odd integer, composite number
47. even integer   **49.** true; $4 \times 5 = 20$ **51.** False;   0 is a whole number but not a natural number.
53. False; $3 + 5 = 8$ and 8 is a composite.   **55.** true; $6 + 8 = 14$
57. false; $5 + 9 = 14$ and 14 is even.   **59.** false; $4 + 9 = 13$ and 13 is prime.
61. true; $5 \times 11 = 55$ **63.** true; $0 + 8 = 8$
65. true;   all other even natural numbers are divisible by 2.   **67.** true; $7 = \frac{7}{1} = \frac{14}{2} = \frac{21}{3}$, and so on
69. 0.875;   terminating decimal   **71.** $-0.733\ldots$;   repeating decimal   **73.** $\frac{1}{2}$ **75.** $\frac{3}{4}$

Exercise 1.2   (page 13)

1. $=$ **3.** $\neq$ **5.** symmetric property of equality   **7.** reflexive property of equality
9. transitive property of equality   **11.** substitution property of equality
13. $5 + (2 + x) = (5 + 2) + x = 7 + x$ **15.** $5(3b) = (5 \cdot 3)b = 15b$
17. $(3 + b) + 7 = 7 + (3 + b) = (7 + 3) + b = 10 + b$ **19.** $(3y)2 = 2(3y) = (2 \cdot 3)y = 6y$
21. $3(x + 2) = 3x + 3 \cdot 2 = 3x + 6$ **23.** $5(x + y + 4) = 5x + 5y + 5 \cdot 4 = 5x + 5y + 20$
25. closure property of multiplication   **27.** commutative property of addition
29. distributive property   **31.** commutative property of addition   **33.** additive identity property
35. multiplicative inverse property   **37.** associative property of addition
39. commutative property of multiplication   **41.** The additive inverse of 1 is -1.
43. The additive inverse of -8 is 8.   **45.** The additive inverse of 0 is 0.
47. The additive inverse of π is $-\pi$.   **49.** The additive inverse of 10 is -10.
51. The additive inverse of -3 is 3.   **53.** The multiplicative inverse of 1 is 1.
55. The multiplicative inverse of $\frac{1}{2}$ is 2.   **57.** The multiplicative inverse of -0.25 (or $-\frac{1}{4}$) is -4.
59. 0 does not have a multiplicative inverse.
61. $(a + b) + c = a + (b + c)$ associative property of addition
$\qquad\qquad\qquad = a + (c + b)$ commutative property of addition
63. $(b + c)a = a(b + c)$ commutative property of multiplication
$\qquad\qquad = ab + ac$ distributive property
$\qquad\qquad = ba + ac$ commutative property of multiplication
$\qquad\qquad = ba + ca$ commutative property of multiplication

Exercise 1.3   (page 19)

1.  [number line: dots at 2, 3, 5, 7; marked 0–10]

3.  [number line: dots at 11, 13, 15, 17, 19; marked 10–20]   **5.** $<$ **7.** $>$ **9.** $<$

11. $12 < 19$ **13.** $-5 \geq -6$ **15.** $-3 \leq 5$ **17.** $x > 3$ **19.** $z < 4$ **21.** $x \geq 7$
23. $x \leq -3$ **25.** 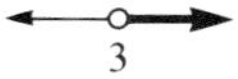 [ray open circle at 3, right]   **27.** 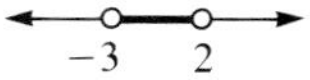 [segment open at -3 to 2]   **29.**  [segment from 0 to 5]   **31.** 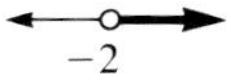 [ray open at -2, right]

33. 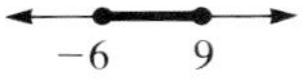 [segment -6 to 9]   **35.**  [segment open at 2 to 4]   **37.**  [segment 2 to 4, closed]   **39.**  [segment -4 to open 8]

41.  [segment 2 to 4]   **43.** 20   **45.** -6 **47.** 5   **49.** 7   **51.** 3   **53.** 99

55. all positive numbers and 0   **57.** Both are 0.   **59.** yes   **61.** 3 or -3

Exercise 1.4   (page 29)

1. -8 **3.** -9 **5.** -6 **7.** -5 **9.** 6   **11.** 17   **13.** -93 **15.** -2
17. -7 **19.** 0   **21.** -12 **23.** 21   **25.** -2 **27.** 4   **29.** -1 **31.** 0
33. 2   **35.** -13 **37.** 1   **39.** 4   **41.** -1 **43.** -4 **45.** -12
47. -20 **49.** 1   **51.** -8 **53.** -9 **55.** $-\frac{5}{4}$ **57.** $-\frac{1}{8}$ **59.** 4   **61.** 14
63. $\frac{20}{21}$ **65.** $22.17 + 39.56 = 61.73$; $\$61.73$ **67.** $7 + (-3) = 4$; $+4$ degrees
69. $437 + 25 + 37 + 45 + (-17) + (-83) + (-22) = 422$; $\$422$
71. $15(-30) = -450$;   Harry would lose $\$450$.   **73.** $-120(-12) = 1440$;   1440 gal   **75.** equal
77. $\frac{4}{5}$ **79.** $-\frac{2}{3}$ **81.** $\frac{3}{20}$ **83.** $\frac{14}{9}$ **85.** $\frac{5}{27}$ **87.** 2   **89.** $-\frac{17}{45}$ **91.** $-\frac{17}{35}$
93. 16   **95.** 26 lbs

REVIEW EXERCISES   (page 34)

1. true   **3.** false; $B \subseteq A$ **5.** true   **7.** integer, rational number, real number
9. irrational number, real number   **11.** rational number, real number
13. $5 - 5 = 0$, whole number, integer, rational number, real number   **15.** even number, composite number
17. odd number   **19.** odd number   **21.** odd number   **23.** distributive property
25. commutative property of addition   **27.** additive identity property
29. reflexive property of equality   **31.** associative property of multiplication
33. multiplicative inverse property   **35.** -1; 1   **37.** 0;   no multiplicative inverse exists.
39. $a < 4$ **41.** $10 \geq 3$ **43.** [number line: dots at 23, 29; marked 20–30]

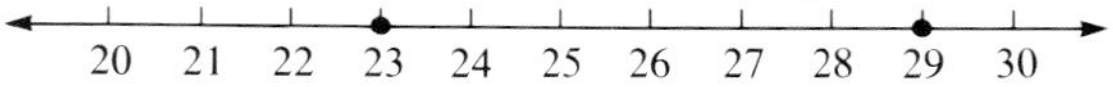

45.  [ray closed at -4, right]   **47.**  [segment open -2 to 3]   **49.** 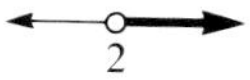 [ray open at 2, right]   **51.** 0   **53.** -8 **55.** -2

57. 3   **59.** -5 **61.** -12 **63.** 12   **65.** -4 **67.** 4   **69.** -1
71. $-\frac{19}{6}$ **73.** $-\frac{4}{3}$ **75.** $-\frac{3}{4}$ **77.** $-\frac{27}{8}$

CHAPTER ONE TEST   (page 35)

1. $\in$ **3.** $\subseteq$ **5.** $\{1, 2, 3, 4, 5, 6\}$ **7.** $\varnothing$ **9.** 1, 2, 5   **11.** $-2, 0, 1, 2, \frac{6}{5}, 5$
13. $0.77\overline{7}$ **15.** commutative property of addition   **17.** associative property of addition
19.  [number line: dots at -3, -1, 2, 5; marked -5 to 6]   **21.** 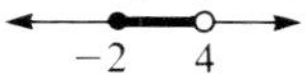 [segment -2 to open 4]   **23.** -3

25. -6 **27.** 6   **29.** 1

Exercise 2.1   (page 44)

1. 9   **3.** -9 **5.** 9   **7.** $-32x^5$ **9.** $-128x^7$ **11.** $64x^6$ **13.** $\frac{1}{25}$
15. $-\frac{1}{25}$ **17.** $\frac{1}{25}$ **19.** 1   **21.** -1 **23.** 1   **25.** x^5 **27.** k^7 **29.** x^{10}

31. p^{10} **33.** a^4b^5 **35.** x^5y^4 **37.** x^{28} **39.** $\frac{1}{b^{72}}$ **41.** $x^{12}y^8$ **43.** $\frac{s^3}{r^9}$

45. a^{20} **47.** $-\frac{1}{d^3}$ **49.** x^2y^{10} **51.** $\frac{a^{15}}{b^{10}}$ **53.** $\frac{a^6}{b^4}$ **55.** a^5 **57.** c^7

59. m **61.** a^4 **63.** m **65.** $\frac{64b^{12}}{27a^9}$ **67.** 1   **69.** $\frac{-b^3}{8a^{21}}$ **71.** $\frac{27}{8a^{18}}$

73. $\frac{1}{9x^3}$ **75.** $\frac{-3y^2}{x^2}$ **77.** $\frac{-n^3}{48}$ **79.** 108   **81.** -8 **83.** $-\frac{1}{216}$ **85.** $\frac{1}{324}$

87. $\frac{27}{2}$ **89.** $\frac{27}{8}$ **91.** a^{n-1} **93.** b^{3n-9} **95.** a^{-n-1} or $\frac{1}{a^{n+1}}$ **97.** a^{-n+2} or $\frac{1}{a^{n-2}}$
107. $2^2 + 2^3 \neq 2^{2+3}$

Exercise 2.2   (page 48)

1. 3.9×10^3 **3.** 7.8×10^{-3} **5.** 1.76×10^7 **7.** 9.6×10^{-6} **9.** 3.23×10^7
11. 6.0×10^{-4} **13.** 5.27×10^3 **15.** 3.17×10^{-4} **17.** 7.31×10^6 **19.** 9.137×10^1
21. 270   **23.** 0.00323   **25.** 796,000   **27.** 0.00037   **29.** 5.23   **31.** 23,650,000,000
33. 0.04   **35.** 14,400,000   **37.** 6000   **39.** 0.64   **41.** 1.1916×10^8 cm/hr
43. 1.67248×10^{-18} g   **45.** 1.48896×10^{10} in.   **47.** 5.58×10^7 mi to 1.674×10^9 mi
49. about 2.49×10^{13} mi   **51.** about 1.29×10^{13} **53.** about 5.67×10^{10}
55. about 3.62×10^{25}

Exercise 2.3   (page 54)

1. monomial   **3.** trinomial   **5.** binomial   **7.** monomial   **9.** 2   **11.** 8
13. 10   **15.** 1   **17.** 0   **19.** 2   **21.** $3x^3 - 4x^2 + 2x + 7$
23. $-x^4 + 2x^3y - 3x^2y^2 + 5xy^3 + y^4$ **25.** $-4x^6y + 3x^3z - 4x + 3$ **27.** $P(0) = 2$
29. $P(4) = 38$ **31.** $P(1) = -2$ **33.** $P(-2) = -23$ **35.** $P(t) = -3t^2 + 4t - 3$
37. $P(-x) = -3x^2 - 4x - 3$ **39.** $P(2x) = -12x^2 + 8x - 3$ **41.** $P(P(0)) = P(-3) = -42$
43. $P(P(-1)) = P(-10) = -343$ **45.** -2 **47.** 13   **49.** 35   **51.** -90 **53.** 84
55. $-\frac{6}{19}$ **57.** $\frac{78}{77}$ **59.** about -34.225 **61.** about 0.1728   **63.** about -0.1227
65. like terms; $10x$ **67.** unlike terms   **69.** like terms; 12   **71.** like terms; $12x^2$
73. $12x$ **75.** $2x^3y^2z$ **77.** $-7x^2y^3 + 3xy^4$ **79.** $10x^4y^2$ **81.** $x^2 - 5x + 6$
83. $-5a^2 + 4a + 4$ **85.** $-y^3 + 4y^2 + 6$ **87.** $4x^2 - 11$ **89.** $3x^3 - x + 13$
91. $4y^2 - 9y + 3$ **93.** $6x^3 - 6x^2 + 14x - 17$ **95.** $-9y^4 + 3y^3 - 15y^2 + 20y + 12$
97. $x^2 - 8x + 22$ **99.** $-3y^3 + 18y^2 - 28y + 35$ **101.** $8x^3 - x^2$ **103.** $-16x^3 - 27x^2 - 12x$
105. $-8z^2 - 40z + 54$ **107.** $-2x + 9$ **109.** $-8x^2 - 2x + 2$

Exercise 2.4   (page 60)

1. $-6a^3b$ **3.** $-15a^2b^2c^3$ **5.** $-120a^9b^3$ **7.** $12x^5y^9$ **9.** $25x^8y^8$ **11.** $-405x^7y^4$
13. $100x^{10}y^6$ **15.** $3x + 6$ **17.** $-a^2 + ab$ **19.** $3x^3 + 9x^2$ **21.** $-6x^3 + 6x^2 - 4x$
23. $10a^6b^4 - 25a^2b^6$ **25.** $7r^3st + 7rs^3t - 7rst^3$ **27.** $-12x^4y^3 + 16x^3y^4 - 4x^2y^5$
29. $-12m^4n^2 - 12m^3n^3$ **31.** $x^2 + 4x + 4$ **33.** $a^2 - 8a + 16$ **35.** $a^2 + 2ab + b^2$
37. $4x^2 - 4xy + y^2$ **39.** $x^2 - 4$ **41.** $a^2 - b^2$ **43.** $x^2 + 5x + 6$ **45.** $z^2 - 9z + 14$
47. $2a^2 - 3a - 2$ **49.** $6y^2 - 5yz + z^2$ **51.** $2x^2 + xy - 6y^2$ **53.** $9 + 6x - 8x^2$

55. $9x^2 - 6xy - 3y^2$ **57.** $8a^2 + 14a - 15$ **59.** $u^2 - 2uv + v^2$ **61.** $4x^2 + 4x + 1$
63. $9x^2 + 12xy + 4y^2$ **65.** $6y^3 + 11y^2 + 9y + 2$ **67.** $6a^3 - 7a^2b + 6ab^2 - 2b^3$
69. $2a^2 + ab - b^2 - 3bc - 2c^2$ **71.** $x^2 + 4xy + 6xz + 4y^2 + 12yz + 9z^2$ **73.** $r^4 - 2r^2s^2 + s^4$
75. $4x^3 - 8x^2 - 9x + 6$ **77.** $-27x^6 + 135x^5 - 225x^4 + 125x^3$ **79.** $a^3 - 3a^2b - ab^2 + 3b^3$

81. $2x^5 + x$ **83.** $\dfrac{3x}{y^4z} - \dfrac{x^6}{y^{10}z^2}$ **85.** $\dfrac{1}{x^2} - y^2$ **87.** $2x^3y^3 - \dfrac{2}{x^3y^3} + 3$

89. $8x^6 + 24x^4y^2 + 18x^2y^4 - \dfrac{12x^4}{y^2} - 36x^2 - 27y^2$ **91.** $x^{3n} - x^{2n}$ **93.** $x^{2n} - 1$

95. $x^{2n} - x^ny^{-n} - x^ny^n + 1$ **97.** $x^{4n} - y^{4n}$ **99.** $-3x^{-n}y^{2n} + 2x^ny^{-2n} + 5$
101. $x^{2n} - y^{2n} + 2y^n - 1$ **103.** $5x^2 - 36x + 7$ **105.** $21x^2 - 6xy + 29y^2$
107. $24y^2 - 4yz + 21z^2$ **113.** $9.2127x^2 - 7.7956x - 36.0315$ **115.** $299.29y^2 - 150.51y + 18.9225$

Exercise 2.5   (page 68)

1. $\dfrac{y}{2x^3}$ **3.** $\dfrac{3b^4}{4a^4}$ **5.** $\dfrac{-5}{7xy^7t^2}$ **7.** $\dfrac{13a^nb^{2n}c^{3n-1}}{3}$ **9.** $\dfrac{2x}{3} - \dfrac{x^2}{6}$ **11.** $\dfrac{2xy^2}{3} + \dfrac{x^2y}{3}$

13. $\dfrac{x^4y^4}{2} - \dfrac{x^3y^9}{4} + \dfrac{3}{4xy^2}$ **15.** $\dfrac{b^2}{4a} - \dfrac{a^3}{2b^4} + \dfrac{3}{4ab}$ **17.** $1 - 3x^ny^n + 6x^{2n}y^{2n}$ **19.** $x + 2$

21. $x + 7$ **23.** $3x - 5 + \dfrac{3}{2x + 3}$ **25.** $3x^2 + x + 2 + \dfrac{8}{x - 1}$ **27.** $2x^2 + 5x + 3 + \dfrac{4}{3x - 2}$

29. $3x^2 + 4x + 3$ **31.** $a + 1$ **33.** $2y + 2$ **35.** $6x - 12$ **37.** $3x^2 - x + 2$

39. $4x^3 - 3x^2 + 3x + 1$ **41.** $a^2 + a + 1 + \dfrac{2}{a - 1}$ **43.** $5a^2 - 3a - 4$ **45.** $6y - 12$

47. $16x^4 - 8x^3y + 4x^2y^2 - 2xy^3 + y^4$ **49.** $x^4 + x^2 + 4$ **51.** $x^2 + x + 1$ **53.** $x^2 + 3$

55. $9.8x + 16.4 + \dfrac{-36.5}{x - 2}$

Exercise 2.6   (page 73)

1. $x + 2$ **3.** $x - 3$ **5.** $x + 2$ **7.** $x - 7 + \dfrac{28}{x + 2}$ **9.** $3x^2 - x + 2$

11. $2x^2 + 4x + 3$ **13.** $6x^2 - x + 1 + \dfrac{3}{x + 1}$ **15.** $7.2x - 0.66 + \dfrac{0.368}{x - 0.2}$

17. $2.7x - 3.59 + \dfrac{0.903}{x + 1.7}$ **19.** $9x^2 - 513x + 29{,}241 + \dfrac{-1{,}666{,}762}{x + 57}$ **21.** $P(1) = -1$

23. $P(-2) = -37$ **25.** $P(3) = 23$ **27.** $P(0) = -1$ **29.** $Q(-1) = 2$ **31.** $Q(2) = -1$

33. $Q(3) = 18$ **35.** $Q(-3) = 174$ **37.** -8 **39.** 59 **41.** 44 **43.** $\dfrac{29}{32}$ **45.** 64

REVIEW EXERCISES   (page 75)

1. 729 **3.** -64 **5.** $-6x^6$ **7.** $\dfrac{1}{x}$ **9.** $27x^6$ **11.** $-32x^{10}$ **13.** $\dfrac{1}{x^{10}}$

15. $\dfrac{x^6}{9}$ **17.** x^2 **19.** $\dfrac{1}{a^5}$ **21.** $\dfrac{1}{y^7}$ **23.** $\dfrac{1}{x}$ **25.** $9x^4y^6$ **27.** $\dfrac{64y^9}{27x^6}$

29. 1.93×10^{10} **31.** $72,000,000$ **33.** 6 **35.** $-t^2 - 4t + 6$ **37.** 5 **39.** $5x^2 + 3x$

41. $4x^2 - 9x + 19$ **43.** $-16a^3b^3c$ **45.** $2x^4y^3 - 8x^2y^7$ **47.** $16x^2 + 14x - 15$

49. $15x^4 - 22x^3 + 73x^2 - 50x + 50$ **51.** $3x^2 - 13x + 42 + \dfrac{-124}{x + 3}$ **53.** $x^4 + x^3 + x^2 + x + 1$

55. $2x^2 + 3x + 1 + \dfrac{10}{3x - 2}$ **57.** $x^2 - 2x + \dfrac{6x - 3}{x^2 + 2x + 3}$ **59.** $x^2 + 4x + 3$ **61.** $P(2) = 11$

CHAPTER TWO TEST   (page 77)

1. x^8 **3.** $\dfrac{1}{m^8}$ **5.** 3 **7.** 4.7×10^6 **9.** $653,000$ **11.** 3.76×10^5 km

13. $P(2) = -9$ **15.** 5 **17.** $5y^2 + y - 1$ **19.** $10a^2 + 22$ **21.** $-6x^4yz^4$

23. $z^2 - 16$ **25.** $2x^3 - x^2 - 7x - 3$ **27.** $\dfrac{-6x}{y} + \dfrac{4x^2}{y^2} - \dfrac{3}{y^3}$ **29.** -7

Exercise 3.1   (page 81)

1. $2 \cdot 3$ **3.** $3^3 \cdot 5$ **5.** 2^7 **7.** $5^2 \cdot 13$ **9.** 12 **11.** 2 **13.** $4a^2$

15. $6xy^2z^2$ **17.** $2(x + 4)$ **19.** $2x(x - 3)$ **21.** $5xy(1 + 2y)$ **23.** $5x^2y(3 - 2y)$

25. $3rt^4(4rs^3 + 5t^2)$ **27.** $6rs(4rs^2 - 2r^2st + t^2)$ **29.** $9x^7y^3(5x^3 - 7y^4 + 9x^3y^7)$ **31.** prime

33. $8a^3b^3(3b^2 + 4a^2 - 8a^2b^2c^5)$ **35.** $(x + y)(4 + t)$ **37.** $(a - b)(r - s)$

39. $(m + n + p)(3 + x)$ **41.** $b(x - a)$ **43.** $(x + y)(x + y + z)$ **45.** $(u + v)(1 - u - v)$

47. $-(x - y)$ **49.** $-6ab(3a + 2b)$ **51.** $-7u^2v^3z^2(9uv^3z^7 - 4v^4 + 3uz^2)$ **53.** $-(x + y)(a - b)$

55. $-8x^2(m - n + p)(4x + 5 - 2x^2)$ **57.** $x^2(x^n + x^{n+1})$ **59.** $y^n(y^2 - y^3)$ **61.** $x^{-2}(x^6 - 5x^8)$

63. $y^{-2n}(y^{4n} + y^{2n} + 1)$ **69.** relatively prime   **71.** not relatively prime

73. relatively prime   **75.** relatively prime

Exercise 3.2   (page 86)

1. $(x + 2)(x - 2)$ **3.** $(3y + 8)(3y - 8)$ **5.** prime   **7.** $(25a + 13b^2)(25a - 13b^2)$

9. $(9a^2 + 7b)(9a^2 - 7b)$ **11.** $(6x^2y + 7z^2)(6x^2y - 7z^2)$ **13.** $(x + y + z)(x + y - z)$

15. $(a - b + c + d)(a - b - c - d)$ **17.** $(x^2 + y^2)(x + y)(x - y)$

19. $(16x^2y^2 + z^4)(4xy + z^2)(4xy - z^2)$ **21.** $2(x + 12)(x - 12)$ **23.** $2x(x + 4)(x - 4)$

25. $5x(x + 5)(x - 5)$ **27.** $t^2(rs + x^2y)(rs - x^2y)$ **29.** $2(c - d)(x + 3)(x - 3)$

31. $(r + s)(r^2 - rs + s^2)$ **33.** $(x - 2y)(x^2 + 2xy + 4y^2)$ **35.** $(4a - 5b^2)(16a^2 + 20ab^2 + 25b^4)$

37. $27(xy^2 + 2z^3)(x^2y^4 - 2xy^2z^3 + 4z^6)$ **39.** $[3a + (x + y)^2][9a^2 - 3a(x + y)^2 + (x + y)^4]$

41. $(x^2 + y^2)(x^4 - x^2y^2 + y^4)$ **43.** $5(x + 5)(x^2 - 5x + 25)$ **45.** $4x^2(x - 4)(x^2 + 4x + 16)$

47. $2u^2(4v - t)(16v^2 + 4vt + t^2)$ **49.** $(a + b)(x + 3)(x^2 - 3x + 9)$

51. $6[(a + b) - z][(a + b)^2 + z(a + b) + z^2]$ **53.** $(x^m + y^{2n})(x^m - y^{2n})$

55. $(10a^{2m} + 9b^n)(10a^{2m} - 9b^n)$ **57.** $(x^n - 2)(x^{2n} + 2x^n + 4)$ **59.** $(a^m + b^n)(a^{2m} - a^mb^n + b^{2n})$

61. $2(x^{2m} + 2y^m)(x^{4m} - 2x^{2m}y^m + 4y^{2m})$

Exercise 3.3   (page 96)

1. $(x + 1)(x + 1)$ **3.** $(a - 9)(a - 9)$ **5.** $(2y + 1)(2y + 1)$ **7.** $(3b - 2)(3b - 2)$

9. $(3z + 4)(3z + 4)$ **11.** $(x + 3)(x + 2)$ **13.** $(x - 2)(x - 2)$ **15.** prime

17. $(x - 6)(x + 5)$ **19.** $(a + 10)(a - 5)$ **21.** $(y - 7)(y + 3)$ **23.** $3(x + 7)(x - 3)$

25. $b^2(a - 11)(a - 2)$ **27.** $x^2(b - 7)(b - 5)$ **29.** $-(a - 8)(a + 4)$ **31.** $-3(x - 3)(x - 2)$

33. $-4(x - 5)(x + 4)$ **35.** $(3y + 2)(2y + 1)$ **37.** $(4a - 3)(2a + 3)$ **39.** $(3x - 4)(2x + 1)$

41. prime   **43.** $(4x - 3)(2x - 1)$ **45.** $(3z - 4)(2z + 5)$ **47.** $(a + b)(a - 4b)$
49. $(2y - 3t)(y + 2t)$ **51.** $x(3x - 1)(x - 3)$ **53.** $-(3a + 2b)(a - b)$ **55.** $(3t + 2)(3t - 1)$
57. $(3x - 2)(3x - 2)$ **59.** $-(2x - 3)(2x - 3)$ **61.** $(5x - 1)(3x - 2)$ **63.** $5(a - 3b)(a - 3b)$
65. $z(8x^2 + 6xy + 9y^2)$ **67.** $(15x - 1)(x + 5)$ **69.** $x^2(7x - 8)(3x + 2)$
71. $(3xy - 4z)(2xy - 3z)$ **73.** $(x^2 + 5)(x^2 + 3)$ **75.** $(y^2 - 10)(y^2 - 3)$
77. $(a + 3)(a - 3)(a + 2)(a - 2)$ **79.** $(z^2 + 3)(z + 2)(z - 2)$ **81.** $(x^3 + 3)(x + 1)(x^2 - x + 1)$
83. $(y - 2)(y^2 + 2y + 4)(y - 1)(y^2 + y + 1)$ **85.** $(x + 2)(x + 2)$ **87.** $(a + b + 4)(a + b - 6)$
89. $(3x + 3y + 4)(2x + 2y - 5)$ **91.** $(5x - 9)(x - 3)$ **93.** $(4x - 5)(x - 2)$ **95.** $(x^n + 1)(x^n + 1)$
97. $(2a^{3n} + 1)(a^{3n} - 2)$ **99.** $(x^{2n} + y^{2n})(x^{2n} + y^{2n})$ **101.** $(3x^n - 1)(2x^n + 3)$

Exercise 3.4   (page 100)

1. $(x + y)(a + b)$ **3.** $(x + 2)(x + y)$ **5.** $(3 - c)(c + d)$ **7.** $(a + b)(a - 4)$
9. $(a + b)(x - 1)$ **11.** $(x + y)(x + y + z)$ **13.** $y(x + y)(x + y + 2z)$
15. $n(2n - p + 2m)(n^2p - 1)$ **17.** $(x - 1)(x^3 - x^2 + 1)$ **19.** $(a - b)(a + b + 2)$
21. $(y + 4)(2 + a)$ **23.** $(x + 1)(x - 1 + 3x^4 + 3x^3)$ **25.** $(x + 2 + y)(x + 2 - y)$
27. $(x + 1 + 3z)(x + 1 - 3z)$ **29.** $(2a - b + c)(2a - b - c)$ **31.** $(a + 4 + b)(a + 4 - b)$
33. $(2x + y + z)(2x + y - z)$ **35.** $(x^2 + x + 3)(x^2 - x + 3)$ **37.** $(2a^2 + a + 1)(2a^2 - a + 1)$
39. $(a^2 + 2ab + 2b^2)(a^2 - 2ab + 2b^2)$ **41.** $(x^2 + 3x + 1)(x^2 - 3x + 1)$
43. $(x + 2)(x^2 - 2x + 4)(x - 2)(x^2 + 2x + 4)$ **45.** $(a - 16)(a - 1)$ **47.** $(2u + 3)(u + 1)$
49. $(4r - 3s)(5r + 2s)$

Exercise 3.5   (page 103)

1. $(x + 4)(x + 4)$ **3.** $(2xy - 3)(4x^2y^2 + 6xy + 9)$ **5.** $(x - t)(y + s)$ **7.** $(5x + 4y)(5x - 4y)$
9. $(6x + 5)(2x + 7)$ **11.** $2(3x - 4)(x - 1)$ **13.** $(8x - 1)(7x - 1)$ **15.** $y^2(2x + 1)(2x + 1)$
17. $(x + a^2y)(x^2 - a^2xy + a^4y^2)$ **19.** $2(x - 3)(x^2 + 3x + 9)$ **21.** $(a + b)(f + e)$
23. $(2x + 2y + 3)(x + y - 1)$ **25.** $(25x^2 + 16y^2)(5x + 4y)(5x - 4y)$ **27.** $36(x^2 + 1)(x + 1)(x - 1)$
29. $2(x^2 + y^2)(x^4 - x^2y^2 + y^4)$ **31.** $(a + 3)(a - 3)(a + 2)(a - 2)$ **33.** $(x + 3 + y)(x + 3 - y)$
35. $(2x + 1 + 2y)(2x + 1 - 2y)$ **37.** $(z^2 + 4 + z)(z^2 + 4 - z)$ **39.** $(x + 1)(x^2 - x + 1)(x + 1)(x - 1)$
41. $(x + 3)(x - 3)(x + 2)(x^2 - 2x + 4)$ **43.** $2z(x + y)(x - y)(x - y)(x^2 + xy + y^2)$

REVIEW EXERCISES   (page 104)

1. $4(x + 2)$ **3.** $5xy^2(xy - 2)$ **5.** $-4x^2y^3z^2(2z^2 + 3x^2)$ **7.** $9x^2y^3z^2(3xz + 9x^2y^2 - 10z^5)$
9. $5x^2(x + y)^3(1 - 3x^2 - 3xy)$ **11.** $(z + 4)(z - 4)$ **13.** $(xy^2 + 8z^3)(xy^2 - 8z^3)$
15. $(x + z + t)(x + z - t)$ **17.** $2(x^2 + 7)(x^2 - 7)$ **19.** $(x + 7)(x^2 - 7x + 49)$
21. $8(y - 4)(y^2 + 4y + 16)$ **23.** $(y + 20)(y + 1)$ **25.** $-(x + 7)(x - 4)$ **27.** $(4a - 1)(a - 1)$
29. prime   **31.** $y(y + 2)(y - 1)$ **33.** $-3(x + 2)(x + 1)$ **35.** $3(5x + y)(x - 4y)$
37. $(8x + 3y)(3x - 4y)$ **39.** $(x^2 + x + 7)(x^2 - x + 7)$ **41.** $(x + 2)(y + 4)$
43. $(x^2 + 4)(x^2 + y)$ **45.** $(z - 2)(z + x + 2)$ **47.** $(x + 2 + 2p^2)(x + 2 - 2p^2)$
49. $(a^2 + 4 + 2a)(a^2 + 4 - 2a)$

CHAPTER THREE TEST   (page 105)

1. $2^2 \cdot 3 \cdot 19$ **3.** $3xy(y + 2x)$ **5.** $(u - v)(r + s)$ **7.** $y^n(x^2y^2 + 1)$ **9.** $(x + 7)(x - 7)$
11. $4(y^2 + 4)(y + 2)(y - 2)$ **13.** $(b - 3)(b^2 + 3b + 9)$ **15.** $(3z + 4t^2)(3z - 4t^2)$
17. $(x + 5)(x + 3)$ **19.** $(2a + 3)(a - 4)$ **21.** $3(2u - 1)(u + 2)$ **23.** $(3x - y)(2x + y)$
25. $(x^n + 1)(x^n + 1)$ **27.** $(a - y)(x + y)$ **29.** $(x + 3 + y)(x + 3 - y)$
31. $(x + 2)(x - 2)(x + 4)(x - 4)$

CUMULATIVE REVIEW EXERCISES (CHAPTERS 1–3)   (page 105)

1. rational number, real number, positive number   **3.** odd integer, prime number   **5.** -2
7. $\frac{7}{8}$ **9.** transitive property of equality   **11.** commutative property of addition   **13.** 5
15. 22   **17.** -4 **19.** $-\frac{1}{8}$ **21.** $-\frac{169}{72}$ **23.** $x^8 y^{12}$ **25.** $-b^3/a^2$
27. 4.97×10^{-6} **29.** trinomial   **31.** 18   **33.** $4x^2 - 4x + 14$ **35.** $6x^2 - 7x - 20$
37. $x + 4$ **39.** $3rs^3(r - 2s)$ **41.** $(x + y)(u + v)$ **43.** $(2x - 3y^2)(4x^2 + 6xy^2 + 9y^4)$
45. $(3x - 5)(3x - 5)$ **47.** $(3a + 2b)(9a^2 - 6ab + 4b^2)$ **49.** $(x + 5 + y^2)(x + 5 - y^2)$

Exercise 4.1   (page 116)

1. all real numbers   **3.** all real numbers except 2   **5.** all real numbers except 2 and -3
7. all real numbers except 0, 10, and -10 **9.** $x = 2$ **11.** $z = 14$ **13.** $u = 3$
15. $x = 28$ **17.** $x = \frac{2}{3}$ **19.** $x = 6$ **21.** $x = -8$ **23.** $r = 2$ **25.** $a = -2$
27. $a = 3$ **29.** $x = 4$ **31.** $a = -4$ **33.** $y = -6$ **35.** $y = 6$ **37.** $y = 13$
39. $x = -8$ **41.** no solution   **43.** $x = 24$ **45.** $x = 6$ **47.** $x = 4$ **49.** $x = 3$
51. $a = 0$ **53.** $a = 6$ **55.** an identity   **57.** $x = 2000$ **59.** $x = 5$ **61.** $\frac{1}{3}$
63. $-\frac{691}{1980}$ **65.** 37 and 38   **67.** 32   **69.** 29   **71.** 3 ft, 5 ft, and 9 ft   **73.** 32 ft
75. 12 cm by 24 cm   **77.** 315 sq ft   **79.** 20 ft by 45 ft

Exercise 4.2   (page 125)

1. 6 cm   **3.** 6 in. by 4 in.   **5.** 50 m   **7.** 5 ft from the fulcrum   **9.** 90 lb
11. 2 ft in front of Jim   **13.** 10 nickels, 20 dimes, 40 pennies   **15.** 13 nickels and 11 quarters
17. 3 nickels and 5 dimes   **19.** Heidi invested \$2000 at 8% and \$10,000 at 9%   **21.** 10.8%
23. \$4200   **25.** 25 student and 175 adult tickets   **27.** 3 hr   **29.** 1.5 hr
31. 4 hr at each rate   **33.** 20 lb of the \$0.95 candy and 10 lb of the \$1.10 candy   **35.** 10 oz
37. 2 gal of cream

Exercise 4.3   (page 129)

1. $w = \dfrac{A}{l}$ **3.** $r^2 = \dfrac{A}{\pi}$ **5.** $B = \dfrac{3V}{h}$ **7.** $t = \dfrac{I}{pr}$ **9.** $w = \dfrac{p - 2l}{2}$ **11.** $b_1 = \dfrac{2A}{h} - b_2$

13. $x = z\sigma + \mu$ **15.** $x = \dfrac{y - b}{m}$ **17.** $n = \dfrac{l - a + d}{d}$ **19.** $r_1 = \dfrac{rr_2}{r_2 - r}$

21. $\Sigma x^2 = n(\sigma^2 + \mu^2)$ **23.** $r = \dfrac{S - a}{S - l}$ **25.** $n = \dfrac{-360}{a - 180} = \dfrac{360}{180 - a}$ **27.** $s = \dfrac{f(P - L)}{i}$

29. $r_2 = \dfrac{rr_1}{r_1 - r}$ **31.** $x = \dfrac{y - y_1 + mx_1}{m}$ **33.** $a = \dfrac{Hb}{2b - H}$ **35.** $a^2 = \dfrac{x^2 b^2}{b^2 - y^2}$

37. $h = x^2 - \dfrac{y - k}{a} = \dfrac{ax^2 - y + k}{a}$ **39.** $h = \dfrac{3V}{B_1 + B_2 + \sqrt{B_1 B_2}}$ **41.** $C = \dfrac{5F - 160}{9}$; $0°$, $21.1°$, $100°$

43. $n = \dfrac{C - 6.50}{0.07}$; 620 kwh, 980 kwh, 1700 kwh   **45.** 60 mi; 160 mi   **47.** \$600

Exercise 4.4   (page 134)

1. $0, -2$ **3.** $4, -4$ **5.** $0, -1$ **7.** $0, 5$ **9.** $-3, -5$ **11.** $1, 6$ **13.** $3, 4$
15. $-2, -4$ **17.** $-\frac{1}{3}, -3$ **19.** $\frac{1}{2}, 2$ **21.** $1, -\frac{1}{2}$ **23.** $2, -\frac{1}{3}$ **25.** $3, 3$
27. $\frac{1}{4}, -\frac{3}{2}$ **29.** $2, -\frac{5}{6}$ **31.** $\frac{1}{3}, -1$ **33.** $2, \frac{1}{2}$ **35.** $\frac{1}{5}, -\frac{5}{3}$ **37.** $0, 0, -1$
39. $0, 7, -7$ **41.** $0, 7, -3$ **43.** $3, -3, 2, -2$ **45.** $0, -2, -3$ **47.** $0, \frac{5}{6}, -7$

49. $1, -1, -3$ **51.** $3, -3, -\frac{3}{2}$ **53.** $2, -2, -\frac{1}{3}$ **55.** 16 and 18, or -18 and -16
57. 6 and 7   **59.** 40 m   **61.** 4 units   **63.** 5 ft by 12 ft   **65.** 20 ft by 40 ft
67. $x^2 - 8x + 15 = 0$ **69.** $x^2 + 5x = 0$

Exercise 4.5   (page 138)

1. 8   **3.** 12   **5.** -2 **7.** -30 **9.** 50   **11.** $4 - \pi$ **13.** $|2|$ **15.** $|5|$
17. $|-2|$ **19.** $-|-4|$ **21.** $-|-7|$ **23.** $|x + 1|$ **25.** $8, -8$ **27.** $9, -3$
29. $4, -1$ **31.** $\frac{14}{3}, -6$ **33.** no solutions   **35.** $8, -4$ **37.** -8 **39.** $-4, -28$
41. $-2, -\frac{4}{5}$ **43.** $3, -1$ **45.** 0   **47.** $\frac{4}{3}$ **49.** no solutions

Exercise 4.6   (page 144)

1. (number line, open circle at 1)   **3.** (number line, -2)   **5.** (number line, 2)   **7.** (number line, 1)   **9.** (number line, $-\frac{8}{5}$)

11. (number line, 20)   **13.** (number line, 10)   **15.** (number line, -36)   **17.** (number line, -100)   **19.** (number line, $\frac{45}{7}$)

21. (number line, -2, 5)   **23.** (number line, 8, 11)   **25.** (number line, -4, 6)   **27.** no solutions

29. (number line, -2, 4)   **31.** (number line, 2, 3)   **33.** (number line, 1, $\frac{9}{4}$)   **35.** (number line, -15)

37. (number line, 2, 7)   **39.** (number line, 1)   **41.** no solutions   **43.** $|7| + |-2| \ge |7 + (-2)|$

45. x and y must differ in sign.   **47.** no   **49.** no   **51.** profit $\le \$15$
53. 185 in. $\le p \le$ 260 in.   **55.** score ≥ 88

Exercise 4.7   (page 147)

1. (number line, -4, 4)   **3.** (number line, -21, 3)   **5.** no solutions   **7.** (number line, $-\frac{3}{2}$, 2)

9. (number line, -1, 1)   **11.** (number line, -12, 36)   **13.** (number line, $-\frac{16}{3}$, 4)   **15.** (number line, 0)

17. (number line, -2, 5)   **19.** (number line, $\frac{3}{8}$)   **21.** (number line, -10, 14)   **23.** (number line, $-\frac{5}{3}$, 1)

25. (number line, -4, -1)   **27.** no solutions   **29.** (number line, -24, -18)   **31.** (number line, 25)

33. (number line, $-\frac{65}{9}$, $-\frac{5}{9}$)   **35.** (number line, -4)   **37.** (number line, -7)   **39.** (number line, 5)

REVIEW EXERCISES   (page 149)

1. $x = 5$ **3.** $y = 8$ **5.** $x = 19$ **7.** $y = 12$ **9.** 88, 90, 92

11. \$18,000 at 10% and \$7000 at 9%   **13.** $r^3 = \dfrac{3V}{4\pi}$ **15.** $S_0 = \dfrac{6V}{H} - 4S_1 - S_2$ **17.** $\frac{1}{2}, -\frac{5}{6}$

19. $0, -\frac{2}{3}, \frac{4}{5}$ **21.** $3, -\frac{11}{3}$ **23.** $\frac{1}{5}, -5$ **25.** (number line, -24)   **27.** (number line, $-\frac{1}{3}$, 2)

29. (number line, -5, -2)   **31.** all numbers x

CHAPTER FOUR TEST   (page 150)

1. all real numbers except 3 and -2 **3.** $y = 6$ **5.** 36 sq cm   **7.** 330 mi

9. $i = \dfrac{f(P - L)}{s}$ **11.** $6, -1$ **13.** 48 units   **15.** 3   **17.** $4, -7$

19.   **21.**

Exercise 5.1   (page 155)

1. $\dfrac{2}{3}$ **3.** $-\dfrac{28}{9}$ **5.** $\dfrac{12}{13}$ **7.** $-\dfrac{122}{37}$ **9.** $4x^2$ **11.** $-\dfrac{4y}{3x}$ **13.** x^2 **15.** $-\dfrac{x}{2}$

17. $\dfrac{3y}{7(y - z)}$ **19.** $\dfrac{1}{x - y}$ **21.** $\dfrac{5}{x - 2}$ **23.** $\dfrac{-3(x + 2)}{x + 1}$ **25.** 3   **27.** $x + 2$

29. $\dfrac{x + 1}{x + 3}$ **31.** $\dfrac{m - 2n}{n - 2m}$ **33.** $\dfrac{x + 4}{2(2x - 3)}$ **35.** $\dfrac{3(x - y)}{x + 2}$ **37.** $\dfrac{2x + 1}{2 - x}$

39. $\dfrac{a^2 - 3a + 9}{4(a - 3)}$ **41.** in lowest terms   **43.** $m + n$ **45.** $\dfrac{x - y}{x + y}$ **47.** $\dfrac{2a - 3b}{a - 2b}$

49. $\dfrac{1}{x^2 + xy + y^2 - 1}$ **51.** $x^2 - y^2$ **53.** $x^2 + 8 + x$ **55.** $\dfrac{(x + 1)^2}{(x - 1)^3}$ **57.** $\dfrac{3a + b}{y + b}$

Exercise 5.2   (page 160)

1. $\dfrac{10}{7}$ **3.** $-\dfrac{5}{6}$ **5.** $\dfrac{xy^2 d}{c^3}$ **7.** $-\dfrac{x^{10}}{y^2}$ **9.** $x + 1$ **11.** 1   **13.** $\dfrac{x - 4}{x + 5}$

15. $\dfrac{(a + 7)^2(a - 5)(a - 3)}{12x^2}$ **17.** $\dfrac{1}{x + 1}$ **19.** $(x + 1)^2$ **21.** $x - 5$ **23.** $\dfrac{x + y}{x - y}$

25. $-\dfrac{x + 3}{x + 2}$ **27.** $\dfrac{a + b}{(x - 3)(c + d)}$ **29.** $-\dfrac{x^7}{18y^4}$ **31.** $x^2(x + 3)$ **33.** $\dfrac{3x}{2}$ **35.** $\dfrac{t + 1}{t}$

37. $\dfrac{x^2 + 4 + x}{x^3}$ **39.** $\dfrac{x + 2}{x - 2}$ **41.** $\dfrac{x - 1}{3x + 2}$ **43.** $\dfrac{x - 7}{x + 7}$ **45.** 1

Exercise 5.3   (page 165)

1. $\dfrac{5}{2}$ **3.** $-\dfrac{1}{3}$ **5.** $\dfrac{11}{4y}$ **7.** $\dfrac{3 - a}{a + b}$ **9.** $\dfrac{2(x + 2)}{x + 1}$ **11.** 3   **13.** 3

15. $\dfrac{6x}{(x - 3)(x - 2)}$ **17.** 72   **19.** $x(x + 3)(x - 3)$ **21.** $(x + 3)^2(x^2 - 3x + 9)$

23. $(2x + 3)^2(x + 1)^2$ **25.** $\dfrac{5}{6}$ **27.** $-\dfrac{16}{75}$ **29.** $\dfrac{9a}{10}$ **31.** $\dfrac{21a - 8b}{14}$ **33.** $\dfrac{17}{12x}$

35. $\dfrac{9a^2 - 4b^2}{6ab}$ **37.** $\dfrac{10a + 4b}{21}$ **39.** $\dfrac{8x - 2}{(x + 2)(x - 4)}$ **41.** $\dfrac{7x + 29}{(x + 5)(x + 7)}$ **43.** $\dfrac{x^2 + 1}{x}$

45. $\dfrac{2x^2 + x}{(x + 3)(x + 2)(x - 2)}$ **47.** $\dfrac{-x^2 + 11x + 8}{(3x + 2)(x + 1)(x - 3)}$ **49.** $\dfrac{-4x^2 + 14x + 54}{x(x + 3)(x - 3)}$

51. $\dfrac{2x^2 + 5x + 4}{x + 1}$ **53.** $\dfrac{x^2 - 5x - 5}{x - 5}$ **55.** $\dfrac{-x^3 - x^2 + 5x}{x - 1}$ **57.** $\dfrac{-y^2 + 48y + 161}{(y + 4)(y + 3)}$

59. $\dfrac{2}{x + 1}$ **61.** $\dfrac{3x + 1}{x(x + 3)}$ **63.** $\dfrac{2x^3 + x^2 - 43x - 35}{(x + 5)(x - 5)(2x + 1)}$ **65.** $\dfrac{3x^2 - 2x - 17}{(x - 3)(x - 2)}$ **67.** $\dfrac{2a}{a - 1}$

69. $\dfrac{x^2 - 6x - 1}{2(x + 1)(x - 1)}$ **71.** $\dfrac{2b}{a + b}$ **73.** $\dfrac{-7a^2 + 8ab + 2a - 2b - 3b^2}{(2a - b)(2a - b)}$ **75.** $\dfrac{x}{3}$

77. $\dfrac{2}{x}$ **79.** $\dfrac{x^2 - 6x + 9}{x^2}$

Exercise 5.4   (page 171)

1. $\dfrac{2}{3}$ **3.** -1 **5.** $\dfrac{10}{3}$ **7.** $-\dfrac{5}{6}$ **9.** $\dfrac{2y}{3z}$ **11.** $125b$ **13.** $-\dfrac{1}{y}$ **15.** $\dfrac{y - x}{x^2 y^2}$

17. $\dfrac{b + a}{b}$ **19.** $\dfrac{y + x}{y - x}$ **21.** $x^2 + x - 6$ **23.** $\dfrac{5x^2 y^2}{xy + 1}$ **25.** -1 **27.** $\dfrac{x + 2}{x - 3}$

29. $\dfrac{a - 1}{a + 1}$ **31.** $\dfrac{y + x}{x^2 y}$ **33.** $\dfrac{xy^2}{y - x}$ **35.** $\dfrac{y + x}{y - x}$ **37.** xy **39.** $\dfrac{x^3 y^2 - x^2}{x^2 y^3 - y^2}$

41. $\dfrac{(b + a)(b - a)}{b(b - a - ab)}$ **43.** $\dfrac{x - 1}{x}$ **45.** $\dfrac{5b}{5b + 4}$ **47.** $\dfrac{3a^2 + 2a}{2a + 1}$

49. $\dfrac{(-x^2 + 2x - 2)(3x + 2)}{(2 - x)(-3x^2 - 2x + 9)}$ or $\dfrac{-3x^3 + 4x^2 - 2x - 4}{3x^3 - 4x^2 - 13x + 18}$

Exercise 5.5   (page 177)

1. $x = 12$ **3.** $x = 40$ **5.** $y = \frac{1}{2}$ **7.** no solution   **9.** $x = \frac{17}{25}$ **11.** $y = 0$

13. $a = 1$ **15.** $x = 2$ **17.** $x = 2$ **19.** $x = \frac{1}{3}$ **21.** $a = 0$ **23.** $2, -5$

25. $-4, 3$ **27.** $6, \frac{17}{3}$ **29.** $1, -11$ **31.** $1\frac{7}{8}$ days   **33.** $4\frac{1}{2}$ hr   **35.** $3\frac{3}{7}$ hr

37. 3 mph   **39.** 60 mph and 40 mph   **41.** 2 **43.** 7 motors

REVIEW EXERCISES   (page 180)

1. $\dfrac{31x}{72y}$ **3.** $\dfrac{x - 7}{x + 7}$ **5.** $\dfrac{1}{2(x + 2)}$ **7.** 1 **9.** $\dfrac{5y - 3}{x - y}$ **11.** $\dfrac{5x + 13}{(x + 2)(x + 3)}$

13. $\dfrac{3x(x - 1)}{(x - 3)(x + 1)}$ **15.** $\dfrac{5x^2 + 11x}{(x + 1)(x + 2)}$ **17.** $\dfrac{5x^2 + 23x + 4}{(x + 1)(x - 1)(x - 1)}$ **19.** $\dfrac{2x^3 + 13x^2 + 31x + 31}{(x + 3)(x + 2)(x - 3)}$

21. $\dfrac{3y - 2x}{x^2 y^2}$ **23.** $\dfrac{2x + 1}{x + 1}$ **25.** $\dfrac{1}{x}$ **27.** $\dfrac{x^2 y^2}{(x - y)^2(y^2 - x^2)}$ **29.** $\dfrac{y(1 + xy)}{x(xy - 1)}$

31. $x = 5$ **33.** no solution   **35.** 50 mph

CHAPTER FIVE TEST   (page 181)

1. $\dfrac{-2}{3xy}$ **3.** -3 **5.** $\dfrac{xz}{y^4}$ **7.** 1 **9.** $\dfrac{2}{x + 1}$ **11.** 3 **13.** $\dfrac{2s + r^2}{rs}$

15. $\dfrac{u^2}{2vw}$ **17.** $x = \dfrac{5}{2}$ **19.** 10 days

Exercise 6.1   (page 186)

1. 4   3. 3   5. 3   7. 2   9. $\dfrac{1}{2}$ 11. $\dfrac{1}{2}$ 13. -2 15. -3

17. -4 19. 0   21. 216   23. 27   25. 1728   27. $\dfrac{1}{4}$ 29. $\dfrac{4}{9}$ 31. $\dfrac{1}{8}$

33. $\dfrac{1}{64}$ 35. $\dfrac{1}{9}$ 37. $\dfrac{1}{4}$ 39. 8   41. $\dfrac{16}{81}$ 43. $-\dfrac{3}{2}$ 45. $5^{5/7}$ 47. $4^{3/5}$

49. $9^{1/5}$ 51. $7^{1/2}$ 53. $\dfrac{1}{36}$ 55. $2^{2/3}$ 57. $2x^{1/3}$ 59. $9x^{4/3}y^{2/3}$

61. $125x^3y^{3/2}$ 63. $\dfrac{1}{2x^{1/2}y^{3/2}}$ 65. $\dfrac{2x}{3}$ 67. $4y$ 69. $x^{5a/6}$ 71. $\dfrac{1}{x^{a/12}}$

73. $\dfrac{1}{x^{a/5}}$ 75. x^{5b-a} 77. $y+y^2$ 79. a^2+1 81. $x^2-x+x^{3/5}$

83. $y^{1/2}+z^{1/3}y^{1/2}-z^{1/3}$ 85. $x-4$ 87. $x^{4/3}-x^2$ 89. $2+x^{1/2}y^{1/2}+\dfrac{1}{x^{1/2}y^{1/2}}$

91. $x^{4/3}+2x^{2/3}y^{2/3}+y^{4/3}$ 93. $a^3-2a^{3/2}b^{3/2}+b^3$ 95. $x+1$ 97. $729-54x+x^2$

Exercise 6.2   (page 195)

1. 11   3. -8 5. 1   7. -5 9. 3   11. -3 13. -2 15. 27
17. 8   19. -4 21. $-\frac{1}{4}$ 23. $\frac{1}{9}$ 25. $2|x|$ 27. $2a$ 29. $|x|$ 31. $|x^3|$
33. $-x$ 35. $-3a^2$ 37. 5   39. 2   41. t 43. $2\sqrt{5}$ 45. $2\sqrt{6}$
47. $10\sqrt{2}$ 49. $-5x\sqrt{2}$ 51. $4\sqrt{2b}$ 53. $-4a\sqrt{7a}$ 55. $5ab\sqrt{7b}$ 57. $-10\sqrt{3xy}$
59. $3\sqrt[3]{3}$ 61. $-2\sqrt[3]{10}$ 63. $-3x^2\sqrt[3]{2}$ 65. $-2x^4y\sqrt[3]{2}$ 67. $2x^3y\sqrt[4]{2}$
69. $-2x^2y\sqrt[5]{2}$ 71. -10 73. 7   75. $6b$ 77. $4x^2\sqrt{x}$ 79. 2   81. $3a$
83. $\dfrac{\sqrt{7}}{3}$ 85. $\dfrac{1}{4x}$ 87. $\dfrac{c\sqrt{5}}{7ab^2}$ 89. $\dfrac{x\sqrt{11}}{11}$ 91. $\dfrac{\sqrt[3]{4}}{3a}$ 93. $\dfrac{a^3\sqrt[3]{6}}{2}$ 95. $\dfrac{\sqrt{7}}{7}$
97. $\dfrac{\sqrt{6}}{3}$ 99. $\dfrac{\sqrt{10}}{4}$ 101. 2   103. $\dfrac{\sqrt[3]{4}}{2}$ 105. $\sqrt[3]{3}$ 107. $\dfrac{\sqrt[3]{18}}{3}$ 109. $2\sqrt{2x}$
111. $\dfrac{\sqrt{5y}}{y}$ 113. $\dfrac{\sqrt[3]{2ab^2}}{b}$ 115. $xz^2\sqrt[4]{xy^3}$ 117. $-2ab\sqrt[3]{2a^2c^2}$ 119. $-2abc^2\sqrt[3]{2abc}$
121. $x+1$ 123. $x+4$

Exercise 6.3   (page 198)

1. $10\sqrt{2}$ 3. $\sqrt[5]{7}$ 5. $14\sqrt{x}$ 7. $4\sqrt{3}$ 9. $-\sqrt{2}$ 11. $2\sqrt{2}$ 13. $9\sqrt{6}$
15. $3\sqrt[3]{3}$ 17. $-\sqrt[3]{4}$ 19. -10 21. $-41\sqrt[3]{2}$ 23. $-17\sqrt[4]{2}$ 25. $-4\sqrt{2}$
27. $3\sqrt{2}+\sqrt{3}$ 29. $-11\sqrt[3]{2}$ 31. $y\sqrt{z}$ 33. $(x^2y-x^2y^2-x^2y^3)\sqrt{y}$
35. $(3x+x^2)\sqrt[5]{xy^2}$ 37. $2x+3$ 39. $(2x+1)\sqrt{3}$ 41. 0   43. $3\sqrt{x}$
45. $\dfrac{5}{2}\sqrt{2}-\dfrac{5}{3}\sqrt{3}$ 47. $\dfrac{\sqrt{3a}}{a}$ 49. $\dfrac{3\sqrt{3x}}{x}$ 51. $\dfrac{5x\sqrt{7xy}}{6}$

Exercise 6.4   (page 202)

1. 4   3. $5\sqrt{2}$ 5. $3\sqrt{2}$ 7. 5   9. 3   11. $2\sqrt[3]{3}$ 13. ab^2 15. $5a\sqrt{b}$
17. $r\sqrt[3]{10s}$ 19. $2a^2b^2\sqrt[3]{2c^2}$ 21. $x^2(x+3)$ 23. $3x(y+z)\sqrt[3]{4}$ 25. $12\sqrt{5}-15$

27. $12\sqrt{6} + 6\sqrt{14}$ **29.** $-8\sqrt{10} + 6\sqrt{15}$ **31.** $-1 - 2\sqrt{2}$ **33.** $9 - 14\sqrt{3}$

35. $8 + 2\sqrt{15}$ **37.** 1 **39.** $-9 + 5\sqrt{15}$ **41.** $22 - 12\sqrt{2}$ **43.** $-20\sqrt{3} - 12\sqrt{7}$

45. $\sqrt{2} + 1$ **47.** $\dfrac{6(\sqrt{5} - 4)}{11}$ **49.** $\sqrt{3} - 1$ **51.** $5(\sqrt{6} - 1)$ **53.** $\dfrac{3\sqrt{2} - \sqrt{10}}{4}$

55. $-2\sqrt{7} - \sqrt{35}$ **57.** $\sqrt{7} + \sqrt{5}$ **59.** $10(\sqrt{3} - 1)$ **61.** $2 + \sqrt{3}$

63. $\dfrac{7 + 2\sqrt{2} - 2\sqrt{7} - \sqrt{14}}{5}$ **65.** $\dfrac{2(\sqrt{x} - 1)}{x - 1}$ **67.** $\dfrac{x(\sqrt{x} + 4)}{x - 16}$ **69.** $\sqrt{2z} + 1$

71. $\dfrac{x - 2\sqrt{xy} + y}{x - y}$

Exercise 6.5   (page 205)

1. $\sqrt{3}$ **3.** $\sqrt{x}$ **5.** x^2 **7.** y^3 **9.** $2x^3$ **11.** $\sqrt{3x}$ **13.** $-x\sqrt[3]{2}$

15. $-4a^4$ **17.** $3\sqrt{3}$ **19.** $-2\sqrt{2}$ **21.** 0 **23.** $3x\sqrt[3]{y}$ **25.** $17xy^2z^3\sqrt[5]{xyz}$

27. $\sqrt[6]{27}$ **29.** $\sqrt[8]{625}$ **31.** $\sqrt[6]{225}$ **33.** $\sqrt[9]{64}$ **35.** $\sqrt{3}$ **37.** $\sqrt[3]{5}$ **39.** $\sqrt[8]{8x^3y^3}$

41. $\sqrt[8]{16x^4y^2}$ **43.** $\sqrt[5]{6125}$ **45.** $\sqrt[6]{1125}$ **47.** $\sqrt[6]{32}$ **49.** $\sqrt[15]{16{,}384}$ **51.** $\sqrt[6]{125x^5y^2}$

53. $\sqrt[15]{5^{10} \cdot 3^3 x^5 y^6}$ **55.** $\sqrt[35]{x^{26}y^{43}} = y\sqrt[35]{x^{26}y^8}$ **57.** $\dfrac{\sqrt[6]{72}}{2}$ **59.** $\dfrac{\sqrt[15]{2^5 \cdot 3^3}}{2}$ or $\dfrac{\sqrt[15]{864}}{2}$

61. $\dfrac{\sqrt[10]{3^7}}{3}$ or $\dfrac{\sqrt[10]{2187}}{3}$ **63.** $\dfrac{\sqrt[14]{(4x)^2(2x)^7}}{2x} = \dfrac{\sqrt[14]{2^{11}x^9}}{2x} = \dfrac{\sqrt[14]{2048x^9}}{2x}$ **65.** $\dfrac{\sqrt[15]{(3x)^3 \cdot 9^5}}{3} = \dfrac{\sqrt[15]{3^{13}x^3}}{3}$

Exercise 6.6   (page 209)

1. $x = 2$ **3.** $x = 4$ **5.** $x = 0$ **7.** $n = 4$ **9.** $p = 8$ **11.** $x = \frac{5}{2}, x = \frac{1}{2}$

13. $r = 6, \cancel{r = 5}$ **15.** $x = 4, x = 3$ **17.** $y = 2, \cancel{y = 1}$ **19.** $x = 9, \cancel{x = 25}$

21. $x = 2, x = -1$ **23.** $x = 1, \cancel{x = 1}$ **25.** no solution   **27.** $y = 0, \cancel{y = 4}$

29. no solution   **31.** $v = 0$ **33.** $u = 1, u = 9$ **35.** $t = 4, \cancel{t = 0}$ **37.** $x = 2, \cancel{x = 142}$

39. $z = 2$ **41.** no solution   **43.** $x = -\frac{3}{2}$ **45.** $x = 0, \cancel{x = 1}$ **47.** $a = 1$

49. $x = 4, \cancel{x = 9}$

REVIEW EXERCISES   (page 211)

1. 5 **3.** 27 **5.** -2 **7.** $\frac{1}{4}$ **9.** $-16{,}807$ **11.** 8 **13.** $3xy^{1/3}$

15. $125x^9y^6$ **17.** $u - 1$ **19.** $x + 2x^{1/2}y^{1/2} + y$ **21.** 7 **23.** -6 **25.** -3

27. 5 **29.** $4\sqrt{15}$ **31.** $2\sqrt[4]{2}$ **33.** $2|x|\sqrt{2x}$ **35.** $2xyz\sqrt[3]{2x^2y}$ **37.** 5

39. $3x$ **41.** $-2x$ **43.** $\dfrac{\sqrt{3}}{3}$ **45.** $\dfrac{\sqrt{xy}}{y}$ **47.** $x + 3$ **49.** $3\sqrt{2}$ **51.** 0

53. $29\sqrt{2}$ **55.** $13\sqrt[3]{2}$ **57.** 4 **59.** $\sqrt{10} - \sqrt{5}$ **61.** 1 **63.** $x - y$

65. $2(\sqrt{2} + 1)$ **67.** $2(\sqrt{x} - 4)$ **69.** $\sqrt{5}$ **71.** $\sqrt{2}$ **73.** x^2 **75.** $x^2y^2\sqrt{x}$

77. $\sqrt[6]{5^3 \cdot 2^2} = \sqrt[6]{500}$ **79.** $\sqrt[6]{3^2 \cdot 2^3} = \sqrt[6]{72}$ **81.** $\dfrac{\sqrt[6]{2000}}{2}$ **83.** $\dfrac{\sqrt[10]{6075}}{3}$ **85.** $y = 22$

87. $r = 3, r = 9$ **89.** $x = 2$

CHAPTER SIX TEST   (page 213)

1. 2 **3.** $\dfrac{1}{216}$ **5.** $2^{4/3}$ **7.** $4\sqrt{3}$ **9.** $2x^5y\sqrt[3]{3}$ **11.** $\dfrac{\sqrt{5}}{5}$ **13.** $2\sqrt[3]{3}$

15. $2\sqrt{3}$ **17.** $2y^2\sqrt{3y}$ **19.** $-6x\sqrt{y} - 2xy^2$ **21.** $\dfrac{\sqrt{2}(\sqrt{5} - 3)}{4}$ **23.** $2\sqrt{2}$

25. $4\sqrt{6}$ **27.** $\sqrt[6]{5^2 \cdot 7^3} = \sqrt[6]{8575}$ **29.** $n = 10$

CUMULATIVE REVIEW EXERCISES (CHAPTERS 4–6)   (page 214)

1. $x = 8$ **3.** $y = -1$ **5.** 28, 30, 32   **7.** $a = \dfrac{2S}{n} - l$ **9.** $x = -\frac{1}{3}, x = -\frac{7}{2}$

11. $x = -5, x = -\frac{3}{5}$ **13.** $-3 < x < 3$ **15.** $-\frac{2}{3} \le x \le 2$ **17.** $\dfrac{2x - 3}{3x - 1}$ **19.** $\dfrac{4}{x - y}$

21. $x = 0$ **23.** 16   **25.** $x^{17/12}$ **27.** $-3x$ **29.** $4x$ **31.** $7\sqrt{2}$ **33.** $-18\sqrt{6}$

35. $\dfrac{x + 3\sqrt{x} + 2}{x - 1}$ **37.** $x = 2, x = 7$

Exercise 7.1   (page 223)

1.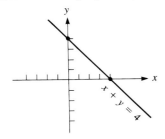

3.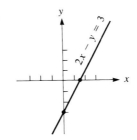

5.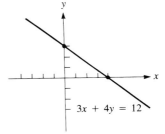

7.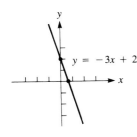

9.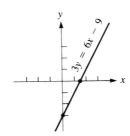

11.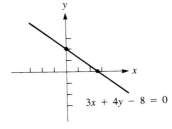

13. 5   **15.** 5   **17.** 13   **19.** 10   **21.** $\sqrt{104}$ or $2\sqrt{26}$ **23.** $(\frac{7}{2}, 6)$ **25.** $(\frac{1}{2}, -2)$

27. $(9, 12)$ **29.** $(-4, 0)$ **31.** $(\frac{3}{2}, -2)$ **33.** $\left(\dfrac{a + c}{2}, \dfrac{b + d}{2}\right)$ **35.** $\left(\dfrac{\sqrt{2} + \sqrt{3}}{2}, \dfrac{\sqrt{3} + \sqrt{2}}{2}\right)$

39. $(4, 1)$ **41.** $x = 7$ **43.** $(7, 0), (3, 0)$

Exercise 7.2   (page 230)

1. 3   **3.** -1 **5.** $-\frac{1}{3}$ **7.** 0   **9.** no defined slope   **11.** $-\frac{3}{2}$ **13.** $\frac{3}{4}$

15. $\frac{1}{2}$ **17.** 0   **19.** $-\frac{2}{3}$ **21.** negative   **23.** positive   **25.** no defined slope

27. perpendicular   **29.** parallel   **31.** perpendicular   **33.** neither   **35.** parallel

37. perpendicular   **39.** neither   **41.** on same line   **43.** not on same line

45. on same line   **47.** $y = 0$; slope is 0   **55.** $a = 4$

Exercise 7.3   (page 238)

1. $5x - y = -7$ **3.** $3x + y = 6$ **5.** $3x - 2y = -4$ **7.** $y = x$ **9.** $y = \frac{7}{3}x - 3$

11. $y = -\frac{9}{5}x + \frac{2}{5}$ **13.** $y = 3x + 17$ **15.** $y = -7x + 54$ **17.** $y = -4$ **19.** $y = -\frac{1}{2}x + 11$

21. $m = 1; \quad b = -1$ **23.** $m = \frac{2}{3}; \quad b = 2$

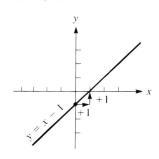
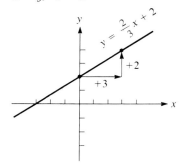

25. $m = -\frac{2}{3}; \quad b = 6$ **27.** $m = \frac{3}{2}; \quad b = -4$

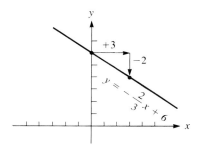

29. $m = -\frac{1}{3}; \quad b = -\frac{5}{6}$ **31.** $m = \frac{7}{2}; \quad b = 2$ **33.** parallel   **35.** perpendicular

37. parallel   **39.** perpendicular   **41.** perpendicular   **43.** perpendicular   **45.** $y = 4x$

47. $y = 4x - 3$ **49.** $y = \frac{4}{5}x - \frac{26}{5}$ **51.** $y = -\frac{1}{4}x$ **53.** $y = -\frac{1}{4}x + \frac{11}{2}$ **55.** $y = -\frac{5}{4}x + 3$

57. perpendicular   **59.** parallel   **61.** $x = -2$ **63.** $x = 5$

Exercise 7.4   (page 244)

1. a function   **3.** a function   **5.** not a function   **7.** not a function   **9.** a function

11. Both the domain and range are the set of real numbers.

13. The domain is the set of all real numbers except 2; the range is the set of all real numbers except 0.

15. The domain is the set of all real numbers; the range is the set of all nonnegative real numbers.

17. The domain is the set of all real numbers; the range is $\{3\}$.

19. The domain is the set of all real numbers greater than or equal to 2; the range is the set of all nonnegative real numbers.

21. 7   **23.** -8 **25.** 0   **27.** $5x + 12$ **29.** 4   **31.** 5   **33.** $\frac{40}{9}$

35. $x^4 + 4$ **37.** 7   **39.** 24   **41.** $2x^2 - 1$ **43.** 58   **45.** 110

47. $9x^2 - 9x + 2$ **53.** $2x + h$ **55.** $3x - 2$; The domain is the set of real numbers.

57. $2x^2 - 5x - 3$; The domain is the set of real numbers.

59. $-2x^2 + 3x - 3$; The domain is the set of real numbers.

61. $\dfrac{3x - 2}{2x^2 + 1}$; The domain is the set of real numbers.   **63.** 3; The domain is set of real numbers.

65. $\dfrac{x^2 - 4}{x^2 - 1}$; The domain is the set of real numbers except 1 and -1.

Exercise 7.5   (page 249)

1.   a linear function   **3.**   a linear function   **5.**   not a linear function   **7.**   a linear function
9.   not a linear function   **11.**   The domain is $\{1, 3, 5\}$; the range is $\{2, 4, 9, 12\}$; not a function
13.   The domain is $\{1, -1, 4, -4\}$; the range is $\{2, 3, 4, 5\}$; a function
15.   The domain is $\{5, 6\}$; the range is $\{8, 9, 10\}$; not a function   **17.** $\{(2, 3), (1, 2), (0, 1)\}$;   a function
19. $\{(2, 1), (3, 2), (3, 1), (5, 1)\}$;   not a function   **21.** $\{(1, 1), (4, 2), (9, 3), (16, 4)\}$;   a function
23. $f^{-1}(x) = \frac{1}{3}x - \frac{1}{3}$;   a linear function   **25.** $f^{-1}(x) = 5x - 4$;   a linear function
27. $f^{-1}(x) = 5x + 4$;   a linear function   **29.** $y = \frac{5}{4}x^2 + 5$;   a function but not a linear function

31. $f^{-1}(x) = \dfrac{x + 3}{2}$ **33.** $f^{-1}(x) = \dfrac{x - 2}{3}$

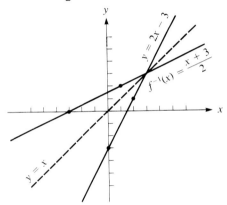

The axis of symmetry is the line $y = x$.

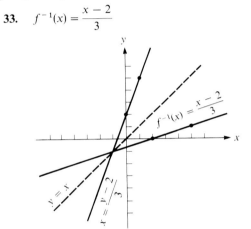

The axis of symmetry is the line $y = x$.

35. $f^{-1}(x) = \dfrac{x + 5}{3}$ **37.** $f^{-1}(x) = -3x + 4$

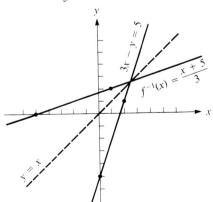

The axis of symmetry is the line $y = x$.

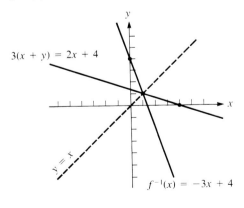

The axis of symmetry is the line $y = x$.

39. $f^{-1}(x) = -\frac{2}{3}x + 4$ **41.** $g = 5l$ **43.** $c = 10 + n$

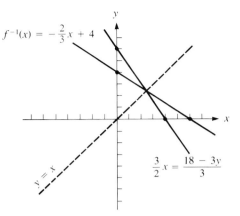

The axis of symmetry is the line $y = x$.

45. $C = \frac{5}{9}F - \frac{160}{9}$ or $C = \frac{5}{9}(F - 32)$

Exercise 7.6   (page 255)

1. $x = 3$ **3.** $r = 5$ **5.** $y = 4$ or $y = -4$ **7.** $n = -3$

9. $x = 5$ **11.** $t = -3$ is extraneous   **13.** $A = kp^2$ **15.** $v = \dfrac{k}{\sqrt[4]{r}}$

17. $B = kmn$ **19.** $P = \dfrac{ka^2}{j^3}$ **21.** $F = \dfrac{km_1 m_2}{d^2}$

23. L varies directly with the product of m and n, or L varies jointly with m and n.
25. E varies directly with the product ab^2, or E varies jointly with a and the square of b.
27. X varies directly with the square of x and inversely with the square of y.
29. R varies directly with L and inversely with the square of d.
31. 36π sq in.   **33.** 432 mi   **35.** 25 days   **37.** 12 cu in.   **39.** approximately 85.3
41. The volume is multiplied by 12.   **43.** 1125π gallons   **45.** 3 ohms
47. 4.4 in. (on side);   0.275 in. (on edge)

Exercise 7.7   (page 260)

1.

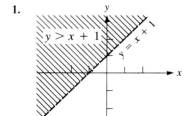

$y > x + 1$

3.

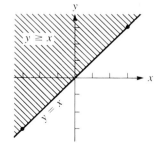

$y \geq x$

5.

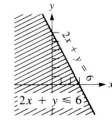

$2x + y = 6$

$2x + y \leqslant 6$

7.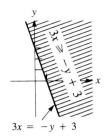

9.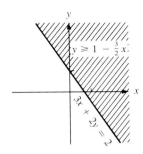

11.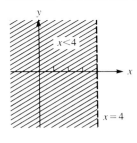

13.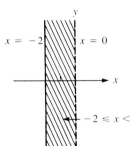

15.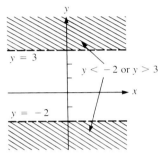

17.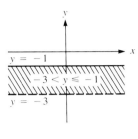

19. $3x + 2y > 6$ **21.** $x \le 3$ **23.** $y \le x$ **25.** $-2 \le x \le 3$ **27.** $y > -1$ or $y \le -3$

REVIEW EXERCISES   (page 263)

1.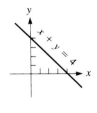

3.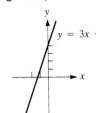

5. 5   **7.** $\sqrt{233}$ **9.** $(2, 9)$ **11.** $(\frac{7}{2}, 2)$

13. 1   **15.** 5

17. $y - 5 = -\frac{3}{2}(x + 2)$ or $y = -\frac{3}{2}x + 2$ **19.** $3x - y = -29$ **21.** $3x - 2y = 1$
23. The domain is the set of real numbers; the range is the set of real numbers; a function
25. The domain is the set of real numbers; the range is the set of real numbers greater than or equal to 1; a function
27. The domain is the set of real numbers; the range is the set of real numbers; a function
29. -7 **31.** 12   **33.** $3x^2 - 10$ **35.** $5x - 1$; the domain is the set of real numbers.

37. $6x^2 - x - 2$; the domain is the set of real numbers.   **39.** $f^{-1}(x) = \dfrac{x - 2}{7}$;   a function

41. $x = 5$ **43.** 72   **45.** $k = 2$ **47.**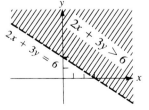

49.

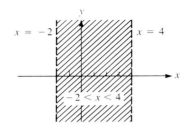

CHAPTER SEVEN TEST   (page 264)

1.

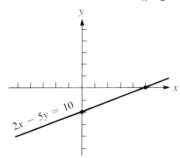

3. $\sqrt{116} = 2\sqrt{29}$

5. $\frac{2}{5}$ **7.** $y = \frac{2}{3}x - \frac{23}{3}$ **9.** $m = -\frac{1}{3}$; $b = -\frac{3}{2}$ **11.**   perpendicular   **13.** $y = \frac{3}{2}x + \frac{21}{2}$
15.   The domain is the set of all real numbers except 2; the range is the set of all real numbers except 0.
17. $g(0) = -2$ **19.** $g(f(x)) = 9x^2 + 6x - 1$ **21.** $(f \cdot g)x = 3x^3 + x^2 - 6x - 2$ **23.**   yes
25. $x = 6$ or $x = -1$ **27.** $\frac{135}{2}$ **29.**

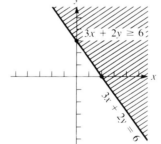

Exercise 8.1   (page 271)

1. $0, -2$ **3.** $0, -1$ **5.** $5, -5$ **7.** $-2, -4$ **9.** $1, 2$ **11.** $6, 1$ **13.** $7, -1$
15. $\frac{1}{2}, 2$ **17.** $\frac{2}{3}, -\frac{5}{2}$ **19.** $\frac{2}{3}, 1$ **21.** $0, 2$ **23.** $3, 3$ **25.** $6, -6$ **27.** $\sqrt{5}, -\sqrt{5}$
29. $\frac{4\sqrt{3}}{3}, -\frac{4\sqrt{3}}{3}$ **31.** $0, -2$ **33.** $10, 4$ **35.** $-5 + \sqrt{3}, -5 - \sqrt{3}$ **37.** $2, -4$

39. $2, 4$ **41.** $-1, -4$ **43.** $1, -\frac{1}{2}$ **45.** $-\frac{1}{3}, -\frac{3}{2}$ **47.** $\frac{3}{4}, -\frac{3}{2}$

49. $\frac{-7 + \sqrt{29}}{10}, \frac{-7 - \sqrt{29}}{10}$ **51.** $16, 18$ or $-18, -16$ **53.** $6, 7$ **55.**   8 ft by 12 ft

57.   16 units   **59.**   either \$4.80 or \$5.20   **61.**   4000 subscribers   **63.**   about 2.26 in.

65. $x^2 + 4\sqrt{7}x - 35 = 0$ **67.** $x^2 - (\sqrt{3} + 1)x + \sqrt{3} = 0$

Exercise 8.2   (page 278)

1. $-1, -2$ **3.** $2, -1$ **5.** $0, -2$ **7.** $6, -6$ **9.** $2, -1$ **11.** $-6, -6$

13. $-\dfrac{3}{2}, -\dfrac{1}{2}$ **15.** $\dfrac{5}{3}, -\dfrac{1}{3}$ **17.** $\dfrac{1}{4}, -\dfrac{3}{4}$ **19.** $\dfrac{-5 + \sqrt{17}}{2}, \dfrac{-5 - \sqrt{17}}{2}$

21. $\dfrac{-5 + \sqrt{5}}{10}, \dfrac{-5 - \sqrt{5}}{10}$ **23.** $\dfrac{3 + \sqrt{21}}{6}, \dfrac{3 - \sqrt{21}}{6}$ **25.**   10 ft by 5 ft   **27.** $b = \dfrac{4}{3}$ cm

29. $\sqrt{17}$ in.   **31.**   4 m   **33.** $r = 30$ mi/h   **35.** $b = 12, r_2 = -1$

Exercise 8.3   (page 285)

1. $3i, -3i$ **3.** $\dfrac{4\sqrt{3}}{3}i, -\dfrac{4\sqrt{3}}{3}i$ **5.** $-1 + i, -1 - i$ **7.** $-\dfrac{1}{4} + \dfrac{\sqrt{7}}{4}i, -\dfrac{1}{4} - \dfrac{\sqrt{7}}{4}i$

9. $\dfrac{2}{3} + \dfrac{\sqrt{2}}{3}i, \dfrac{2}{3} - \dfrac{\sqrt{2}}{3}i$ **11.** i **13.** $-i$ **15.**   1   **17.** i **19.** $8 - 2i$ **21.** $3 - 5i$

23. $15 + 7i$ **25.** $-15 + 2\sqrt{3}i$ **27.** $3 + 6i$ **29.** $7 + i$ **31.** $14 - 8i$ **33.** $8 + \sqrt{2}i$

35. $6 - 8i$ **37.** $6 + \sqrt{6} + (3\sqrt{3} - 2\sqrt{2})i$ **39.** $-16 - \sqrt{35} + (2\sqrt{5} - 8\sqrt{7})i$ **41.** $0 - i$

43. $0 + \dfrac{4}{5}i$ **45.** $\dfrac{1}{8} + 0i$ **47.** $0 + \dfrac{3}{5}i$ **49.** $0 + \dfrac{3\sqrt{2}}{4}i$ **51.** $\dfrac{15}{26} - \dfrac{3}{26}i$

53. $-\dfrac{42}{25} - \dfrac{6}{25}i$ **55.** $\dfrac{1}{4} + \dfrac{3}{4}i$ **57.** $\dfrac{5}{13} - \dfrac{12}{13}i$ **59.** $\dfrac{6 + \sqrt{10}}{9} + \dfrac{2\sqrt{2} - 3\sqrt{5}}{9}i$ **61.**   10

63.   13   **65.** $\sqrt{74}$ **67.** $3\sqrt{2}$ **69.** $\sqrt{69}$

Exercise 8.4   (page 289)

1.   rational and equal   **3.**   nonreal and complex conjugates   **5.**   irrational and unequal

7.   rational and unequal   **9.** $6, -6$ **11.** $12, -12$ **13.**   5   **15.** $12, -3$

17.   roots are real   **19.** $k < -\dfrac{4}{3}$ **21.** $\dfrac{-\sqrt{5} + 1}{2}, \dfrac{-\sqrt{5} - 1}{2}$

Exercise 8.5   (page 291)

1. $1, -1, 4, -4$ **3.** $1, -1, \sqrt{2}, -\sqrt{2}$ **5.** $1, -1, \sqrt{5}, -\sqrt{5}$ **7.** $1, -1, 2, -2$ **9.**   1

11.   no solution   **13.** $-8, -27$ **15.** $27, -1$ **17.** $-1, -4$ **19.** $4, -5$

21. $0, 2$ **23.** $-1, -\frac{27}{13}$ **25.** $1, 1, -1, -1$ **27.** $1, -1, 2, -2$ **29.** $1, -1, \sqrt{5}, -\sqrt{5}$

31. $x = \pm\sqrt{r^2 - y^2}$ **33.** $d = \pm\sqrt{\dfrac{k}{I}} = \dfrac{\pm\sqrt{kI}}{I}$ **35.** $y = \dfrac{-3x \pm \sqrt{9x^2 - 28x}}{2x}$

37. $\mu^2 = \dfrac{\sum x^2}{N} - \sigma^2$ **39.**   either $\frac{2}{5}$ or $\frac{5}{2}$ **41.**   37 decks

Exercise 8.6   (page 295)

1.   **3.**   **5.**   **7.**

9.   no solutions   **11.**   **13.**   **15.**

17. 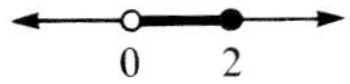

19. 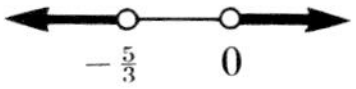

21. 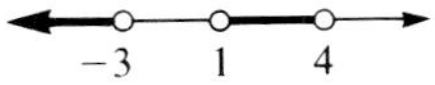

23. 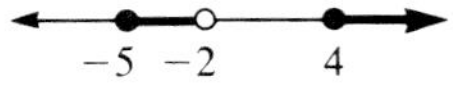

25. 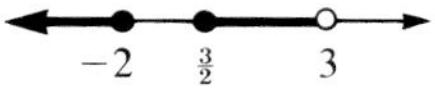

27. 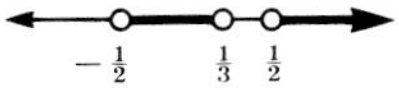

29. 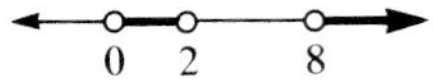

31. 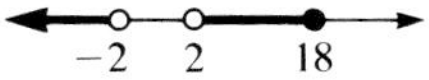

33. 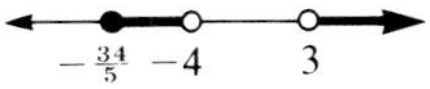

35. 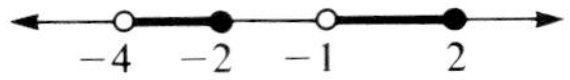

37. 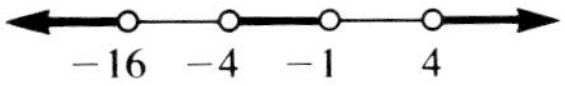

39. 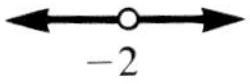

REVIEW EXERCISES (page 296)

1. $\frac{2}{3}, -\frac{3}{4}$ **3.** $\frac{2}{3}, -\frac{4}{5}$ **5.** $5, -3$ **7.** $1, \frac{7}{2}$ **9.** $9, -1$ **11.** $\frac{1}{2}, -7$ **13.** $\frac{14}{3}$

15. 4 in. by 6 in. **17.** $\dfrac{-1+\sqrt{31}\,i}{4}, \dfrac{-1-\sqrt{31}\,i}{4}$ **19.** $12 - 8i$ **21.** $-96 + 3i$

23. $22 + 29i$ **25.** $-12 + 28\sqrt{3}i$ **27.** $0 - \frac{3}{4}i$ **29.** $\frac{12}{5} - \frac{6}{5}i$ **31.** $\frac{15}{17} + \frac{8}{17}i$

33. $\dfrac{15}{29} - \dfrac{6}{29}i$ **35.** $\dfrac{6+\sqrt{2}}{6} + \dfrac{2-3\sqrt{2}}{6}i$ **37.** 15 **39.** irrational and unequal

41. 12, 152 **43.** $3, -3, 2, -2$ **45.** 4, 11 **47.** $\frac{9}{16}$ **49.** 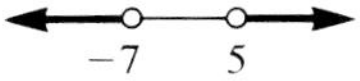

51. 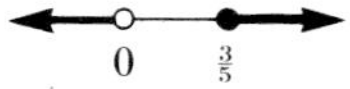

53. 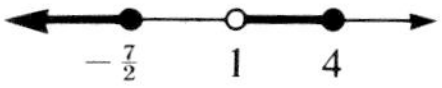

55. 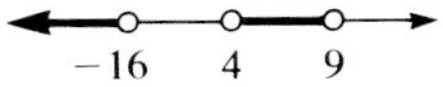

CHAPTER EIGHT TEST (page 298)

1. $3, -6$ **3.** 144 **5.** $-2 + \sqrt{3}, -2 - \sqrt{3}$ **7.** 10 in. **9.** $0 + 4i, 0 - 4i$

11. $-1 + 11i$ **13.** $8 + 6i$ **15.** $0 - \dfrac{\sqrt{2}}{2}i$ **17.** nonreal **19.** $1, \dfrac{1}{4}$

21. 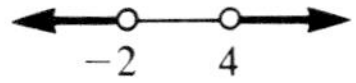

Exercise 9.1 (page 303)

1. 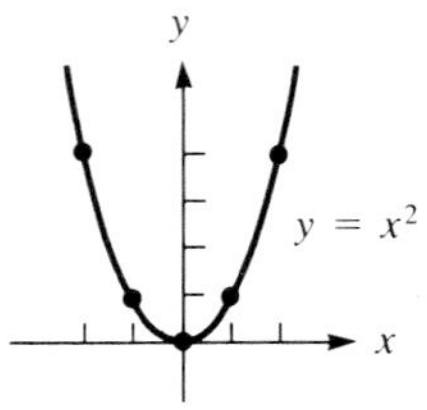

3. 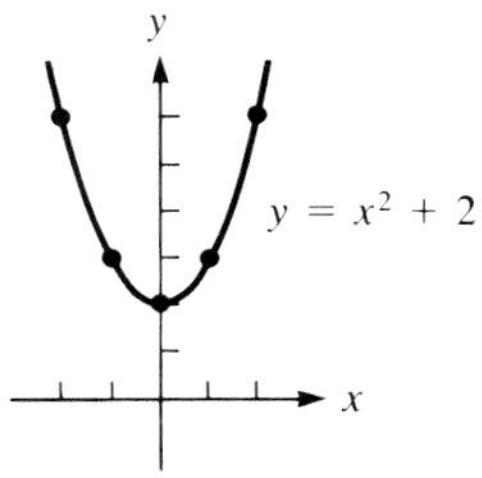

5. 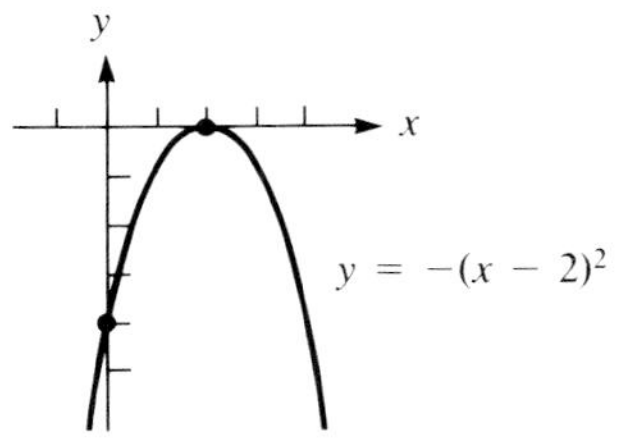

7.
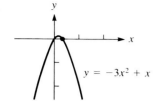
$y = -3x^2 + x$

9.
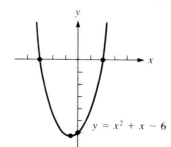
$y = x^2 + x - 6$

11.
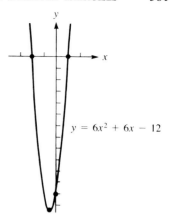
$y = 6x^2 + 6x - 12$

13. vertex at $(1, 2)$; axis of symmetry is $x = 1$ **15.** vertex at $(-3, -4)$; axis of symmetry is $x = -3$
17. vertex at $(0, 0)$; axis of symmetry is $x = 0$
19. vertex at $(1, -2)$; axis of symmetry is $x = 1$ **21.** vertex at $(2, 21)$; axis of symmetry is $x = 2$
23. vertex at $\left(\frac{5}{12}, \frac{143}{24}\right)$; axis of symmetry is $x = \frac{5}{12}$ **25.** vertex at (h, k) **27.** both are 25
29. 36 ft; 3 s   **31.** 50 ft by 50 ft; 2500 sq ft   **33.** \$35

Exercise 9.2   (page 308)

1. no   **3.** yes   **5.** no   **7.** yes   **9.** yes   **11.** yes   **13.** no   **15.** yes
17. no   **19.** yes   **21.** yes   **23.** no   **25.** yes   **27.** no   **29.** no

31.
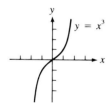
$y = x^3$

33.
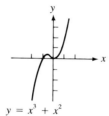
$y = x^3 + x^2$

35.
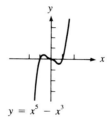
$y = x^5 - x^3$

37.
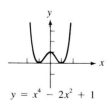
$y = x^4 - 2x^2 + 1$

39.
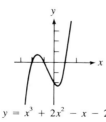
$y = x^3 + 2x^2 - x - 2$

41.
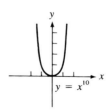
$y = x^{10}$

43. increasing when $x \leq 0$;
decreasing when $0 \leq x \leq 1$;
increasing when $x \geq 1$

45. increasing when $x \leq -2$;
decreasing when $-2 \leq x \leq 0$;
increasing when $x \geq 0$

47. always increasing

Exercise 9.3   (page 315)

1.
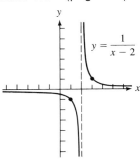

3.
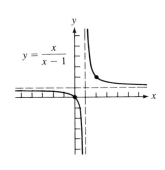

5.
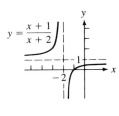

7.
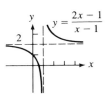

9.
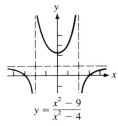

11.
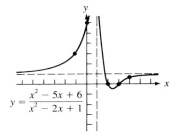

13.
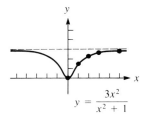

15.
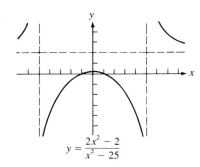

17.
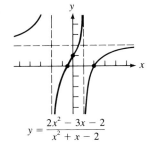

19.
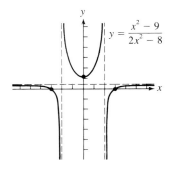

21.
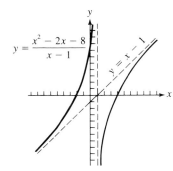

23.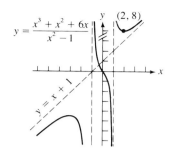
$$y = \frac{x^3 + x^2 + 6x}{x^2 - 1}$$

25.   no

Exercise 9.4   (page 319)

1.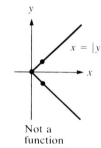
$x = |y|$

Not a function

3.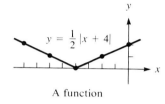
$y = \frac{1}{2}|x + 4|$

A function

5.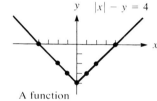
$|x| - y = 4$

A function

7.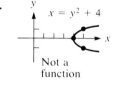
$x = y^2 + 4$

Not a function

9.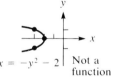
$x = -y^2 - 2$

Not a function

11.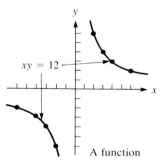
$xy = 12$

A function

13.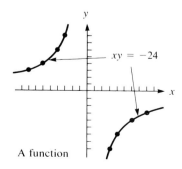
$xy = -24$

A function

15.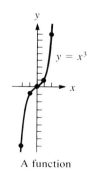
$y = x^3$

A function

17.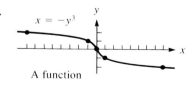
$x = -y^3$

A function

19.

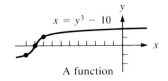

$x = y^3 - 10$

A function

21.

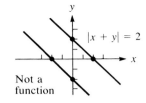

$|x + y| = 2$

Not a function

23.

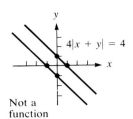

$4|x + y| = 4$

Not a function

25.

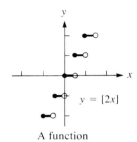

$y = [2x]$

A function

27.

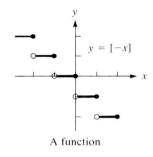

$y = [-x]$

A function

29.

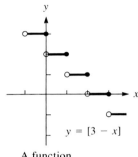

$y = [3 - x]$

A function

31.

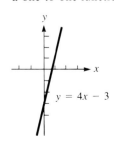

$y = \operatorname{sgn} x$

Exercise 9.5   (page 326)

1. $y = \dfrac{x - 1}{3}$; a function

3. $y = 5x - 4$; a function

5. $y = \pm\sqrt{x - 4}$; not a function

7. $y = \sqrt[3]{x + 1}$; a function

9. $y = \pm\sqrt{1 - x^2}$; not a function

11. $y = x^2$; a function

13. a one-to-one function

15. not a one-to-one function

17.

$y = 4x - 3$

a one-to-one function

19.

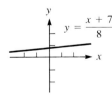

$y = \dfrac{x + 7}{8}$

a one-to-one function

21.

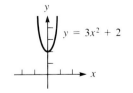

$y = 3x^2 + 2$

not a one-to-one function

23.

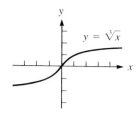

$y = \sqrt[3]{x}$

a one-to-one function

25.

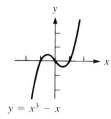

$y = x^3 - x$

not a one-to-one function

27.

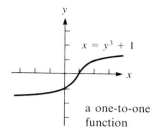

$x = y^3 + 1$

a one-to-one
function

29. $y = f^{-1}(x) = \frac{1}{3}x;$ $\begin{cases} (f \circ f^{-1})(x) = f(f^{-1}(x)) = 3(\frac{1}{3}x) = x \\ (f^{-1} \circ f)(x) = f^{-1}(f(x)) = \frac{1}{3}(3x) = x \end{cases}$

31. $y = f^{-1}(x) = \dfrac{x+4}{2};$ $\begin{cases} (f \circ f^{-1})(x) = f(f^{-1}(x)) = 2\left(\dfrac{x+4}{2}\right) - 4 = x \\ \\ (f^{-1} \circ f)(x) = f^{-1}(f(x)) = \dfrac{2x - 4 + 4}{2} = x \end{cases}$

33. $y = f^{-1}(x) = \dfrac{1 - 3x}{x};$ $\begin{cases} (f \circ f^{-1})(x) = f(f^{-1}(x)) = \dfrac{1}{\dfrac{1 - 3x}{x} + 3} = x \\ \\ (f \circ f^{-1})(x) = f^{-1}(f(x)) = \dfrac{1 - 3\left(\dfrac{1}{x+3}\right)}{\dfrac{1}{x+3}} = x \end{cases}$

35. $y = f^{-1}(x) = \dfrac{1}{2x};$ $\begin{cases} (f \circ f^{-1})(x) = f(f^{-1}(x)) = \dfrac{1}{2\left(\dfrac{1}{2x}\right)} = x \\ \\ (f^{-1} \circ f)(x) = f^{-1}(f(x)) = \dfrac{1}{2\left(\dfrac{1}{2x}\right)} = x \end{cases}$

37. $y = f^{-1}(x) = -\sqrt{x+3} \ (y \le 0)$ **39.** $y = f^{-1}(x) = \sqrt[4]{x+8} \ (y \ge 0)$
41. $y = f^{-1}(x) = \sqrt{4 - x^2} \ (0 \le y \le 2)$
43. domain is the set of all real numbers except 1, range is the set of all real numbers except 1
45. domain is the set of all real numbers except 0, range is the set of all real numbers except -2

Exercise 9.6   (page 328)

1.

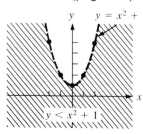

$y = x^2 + 1$

$y < x^2 + 1$

3.

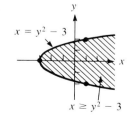

$x = y^2 - 3$

$x \ge y^2 - 3$

5. $y = x^2 + 5x + 6$

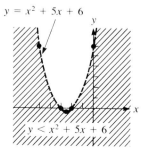

$y < x^2 + 5x + 6$

7.

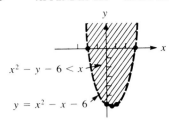

$x^2 - y - 6 < x$

$y = x^2 - x - 6$

9.

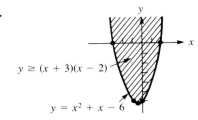

$y \geq (x + 3)(x - 2)$

$y = x^2 + x - 6$

11.

$y = (x + 2)^2$

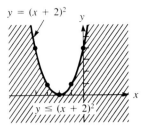

$y \leq (x + 2)^2$

13.

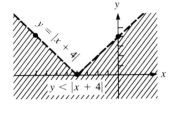

$y = |x + 4|$

$y < |x + 4|$

15.

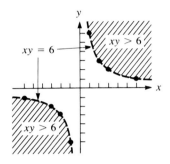

$xy = 6$

$xy > 6$

$xy > 6$

17.

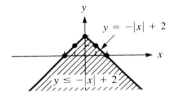

$y = -|x| + 2$

$y \leq -|x| + 2$

REVIEW EXERCISES   (page 330)

1.

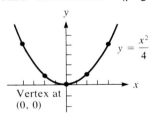

$y = \dfrac{x^2}{4}$

Vertex at (0, 0)

3.

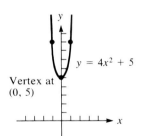

$y = 4x^2 + 5$

Vertex at (0, 5)

5.   symmetric to the y-axis

7.   symmetric to the x-axis

9.

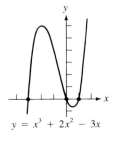

$y = x^3 + 2x^2 - 3x$

11.   increasing when $x \leq -2$,
decreasing when $-2 \leq x \leq 2$,
increasing when $x \geq 2$

13.

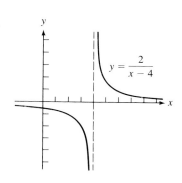

$$y = \frac{2}{x - 4}$$

15

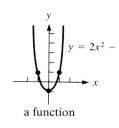

$y = 2x^2 - 1$

a function

17.

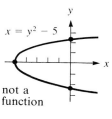

$x = y^2 - 5$

not a function

19. $f^{-1}(x) = y = \dfrac{7 - x}{2}$; the inverse is a function

21. $f^{-1}(x) = y = \dfrac{-8}{x}$; the inverse is a function

23.

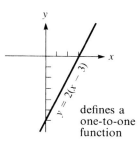

$y = 2(x - 3)$

defines a one-to-one function

25. $y = f^{-1}(x) = \dfrac{1 - 2x}{x}$;

$$\begin{cases} (f \circ f^{-1})(x) = f(f^{-1}(x)) = \dfrac{1}{\dfrac{1 - 2x}{x} + 2} = x \\[4mm] (f^{-1} \circ f)(x) = f^{-1}(f(x)) = \dfrac{1 - 2\left(\dfrac{1}{x + 2}\right)}{\dfrac{1}{x + 2}} = x \end{cases}$$

27. The domain is the set of all real numbers except $\frac{1}{2}$; the range is the set of all real numbers except 1.

29.

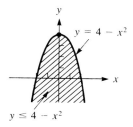

$y = 4 - x^2$

$y \le 4 - x^2$

CHAPTER NINE TEST   (page 331)

1.

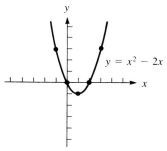

$y = x^2 - 2x$

3. $x = 2$ **5.**

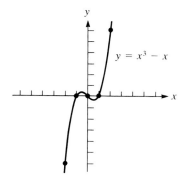

$y = x^3 - x$

7. $x = 3$ **9.** $x = 2$ **11.** no   **13.**

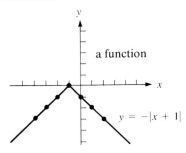

a function

$y = -|x + 1|$

15.

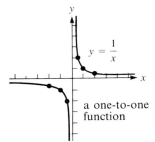

$y = \dfrac{1}{x}$

a one-to-one function

17. The range is the set of real numbers.

CUMULATIVE REVIEW EXERCISES (CHAPTERS 7–9)   (page 332)

1.

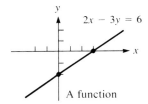

$2x - 3y = 6$

A function

3. $(3, -2)$ **5.** $y = -\frac{7}{5}x + \frac{11}{5}$ **7.** 5   **9.** $12x^2 - 12x + 5$

11. $y = f^{-1}(x) = 3x - 3$; a function   **13.** $y = \dfrac{kxz}{rs}$ **15.**

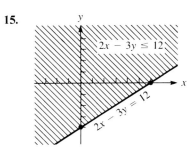

$2x - 3y \le 12$

$2x - 3y = 12$

17. $x = \dfrac{-2 + \sqrt{7}}{3}; x = \dfrac{-2 - \sqrt{7}}{3}$ **19.** $x = 16$ **21.**

$-1 \quad 1 \quad 4$

23. $\dfrac{3 + 10\sqrt{13}}{10} + \dfrac{1}{10}i$ **25.** $k = -2$ **27.**

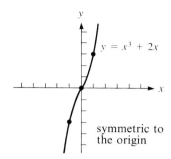

symmetric to
the origin

29.

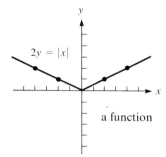

a function

31. The range is the set of all real numbers except 2.

Exercise 10.1 (page 336)

1.

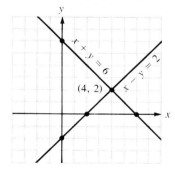

3.

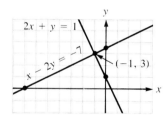

5.

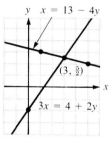

7.

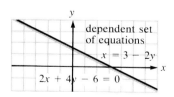

9.

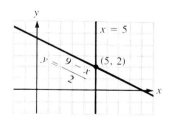

11.

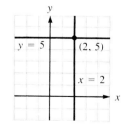

13.

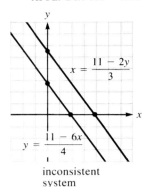

inconsistent system

15.

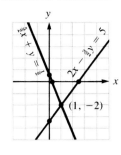

17.

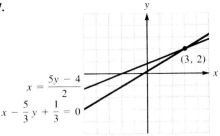

19.

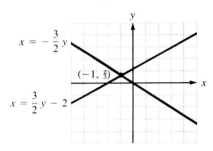

21. One possible solution is $\begin{cases} x + y = -3 \\ x - y = -7 \end{cases}$.

Exercise 10.2 (page 343)

1. $(2, 2)$ **3.** $(5, 3)$ **5.** $(-2, 4)$ **7.** no solution **9.** $(5, \frac{3}{2})$ **11.** $(5, 2)$
13. $(-4, -2)$ **15.** $(1, 2)$ **17.** $(\frac{1}{2}, \frac{2}{3})$ **19.** dependent equation **21.** $(4, 8)$
23. $(20, -12)$ **25.** $(\frac{2}{3}, \frac{3}{2})$ **27.** $(\frac{1}{2}, -3)$ **29.** $(2, 3)$ **31.** $(-\frac{1}{3}, 1)$ **33.** 28 and 21
35. 16 in. by 20 in. **37.** $40°$ **39.** 40 oz of 8% solution; 60 oz of 15% solution **41.** 55 mph
43. \$270

Exercise 10.3 (page 349)

1. 8 **3.** -2 **5.** $x^2 - y^2$ **7.** $-2x^2$ **9.** $-2x - 2$ **11.** $(4, 2)$ **13.** $(-1, 3)$
15. $(-\frac{1}{2}, \frac{1}{3})$ **17.** $(2, -1)$ **19.** no solution **21.** $(5, \frac{14}{5})$ **23.** $x = \dfrac{kd - q}{ad - 1}$, $y = \dfrac{aq - k}{ad - 1}$
25. $x = 2$ **27.** $x = 2$

Exercise 10.4 (page 353)

1. $(1, 1, 2)$ **3.** $(0, 2, 2)$ **5.** $(3, 2, 1)$ **7.** inconsistent system; no solution
9. dependent equations; one possible solution is $(\frac{1}{2}, \frac{5}{3}, 0)$ **11.** $(2, 6, 9)$ **13.** $-2, 4, 16$
15. 9, 10, 11 **17.** 10 nickels, 5 dimes, 2 quarters
19. 50 expensive footballs, 75 middle-priced footballs, 1000 cheap footballs
21. 250 five-dollar tickets, 375 three-dollar tickets, 125 two-dollar tickets

Exercise 10.5 (page 359)

1. 0 **3.** -13 **5.** 26 **7.** 0 **9.** $10a$ **11.** $(1, 1, 2)$ **13.** $(3, 2, 1)$
15. Cramer's Rule fails **17.** $(3, -2, 1)$ **19.** Cramer's Rule fails **21.** $(-2, 3, 1)$
23. Cramer's Rule fails

Exercise 10.6   (page 367)

1. $(1, 1)$ **3.** $(2, -3)$ **5.** $(0, -3)$ **7.** $(1, 2, 3)$ **9.** $(-1, -1, 2)$ **11.** $(2, 1, 0)$
13. $(1, 2)$ **15.** $(2, 0)$ **17.** no solution   **19.** $x = -6 - z, y = 2 - z, z$ can be any number
21. $x = 2 - z, y = 1 - z, z$ can be any number   **23.** $(1, 0, 1, 2)$ **25.** $(-1, 1, 4, 0)$
27. $(1, 1, 2, 1)$

Exercise 10.7   (page 372)

1. $\dfrac{1}{x + 1} + \dfrac{2}{x - 1}$ **3.** $\dfrac{1}{x^2 + 2} - \dfrac{3}{x + 1}$ **5.** $\dfrac{1}{x} + \dfrac{2}{x^2} - \dfrac{3}{x - 1}$ **7.** $\dfrac{1}{x^2} + \dfrac{1}{x^2 + 1}$

9. $\dfrac{2}{x} + \dfrac{3x + 2}{x^2 + 1}$ **11.** $\dfrac{1}{x} + \dfrac{1}{x^2} + \dfrac{2}{x^2 + x + 1}$ **13.** $\dfrac{1}{x^2 + x + 5} + \dfrac{x + 1}{x^2 + 1}$

15. $\dfrac{-1}{x^2 + 1} - \dfrac{x}{(x^2 + 1)^2} + \dfrac{1}{x}$ **17.** $\dfrac{1}{x^2 + 1} + \dfrac{x + 2}{x^2 + x + 2}$ **19.** $\dfrac{1}{x} + \dfrac{x}{x^2 + 2x + 5} + \dfrac{x + 2}{(x^2 + 2x + 5)^2}$

21. $2 + \dfrac{1}{x} + \dfrac{2}{x^2} + \dfrac{3}{x + 1}$ **23.** $x^2 + x + 1 + \dfrac{1}{x} + \dfrac{1}{x^2}$

Exercise 10.8   (page 375)

1. $y = -2x + 3$ y

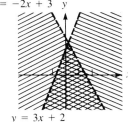

$y = 3x + 2$

3.

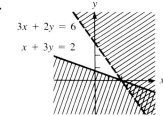

$3x + 2y = 6$

$x + 3y = 2$

5.

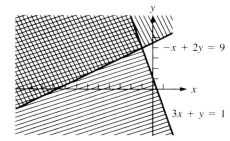

$-x + 2y = 9$

$3x + y = 1$

7. y $2x - y = 4$

$y = -x^2 + 2$

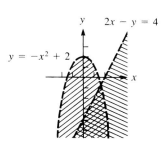

9.

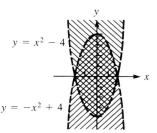

$y = x^2 - 4$

$y = -x^2 + 4$

11.

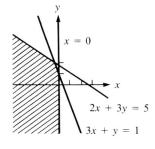

$x = 0$

$2x + 3y = 5$

$3x + y = 1$

13.

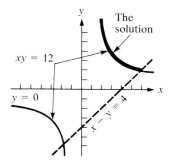

The solution

$xy = 12$

$y = 0$

$x - y = 4$

15.

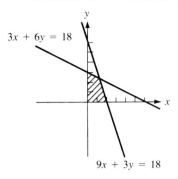

$3x + 6y = 18$

$9x + 3y = 18$

Exercise 10.9   (page 378)

1.

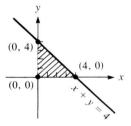

P attains maximum of
12 at $(0, 4)$

3.

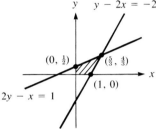

$y - 2x = -2$

$2y - x = 1$

P attains maximum of $\dfrac{13}{6}$

at $\left(\dfrac{5}{3}, \dfrac{4}{3}\right)$

5.

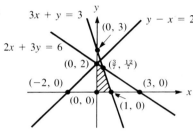

$3x + y = 3$ $y - x = 2$

$2x + 3y = 6$

P attains maximum value

of $\dfrac{18}{7}$ at $\left(\dfrac{3}{7}, \dfrac{12}{7}\right)$

7.   2 tables, no chairs   **9.**   10 m^2 of strawberries, 30 m^2 of pumpkins
11.   10 oz of X and 25 oz of Y per day

REVIEW EXERCISES   (page 381)

1. $(3, 5)$ **3.**   dependent equations   **5.** $(-1, 3)$ **7.** $(3, 4)$ **9.** $(-3, 1)$ **11.** $(9, -4)$
13. $(1, 2, 3)$ **15.**   18   **17.** -3 **19.** $(2, 1)$ **21.** $(1, -2, 3)$ **23.** $(2, 1)$

25. $\dfrac{1}{x} + \dfrac{3x + 4}{x^2 + 1}$ **27.**

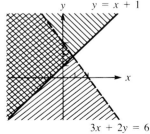

$y = x + 1$

$3x + 2y = 6$

29.

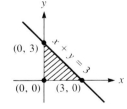

$x + y = 3$

P attains maximum
of 6 at $(3, 0)$

31.   1000 bags of X, 1400 bags of Y

CHAPTER TEN TEST   (page 383)

1.

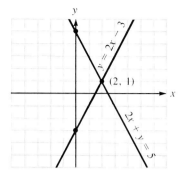

3. consistent   **5.** $y = 4$ **7.** -17 **9.** $\begin{vmatrix} 1 & -1 \\ 3 & 1 \end{vmatrix}$

11. $x = 3$ **13.** $z = -1$ **15.** $\begin{bmatrix} 1 & 1 & 1 & | & 4 \\ 1 & 1 & -1 & | & 6 \\ 2 & -3 & 1 & | & -1 \end{bmatrix}$ **17.** $\dfrac{1}{x+1} + \dfrac{-2}{(x+1)^2} + \dfrac{2}{(x+1)^3}$

19.

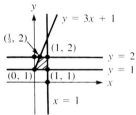

P attains maximum
of 2 at $(1, 1)$

Exercise 11.1   (page 388)

1. $P(2) = 35$ **3.** $P(0) = -1$ **5.** $P(-4) = 719$ **7.** $P(2) = 31$ **9.** true   **11.** true
13. false   **15.** true   **17.** $3, -1, -5$ **19.** $x^3 - 3x^2 + 3x - 1$ **21.** $x^3 - 11x^2 + 38x - 40$
23. $x^4 - 3x^2 + 2$ **25.** $x^3 - \sqrt{2}x^2 + x - \sqrt{2}$ **27.** $x^3 - 2x^2 + 2x$
29. $1, \dfrac{-1 + \sqrt{3}i}{2}, \dfrac{-1 - \sqrt{3}i}{2}$ **31.** $-5, \dfrac{5 + 5\sqrt{3}i}{2}, \dfrac{5 - 5\sqrt{3}i}{2}$ **33.** $3, 2, i, -i$ **35.** $4, -1, 1, -2$
37. $a_1 = 0$

Exercise 11.2   (page 395)

1. 10   **3.** 4   **5.** 0 or 2 positive; 1 negative; 0 or 2 nonreal
7. 0 positive; 1 or 3 negative; 0 or 2 nonreal   **9.** 0 positive; 0 negative; 4 nonreal
11. 1 positive; 1 negative; 2 nonreal   **13.** 0 positive; 0 negative; 10 nonreal
15. 0 positive; 0 negative; 8 nonreal; 1 root of 0   **17.** 1 positive; 1 negative; 2 nonreal
19. $-1, 6$ **21.** $-4, 6$ **23.** $-4, 3$ **25.** $-5, 2$
27. An odd-degree polynomial equation must have an odd number of roots. Since complex roots occur in conjugate pairs, one root must be left over, and it is real.

Exercise 11.3   (page 400)

1. $-1, 1, 2$ **3.** $1, 2, 3, 4$ **5.** $-1, -1, 1, 1, 2$ **7.** $-5, 2, \sqrt{3}, -\sqrt{3}$
9. $0, -2, -2, -2, 2, 2, 2$ **11.** $-3, -\frac{1}{3}, \frac{1}{2}, 2, 2$ **13.** $-\frac{1}{2}, \frac{1}{2}, 3, 2i, -2i$ **15.** $-1, \frac{2}{3}, 2, 3$
17. $-1, \frac{1}{2}, 1, \frac{3}{2}$ **19.** $-\frac{3}{5}, \frac{2}{3}, \frac{3}{2}$ **21.** $2, -\frac{1}{2} + \frac{\sqrt{3}}{2}i, -\frac{1}{2} - \frac{\sqrt{3}}{2}i$

23.   There can be no positive or negative roots. 0 is not a root. Hence, all roots are nonreal.

Exercise 11.4   (page 403)

1. $P(-2) = 3; P(-1) = -2$ **3.** $P(4) = -40; P(5) = 30$ **5.** $P(1) = 8; P(2) = -1$
7. $P(2) = -72; P(3) = 154$ **9.** $P(0) = 10; P(1) = -60$ **11.** $\sqrt{3} \approx 1.73$ **13.** $\sqrt{5} \approx 2.236$
15. $x \approx 0.50$

REVIEW EXERCISES   (page 404)

1. $P(0) = -2$ **3.** $P(-3) = 277$ **5.** false   **7.** true   **9.** $-4, 2 + 2\sqrt{3}i, 2 - 2\sqrt{3}i$
11. $2x^3 - 5x^2 - x + 6$ **13.** $3x^3 + 9x^2 + 29x + 90$ with a remainder of 277 **15.** 6
17. 2 or 0 positive; 2 or 0 negative; 0, 2, or 4 nonreal   **19.** 0 positive; 0 negative; 4 nonreal
21. $-5, -\frac{3}{2}, -2$ **23.** $P(0) = 18; P(-1) = -9$ **25.** $\sqrt{7} \approx 2.65$

CHAPTER ELEVEN TEST   (page 405)

1. 1   **3.** True   **5.** $x^2 - 5x + 6$ **7.** $P(2) = 15$ **9.** 5   **11.** 1
13. -2 is a lower bound   **15.** $+i, -i$ **17.** There are no nonreal solutions.
19. Yes; it is -2.

Exercise 12.1   (page 412)

1.

3. **5.** **7.**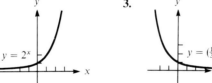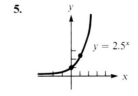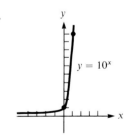

9. **11.** **13.**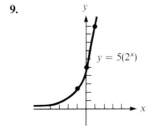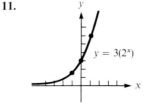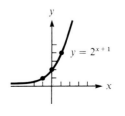

15.

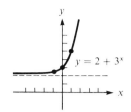

$y = 2 + 3^x$

17.

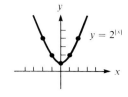

$y = 2^{|x|}$

19. $b = 5$ **21.**   no value of b

23. $b = \frac{1}{2}$ **25.** $\frac{32}{243}A_0$ **27.** $A_0 2^{-3000/5700} \approx 0.6943A_0$ **29.**   \$1342.53   **31.**   \$2,273,996.13
33. 1.68×10^8 **35.**   2.83

Exercise 12.2   (page 417)

1.

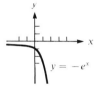

$y = -e^x$

3.

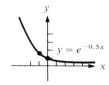

$y = e^{-0.5x}$

5.

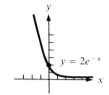

$y = 2e^{-x}$

7.

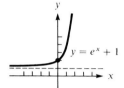

$y = e^x + 1$

9.   yes   **11.**   no   **13.**   no   **15.**   no   **17.**   \$19,171.75   **19.**   \$4500   **21.**   \$8753.36
23. 9.44×10^5 **25.**   2.6   **27.**   202

Exercise 12.3   (page 426)

1. $3^4 = 81$ **3.** $(\frac{1}{2})^3 = \frac{1}{8}$ **5.** $4^{-3} = \frac{1}{64}$ **7.** $x^z = y$ **9.** $\log_8 64 = 2$
11. $\log_4 \frac{1}{16} = -2$ **13.** $\log_{1/2} 32 = -5$ **15.** $\log_x z = y$ **17.**   3   **19.** -3 **21.**   2
23.   2   **25.**   7   **27.**   4   **29.** $-\frac{3}{2}$ **31.** $\frac{2}{3}$ **33.**   5   **35.** $\frac{3}{2}$ **37.** $\frac{1}{9}$
39.   8   **41.**

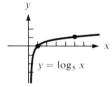

$y = \log_5 x$

43.

$y = \log_{\frac{1}{3}} x$

45.

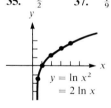

$y = \ln x^2$
$= 2 \ln x$

47.

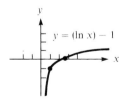

$y = (\ln x) - 1$

49.

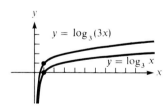

$y = \log_3 (3x)$
$y = \log_3 x$

51.

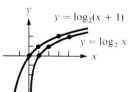

$y = \log_2 (x + 1)$
$y = \log_2 x$

53.

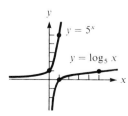

$y = 5^x$
$y = \log_5 x$

55.   no value of b **57.**   3   **59.**   no value of b **61.**   yes

63. no   **65.** $\log_b xyz = \log_b x + \log_b y + \log_b z$ **67.** $\log_b\left(\dfrac{x}{y}\right)^2 = 2\log_b x - 2\log_b y$

69. $\log_b x\sqrt{z} = \log_b x + \frac{1}{2}\log_b z$ **71.** $\log_b \sqrt[4]{\dfrac{x^3 y^2}{z^4}} = \frac{3}{4}\log_b x + \frac{1}{2}\log_b y - \log_b z$

73. $\log_b(x+1) - \log_b x = \log_b \dfrac{x+1}{x}$ **75.** $2\log_b x + \frac{1}{3}\log_b y = \log_b x^2 y^{1/3}$

77. $-3\log_b x - 2\log_b y + \dfrac{1}{2}\log_b z = \log_b \dfrac{z^{1/2}}{x^3 y^2}$ **79.** $\log_b\left(\dfrac{x}{z}+x\right) - \log_b\left(\dfrac{y}{z}+y\right) = \log_b \dfrac{\dfrac{x}{z}+x}{\dfrac{y}{z}+y} = \log_b \dfrac{x}{y}$

81. true   **83.** false   **85.** true   **87.** false   **89.** true   **91.** false   **93.** false
95. true   **97.** true   **99.** false   **101.** true   **103.** 1.4472   **105.** 0.3521
107. 1.1972   **109.** 2.4014   **111.** 2.0493

Exercise 12.4   (page 433)

1. 0.5119   **3.** −0.0726   **5.** −0.2752   **7.** 69.4079   **9.** 0.0002   **11.** 120.0719
19. 4.77   **21.** from 0.000501 to 0.00126   **23.** 0.71 V
25. $10\log\dfrac{P_O}{P_1} = 10\log\dfrac{kE_O^2}{kE_I^2} = 10\log\left(\dfrac{E_O}{E_I}\right)^2 = 20\log\dfrac{E_O}{E_I}$ **27.** 4.4   **29.** 2500 μm   **31.** 19.9 h
33. $L = L_0 + k\ln 2$ where $L_0 = k\ln I$ **35.** about 5.8 years   **37.** 3 years old
39. about 10.8 years   **43.** because log 0.9 is a negative number

Exercise 12.5   (page 439)

1. $x = \dfrac{\log 5}{\log 4} \approx 1.16$ **3.** $x = \dfrac{\log 2}{\log 13} + 1 \approx 1.27$ **5.** $x = \dfrac{\log 2}{\log 3 - \log 2} \approx 1.71$ **7.** $x = 0$

9. $x = \sqrt{\dfrac{1}{\log 7}} \approx 1.09$ **11.** $x = 0$ or $x = \dfrac{\log 9}{\log 8} \approx 1.06$ **13.** 7   **15.** 4   **17.** 10, −10

19. 50   **21.** 20   **23.** 10   **25.** 3, 4   **27.** 1, 100   **29.** 9   **31.** 1.771
33. 2.322   **35.** about 5.146 years   **37.** about 42.7 days   **39.** about 4200 years old
41. 4.03 years, 3.92 years   **43.** approximately 6.96%   **45.** about 3.15 days

Exercise 12.6   (page 445)

1. 0.7760   **3.** 0.6263   **5.** 5.6355   **7.** −2.8633   **9.** 3.14   **11.** 8380
13. 0.00284   **15.** 0.8384   **17.** −2.4614   **19.** 4.281   **21.** 1598   **23.** 0.007702
25. 0.1913   **27.** 3.388   **29.** 4.354   **31.** 15.33   **33.** 2.022   **35.** 1.5369
37. 7.73   **39.** 3.3810   **41.** −4.8000

REVIEW EXERCISE (page 447)

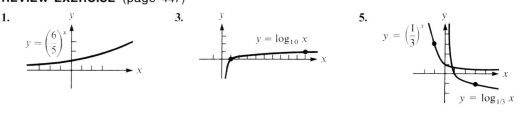

7.

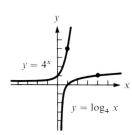

9. 8 **11.** 3 **13.** 1 **15.** $\frac{1}{6}$ **17.** -2 **19.** 27

21. 32 **23.** 27 **25.** $\frac{1}{8}$ **27.** 4 **29.** 10 **31.** $\frac{1}{2} \log_b x - \frac{1}{2} \log_b y - \log_b z$

33. 2.64 **35.** $x = \dfrac{\log 7}{\log 3}$ **37.** $x = \dfrac{\log 3}{\log 3 - \log 2}$ **39.** $x = 4$ **41.** $x = \dfrac{\ln 9}{\ln 2}$

43. $x = \dfrac{e}{e - 1}$ **45.** approximately 9034 year old

47. $\text{pH} = \log_{10} \dfrac{1}{[\text{H}^+]} = \log_{10}[\text{H}^+]^{-1} = -\log_{10}[\text{H}^+]$ **49.** 8.141 **51.** 0.0001617

CHAPTER TWELVE TEST (page 448)

1.

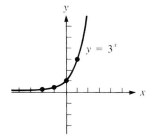

3. 2 **5.** 4 **7.** 2 **9.**

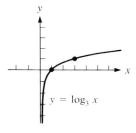

11. $\log_b x + \frac{1}{2} \log_b y - 2 \log_b z$ **13.** 4 **15.** 1.2 **17.** 4.2 **19.** $x = \dfrac{\log 3}{\log 5}$

21. $x = 1$ **23.** $\frac{10}{3}$

CUMULATIVE REVIEW EXERCISES (CHAPTERS 10–12) (page 449)

1.

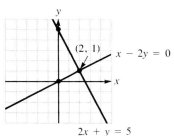

3. $(2, -2)$ **5.** -1 **7.** $(-1, 2, 0)$ **9.** $(2, -1, 1)$

11.   not a factor   **13.** $-5, -\frac{3}{2}, -2$ **15.**

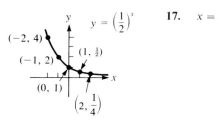

17. $x = 5$

19. $x = 1$ **21.** $y = 2^x$ **23.**   1.9912   **25.**   1.6902   **27.** $x = \dfrac{2 \log 2}{\log 3 - \log 2}$

29.   \$2848.31

Exercise 13.1   (page 454)

1. $x^2 + y^2 = 1$ **3.** $(x - 6)^2 + (y - 8)^2 = 16$ **5.** $(x + 5)^2 + (y - 3)^2 = 25$
7. $(x - 3)^2 + (y + 4)^2 = 2$ **9.** $(x - 3)^2 + (y - 3)^2 = 25$ **11.** $(x + 5)^2 + (y - 1)^2 = 65$
13. $(x + 3)^2 + (y - 4)^2 = 25$ **15.** $(x + 2)^2 + (y + 6)^2 = 40$ **17.** $x^2 + (y + 3)^2 = 157$
19. $(x - 5)^2 + (y - 8)^2 = 338$ **21.** $(x + 4)^2 + (y + 2)^2 = 98$ **23.** $(x - 1)^2 + (y + 2)^2 = 36$
25. $x^2 + (y + 12)^2 = 10$ **27.**   no   **29.**

$x^2 + y^2 - 25 = 0$

31.

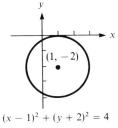

$(x - 1)^2 + (y + 2)^2 = 4$

33.

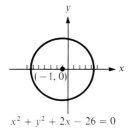

$x^2 + y^2 + 2x - 26 = 0$

35.

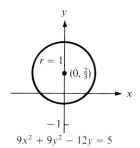

$9x^2 + 9y^2 - 12y = 5$

37.

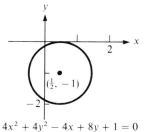

$4x^2 + 4y^2 - 4x + 8y + 1 = 0$

39. $x^2 + (y - 3)^2 = 25$ **41.** $A = 5\pi$

Exercise 13.2   (page 460)

1. $x^2 = 12y$ **3.** $y^2 = 12x$ **5.** $(x - 3)^2 = -12(y - 5)$ **7.** $(x - 3)^2 = -28(y - 5)$
9. $(x - 2)^2 = -2(y - 2)$ or $(y - 2)^2 = -2(x - 2)$ **11.** $(x + 4)^2 = -\frac{16}{3}(y - 6)$ or $(y - 6)^2 = \frac{9}{4}(x + 4)$
13. $(y - 8)^2 = -4(x - 6)$ **15.** $(x - 3)^2 = \frac{1}{2}(y - 1)$

17.

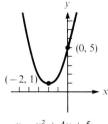

$$y = x^2 + 4x + 5$$
or
$$y - 1 = (x + 2)^2$$

19.

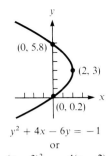

$$y^2 + 4x - 6y = -1$$
or
$$(y - 3)^2 = -4(x - 2)$$

21.

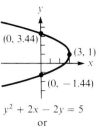

$$y^2 + 2x - 2y = 5$$
or
$$(y - 1)^2 = -2(x - 3)$$

23.

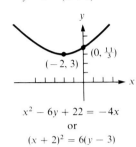

$$x^2 - 6y + 22 = -4x$$
or
$$(x + 2)^2 = 6(y - 3)$$

25.

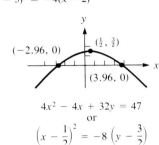

$$4x^2 - 4x + 32y = 47$$
or
$$\left(x - \frac{1}{2}\right)^2 = -8\left(y - \frac{3}{2}\right)$$

27. $x^2 = -\frac{45}{2}y$ **29.** 8 cabins

31. $\frac{80}{7}$ m   **33.** $\frac{1}{36}$ ft

37. $y = x^2 + 4x + 3$

Exercise 13.3   (page 468)

1. $\dfrac{x^2}{25} + \dfrac{y^2}{16} = 1$ **3.** $\dfrac{9x^2}{16} + \dfrac{9y^2}{25} = 1$ **5.** $\dfrac{x^2}{7} + \dfrac{y^2}{16} = 1$ **7.** $\dfrac{(x - 3)^2}{4} + \dfrac{(y - 4)^2}{9} = 1$

9. $\dfrac{(x - 3)^2}{9} + \dfrac{(y - 4)^2}{4} = 1$ **11.** $\dfrac{(x - 3)^2}{41} + \dfrac{(y - 4)^2}{16} = 1$ **13.** $\dfrac{x^2}{36} + \dfrac{(y - 4)^2}{20} = 1$

15. $\dfrac{x^2}{100} + \dfrac{y^2}{64} = 1$ **17.**

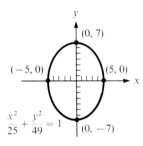

$$\frac{x^2}{25} + \frac{y^2}{49} = 1$$

19.

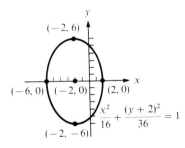

$$\frac{x^2}{16} + \frac{(y + 2)^2}{36} = 1$$

21.

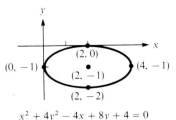

$$x^2 + 4y^2 - 4x + 8y + 4 = 0$$

23.

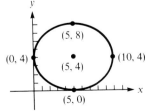

$$16x^2 + 25y^2 - 160x - 200y + 400 = 0$$

25. 199,395 mi   **27.** $\dfrac{x^2}{2500} + \dfrac{y^2}{900} = 1$; 36 m

29. In the ellipse, $b^2 = a^2 - c^2$, or $a = \sqrt{b^2 + c^2}$. Using the distance formula, you have $d(FB) = \sqrt{b^2 + c^2}$.

31. Substitute c for x in the equation $\dfrac{x^2}{a^2} + \dfrac{y^2}{b^2} = 1$. Use the fact that $c^2 = a^2 - b^2$, and solve for y to determine

FA'. The focal width is $2y$.

33. The thumbtacks are the foci at $(\pm 1, 0)$. Hence, $c = 1$. The string is 6 meters, so $2a = 6$, or $a^2 = 9$. Because

$b^2 = a^2 - c^2$, you have $b^2 = 8$. The equation is $\dfrac{x^2}{9} + \dfrac{y^2}{8} = 1$.

Exercise 13.4   (page 476)

1. $\dfrac{x^2}{25} - \dfrac{y^2}{24} = 1$ **3.** $\dfrac{(x-2)^2}{4} - \dfrac{(y-4)^2}{9} = 1$ **5.** $\dfrac{(y-3)^2}{9} - \dfrac{(x-5)^2}{9} = 1$ **7.** $\dfrac{y^2}{9} - \dfrac{x^2}{16} = 1$

9. $\dfrac{(x-1)^2}{4} - \dfrac{(y+3)^2}{16} = 1$ or $\dfrac{(y+3)^2}{4} - \dfrac{(x-1)^2}{16} = 1$ **11.** $\dfrac{x^2}{10} - \dfrac{3y^2}{20} = 1$ **13.** 24 square units

15. 12 square units   **17.** $\dfrac{(x+2)^2}{4} - \dfrac{4(y+4)^2}{81} = 1$ **19.** $\dfrac{x^2}{36} - \dfrac{16y^2}{25} = 1$

21.

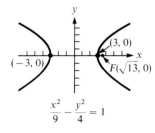

$\dfrac{x^2}{9} - \dfrac{y^2}{4} = 1$

23.

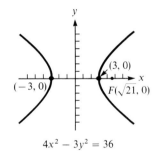

$4x^2 - 3y^2 = 36$

25.

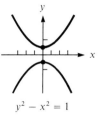

$y^2 - x^2 = 1$

27.

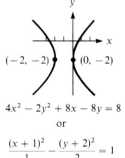

$4x^2 - 2y^2 + 8x - 8y = 8$
or
$\dfrac{(x+1)^2}{1} - \dfrac{(y+2)^2}{2} = 1$

29.

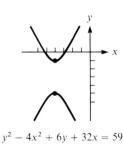

$y^2 - 4x^2 + 6y + 32x = 59$

31.

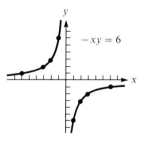

$-xy = 6$

33. $\dfrac{(x-3)^2}{9} - \dfrac{(y-1)^2}{16} = 1$ **35.** $4x^2 - 5y^2 - 60y = 0$

37. From the geometry of Figure 13-17, $PF + F'F > F'P$. This is equivalent to $F'P - PF < F'F$ or $2a < 2c$, which implies that $c > a$.

Exercise 13.5   (page 480)

1.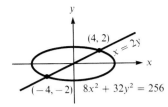

(4, 2)
$x = 2y$
$(-4, -2)$ $8x^2 + 32y^2 = 256$

3.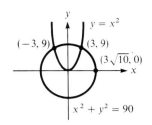

$y = x^2$
$(-3, 9)$ (3, 9)
$(3\sqrt{10}, 0)$
$x^2 + y^2 = 90$

5.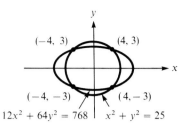

$(-4, 3)$ (4, 3)
$(-4, -3)$ $(4, -3)$
$12x^2 + 64y^2 = 768$ $x^2 + y^2 = 25$

7.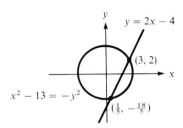

$y = 2x - 4$
(3, 2)
$x^2 - 13 = -y^2$
$(\frac{1}{5}, -\frac{18}{5})$

9.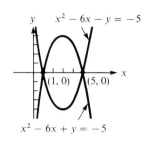

$x^2 - 6x - y = -5$
(1, 0)   (5, 0)
$x^2 - 6x + y = -5$

11.   (3, 0), (0, 5)   **13.**   (1, 1)

15.   (1, 2), (2, 1)   **17.** $(-2, 3), (2, 3)$ **19.** $(\sqrt{5}, 5), (-\sqrt{5}, 5)$ **21.** $(3, 2), (3, -2), (-3, 2), (-3, -2)$
23. $(2, 4), (2, -4), (-2, 4), (-2, -4)$ **25.** $(-\sqrt{15}, 5), (\sqrt{15}, 5), (-2, -6), (2, -6)$
27. $(0, -4), (-3, 5), (3, 5)$ **29.** $(-2, 3), (2, 3), (-2, -3), (2, -3)$ **31.**   (3, 3)
33. $(6, 2), (-6, -2), (\sqrt{42}, 0), (-\sqrt{42}, 0)$ **35.** $(\frac{1}{2}, \frac{1}{3}), (\frac{1}{3}, \frac{1}{2})$ **37.**   7 by 9 cm   **39.**   14 and -5
41.   Either \$750 at 9% or \$900 at 7.5%

Exercise 13.6   (page 485)

1. $P(3, 1)$ **3.** $R(1, -3)$ **5.** $P(4, -8)$ **7.** $R(2, -4)$

9.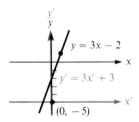

$y = 3x - 2$
$y' = 3x' + 3$
$(0, -5)$

11.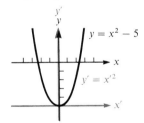

$y = x^2 - 5$
$y' = x'^2$

13.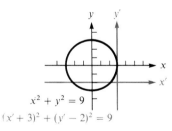

$x^2 + y^2 = 9$
$(x' + 3)^2 + (y' - 2)^2 = 9$

15.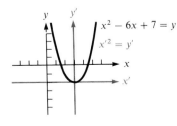

$x^2 - 6x + 7 = y$
$x'^2 = y'$

17.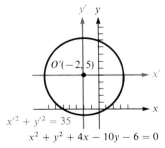

$O'(-2, 5)$
$x'^2 + y'^2 = 35$
$x^2 + y^2 + 4x - 10y - 6 = 0$

19.

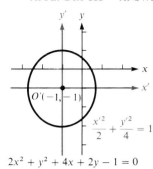

$$\frac{x'^2}{2} + \frac{y'^2}{4} = 1$$

$$2x^2 + y^2 + 4x + 2y - 1 = 0$$

21.

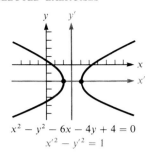

$$x^2 - y^2 - 6x - 4y + 4 = 0$$

$$x'^2 - y'^2 = 1$$

REVIEW EXERCISES   (page 488)

1. $x^2 + y^2 = 50$ **3.** $(x - 5)^2 + (y - 10)^2 = 85$ **5.**   **7.** $y^2 = -2x$

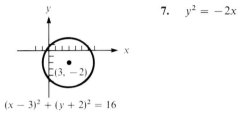

$$(x - 3)^2 + (y + 2)^2 = 16$$

9. $\left(x + \dfrac{b}{2a}\right)^2 = \dfrac{1}{a}\left(y + \dfrac{b^2 - 4ac}{4a}\right)$ **11.**   **13.**

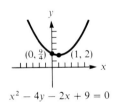

$$x^2 - 4y - 2x + 9 = 0$$

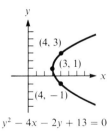

$$y^2 - 4x - 2y + 13 = 0$$

15. $\dfrac{(x + 2)^2}{16} + \dfrac{(y - 3)^2}{9} = 1$ **17.**   **19.**

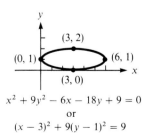

$$x^2 + 9y^2 - 6x - 18y + 9 = 0$$
$$\text{or}$$
$$(x - 3)^2 + 9(y - 1)^2 = 9$$

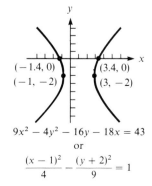

$$9x^2 - 4y^2 - 16y - 18x = 43$$
$$\text{or}$$
$$\frac{(x - 1)^2}{4} - \frac{(y + 2)^2}{9} = 1$$

21.

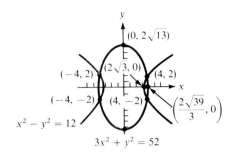

$(0, 2\sqrt{13})$
$(-4, 2)$ $(2\sqrt{3}, 0)$ $(4, 2)$
$(-4, -2)$ $(4, -2)$
$\left(\frac{2\sqrt{39}}{3}, 0\right)$
$x^2 - y^2 = 12$
$3x^2 + y^2 = 52$

23.

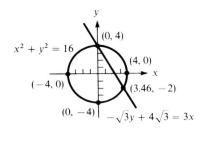

$(0, 4)$
$x^2 + y^2 = 16$
$(4, 0)$
$(-4, 0)$
$(3.46, -2)$
$(0, -4)$
$-\sqrt{3}y + 4\sqrt{3} = 3x$

25.

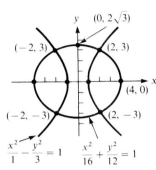

$(0, 2\sqrt{3})$
$(-2, 3)$ $(2, 3)$
$(4, 0)$
$(-2, -3)$ $(2, -3)$
$\frac{x^2}{1} - \frac{y^2}{3} = 1$ $\frac{x^2}{16} + \frac{y^2}{12} = 1$

27.

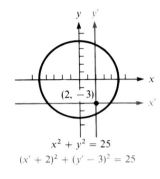

$(2, -3)$
$x^2 + y^2 = 25$
$(x' + 2)^2 + (y' - 3)^2 = 25$

29.

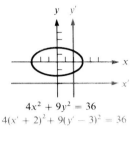

$4x^2 + 9y^2 = 36$
$4(x' + 2)^2 + 9(y' - 3)^2 = 36$

31.

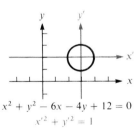

$x^2 + y^2 - 6x - 4y + 12 = 0$
$x'^2 + y'^2 = 1$

CHAPTER THIRTEEN TEST   (page 490)

1. $x^2 + y^2 = 4$ **3.** $(x - 3)^2 + (y - 4)^2 = 25$ **5.** $(y - 3)^2 = -\frac{9}{2}(x - 2)$ **7.** $\frac{y^2}{169} + \frac{x^2}{144} = 1$

9. $\frac{(x - 2)^2}{4} + \frac{(y - 4)^2}{16} = 1$ **11.** 60 sq. units   **13.** $(4, 2)$ **15.** $(3, 4)$ and $(-3, 4)$

17. Place origin of $x'y'$ system at $(-3, 2)$.

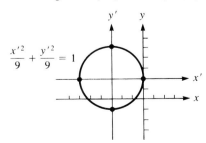

$\frac{x'^2}{9} + \frac{y'^2}{9} = 1$

Exercise 14.1   (page 496)

25. no

Exercise 14.2   (page 501)

1. 0, 10, 30, 60, 100, 150, 210, 280   **3.** 21   **5.** $a + 4d$ **7.** 15   **9.** 15
11. 15   **13.** $\frac{242}{243}$ **15.** 35   **17.** 30   **19.** -50 **21.** 40   **23.** 500
25. $\frac{7}{12}$ **27.** 160

Exercise 14.3   (page 509)

1. 1, 3, 5, 7, 9, 11   **3.** $5, \frac{7}{2}, 2, \frac{1}{2}, -1, -\frac{5}{2}$ **5.** $9, \frac{23}{2}, 14, \frac{33}{2}, 19, \frac{43}{2}$ **7.** 285   **9.** 555
11. $157\frac{1}{2}$ **13.** 44   **15.** $\frac{25}{2}, 15, \frac{35}{2}$ **17.** $-\frac{82}{15}, -\frac{59}{15}, -\frac{36}{15}, -\frac{13}{15}$ **19.** 10, 20, 40, 80
21. $-2, -6, -18, -54$ **23.** $3, 3\sqrt{2}, 6, 6\sqrt{2}$ **25.** 2, 6, 18, 54   **27.** 124   **29.** $-29, 524$
31. $\frac{1995}{32}$ **33.** 18   **35.** 8   **37.** $10\sqrt[4]{2}, 10\sqrt{2}, 10\sqrt[4]{8}$ **39.** 8, 32, 128, 512
41. $\frac{5}{9}$ **43.** $\frac{25}{99}$ **47.** \$21,474,836.47
49. Arithmetic mean is $\frac{11}{16}$; geometric mean is $\sqrt{7}/4$; the arithmetic mean is larger.   **51.** $1 - \frac{1}{101} = \frac{100}{101}$

Exercise 14.4   (page 513)

1. 23   **3.** 5.13 m   **5.** 1,048,576   **7.** She will earn \$0.19 more on the $7\frac{1}{4}\%$ investment.
9. approximately 6.87×10^{19} **11.** \$180,176.87   **13.** \$2001.60   **15.** \$2013.62
17. \$264,094.58   **19.** 1.8447×10^{19} grains
21. No, because $0.999999 = \dfrac{999,999}{1,000,000}$, which does not equal 1.

Exercise 14.5   (page 518)

1. 24   **3.** 720   **5.** 1440   **7.** $\frac{1}{1320}$ **9.** 18,564   **11.** $a^4 + 4a^3b + 6a^2b^2 + 4ab^3 + b^4$
13. $a^5 - 5a^4b + 10a^3b^2 - 10a^2b^3 + 5ab^4 - b^5$ **15.** $8x^3 - 12x^2y + 6xy^2 - y^3$
17. $16x^4 + 32x^3y + 24x^2y^2 + 8xy^3 + y^4$ **19.** $256x^4 - 768x^3y + 864x^2y^2 - 432xy^3 + 81y^4$
21. $36x^2 - 36xy + 9y^2$ **23.** $6a^2b^2$ **25.** $35a^3b^4$ **27.** $-b^5$ **29.** $28x^2y^6$

31. $20\sqrt{2}x^3y^2$ **33.** $4608x^2y^7$ **35.** $\dfrac{r!}{3!(r-3)!}\,a^{r-3}b^3$ **37.** $\dfrac{n!}{(r-1)!(n-r+1)!}\,a^{n-r+1}b^{r-1}$

39. 1, 2, 4, 8, 16, 32, 64, 128, 256, 512. They are sequential powers of 2.

41. The sixth term is $\dfrac{10!}{5!(10-5)!}\,a^5\left(-\dfrac{1}{a}\right)^5$, or -252.

43. $(x^{1/2})^{25-r}\left(\dfrac{1}{x}\right)^r$ must be x^8. Hence, $r = 3$. Coefficient is $\dfrac{25!}{3!(25-3)!}\cdot\dfrac{1}{2^3} = \dfrac{575}{2}$.

Exercise 14.6   (page 525)

1. 144   **3.** 8,000,000   **5.** 240   **7.** 6   **9.** 840   **11.** 35   **13.** 120
15. 5   **17.** 1   **19.** 1200   **21.** 40   **23.** 2278   **25.** 40,320   **27.** 14,400
29. 24,360   **31.** 5040   **33.** 48   **35.** 144   **37.** 210   **39.** approximately 6.35×10^{11}
41. 3360   **43.** 2,721,600   **45.** 1120   **47.** 59,400   **49.** 272   **51.** 28   **53.** 56
55. 2,042,975 (ignoring the order of the players)

Exercise 14.7   (page 530)

1. $\frac{1}{6}$ **3.** $\frac{2}{3}$ **5.** $\frac{19}{42}$ **7.** $\frac{13}{42}$ **9.** $\frac{3}{8}$ **11.** 0   **13.** $\frac{1}{12}$ **15.** $\frac{1}{169}$ **17.** $\frac{5}{12}$
19. approximately 6.3×10^{-12} **21.** 0   **23.** $\frac{3}{13}$ **25.** $\frac{1}{6}$ **27.** $\frac{1}{8}$ **29.** $\frac{5}{16}$
31. (S-survive; F-fail) SSSS, SSSF, SSFS, SFSS, FSSS, SSFF, SFSF, FSSF, SFFS, FSFS, FFSS, SFFF, FSFF, FFSF, FFFS, FFFF   **33.** $\frac{1}{4}$ **35.** $\frac{1}{4}$
37. 1; Exercises 32 through 36 exhaust all possibilities and are mutually exclusive.   **39.** $\frac{32}{119}$

Exercise 14.8   (page 535)

1. $\frac{1}{2}$ **3.** $\frac{7}{13}$ **5.** $\frac{1}{221}$ **7.** $\frac{25}{204}$ **9.** $\frac{11}{36}$ **11.** $\frac{7}{12}$ **13.** $\frac{5}{8}$ **15.** $\frac{13}{16}$
17. $\frac{21}{128}$ **19.** $\frac{3}{20}$ **21.** $\frac{1}{49}$ **23.** 0.973   **25.** $\frac{11}{20}$ **27.** $\frac{1}{8}, \frac{1}{12}, \frac{3}{8}, \frac{5}{12}, 1$

REVIEW EXERCISES   (page 538)

3. 1718   **5.** 117   **7.** -92 **9.** $\frac{1}{3^6}$ **11.** $\frac{9}{2^{14}}$ **13.** 3320   **15.** -5220

17. $\frac{3280}{27}$ **19.** $\frac{2295}{128}$ **21.** $\frac{2}{3}$ **23.** no sum   **25.** $\frac{1}{3}$ **27.** $\frac{17}{99}$ **29.** $\frac{7}{2}, 5, \frac{13}{2}$

31. $2\sqrt{2}, 4, 4\sqrt{2}$ **33.** $\frac{3280}{3}$ **35.** 16   **37.** 6516, 3134   **39.** $x^3 - 3x^2y + 3xy^2 - y^3$
41. $1024a^5 - 6400a^4b + 16000a^3b^2 - 20000a^2b^3 + 12500ab^4 - 3125b^5$ **43.** $56a^5b^3$ **45.** $84x^3y^6$
47. 720   **49.** 1   **51.** 564,480   **53.** 21   **55.** 120   **57.** $\frac{1}{6}$ **63.** 0.00000923
65. 20,160   **67.** approximately 6.30×10^{-12} **69.** $\frac{1}{2}$ **71.** $\frac{1}{2,598,960}$ **73.** $\frac{15}{16}$

CHAPTER FOURTEEN TEST   (page 540)

3. 31   **5.** 256   **7.** -3 **9.** 14, 18, 22   **11.** 10   **13.** $\frac{3}{4}$ **15.** $15x^4y^2$
17. 3024   **19.** 6! or 720   **21.** $\frac{1}{18}$ **23.** $\frac{1}{2}$

CUMULATIVE REVIEW EXERCISES (CHAPTERS 13–14)   (page 541)

1. $x^2 + y^2 = 98$ **3.** $(x - 3)^2 + (y + 2)^2 = 16$;

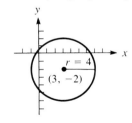

5.

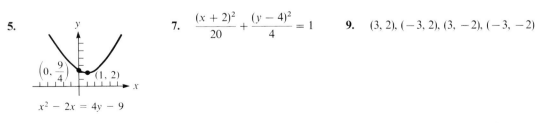

$x^2 - 2x = 4y - 9$

7. $\frac{(x + 2)^2}{20} + \frac{(y - 4)^2}{4} = 1$ **9.** $(3, 2), (-3, 2), (3, -2), (-3, -2)$

13. 27   **15.** 690   **17.** 27   **19.** 12, -48 **21.** 30, 240   **23.** $112x^2y^6$ **25.** 120
27. 84   **29.** $\frac{1}{221}$

Exercise I.1   (page 550)

1. $x = 2, y = 5$ **3.** no values   **5.** $x = 1, y = 2$ **7.** $x = 2, y = 2$ **9.** $\begin{bmatrix} -1 & 2 & 1 \\ -6 & 0 & 0 \end{bmatrix}$

11. $\begin{bmatrix} 5 & -4 & 3 \\ -7 & -4 & -2 \\ 0 & 4 & -8 \end{bmatrix}$ **13.** not possible   **15.** $\begin{bmatrix} 5 & 7 & 9 \end{bmatrix}$ **17.** $\begin{bmatrix} 3 & 2 & -7 \\ 9 & 19 & 15 \\ 0 & -4 & -1 \end{bmatrix}$

19. $\begin{bmatrix} 2 & -2 \\ 3 & 10 \end{bmatrix}$ **21.** $\begin{bmatrix} -22 & -22 \\ -105 & 126 \end{bmatrix}$ **23.** $\begin{bmatrix} 4 & 2 & 10 \\ 5 & -2 & 4 \\ 2 & -2 & 1 \end{bmatrix}$ **25.** $\begin{bmatrix} 32 \end{bmatrix}$

27. not possible   **29.** $\begin{bmatrix} 30 & 36 & 42 \end{bmatrix}$ **31.** $\begin{bmatrix} 2 & 0 & 3 \\ 3 & 0 & 5 \end{bmatrix}$ **33.** $\begin{bmatrix} 12 & -4 & 9 \\ 16 & -2 & 2 \\ 10 & -2 & 1 \end{bmatrix}$

35. $\begin{bmatrix} 7 \\ 6 \end{bmatrix}$ **37.** $\begin{bmatrix} 4 & 5 \\ -7 & -1 \end{bmatrix}$ **39.** not possible   **41.** $\begin{bmatrix} 24 & 16 \\ 39 & 26 \end{bmatrix}$ **43.** $\begin{bmatrix} 64 & 64 \\ 64 & 64 \end{bmatrix}$

45. One example is $\begin{bmatrix} 1 & 0 \\ 0 & 0 \end{bmatrix}$

Exercise I.2   (page 556)

1. $\begin{bmatrix} 3 & 4 \\ 2 & 3 \end{bmatrix}$ **3.** $\begin{bmatrix} 5 & -7 \\ -2 & 3 \end{bmatrix}$ **5.** $\begin{bmatrix} -40 & 16 & 9 \\ 13 & -5 & -3 \\ 5 & -2 & -1 \end{bmatrix}$ **7.** $\begin{bmatrix} 4 & 1 & -3 \\ -5 & -1 & 4 \\ -1 & -1 & 1 \end{bmatrix}$

9. no inverse   **11.** $\begin{bmatrix} 1 & -2 & 1 \\ 0 & 1 & -2 \\ 0 & 0 & 1 \end{bmatrix}$ **13.** no inverse   **15.** $\begin{bmatrix} 1 & -2 & 1 & 0 \\ 0 & 1 & -2 & 1 \\ 0 & 0 & 1 & -2 \\ 0 & 0 & 0 & 1 \end{bmatrix}$

17. $x = 23, y = 17$ **19.** $x = 70, y = -30$ **21.** $x = -10, y = 4, z = 1$
23. $x = 7, y = -9, z = -1$ **25.** $x = 4, y = -6, z = 3$

29. $A^2 = \begin{bmatrix} 1 & 0 \\ 0 & 1 \end{bmatrix}$, $A^3 = \begin{bmatrix} 0 & 1 \\ 1 & 0 \end{bmatrix}$, $A^4 = \begin{bmatrix} 1 & 0 \\ 0 & 1 \end{bmatrix}$. $A^n = \begin{bmatrix} 0 & 1 \\ 1 & 0 \end{bmatrix}$ if n is odd, $A^n = \begin{bmatrix} 1 & 0 \\ 0 & 1 \end{bmatrix}$ if n is even.

33. $A^2 = \begin{bmatrix} 1 & 0 \\ 2 & 1 \end{bmatrix}$, $A^3 = \begin{bmatrix} 1 & 0 \\ 3 & 1 \end{bmatrix}$, $A^n = \begin{bmatrix} 1 & 0 \\ n & 1 \end{bmatrix}$

35. $x = \pm 4$ **39.** $E = \begin{bmatrix} 1 & 0 & 0 \\ 0 & 1 & 0 \\ 3 & 0 & 1 \end{bmatrix}$, $E^{-1} = \begin{bmatrix} 1 & 0 & 0 \\ 0 & 1 & 0 \\ -3 & 0 & 1 \end{bmatrix}$

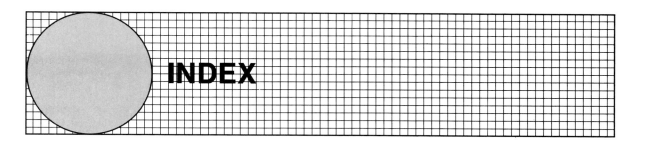

INDEX

7.4 FUNCTIONS AND FUNCTION NOTATION

$(f \circ g)(x) = f(g(x))$
$(f + g)(x) = f(x) + g(x)$
$(f - g)(x) = f(x) - g(x)$
$(f \cdot g)(x) = f(x)g(x)$

$(f/g)(x) = \dfrac{f(x)}{g(x)}$ $(g(x) \neq 0)$

7.6 PROPORTION AND VARIATION

$y = kx$ y varies directly as x

$y = \dfrac{k}{x}$ y varies inversely as x

$y = kxz$ y varies jointly with x and z

$y = \dfrac{kx}{z}$ y varies directly as x, but inversely as z

8.1 SOLVING QUADRATIC EQUATIONS BY COMPLETING THE SQUARE

The solutions of $x^2 = c$ are
$x = \sqrt{c}$ and $x = -\sqrt{c}$

8.2 THE QUADRATIC FORMULA

$x = \dfrac{-b \pm \sqrt{b^2 - 4ac}}{2a}$ $(a \neq 0)$

If x_1 and x_2 are solutions of the equation $ax^2 + bx + c = 0$, then

$x_1 + x_2 = -\dfrac{b}{a}$

$x_1 x_2 = \dfrac{c}{a}$

8.3 COMPLEX NUMBERS

$i^2 = -1$
$a + bi = c + di$ if and only if $a = c$ and $b = d$
$(a + bi) + (c + di) = (a + c) + (b + d)i$
$(a + bi)(c + di) = (ac - bd) + (ad + bc)i$
$a + bi$ and $a - bi$ are complex conjugates
$|a + bi| = \sqrt{a^2 + b^2}$

8.4 THE DISCRIMINANT AND THE SOLUTIONS OF QUADRATIC EQUATIONS

If $\left\{\begin{array}{l} b^2 - 4ac > 0 \\ b^2 - 4ac = 0 \\ b^2 - 4ac < 0 \end{array}\right\}$, then the solutions

of $ax^2 + bx + c = 0$ are $\left\{\begin{array}{l} \text{real and unequal} \\ \text{real and equal} \\ \text{nonreal} \end{array}\right.$

9.1 GRAPHS OF QUADRATIC FUNCTIONS

The vertex of the parabola determined by
$y = a(x - h)^2 + k$ has coordinates of (h, k).

The vertex of the parabola determined by
$y = ax^2 + bx + c$ has coordinates of

$\left(-\dfrac{b}{2a}, c - \dfrac{b^2}{4a}\right)$

9.2 GRAPHS OF POLYNOMIAL FUNCTIONS

If $y = f(x)$ and $y = f(-x)$ are equivalent, then the graph of $y = f(x)$ is symmetric about the y-axis.

If $(x, -y)$ lies on a graph whenever (x, y) does, then the graph is symmetric about the x-axis.

If $y = f(x)$ and $-y = f(-x)$ are equivalent, then the graph of $y = f(x)$ is symmetric about the origin.

10.3 SOLUTION BY DETERMINANTS

$\begin{vmatrix} a & b \\ c & d \end{vmatrix} = ad - bc$

The solutions of $\left\{\begin{array}{l} ax + by = e \\ cx + dy = f \end{array}\right.$ are

$x = \dfrac{D_x}{D}$ and $y = \dfrac{D_y}{D}$

where $D = \begin{vmatrix} a & b \\ c & d \end{vmatrix}$, $D_x = \begin{vmatrix} e & b \\ f & d \end{vmatrix}$, and $D_y = \begin{vmatrix} a & e \\ c & f \end{vmatrix}$

10.5 SOLUTIONS OF THREE EQUATIONS IN THREE VARIABLES BY DETERMINANTS

The solutions of $\left\{\begin{array}{l} ax + by + cz = j \\ dx + ey + fz = k \\ gx + hy + iz = l \end{array}\right.$ are

$x = \dfrac{D_x}{D}$, $y = \dfrac{D_y}{D}$, $z = \dfrac{D_z}{D}$

where $D = \begin{vmatrix} a & b & c \\ d & e & f \\ g & f & i \end{vmatrix}$, $D_x = \begin{vmatrix} j & b & c \\ k & e & f \\ l & h & i \end{vmatrix}$

$D_y = \begin{vmatrix} a & j & c \\ d & k & f \\ g & l & i \end{vmatrix}$, and $D_z = \begin{vmatrix} a & b & j \\ d & e & k \\ g & h & l \end{vmatrix}$

12.1 EXPONENTIAL FUNCTIONS

If $b > 0$, $b \neq 1$, and $b^r = b^s$, then $r = s$.

$A = A_0 2^{-t/h}$ Radioactive decay formula

$A = A_0\left(1 + \dfrac{r}{k}\right)^{kt}$ Compound interest formula

12.2 BASE-e EXPONENTIAL FUNCTIONS

$A = A_0 e^{rt}$ Continuous compound interest formula

$P = P_0 e^{kt}$ Population growth formula